*introduction to switching
and automata theory*

McGraw-Hill Series in Systems Science

Editorial Consultants

A. V. Balakrishnan
George Dantzig
Lotfi Zadeh

introduction to switching and automata theory

MICHAEL A. HARRISON

Department of Electrical Engineering
University of California
Berkeley, California

McGRAW–HILL BOOK COMPANY
New York   St. Louis   San Francisco
Toronto   London   Sydney

INTRODUCTION TO SWITCHING AND AUTOMATA THEORY

TO EVALEE AND CRAIG

preface

Switching theory was developed to provide the communications engineer with techniques for the analysis and synthesis of large-scale switching systems. With the advent of electronic digital computers it was soon seen that some knowledge of switching theory was useful in logical design. At roughly the same time many people became interested in finding models for describing digital computers which were different from the classical model of a Turing machine, studied by logicians in recursive function theory. The Turing machine possesses an infinite tape; such machines (with modifications) are reasonable models for digital computers. A different model is needed for sequential circuits, so people turned to the model of a finite automaton described in this book.

In recent years a great deal of research in switching and automata theory has been carried out. Much of this research has gotten away from the original ideas of design. The approach taken in this book toward design is not the customary one of trying to design a particular system, but is instead one of formulating methods or algorithms for the investigation of whole classes of systems.

This book represents a general point of view toward discrete systems which this writer believes is fundamental. The basic idea behind the presentation is to abstract the pertinent information from the physical systems, construct and investigate tractable mathematical models of the systems, and interpret the results. The rapid pace of modern technology has affected the teaching of college science courses. It is no longer appropriate to teach "state of the art" courses in some fields because the student will find that his skills are obsolete even before graduation. It is necessary to teach fundamental methods and hope that the student's education will not terminate upon graduation. For this reason, some topics were left out of this book and others which may appear unconventional were included. The main criterion for including material was the belief that the subject matter was basic and would not be bypassed by new technological development. The material on complexity, for example, is of this nature.

Certain special topics were not included for different reasons. Almost no mention is made of the new and interesting developments in threshold logic, since an entire book on this subject is being prepared by R. O. Winder. Functional decomposition has been mentioned only briefly, despite its importance, because of the recent appearance of a book by Curtis which thoroughly exploits this point of view. Linear machines, error-correcting codes, adaptive systems, self-reproducing automata, neural nets, and the semigroup approach to automata were all excluded because a more sophisticated background would be required of the student.

Many problems in combinatorial switching circuits depend on the components involved. Instead of working with components, we have presented what might be called *intrinsic* switching theory, i.e., those aspects of the field appropriate to all components. When it was necessary to mention components explicitly, the classification into branch-type and gate-type elements was used. Parallel discussions were then given for each class of elements.

This book is intended as a textbook; as such it is self-contained except for an occasional use of probability theory. The author has taught this material to juniors in engineering, but the abstract treatment is more suitable for a second course. Some of the more advanced topics (such as Chapter 5) were taught only to graduate students. There is enough material for a full year. For a one-year sequence, the following outline was used.

First semester	*Second semester*
Chapter 1	Chapter 2, Sections 7, 8
Chapter 2, Sections 1 to 6, 9 to 10	Chapter 3, Section 6
Chapter 3, except Section 6	Chapter 5
Chapter 4	Chapter 6, Sections 5 to 8
Chapter 6, Sections 1 to 4	Chapter 7, Sections 4 to 10
Chapter 7, Sections 1 to 3	Chapter 8
Chapter 9	Chapter 12
Chapter 10	Chapter 13
Chapter 11	Chapter 14

The second half of the book can be used as a one-semester course in automata theory.   The following outline was actually used at Berkeley in 1963.

Chapter 1, Sections 2 to 7

Chapters 9 to 14

Similarly, one can teach a one-semester course in combinational switching theory from the first half of the book.

The problems form an integral part of this book, and results stated in the problems are used freely.   Very few computational problems are included, since the reader can construct these problems as well as this writer can.   While many of the problems are straightforward, there are a few which are challenging.

Many people contributed, in one form or another, to the production of this book.   I have acknowledged my scientific indebtedness in the body of the book, but I would like to explicitly thank the following people: R. F. Arnold, R. L. Ashenhurst, W. G. Dow, I. T. Frisch, H. L. Garner, A. Gill, H. H. Glover, E. I. Jury, E. S. Kuh, P. L. Morton, I. Ninomiya, D. O. Pederson, T. F. Piatowski, W. C. Ripperger, W. J. Sanders, A. J. Thomasian, I. Toda, and L. A. Zadeh.   Special thanks are also due to Billie Crownover, Dorothy Landreth, and Kim Teramoto for their assistance in typing the manuscript.

Michael A. Harrison

note to the reader:

The following device is used for the numbering of results. Definitions, lemmas, propositions, and theorems are numbered sequentially within a given section. Thus a reference to Theorem 5 means Theorem 5 of the section in which the reference appears. A reference to Proposition 7.9 means Proposition 9 of Section 7 of the chapter in which the reference appears. A reference to Problem 3-5.2 means Problem 2 in Section 5 of Chapter 3. The symbol ▌ is used to mark the end of a proof.

Equations are not numbered unless reference is made to them. References to the bibliography are made by mentioning a person's name, as in "the book of Peterson." A glance at the bibliography shows that there is only one item under the name of Peterson, and the reference is unambiguous. Superscripts are used when more than one reference appears under a name, as in "Polya[2]."

contents

CHAPTER 1 *mathematical background*

1 INTRODUCTION

In Chap. 1 the mathematical conventions of this book are introduced, along with the basic background that is assumed. The mathematics which is best suited for the description of digital systems is not analysis, as in conventional engineering, but discrete mathematics.

This chapter is a collection of basic results of set theory, algebra, number theory, etc. The reader who finds this material completely novel should consult the books mentioned in Sec. 11.

2 SET THEORY

The intuitive idea of a collection of objects is assumed to be familiar. The words *set, class, collection,* and *aggregate* will be all taken as synonyms. The objects in the set will be called *elements.* "x is an element of A" will be written as "$x \in A$," and "x is not an element of A" will be written "$x \notin A$." For example, the aggregate of prime numbers between 1 and 10 is a set of four elements. The set of all people who will read this book is an example of a collection whose exact size is unknown. The collection of all Martians is a set which may not contain any members at all.

It is conventional to use braces to represent sets. For instance, the set of the first example is written

$$\{2,3,5,7\}$$

Definition 1. Two sets A and B are *equal* (written $A = B$) if and only if they are actually the same set.

EXAMPLE. $\{1,2,3\} = \{1,3,2\}$. The two sets are the same because the order of listing is immaterial.

Many of the statements about the subject matter in this book can be considerably shortened if some of the symbolism of logic is used.

Definition 2. If P and Q denote propositions, then the statement "if P, then Q" is written symbolically "$P \Rightarrow Q$." The statement "P if and only if Q" is written "$P \Leftrightarrow Q$." In the following statements, "if and only if" will be written "iff." The phrase "for all x" is written $\forall x$, and the phrase "there exists an x" is written $\exists x$. "There is a unique x" will be denoted by $\exists ! x$. We shall often write $(\forall x)_X$ to stand for the phrase "for every x in X," and similarly for $\exists$. Sometimes, "P and Q" is written $P \wedge Q$ and "P or Q" is written $P \vee Q$.

EXAMPLE. Using the symbolic notation, the definition of set equality may be written as

$$A = B \Leftrightarrow (\forall x)(x \in A \Leftrightarrow x \in B)$$

Definition 3. A is called a *subset* of B (written $A \subseteq B$) iff every element of A is an element of B. Symbolically, this is expressed as

$$A \subseteq B \Leftrightarrow (\forall x)(x \in A \Rightarrow x \in B)$$

For instance, the collection of married women is a subset of the set of all women. Every set is counted as a subset of itself; that is, $A \subseteq A$ is always true.

It is often convenient to specify the set of elements which do not have a certain property. This set is called the *complement* of the set which does have the prescribed property.

Definition 4. Let A and B denote sets. The *absolute complement* of A is written $-A$ or $\bar{A}$ and is the set of all elements which do not belong to A. The *difference between A and B*, or *relative complement*, written $A - B$, is the set of all elements which are members of A but not members of B. Symbolically, the first definition is written as

$$-A = \{x | x \notin A\}$$

where $\{x | x \notin A\}$ is read "the set of all x such that x is not in A." In general, we write $\{x | P(x)\}$, where $P(x)$ denotes some proposition involving x. This latter set means the set of x such that $P(x)$ is true. For the relative complement, we have

$$A - B = \{x | x \in A \wedge x \notin B\}$$

For instance, let N denote the class of natural numbers

$$N = \{0,1,2,3, \ldots\}$$

and let I denote the set of integers

$$I = \{0, \pm 1, \pm 2, \ldots\}$$

Then

$$I - N = \{-1, -2, -3, \ldots\}$$

There is one set which plays a special role in many of our considerations.

Definition 5.   The *null set* (also called the *empty* set or *void* set) is defined as the set with no elements and is denoted by $\emptyset$.

The null set can be generated from any set A by taking $A - A = \emptyset$. Note that the null set is a subset of every set, that is, $\emptyset \subseteq A$ for any A.

There are two important ways to combine sets.

Definition 6.   If A and B are sets, then the *union* of A and B, written $A \cup B$, is defined to be the set of all elements which are in A or are in B.   The *intersection* of A and B, written $A \cap B$, is the set of all elements in A and in B.

It may well happen that for a given pair of sets A and B there are no elements that are both in A and in B.   In this case, one writes

$$A \cap B = \emptyset$$

and we say that A and B are *disjoint* or *mutually exclusive*.

EXAMPLE.   The set of integers is the union of the natural numbers and the negative integers.   The intersection of the set of nonpositive integers with the set of natural numbers is the set whose only element is zero.   Also,

$$\{1,2,3\} \cap \{4,5,6\} = \emptyset$$

A variety of theorems about the relationship of the operations can be proved.   The following example indicates the method of proof.

EXAMPLE.   Show that, for any sets A and B,

$$A \cap (A \cup B) = A$$

PROOF.   Suppose $x \in A$; then $x \in A \cup B$.   Since $x \in A$ and $x \in A \cup B$, then $x \in A \cap (A \cup B)$.   We have shown that $A \subseteq A \cap (A \cup B)$.   Conversely, if $x \in A \cap (A \cup B)$, then $x \in A$.   This shows that $A \cap (A \cup B) \subseteq A$.   Having shown that both sets contain one another, we conclude that they are equal. |

There is a convenient graphical representation of sets known as the Venn diagram.   Suppose that A and B are sets contained in some universal set X. X, often called the *universe of discourse*, contains all the sets of the type under discussion.   We represent X as a large rectangle with A and B drawn as, say, circles; see Fig. 1 for an example.   The intersection of A and B is represented by the shaded region, while $A \cup B$ is the interior of the region of the form $\bigcirc\!\!\bigcirc$.   It is clear from the diagram that the statement $A \cap (A \cup B) = A$ of the preceding

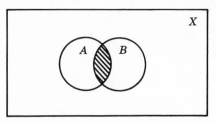

Fig. 1   A Venn diagram.

example is true.   Although Venn diagrams are convenient representations, they do not constitute a proof of the relation under study.   It is too easy to make a mistake in the pictorial interpretation.   Thus, formal proofs should always be written out; as mentioned, they generally establish results for sets by reasoning about their members.

Before proceeding to a further discussion of the mathematics involved in switching and automata theory, it is convenient to list the axioms which will be presupposed.   Many of the results to be obtained ultimately rest on these principles.

Definition 7.   Let S be a set of numbers with an ordering relation† on the set.   A set of numbers S is called *well ordered* if every nonvoid subset of S has a least element.

Axiom 1.   The set of natural numbers N is well ordered.

Axiom 2.   If a and b are positive integers, then there exists a positive integer n such that $na > b$.

Axiom 3.   Let n be a positive integer.   If a set of $n + 1$ elements is subdivided into n or fewer subsets in such a way that each element belongs to precisely one subset, then some subset contains more than one element.

Axiom 2 is often called the axiom of Archimedes.   Axiom 3 is known as Dirichlet's principle.   Dirichlet's principle is useful in automata theory.

PROBLEMS

1.   Prove for all sets A, B, C, and X, where X is a universal set containing A, B, and C:

(a) $(A \cup B) \cup C = A \cup (B \cup C)$ $(A \cap B) \cap C = A \cap (B \cap C)$

(b) $A \cup A = A$ $A \cap A = A$

(c) $A \cup (A \cap B) = A$

(d) $A \subseteq B \Leftrightarrow A \cup B = B$ $A \subseteq B \Leftrightarrow A \cap B = A$

(e) $A \cup B = B \cup A$ $A \cap B = B \cap A$

† See Sec. 6.

(f) $A \cup (B \cap C) = (A \cup B) \cap (A \cup C)$
$A \cap (B \cup C) = (A \cap B) \cup (A \cap C)$
(g) $X - (A \cup B) = (X - A) \cap (X - B)$
$X - (A \cap B) = (X - A) \cup (X - B)$
(h) $A \cap (X - B) = \emptyset \Leftrightarrow A \subseteq B$
$(X - A) \cup B = X \Leftrightarrow A \subseteq B$
(i) Let $\emptyset$ be the empty set. Then

$$A \cap \emptyset = \emptyset \qquad A \cup \emptyset = A$$

2. Let S be a set containing n elements. Shown that S has 2^n subsets. (HINT: Don't forget to count the empty set.)

3 PROOFS

Two methods of proof which will be employed are proof by contradiction and proof by induction. Most theorems are of the form "If P, then Q," where P and Q are propositions. To prove a theorem of this form by contradiction, one assumes that proposition P is true and that proposition Q is false. From these assumptions, one derives a contradiction which establishes the theorem. Two simple examples will illustrate the method.

EXAMPLE. $\sqrt{2}$ is irrational. (The reader will recall that a number is *rational* if it is the ratio of two integers, say p/q with $q \neq 0$.)

PROOF. Assume $\sqrt{2}$ is rational, that is, $\sqrt{2} = a/b$, where a and b have no factors larger than 1 in common. (This is possible because any common factor could be divided out of the quotient.)

Thus $\qquad\qquad a^2 = 2b^2$

so a is an even number, say, $a = 2j$.

Then $\qquad\qquad a^2 = 4j^2 = 2b^2$
or $\qquad\qquad b^2 = 2j^2$

so that b is also an even number.
We have now shown that a and b are both even; i.e., they have 2 as a common factor. This contradicts the assumption that the greatest common divisor of a and b is 1 and shows that the $\sqrt{2}$ is not rational. $\quad\blacksquare$

EXAMPLE. $e = \sum_{i=0}^{\infty} \frac{1}{i!} = 2.718 \cdots$ is irrational.

PROOF. Assume e is rational, so that

$$e = \frac{a}{b}$$

where we may assume $b > 1$ since e is not an integer.   If $k \geq b$, then $k! = k(k - 1)$ $\cdots 2 \cdot 1$ so that b divides $k!$ evenly.   Let

$$t = k! \left(\frac{a}{b} - 1 - \frac{1}{1!} - \frac{1}{2!} - \frac{1}{3!} - \cdots - \frac{1}{k!} \right)$$

Since b divides $k!$ and every other term on the right is an integer, t *is an integer.*

$$0 < t = \frac{1}{k + 1} + \frac{1}{(k + 1)(k + 2)} + \frac{1}{(k + 1)(k + 2)(k + 3)} + \cdots < \frac{1}{k + 1}$$

$$+ \frac{1}{(k + 1)^2} + \frac{1}{(k + 1)^3} + \cdots = \frac{1}{k} < 1$$

This is certainly a contradiction, since we have shown that t is an integer greater than 0 and less than 1. ▮

Mathematical induction is a useful method of proof for statements of the form $P(n)$, where the proposition $P(n)$ depends on a number n which ranges over the natural numbers.   Let θ denote the least element of the well-ordered set S over which n runs.

First Statement of the Induction Principle.   If $P(\theta)$ is true and if $P(k)$ is true implies that $P(k + 1)$ is true, then for all $n \, \epsilon \, S$, $P(n)$ is true.

The part of the proof in which $P(\theta)$ is shown to be true is called the *basis* of the induction, and the second part of the procedure is called the *induction step*.   The induction step is established by an argument in which the truth of $P(k + 1)$ is shown to follow from the truth of $P(k)$ for any k.

Second Statement of the Induction Principle.   If $P(\theta)$ is true and if $P(k)$ is true for all $k < m$ implies $P(m)$ is true, then $P(n)$ is true for every $n \, \epsilon \, S$.

It is easy to show that the two statements of the induction principle are equivalent.   The mechanics of using the induction principle are illustrated by the following examples.

EXAMPLE $1 + 2 + \cdots + n = \sum_{i=1}^{n} i = \frac{n(n + 1)}{2}$

PROOF.   The argument is an induction on n.

BASIS. $n = 1$. $1 = \frac{1(2)}{2} = 1$, so the basis step is completed.

INDUCTION STEP.   Assume $\sum_{i=1}^{k} i = \frac{k(k + 1)}{2}$

Now, by the nature of summation,

$$\sum_{i=1}^{k+1} i = \sum_{i=1}^{k} i + (k + 1)$$

The result will be established if the assumed expression is substituted for the Σ part and the resulting expression is the assumed result for $k + 1$. Thus

$$\sum_{i=1}^{k+1} i = \frac{k(k+1)}{2} + k + 1 = \frac{k^2 + 3k + 2}{2} = \frac{(k+1)(k+2)}{2}$$

The proof is complete. |

Theorem 1. (The Binomial Theorem)

$$(a + b)^n = \sum_{i=0}^{n} \binom{n}{i} a^{n-i} b^i$$

where the binomial coefficient $\binom{n}{i}$ is defined as

$$\binom{n}{i} = \begin{cases} \dfrac{n!}{i!(n-i)!} & \text{for } i = 0, 1, \ldots, n \\ 0 & \text{for } i > n \text{ or } i < 0 \end{cases}$$

$\binom{n}{i}$ is the number of different ways that i objects can be selected from a set of n objects.

PROOF. The argument will be an induction on n.

BASIS. $n = 0$; so $1 = \binom{n}{0} = 1$, since $0! = 1$.

INDUCTION STEP. Assume

$$(a + b)^n = \sum_{i=0}^{n} \binom{n}{i} a^{n-i} b^i$$

then
$$(a + b)^{n+1} = (a + b) \sum_{i=0}^{n} \binom{n}{i} a^{n-i} b^i$$

$$= \sum_{i=0}^{n} \binom{n}{i} a^{n+1-i} b^i + \sum_{i=0}^{n} \binom{n}{i} a^{n-i} b^{i+1}$$

The coefficient of $a^{n+1-i} b^i$ in the above sum is

$$\binom{n}{i} + \binom{n}{i-1} = \frac{n!}{i!(n-i)!} + \frac{n!}{(i-1)!(n+1-i)!}$$

$$= \frac{n!}{(i-1)!(n-i)!} \frac{n+1}{i(n-i+1)} = \frac{(n+1)!}{i!(n-i+1)!} = \binom{n+1}{i}$$

Thus
$$(a + b)^{n+1} = \sum_{i=0}^{n+1} \binom{n+1}{i} a^{n+1-i} b^i$$

To select i objects from a set of n elements, there are n choices for the first elements, $n - 1$ choices for the second elements, . . . , $n - i + 1$ choices for the ith element. Thus $n(n - 1) \cdots (n - i + 1)$ ways to choose i elements exist, but we want the number of different ways that the selection can be made. Each set of i elements has $i!$ permutations, so the desired number is

$$\frac{n(n - 1) \cdots (n - i + 1)}{i!} = \frac{n(n - 1) \cdots (n - i + 1)(n - i)!}{i!(n - i)!}$$

$$= \frac{n!}{i!(n - i)!} = \binom{n}{i} \quad \blacksquare$$

Corollary 2. $\binom{n}{i} + \binom{n}{i - 1} = \binom{n + 1}{i}$ for any $i = 1, \ldots , n$.

PROBLEMS

1. Prove by contradiction that there is no integer between 0 and 1.

2. Prove by induction that

$$1 + 4 + 9 + \cdots + n^2 = \frac{n(n + 1)(2n + 1)}{6}$$

3. Prove by induction that

$$1 + 16 + 81 + \cdots + n^4 = \frac{n}{30}(n + 1)(2n + 1)(3n^2 + 3n - 1)$$

4. Prove that

$$\binom{n}{0} + \binom{n}{1} + \cdots + \binom{n}{n} = 2^n$$

$$\binom{n}{1} + 2\binom{n}{2} + 3\binom{n}{3} + \cdots + n\binom{n}{n} = n2^{n-1}$$

$$\binom{n}{0} - \binom{n}{1} + \binom{n}{2} - \binom{n}{3} + \cdots + (-1)^n\binom{n}{n} = 0 \quad \text{for } n \neq 0$$

$$-\binom{n}{1} + 2\binom{n}{2} - 3\binom{n}{3} + \cdots + (-1)^n\binom{n}{n} = 0 \quad \text{for } n \neq 0$$

5. Find the error in the "proof" of the following assertion.

ASSERTION.   Any set of n elements has the property that all the elements are the same.

PROOF(?).   The argument is an induction on n.

BASIS. $n = 1$.   The set has one element a, and clearly $a = a$.

INDUCTION STEP.   Assume the assertion for all sets containing $n - 1$ elements. Consider the set $\{a_1, \ldots , a_n\}$. If we form the subset $\{a_1, \ldots , a_{n-1}\}$, the induction hypothesis guarantees $a_1 = a_2 = \cdots = a_{n-1}$. Also form the subset $\{a_2, \ldots , a_n\}$. Again the induction hypothesis guarantees $a_2 = \cdots = a_n$. Collecting our results, $a_1 = a_2 = \cdots = a_{n-1} = a_n$. The result follows from the induction principle.

6. Show that

$$\binom{a}{0}\binom{b}{n} + \binom{a}{1}\binom{b}{n - 1} + \binom{a}{2}\binom{b}{n - 2} + \cdots + \binom{a}{n}\binom{b}{0} = \binom{a + b}{n}$$

(HINT: $(1 + t)^a(1 + t)^b = (1 + t)^{a+b}$)

7. Show that

$$\sum_{v=0}^{\infty} \binom{n}{v} \binom{n-v}{k-v} t^v = \binom{n}{k} (1 + t)^k$$

The convention of summing over an infinite range is adopted for convenience. The terms will be zero for $v > \min (k,n)$.

8. Prove that $(-1)^k \binom{a+k-1}{k} = \binom{-a}{k}$ where $a > 0$.

9. Show that if

$$a(n) = \sum_{k=0}^{n} \binom{n}{k} b(k)$$

then

$$b(n) = \sum_{k=0}^{n} \binom{n}{k} (-1)^{n-k} a(k)$$

4   RELATIONS

Relations will play a key role in the solution of many problems in automata theory. It is essential that the reader master these concepts, particularly equivalence relations.

Definition 1. Let X and Y be two sets. The *cartesian product* of X and Y, written $X \times Y$, is defined to be the set of all ordered pairs† whose first element is in X and whose second element is in Y. Symbolically,

$$X \times Y = \{(x,y) | x \in X \text{ and } y \in Y\}$$

Definition 2. Let X and Y be two sets. Any subset of $X \times Y$ is said to be a *binary relation between X and Y*. If $X = Y$, we say that any subset R of $X \times X$ is a *binary relation on X*.

The idea of the definition is that (x,y) is in the subset iff x stands in the relation to y.

EXAMPLE.   The relation "is less than" (denoted by $<$) on $\{0,1,2,3,4\}$ is represented by

$$< = \begin{Bmatrix} (0,1),(0,2),(0,3),(0,4),(1,2), \\ (1,3),(1,4),(2,3),(2,4),(3,4) \end{Bmatrix}$$

Since a relation R between sets X and Y is itself a set, we would naturally write $(x,y) \in R$ to indicate that x stands in the relation R to y. It is more suggestive to use the notation xRy to mean $(x,y) \in R$ and to read xRy as "x is R-related to y."

Definition 3. If R is a binary relation between X and Y, then the *converse* of R, written as R^c, is defined to be

$$R^c = \{(y,x) | xRy\}$$

EXAMPLE.   The converse of "less than" is the relation "greater than."

† The idea of an *ordered pair* is assumed to be understood, along with the idea of an n-tuple of elements.

Since relations are sets, it is immediately clear how the union, intersection, and complement relations must be defined.

Definition 4. If R_1, R_2 are binary relations on X, the *composition of R_1 and R_2*, written $R_1 R_2$, is the relation defined by

$$x(R_1 R_2)y \Leftrightarrow (\exists z)_X \quad xR_1 z \wedge zR_2 y$$

EXAMPLE. Let $R_1 = \{(m,n)|(m - n) = 1\}$; then $R_1 R_1 = R_1{}^2 = \{(p,q)|p - q = 2\}$.

Definition 5. A relation R on X is called an *equivalence relation* on X if R satisfies the following three conditions

1. $(\forall x)_X (xRx)$ reflexivity
2. $(\forall x)_X (\forall y)_X (xRy \Rightarrow yRx)$ symmetry
3. $(\forall x)_X (\forall y)_X (\forall z)_X (xRy \wedge yRz \Rightarrow xRz)$ transitivity

Definition 6. If R is an equivalence relation on X, the *equivalence class containing x* is defined to be the set of all elements of X which are R-equivalent to x and is written $R[x]$. Symbolically

$$R[x] = \{y|yRx\}$$

EXAMPLES. The reader should check the following examples to see that all the defining properties are satisfied and should also examine the equivalence classes carefully.

1. The relation R holds between two lines in the plane if they are parallel.
2. The relation of congruence of geometric figures is an equivalence relation.
3. Two automobiles are said to be equivalent if they have the same engine displacement.

Theorem 7. An equivalence relation R partitions a set S into disjoint equivalence classes such that every element of S is in one and only one equivalence class.

PROOF. First it will be shown that if two equivalence classes have an element in common, then they are the same class. Second, every element will be shown to be in at least one class.

Assume $z \in R[x]$ and $z \in R[y]$
then zRx and zRy
By symmetry $zRx \Rightarrow xRz$
By transitivity xRz and $zRy \Rightarrow xRy$ so $R[x] \subseteq R[y]$

Since the argument is symmetric, $R[y] \subseteq R[x]$ and therefore

$$R[x] = R[y]$$

This shows that every element of S is in at most one equivalence class. To see that every element is in at least one equivalence class, we use reflexivity. xRx holds for any element x, so that

$$x \in R[x]$$

This shows that every element of S is in exactly one equivalence class.   **|**

Definition 8. If R is an equivalence relation on a set S, the number of equivalence classes of R is called the *rank* of the relation and is written $rk(R)$.

EXAMPLE. Let us say $a \equiv b \bmod 2$ if the two integers a and b are both even or both odd. We partition the set I of integers into two equivalence classes, one consisting of just the even integers and one consisting of the odd integers. The rank of this relation is 2.

EXAMPLE. Let S be a set of elements, say, $\{s_0, \ldots, s_{n-1}\}$. The smallest† equivalence relation on S is the *zero equivalence relation*, written 0 and sometimes called the equality relation ($=$).

$$(=) = 0 = \left\{ \begin{array}{c} (s_0,s_0) \\ (s_1,s_1) \\ \cdots \\ (s_{n-1},s_{n-1}) \end{array} \right\}$$

The largest relation on S is the universal equivalence relation, denoted by 1.

$$1 = S \times S$$

Definition 9. Given a set S and an index set I, a family of sets X_i, $i \, \epsilon \, I$, is said to be a *partition* of S iff

$$\bigcup_{i \, \epsilon \, I} X_i = S$$

and $$X_i \cap X_j = \emptyset \qquad \text{for } i \neq j$$

The content of Theorem 7 is that every equivalence relation induces a partition. The converse is also true; it is given as Prob. 6. Thus, partitions and equivalence relations are essentially the same concept. It is our preference to speak of equivalence relations.

EXAMPLE. Let $S = \{a,b,c,d\}$ and let R be the equivalence relation given by

$$R = \left\{ \begin{array}{ccc} (a,a) & (a,b) & \\ (b,b) & (b,a) & (b,c) \\ (c,c) & (a,c) & (c,b) \\ (d,d) & (c,a) & \end{array} \right\}$$

If we know that we are dealing with an equivalence relation, it is redundant to write (a,a), etc., since R must be reflexive. Similarly, it is redundant to write both (a,b) and (b,a), since R must be symmetric. Therefore, we can abbreviate and write R as

$$R = \left\{ \begin{array}{c} (a,b) \\ (a,c) \\ (b,c) \end{array} \right\}$$

The partition induced by R is

$$\{[a,b,c],[d]\}$$

where the square brackets denote the equivalence classes. Since partitions and equivalence relations are completely interchangeable, we shall also stretch tradition

† "Smallest" refers to the ordering of $\subseteq$ on sets. Note that 0 is the largest relation with respect to ordering by rank.

and write

$$R = \{[a,b,c],[d]\}$$

Many times, a relation R which is not transitive is under consideration, so that one wishes to consider the least transitive relation containing
R. This relation is now defined.

Definition 10. Let R be a relation on X. The *transitive closure of R*,
written $\hat{R}$, is defined as

$$\hat{R} = \bigcup_{i=1}^{\infty} R^i = R \cup (RR) \cup (RRR) \cup \cdots$$

Although $\hat{R}$ is written as an infinite union, if X is finite, then $\hat{R}$ is
finite and for some natural number h, $R^h = R^{h+1}$. Thereafter,

$$R^h = R^{h+m}$$

for all m. Thus $R = \bigcup_{i=1}^{h} R_i$.

Proposition 11. $\hat{R}$ is transitive. If S is a transitive relation on X and
$R \subseteq S$, then $\hat{R} \subseteq S$.

PROOF. Suppose $x\hat{R}y$ and $y\hat{R}z$; then there exist positive integers i and j such that
xR^iy and yR^jz. It is clear that $xR^{i+j}z$, since if $xRw_1, w_1Rw_2, \ldots, w_{i-1}Ry$ and if yRv_1,
$v_1Rv_2, \ldots, v_{j-1}Rz$, then a sequence of length $i + j - 1$ connects x and z, that is,
$xR^{i+j}z$. To prove the second statement, which says that $\hat{R}$ is the least transitive containing R, suppose $x\hat{R}y$. Thus xR^iy for some i. Using a special case of Prob. 9,
since $R \subseteq S$, then $R^i \subseteq S^i$; but since S is transitive, $S^i \subseteq S$. Thus xR^iy implies
xSy. $\blacksquare$

It is important to have algorithms for computing $\hat{R}$ and other operations on relations. This problem will be considered in Chap. 5 when
boolean matrices are introduced.

There is a convenient and useful graphical interpretation of relations.
If the relation R is defined on S, where $S = \{s_0, \ldots, s_{n-1}\}$, draw n
nodes labeled $s_0, \ldots, s_{n-1}$. Draw a directed line (i.e., line with arrow
indicating direction) from s_i to s_j iff s_iRs_j. The corresponding directed
graph (*digraph*, for short) represents the relation.

EXAMPLE. Let $S = \{s_0, \ldots, s_3\}$ and $R = 0$; see Fig. 1. Note that the interpretation of the relation R^2 holding between x and y is that they are connected by a
directed path of length 2. $x\hat{R}y$ means that x and y are connected by some directed
path.

PROBLEMS

1. Find a relation which is reflexive, symmetric, but not transitive.

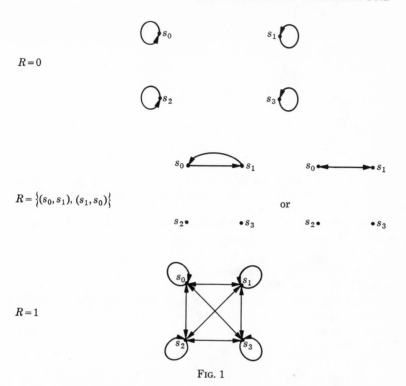

$R=0$

$R=\big\{(s_0,s_1),\,(s_1,s_0)\big\}$

or

$R=1$

FIG. 1

2. Find a relation which is reflexive, transitive, but not symmetric.

3. Is it possible to find a relation which is symmetric, transitive, but not reflexive?

4. Let R be the relation "is the stepfather of." Is R reflexive, symmetric, or transitive? Discuss the special case of Oedipus.

5. Assume the symmetric and transitive properties for a relation R.

What (if anything) is wrong with the following proof that the reflexive property follows from the symmetric and transitive properties?

Assume xRy.

By symmetry, yRx.

By transitivity, $xRy,\ yRx \Rightarrow xRx$.

Therefore, xRx.

6. Prove the following converse of Theorem 7. If a set S is decomposed into disjoint subsets whose union is S, then an equivalence relation R is induced on S.

7. Let A and B be equivalence relations. Prove that if $A \subseteq B$, then $rk(A) \geq rk(B)$. (HINT: Define a mapping from the equivalence classes of A into the equivalence classes of B, and recall what $\geq$ means.)

8. If R is any relation on X, show that $\tilde{R} = R \cup R^c \cup 0$ is the smallest reflexive and symmetric relation containing R. Recall that 0 denotes the equality relation on X.

9. If R_1, R_2, and R_3 are relations on X, show that $R_1 \subseteq R_2$ implies $R_1R_3 \subseteq R_2R_3$ and that $R_1 \subseteq R_2$ implies $R_3R_1 \subseteq R_3R_2$. Show that $R_1 \subseteq R_2$ implies that $R_1{}^c \subseteq R_2{}^c$.

10. Let I be an index set and let R and R_i, $i \, \epsilon \, I$, be relations on X. Show that

(a) $R(\bigcup_{i \, \epsilon \, I} R_i) = \bigcup_{i \, \epsilon \, I} RR_i$

(b) $R(\bigcap_{i \, \epsilon \, I} R_i) \subseteq \bigcap_{i \, \epsilon \, I} RR_i$

(c) $(\bigcup_{i \, \epsilon \, I} R_i)^c = \bigcup_{i \, \epsilon \, I} R_i{}^c$

(d) $(\bigcap_{i \, \epsilon \, I} R_i)^c = \bigcap_{i \, \epsilon \, I} R_i{}^c$

(e) $(R_1 R_2)^c = R_2{}^c R_1{}^c$

(f) $(R^c)^c = R$

11. If R_1 and R_2 are symmetric relations such that $R_1 R_2 \subseteq R_2 R_1$, show that $R_1 R_2 = R_2 R_1$.

12. Show that if R_1 and R_2 are equivalence relations on X, then $R_1 \cup R_2$ is not necessarily an equivalence relation. Show that $R_1 \cap R_2$ is an equivalence relation and that $rk(R_1 \cap R_2) \leq rk(R_1) \cdot rk(R_2)$.

13. If R_1 and R_2 are equivalence relations on X, define the *join* of R_1 and R_2 to be least equivalence relation containing R_1 and R_2. The join of R_1 and R_2 is written as $R_1 \sqcup R_2$. Show that $R_1 \sqcup R_2 = (\widehat{R_1 \cup R_2})$. Show that if R_1 and R_2 are equivalence relations on X such that $R_1 R_2 = R_2 R_1$, then $R_1 R_2$ is an equivalence relation on X and, furthermore, $R_1 R_2 = R_1 \sqcup R_2$.

14. If R_1 and R_2 are equivalence relations on X and if X has n elements, show that $R_1 \sqcup R_2 = (R_1 \cup R_2)^{n-1}$. Can you lower the exponent?

15. Show that if P_n is the number of equivalence relations on a set of n elements, then

$$P_0 = 1 \qquad P_{n+1} = \sum_{k=0}^{n} \binom{n}{k} P_k$$

Note that

$$e^{(e^x - 1)} = \sum_{n=0}^{\infty} \frac{P_n}{n!} x^n$$

5 FUNCTIONS

At least half of this book is concerned with certain types of functions and their properties. The definition of function which we shall give is somewhat narrower than that sometimes assumed.

Definition 1. f is called a *function from X into Y* iff f is a relation between X and Y and for every $x \, \epsilon \, X$ there exists a *unique* element y such that xfy (that is, every x occurs once and only once in R as the first member of a pair).

Definition 2. Let f be a function from X into Y. X is called the *domain* of the function. The *range* of f is defined to be the set of all elements $y \, \epsilon \, Y$ such that there exists an $x \, \epsilon \, X$ for which xfy. Symbolically,

$$\text{Range } (f) = \{y | (\exists x) xfy\}$$

There are many synonyms for a function; they include *mapping*, *transformation*, and *operation*. Our definition of a function is what is more generally called a *completely specified single-valued function*. The function is completely specified, since every $x \in X$ begins an ordered pair; it is single-valued, since X may begin only one ordered pair. Notice that we define a function to be what is often called the graph of the function.

EXAMPLE. $f(x) = x^2$ may be defined as a function from I into I, where I denotes the set of integers. To stay strictly within our definition, we should write

$$f = \left\{ \begin{array}{c} \cdots \cdots \\ (-2,4) \\ (-1,1) \\ (0,0) \\ (1,1) \\ (2,4) \\ \cdots \cdots \end{array} \right\}$$

Clearly, f is a function. Note that the converse relation is not a function, in our sense, because it is neither completely specified nor single-valued. (For real x, $\sqrt{x}$ can be defined for $x \geq 0$ as a function by always choosing the positive root.)

Definition 3. A function f from X is said to be *onto* Y (rather than into Y) when the range of f is Y. Equivalently, f is a function from X onto Y iff $(\forall y)_Y (\exists x)_X \ xfy$.

Definition 4. A function f from X into Y is said to be *one to one* iff $(\forall x_1, x_2)_X (\forall y)_Y \ x_1 f y$ and $x_2 f y$ implies $x_1 = x_2$.

Sometimes one abbreviates the statement "f is a mapping from X into Y" by writing $f \colon X \to Y$ or $f \colon x \to f(x)$.

EXAMPLE. The mapping $f \colon k \to 2k$ for natural numbers k is an example of a one-to-one mapping, but it is not an onto mapping because, for example, the number 3 has no natural number mapped onto it by f.

EXAMPLE. The mapping f from the set $X = \{0,1,2\}$ into the set $\{0,1\}$ given by

$$f(x) = \begin{cases} 0 & \text{if } x \text{ is even} \\ 1 & \text{if } x \text{ is odd} \end{cases}$$

is onto, but not one to one, since 0 and 2 both map into 0.

The situation can be described graphically. Figure 1 shows a function which is not one to one, since x_1 and x_2 both map into y_1, yet f is onto. Figure 2 shows a mapping which is one to one, but not onto, since y_2 has no element x which maps onto it.

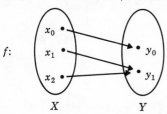

Fig. 1

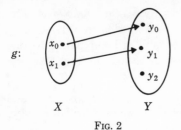

g:

X Y

FIG. 2

Definition 5. If f is a function from X into Y and if f^c is also a function, then we say that f has an *inverse* $f^{-1} = f^c$.

It is clear that for any function f, f^c exists, but in general f^c is not a function.

Lemma 6. f has an inverse iff f is one to one and onto.

PROOF. Suppose f has an inverse, $f^{-1} = f^c = \{(y,x) | xfy\}$. Since f^c is a function, f is one to one and onto. The argument is reversible. ∎

Definition 7. If f is a function from X to Y and if A is a subset of X, then the *restriction* of f to A, denoted by $f \restriction A$, is defined as

$$f \restriction A = f \cap (A \times Y)$$

that is, $f \restriction A$ is a function with domain A such that $y = f(x)$ for all $x \in A$.

In later chapters, it will be important to obtain asymptotic bounds. The following notation, due originally to E. Landau, is helpful.

Definition 8. Assume $g(x)$ is defined and positive for all positive numbers x, and if $f(x)$ is any function defined on an unbounded set S of positive numbers, then we write

$$f(x) = O(g(x)) \qquad \text{iff there is a constant } M \text{ such that } \frac{|f(x)|}{g(x)} < M$$

$$f(x) = o(g(x)) \qquad \text{iff } \lim_{\substack{x \to \infty \\ x \in S}} \frac{f(x)}{g(x)} = 0$$

$$f(x) \sim g(x) \qquad \text{iff } \lim_{\substack{x \to \infty \\ x \in S}} \frac{f(x)}{g(x)} = 1$$

Our applications will usually involve taking S to be the set of natural numbers.

EXAMPLE. $\sin x = O(1)$ $\sin x = o(x)$

PROBLEMS

1. Let X be a set with d elements and Y be a set with r elements. Show that there are r^d functions from X into Y.

2.   A permutation of X is defined to be a one-to-one function from X onto X. Show that there are $n!$ permutations of $S = \{0, 1, \ldots, n - 1\}$.

3.   Let f and g be functions defined from S into S.   Define the composition of f and g to be $fg(x) = f(g(x))$ for $x \epsilon S$.   Show that fg is a function.

4.   Show that the following statements are true.
(a) $x^k = o(2^x)$ for any k.
(b) $\log_2 x = o(x^r)$ for any positive *real* number r.

6   ALGEBRAIC STRUCTURES

Many examples of algebraic systems will occur throughout this book. At this point, some general facts are given and a variety of systems are presented.   All of these concepts will be exploited subsequently.

Definition 1.   An *algebraic system* is defined to be a system

$$\langle D, o_1, \ldots, o_k; R_1, \ldots, R_m; c_1, \ldots, c_n \rangle$$

where D is a nonvoid set; o_i are functions from D^{l_i} into D for some integer l_i; R_i $(i = 1, \ldots, m)$ are relations on D; and c_i $(i = 1, \ldots, n)$ are elements of D, that is, distinguished constants.

This formal system approach is very useful, since one can study a given system D and easily augment D by the addition of extra relations.

EXAMPLE. $\langle I, + \rangle$ denotes the system of integers with the single binary operation of addition. $I' = \langle I, +, \leq \rangle$ is the system of integers with the operation of $+$ and the relation "less than or equal to."

With each algebraic system is associated a given equivalence relation which defines "equality" between the elements of D.

For future reference, we now list some potential axioms.

O1	$(\forall x)$	$x \leq x$	reflexive property
O2	$(\forall x)(\forall y)$	$(x \leq y), (y \leq x) \Rightarrow x = y$	antisymmetric property
O3	$(\forall x)(\forall y)(\forall z)$	$(x \leq y), (y \leq z) \Rightarrow x \leq z$	transitive property
O4	$(\forall x)(\forall y)$	$(x \leq y)$ or $(y \leq x)$	
A1	$(\forall x)(\forall y)(\forall z)$	$(x + y) + z = x + (y + z)$	associative law
A2	$(\exists !0)(\forall x)$	$x + 0 = 0 + x = x$	existence of zero element
A3	$(\forall x)(\exists y)$	$x + y = y + x = 0$	existence of additive inverses

A4	$(\forall x)(\forall y)$	$x + y = y + x$	commutative law
M1	$(\forall x)(\forall y)(\forall z)$	$x \cdot (y \cdot z) = (x \cdot y) \cdot z$	associative law
M2	$(\exists !1)(\forall x)$	$x \cdot 1 = 1 \cdot x = x$	existence of unit element
M3	$(\forall x)(\exists y)$	$x \cdot y = y \cdot x = 1$	existence of multiplicative inverses
M4	$(\forall x)(\forall y)$	$x \cdot y = y \cdot x$	commutative law
D1	$(\forall x)(\forall y)(\forall z)$	$x \cdot (y + z) = x \cdot y + x \cdot z$	distributive law
D2	$(\forall x)(\forall y)(\forall z)$	$(y + z) \cdot x = y \cdot x + z \cdot x$	distributive law

The first four axioms involve an order relation; the next four axioms involve an operation written additively; and the statements numbered with an M are the multiplicative versions of those designated by A. D1 and D2 are distributive laws which give the relation between the additive and multiplicative operations.

Definition 2. A system $P = \langle P, \leq \rangle$ is called a *partially ordered system* provided that the axioms O1, O2, and O3 are satisfied. If O4 is also satisfied, then P is a *totally ordered system*.

It should be noticed that the same symbol is used to designate the system as the domain of the system. This should never result in confusion, because the context will always indicate which is meant if it is necessary to distinguish.

EXAMPLE. Let S be any set and let 2^S denote the set of all subsets of S. The system $\langle 2^S, \subseteq \rangle$ is a partially ordered set, but not a totally ordered set, under the relation of set inclusion.

EXAMPLE. The system $\langle N, \leq \rangle$, where N is the set of natural numbers and $\leq$ is the usual "less than or equal to" relation, is a totally ordered set.

Definition 3. Let $P = \langle P, \leq \rangle$ be a partially ordered set. An element $u \in P$ is said to be an *upper bound* for a subset X of P if every $x \in X$ has the property $x \leq u$. u is called a *least upper bound* for a subset X of P if u is an upper bound for X and for every upper bound v of X, $u \leq v$. Dually for *lower bounds* and *greatest lower bounds*.

Definition 4. Given a partially ordered set $P = \langle P, \leq \rangle$, define the *meet* of two elements $x, y \in P$, written $x \sqcap y$, to be the greatest lower bound of $\{x, y\}$. Similarly, define the *join* of x and y, written $x \sqcup y$, to be the least upper bound of $\{x, y\}$.

EXAMPLE.   For set inclusion $\subseteq$, the meet is the greatest set included in both, i.e., the intersection.

Definition 5.   A *lattice* $L = \langle L, \leq, \sqcap, \sqcup \rangle$ is defined as a system with $\langle L, \leq \rangle$ a partially ordered set having the property that every two elements of L have a greatest lower bound and a least upper bound.

Discrete partially ordered sets and lattices are conveniently represented by diagrams in which the nodes represent the domain elements with a drawn above b if $a > b$, below b if $a < b$, and on the same level as b if neither holds.

EXAMPLE.   Let $S = \{a,b,c\}$ and let E_s be the class of all equivalence relations on S. The system $E_s = \langle E_s, \subseteq, \sqcap, \sqcup \rangle$, where $\subseteq$ is set inclusion, $\sqcap$ is the intersection, and $\sqcup$ is the join of two relations defined in Prob. 4.13.   The diagram of the lattice is shown in Fig. 1.

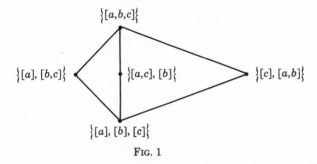

Fig. 1

Later, more will be said about the lattice of equivalence relations (partitions) of a finite set.

Definition 6.   A system $S = \langle S, \cdot, 1 \rangle$ is called a *semigroup with identity*, or *monoid*, iff axioms $M1$ and $M2$ are satisfied.   (The choice of multiplicative notation is unessential.)

EXAMPLE.   The system $N = \langle N, +, 0 \rangle$, where N is the set of natural numbers, forms a monoid.   Note that the operation is written additively here by custom.

EXAMPLE.   Let X be a finite set and let R_1 and R_2 be relations on X.   Let R_X be the set of all relations on X.   The system $R_X = \langle R_X, \circ, 0 \rangle$ is a monoid under the operation of composition of relations.   0 denotes the equality relation on X.

Definition 7.   A *group* is a system $G = \langle G, \cdot, 1 \rangle$ satisfying M1, M2, and M3.   If G also satisfies M4, it is called a *commutative* or *abelian group*.

Again, the definition is written multiplicatively, but it could have been written additively.

EXAMPLE.   The system $I = \langle I, +, 0 \rangle$, where I denotes the class of integers, is an additive abelian group.

EXAMPLE.   The set of all permutations of $\{1, \ldots, n\}$ forms a group under the operation of functional composition (cf. Prob. 5.2).   This famous group, denoted by S_n, is called the *symmetric group of degree n*.   The group S_n is not abelian for $n > 2$.

Definition 8.   A *ring* is a system $R = \langle R, +, \cdot, 0 \rangle$ which satisfies axioms A1 to A4, M1, D1, and D2.   If R also satisfies axiom M4, it is called a *commutative ring*.   A system $R = \langle R, +, \cdot, 0, 1 \rangle$ is called a *ring with identity* if R is a ring and in addition satisfies M2.

EXAMPLE.   The class of polynomials in the symbol or indeterminate x with coefficients in the real field R is denoted by $R[x]$.   The system $R[x] = \langle R[x], +, \cdot, 0 \rangle$ is a commutative ring. $+$ denotes the usual addition of polynomials, and $\cdot$ designates the conventional product of two polynomials.   0 designates $0 + 0 \cdot x + 0 \cdot x^2 + \cdots$.

EXAMPLE.   The system of $n \times n$ matrices whose entries are integers forms a ring. This ring is not abelian under multiplication.

Definition 9.   A *field* is a system $F = \langle F, +, \cdot, 0, 1 \rangle$ satisfying A1 to A4, M1, M2, M_3', M4, D1, and D2, where M_3' is $(\forall x)(\exists y)\ x \neq 0 \Rightarrow x \cdot y = y \cdot x = 1$.

EXAMPLE.   The complex numbers and the real numbers form fields.

PROBLEMS

1.   Let $\cdot$ be an associative binary operation.   Show that the generalized associative law holds, that is

$$\prod_{i=1}^{n} a_i \prod_{j=1}^{m} a_{n+j} = \prod_{k=1}^{n+m} a_k$$

2.   Show that subtraction is not an associative operation.

3.   Consider the set of complex numbers $e^{i\theta}$ whose absolute value is 1 and the operation of multiplication.   Show that this system is a group.

4.   Let G_1 be a nonvoid subset of a group G. $\langle G_1, \cdot, 1 \rangle$ is a subgroup iff this system satisfies axiom M3 and also is closed; i.e., if $a_1 \in G_1$, $a_2 \in G_1$, then $a_1 \cdot a_2 \in G_1$.
  (a)   Is $1 \in G_1$?   Why?
  (b)   Show that if G is finite, G_1 is a subgroup iff the system satisfies $a_1 \in G$, $a_2 \in G \Rightarrow a_1 \cdot a_2 \in G$.

5.   Theorem 3.1, the binomial theorem, holds in some algebraic systems and not in others.   Characterize the weakest algebraic system (i.e., the system with the least number of axioms listed in this section) in which the binomial theorem holds.

6.   Consider the set of $n \times n$ matrices whose elements are from a field.   Let the operations be matrix addition and matrix multiplication.   Show that this system is a ring with identity.   Prove that the ring is not commutative.

7.   Consider numbers of the form $a + b \sqrt{2}$, where a and b are rational numbers. Show that the set of these numbers with $+$ and $\cdot$ forms a field.

7   SUBSYSTEMS, STRUCTURE-PRESERVING MAPS, AND CONGRUENCE RELATIONS

It is often necessary to consider only a subset of a given algebraic system under discussion.

Definition 1. If $D = \langle D, o_1, \ldots, o_k; R_1, \ldots, R_m; c_1, \ldots, c_n \rangle$ is an algebraic system (cf. Definition 6.1), then

$$D' = \langle D', o_1', \ldots, o_k'; R_1', \ldots, R_m'; c_1, \ldots, c_m \rangle$$

is a *subsystem* of D iff $D' \subseteq D$, the o_i' are restrictions of o_i' from D^{l_i} to $(D')^{l_i}$ $(i = 1, \ldots, k)$, and the R_i' are defined as $R_i' = R_i \cap (D' \times D')$ for $i = 1, \ldots, m$.

EXAMPLE. Let $C = \langle C, +_c, \cdot_c, 0, 1 \rangle$ be the field of complex numbers. The field $R = \langle R, +_R, \cdot_R, 0, 1 \rangle$ of real numbers is a subfield of C. Although the same symbol is conventionally used for the operations in both fields, we have used subscripts to distinguish between the different systems.

It is often essential to map one algebraic system into another. Mappings of this type are interesting transformations and, indeed, play a central role in modern mathematics and its applications.

Definition 2. A mapping α from an algebraic system D into (onto) another system E is said to be a *homomorphism* of D into (onto) E if α preserves the algebraic structure of D.

The preceding definition is somewhat vague because the phrase *algebraic structure* is not specified. It is preferable to state, for each system under consideration, exactly what structure is to be preserved.

Definition 3. Two systems D and E are said to be *isomorphic* iff there is a *one-to-one* mapping α from D *onto* E which is a homomorphism. α is then called an *isomorphism*.

Definition 4. A homomorphism from D into D is called an *endomorphism* of D. An isomorphism from D onto D is called an *automorphism* of D.

EXAMPLE. Let $R = \langle R, +, 0 \rangle$ be the group of real numbers under addition and let $C = \langle C, \cdot, 1 \rangle$ be the group of complex numbers whose absolute value is 1. We shall construct a homomorphism α from R onto C. [The structure-preserving property of α for groups is $\alpha(r_1 + r_2) = \alpha(r_1) \cdot \alpha(r_2)$.]

Let $\alpha(r) = e^{ir}$. Clearly, α maps real numbers into complex numbers of absolute value 1. α is *onto*, since given any complex number of absolute value 1, say, $a + bi = \sqrt{a^2 + b^2} \, e^{i \, \tan^{-1}(b/a)}$, the real number $r = \tan^{-1}(b/a)$ must map onto $a + bi$ under α. Note also that $\alpha(0) = e^{i0} = 1$. Finally,

$$\alpha(r_1) = e^{ir_1}$$
$$\alpha(r_2) = e^{ir_2}$$
$$\alpha(r_1 + r_2) = e^{i(r_1 + r_2)} = e^{ir_1} \cdot e^{ir_2} = \alpha(r_1) \cdot \alpha(r_2)$$

so α is indeed a group homomorphism of R onto C.

The study of homomorphic images of an algebraic system can be carried out by studying equivalence relations of a particular type. For the purposes of our development, we consider a new type of system, the *abstract algebra.*†

Definition 5. An *abstract algebra* $A = \langle A, f_0, \ldots, f_{k-1} \rangle$ is a system with a nonvoid domain A and k functions $f_i: A \to A$ for $i = 0, \ldots, k - 1$.

Abstract algebras are usually defined with k finitary functions, but the present definition suffices for our applications.

Definition 6. R is called a *congruence relation* on an abstract algebra A iff R is an equivalence relation on A and R satisfies the *substitution property* with respect to the f_i, namely, for any $a, b \in A$,

$$aRb \Rightarrow f_i(a)Rf_i(b)$$

for $i = 0, \ldots, k - 1$.

EXAMPLE. Consider the system $N = \langle N, ' \rangle$, where $'$ is the successor function. $n' = n + 1$. Let R be the relation of *congruence modulo 2*, that is, $(m,n) \in R$ if m and n are both odd or both even. Clearly, $(m,n) \in R \Rightarrow (m',n') = (m + 1, n + 1) \in R$.

Definition 7. Let $A = \langle A, f_0, \ldots, f_{k-1} \rangle$ be an abstract algebra and let R be a congruence relation on A. The *quotient algebra of A modulo R*, written A/R, is defined as

$$A/R = \langle B, g_0, \ldots, g_{k-1} \rangle$$

where

$$B = \{ R[a] \mid a \in A \} \quad \text{and} \quad g_i(R[a]) = R[f_i(a)] \quad \text{for } i = 0, \cdots, k - 1$$

EXAMPLE. $N/R = \langle N/R, ' \rangle$, where $N/R = \{[2k],[2k + 1] \mid k = 0,1,2, \ldots\}$. Thus N/R has two classes; one consisting of the even numbers, one consisting of the odd ones.

The idea behind Definition 7 is to take an abstract algebra A and partition the domain of A by an equivalence relation. It is desired to make a new abstract algebra whose domain consists of the equivalence classes of A. Whenever one defines a system whose elements are classes, then the functions defined on the classes must be independent of the representatives of the classes. This consistency requirement is usually expressed by saying that the quotient system is *well defined*.

Proposition 8. If A is an abstract algebra and R is a congruence relation on A, then A/R is well defined.

PROOF. Let $A = \langle A, f_0, \ldots, f_{k-1} \rangle$ and $A/R = \langle B, g_0, \ldots, g_{k-1} \rangle$. We must show that if $a_1 R a_2$, then $g_i(R[a_1]) = g_i(R[a_2])$. If $a_1 R a_2$, then $f_i(a_1)Rf_i(a_2)$ because R is a congruence relation. Thus $R[f_i(a_1)] = R[f_i(a_2)]$ and $g_i(R[a_1]) = g_i(R[a_2])$ for $i = 0, \ldots, k - 1$. ∎

---

† These algebras should not be confused with vector spaces with an associative multiplication, although the same name is given to both systems. Our interest in abstract algebras occurs because sequential machines are unary abstract algebras.

The proof indicates that it is just the substitution property on R which allows the definition of a quotient algebra to be well defined. This can be checked in Definition 7, since it did not matter which representatives were chosen.

Definition 9. A mapping φ from an abstract algebra

$$A = \langle A, f_0, \ldots, f_{k-1} \rangle$$

into $B = \langle B, g_0, \ldots, g_{k-1} \rangle$ is a *homomorphism* iff $\varphi(f_i(a)) = g_i(\varphi(a))$ for $i = 0, \ldots, k - 1$.

Next we indicate the connections between the new concepts.

Lemma 10. If φ is a homomorphism from an abstract algebra A_1 into A_2, then the relation R on A_1 defined by $aRb \Leftrightarrow \varphi(a) = \varphi(b)$ is a congruence relation.

PROOF. Let $\varphi: A_1 \rightarrow A_2$ such that $\varphi(f_i(a)) = g_i(\varphi(a))$ for $i = 0, \ldots, k - 1$. The relation R on A_1 is defined as follows:

$$aRb \Leftrightarrow \varphi(a) = \varphi(b)$$

Clearly, R is an equivalence relation. R has the substitution property since if

$$aRb \Leftrightarrow \varphi(a) = \varphi(b)$$

then $\qquad g_i(\varphi(a)) = g_i(\varphi(b)) \qquad$ for $i = 0, \ldots, k - 1$

Because φ is a homomorphism, $g_i(\varphi(a)) = \varphi(f_i(a))$.

Therefore, $\qquad \varphi(f_i(a)) = \varphi(f_i(b)) \Leftrightarrow f_i(a)Rf_i(b)$ |

Theorem 11. Let φ be a homomorphism from $A = \langle A, f_0, \ldots, f_{k-1} \rangle$ onto $B = \langle B, g_0, \ldots, f_{k-1} \rangle$. B is isomorphic to A/R, where R is defined in Lemma 10.

PROOF. Since R is a congruence relation, we construct $A/R = \langle C, h_0, \ldots, h_{k-1} \rangle$. Define a mapping β as

$$\beta: \varphi(a) \rightarrow R[a]$$

Clearly, β is a transformation from B into A/R. β is onto, since given any class $R[a]$, $\varphi(a)$ exists and maps onto it. Clearly, β is one to one, since

$$R[a_1] = R[a_2] \Leftrightarrow a_1Ra_2 \Leftrightarrow \varphi(a_1) = \varphi(a_2)$$

It must be shown that $\beta(g_i(b)) = h_i(\beta(b))$ for $i = 0, \ldots, k - 1$ to complete the proof. Since φ is onto, write $b = \varphi(a)$. Then

$$\beta(g_i(b)) = \beta(g_i(\varphi(a))) = \beta(\varphi(f_i(a)))$$

since φ is a homomorphism.
By the definition of β,

$$\beta(g_i(\varphi(a))) = \beta(\varphi(f_i(a))) = R[f_i(a)] = h_i(R[a]) = h_i(\beta(\varphi(a)))$$

for $i = 0, \ldots, k - 1$. |

We have noted that every homomorphic image of an algebra is a quotient algebra.   The converse is also true.

Theorem 12.   If A/R is a quotient algebra of an abstract algebra A modulo a congruence R, then there is a homomorphism from A onto A/R.

PROOF.   Let $A = \langle A, f_0, \ldots, f_{k-1} \rangle$ and $A/R = \langle B, g_0, \ldots, g_{k-1} \rangle$, where $B = \{R[a] | a \, \epsilon \, A\}$ and $g_i(R[a]) = R[f_i(a)]$ for $i = 0, \ldots, k - 1$.   Define the mapping φ such that $\varphi \colon a \to R[a]$.   Clearly, φ is a mapping from A *onto* A/R. φ is a homomorphism, since

$$\varphi(f_i(a)) = R[f_i(a)] = g_i(R[a]) = g_i(\varphi(a))$$

for $i = 0, \ldots, k - 1$.   ∎

EXAMPLE.   Let A and B be abstract algebras, where $A = \langle \{a_0, \ldots, a_6\}, f_0, f_1 \rangle$ and $B = \langle \{b_0, \ldots, b_2\}, g_0, g_1 \rangle$

The functions are expressed in tabular form as

	a_0	a_1	a_2	a_3	a_4	a_5	a_6
f_0	a_1	a_1	a_2	a_1	a_6	a_5	a_6
f_1	a_2	a_3	a_4	a_5	a_2	a_3	a_6

and

	b_0	b_1	b_2
g_0	b_1	b_1	b_2
g_1	b_2	b_1	b_2

The mapping φ given below can be checked to be a homomorphism of A onto B.

a	a_0	a_1	a_2	a_3	a_4	a_5	a_6
$\varphi(a)$	b_0	b_1	b_2	b_1	b_2	b_1	b_2

The appropriate relation R is $\{[a_0], [a_1, a_3, a_5], [a_2, a_4, a_6]\}$.   It is easily checked (in six steps) that R is a congruence relation; the reader should construct A/R and note that it is isomorphic to B.

PROBLEMS

1.   Let f be a homomorphism from the group $G = \langle G, \cdot, 1_G \rangle$ onto $H = \langle H, *, 1_H \rangle$. Show that $f(1_G) = 1_H$.   Show that if $x \, \epsilon \, G$, $f(x^{-1}) = (f(x))^{-1}$.

2.   Let f be a homomorphism from G onto H (same setup as in Prob. 1).   Let $K = \{x | f(x) = 1_H\}$.   Show that K is a subgroup of G.   (K is called the *kernel* of the homomorphism.)   HINT: Use the preceding problem.

3.   Prove that the complex-number system is isomorphic to the set of matrices of the form

$$\begin{bmatrix} a & b \\ -b & a \end{bmatrix}$$

where a and b are real numbers.   The operations on the matrices are to be matrix addition and matrix multiplication.

4. Let $A = \langle A, f_0, \ldots, f_{k-1} \rangle$ and $B = \langle B, g_0, \ldots, g_{k-1} \rangle$ be abstract algebras. $C = \langle C, h_0, \ldots, h_{k-1} \rangle$ is said to be the *direct product* of A and B, written $A \times B$, iff $C = A \times B$ (cartesian product of the domains A and B) and

$$h_i((a,b)) = (f_i(a), g_i(b)) \qquad \text{for } i = 0, \ldots, k - 1$$

Note that C is an abstract algebra. Show that A (or B) is a homomorphic image of C. Give the appropriate congruence relation.

5. Can you give necessary and sufficient conditions for the decomposition of an abstract algebra as the direct product of two algebras?

6. Show that, if A is an abstract algebra and A/R is a quotient algebra modulo a congruence relation R, there is a one-to-one correspondence between the congruence relations on A/R and the congruence relations on A which include R.

8 NUMBER THEORY

In many of the arguments to be developed later, some of the elementary properties of the ring of integers are needed. These are summarized in this section.

Definition 1. Let x be any real number. Define $[x]$ to be the largest integer not exceeding x and $\{x\} = x - [x]$. $\{x\}$ is called the *fractional part* of x.

EXAMPLES

$$
\begin{array}{ll}
[7] = 7 & \{7\} = 0 \\
[2\frac{1}{3}] = 2 & \{2\frac{1}{3}\} = \frac{1}{3} \\
[\pi] = 3 & \{\pi\} = 0.14159 \ldots \\
[-3\frac{1}{5}] = -4 & \{-3\frac{1}{5}\} = \frac{4}{5}
\end{array}
$$

Proposition 2. $0 \leq \{x\} < 1$ and $x - 1 < [x] \leq x < [x] + 1$.

For the rest of this chapter, all algebraic symbols denote integers.

Definition 3. a *divides* b, written $a|b$, iff there exists an integer c such that $b = ac$. $a \nmid b$ is read "a does not divide b."

EXAMPLE. $2|10$, since $10 = 2 \cdot 5$. $2 \nmid 7$.

Proposition 4. For any integers a, b, and c:

$a|a$

$a|0$

$a|b$ implies $|a| \leq |b|$ if $b \neq 0$

$a|b$, $b|c$ implies $a|c$

$c|a$, $c|b$ implies $c|ax + by$ for any integers x and y

A surprising number of results are consequences of the following simple proposition.

Theorem 5. If a, $b > 0$, then $a = bq + r$, where $0 \leq r < b$. q and r are unique.

PROOF. Let $q = [a/b]$ and therefore

$$q \le \frac{a}{b} < q + 1$$

so that

$$0 \le \frac{a}{b} - q < 1$$

Define

$$r = a - bq$$

so that

$$0 \le \frac{r}{b} = \frac{a}{b} - q < 1$$

We have now shown $a = bq + r$, where $0 \le r < b$. To show uniqueness, we assume

$$a = bq + r = bq' + r'$$

where $0 \le r < b$ and $0 \le r' < b$

Assume $q' > q$, that is, $q \le q' - 1$.

$$r = a - bq$$
$$r \ge a - b(q' - 1) = a - bq' + b$$
$$0 > r - b \ge r'$$

Thus $r' < 0$, which contradicts $r' \ge 0$.

Assume $q > q'$ or $q \ge q' + 1$.

$$r = a - bq$$
$$r \le a - b(q' + 1) = a - bq' - b$$
$$r \le r' - b$$
$$r' \ge r + b \ge b \text{ contradicts } r' < b$$

The only noncontradictory possibility is that $q = q'$, which implies $r = r'$, and the uniqueness is proved. |

Definition 6. A nonempty set A contained in a ring R is called an *ideal* of the ring R if

(1) $a, b \in A \Rightarrow (a - b) \in A$
(2) $a \in A, x \in R \Rightarrow ax \in A$ and $xa \in A$

An ideal A is said to be a *principal ideal* if every element of A is a multiple of some element of R. A ring is said to be a *principal ideal ring* if every ideal in the ring is a principal ideal.

EXAMPLE. The set of multiples of 5 in the ring of integers I is an ideal.

Let R be a commutative ring with identity. Then $R[x]$ is defined to be the set of all polynomials in an indeterminate x with coefficients in R. $R[x]$ is also a ring. The set of multiples of $x^3 + 7$ is an ideal in $R[x]$.

Let $R[x,y]$ be the ring of all polynomials in two indeterminates x, y having coefficients in a commutative ring with identity R. The set of all polynomials with no constant term is an ideal.

Theorem 7. The ring of integers I is a principal ideal ring.

PROOF. Let A be an ideal in I. Assume A is nonempty and let a be an element of A.

By condition (1) $a - a = 0 \in A$
Using (1) again $0 - a = -a \in A$

Thus either $A = \{0\}$ or A contains positive integers because one of a, $-a$ is always positive for $a \neq 0$. The case $A = \{0\}$ is trivial; so let m be the least positive integer in A. (The careful reader has now noticed that we have employed our assumption that the natural numbers are well ordered. *Cf.* Axiom 2.3.) Take $a \in A$. By Theorem 7

$$a = qm + r \qquad \text{with } 0 \leq r < m$$
$$r = a - qm$$

If $m \in A$, then $qm \in A$; since $a \in A$ and $qm \in A$, therefore $a - qm = r \in A$. We have proved that $r \in A$, but $r < m$ and m was the least positive integer in A. The only way to avoid a contradiction is for $r = 0$, which implies that $m|a$. Therefore, for every $a \in A$, $m|a$. ▌

Definition 8. If $d|a$, $d|b$, and if for every t, $t|a$, $t|b$ implies $t|d$, then the absolute value of d is called the *greatest common divisor of a and b* and written (a,b).

Theorem 9. If a and b are two integers not both zero, then a and b have a unique greatest common divisor $d = (a,b)$ and there exist integers x and y such that $d = ax + by$.

PROOF. Let $A = \{xa + by | x, y \in I\}$. Clearly, A is an ideal. By the previous theorem, A is a principal ideal generated by some element, say, d. We write

$$A = (d)$$

$a \in A$, $b \in A$ implies $d|a$ and $d|b$.
Since $d \in A$, there are integers x and y such that

$$d = ax + by$$

$t|a$, $t|b \Rightarrow a = k_1 t$, $b = k_2 t$

$$d = ax + by = t(k_1 x + k_2 y)$$

so that $$t|d$$
Then $$d = (a,b)$$

To show uniqueness, assume there exist two greatest divisors d_1 and d_2.

$$d_1|a, \; d_1|b \Rightarrow d_1|d_2$$
$$d_2|a, \; d_2|b \Rightarrow d_2|d_1$$

Therefore $$d_1 = d_2 \quad ▌$$

At this point we have encountered a certain type of proof which may be new to the reader. The proof of Theorem 9 may be called an *existence proof*. The proof demonstrates that a greatest common divisor exists, but when we are given two numbers, say, 1551 and 243, the proof does not tell how to find that $(1551, 243) = 3$.

A proof which indicates in some sense a method of calculation will be called a *constructive proof*. Since our motivation is the solution of engineering problems, we shall always try to find constructive proofs.

Theorem 10. If $a|bc$, $(a,b) = 1$, then $a|c$.

PROOF. There exist integers x, y such that

$$ax + by = 1 \qquad acx + bcy = c$$

Since $a|bc$, $bc = ta$

$$a(cx + ty) = c$$

Thus $\qquad\qquad a|c$ |

The reader should be careful not to misinterpret the preceding theorem. Notice that the following statement is false. If $a|bc$ and $a\nmid b$, then $a|c$. A counterexample is $9|6\cdot3$, $9\nmid3 \nRightarrow 9|6$.

Theorem 11. If $(a,b) = 1$ and $(a,c) = 1$, then $(a,bc) = 1$

PROOF.

$$ax_1 + by_1 = 1$$
$$ax_2 + cy_2 = 1$$
$$a(ax_1x_2 + by_1x_2 + cx_1y_x) + bcy_1y_2 = 1$$
$$(a,bc)|a, (a,bc)|bc \Rightarrow (a,bc)|1$$

so $\qquad\qquad (a,bc) = 1$

Definition 12. An integer p is said to be a *prime* if $p \neq \pm1$ and the only divisors of p are ±1 and $\pm p$.

Theorem 13. Every integer $a > 1$ can be represented as a product of one or more primes.

PROOF. This theorem is proved by induction on a. It is our first use of the second statement of the induction principle.

BASIS. $a = 2$ is a prime.

INDUCTION STEP. Assume the result for $a = 3, \ldots , n - 1$. If n is a prime, we are through. If n is composite, there exists a divisor of n, namely, d, where $2 \leq d \leq n - 1$. The range of values of d is precisely that covered by the basis and the induction hypothesis. Since d has a prime divisor and $d|n$, the theorem follows from the transitive property of division. |

Theorem 14. If $p \left| \prod_{m=1}^{n} p_m \right.$, where each p_m is a prime, then $p = p_m$ for some m.

PROOF. Suppose $p|p_1p_2 \cdots p_n$ and $p \neq p_i$ for $i = 1, \ldots , n - 1$;$(p,p_i) = 1$ for $i = 1, \ldots , n - 1$. $\left(p, \prod_{i=1}^{n-1} p_i \right) = 1$ by repeated application of Theorem 11. Employing Theorem 10, we have $p|p_n$. |

We now prove the important unique factorization theorem.

Theorem 15. The representation of $a > 1$ as a product of prime is unique up to the order of the factors.

PROOF. Assume $a = \prod_{m=1}^{n_1} p_m = \prod_{m=1}^{n_2} p'_m$, where

$$p_1 \leq p_2 \leq \cdots \leq p_{n_1} \qquad p'_1 \leq p'_2 \leq \cdots \leq p'_{n_2}$$

We must show $n_1 = n_2$ and $p_m = p'_m$ for $1 \leq m \leq n_1$. The argument will be an induction on a.

BASIS. $a = 2$, so $n_1 = n_2 = 1$, $p_1 = p'_1 = 2$.

INDUCTION STEP. Assume the result for $3, \ldots, a - 1$. If a is a prime, we are done; otherwise, $n_1 > 1$, $n_2 > 1$. Note that

$$p_1 \;\Big|\; \prod_{m=1}^{n_2} p'_m \quad \text{and} \quad p'_1 \;\Big|\; \prod_{m=1}^{n_1} p_m$$

By Theorem 14, for at least one r and s

$$p'_1 = p_r \quad \text{and} \quad p_1 = p'_s$$

Thus
$$p_1 \leq p_r = p'_1 \leq p'_s = p_1$$
and we get
$$p_1 \leq p'_1 \quad \text{and} \quad p'_1 \leq p_1$$
Therefore
$$p_1 = p'_1$$
Since
$$1 < p_1 < a \quad \text{and} \quad p_1 | a$$
then
$$1 < \frac{a}{p_1} = \prod_{m=2}^{n_1} p_m = \prod_{m=2}^{n_2} p'_m < a$$

By the induction hypothesis, $n_1 - 1 = n_2 - 1$ and $p_m = p'_m$ for $m = 2, \ldots, n_1$. ▋

PROBLEMS

1. The following procedure of obtaining the greatest common divisor of two integers is known as Euclid's algorithm. Let $a, b > 0$. Assume $a \geq b$.

$$a = bq_1 + r_1 \qquad 0 \leq r_1 < b \leq a$$
$$b = q_2 r_1 + r_2 \qquad 0 \leq r_2 < r_1$$
$$r_1 = q_3 r_2 + r_3 \qquad 0 \leq r_3 < r_2$$
$$\cdots\cdots\cdots$$
$$r_{k-2} = r_{k-1} q_k + r_k \qquad 0 \leq r_k < r_{k-1}$$
$$r_{k-1} = r_k q_{k+1}$$

(a) Why does the algorithm terminate?

(b) Show that $r_k = (a,b)$.

2. Prove that if $m \neq 0$, then $(am, bm) = m(a,b)$.

3. Prove that if $m|a$ and $m|b$, then $(a/m, b/m) = (a,b)/m$.

4. Prove that if $ax + by = m$, then $(a,b)|m$.

5. Two integers a and b are said to be *congruent modulo* m iff $m|(a - b)$, and we write $a \equiv b \bmod m$. Show that congruence modulo m is a congruence relation with respect to addition and multiplication.

6. Show that if $a \equiv b \bmod m$ and if $d|m$, then $a \equiv b \bmod d$.

7. Show that if $ka \equiv kb \bmod m$ and $(k,m) = d$, then $a \equiv b \bmod (m/d)$.

8. Consider the equivalence relation of congruence modulo m and define $\{a_1, \ldots, a_m\}$ to be a *complete residue system modulo* m iff $i \neq j$ implies $a_i \not\equiv a_j \bmod m$ and, if a is any integer, there exists an index $i(1 \leq i \leq m)$ such that $a \equiv a_i \bmod m$. (Example: $\{0,1,2, \ldots, m - 1\}$.) Show that if $\{a_1, \ldots, a_m\}$ is a complete residue system mod m and if $(k,m) = 1$, then $\{ka_1, \ldots, ka_m\}$ is a complete residue system mod m.

9. Prove that if p is a prime and $p > 3$, then $p^2 \equiv 1 \bmod 24$.

10. Prove that if $a \equiv b \bmod m$, then $(a,m) = (b,m)$.

11. Show that $-[-x]$ is the least integer greater than or equal to x.

9   RADIX REPRESENTATION

We now develop the theory of radix representations. In computer work, nondecimal number systems are of considerable importance. Algorithms will be given for the conversion between representations to different bases. First, the theorem which characterizes radix representations is given.

Theorem 1.   Let g be an integer, $g > 1$. Then every integer $a > 0$ can be uniquely represented in the form

$$a = c_0 + c_1 g + \cdots + c_n g^n$$

where $0 \le c_m < g$ for $m = 0, \ldots, n$ and $c_n > 0$.

PROOF.   The argument will be an induction on a.

BASIS. $a = 1$, so $c_0 = 1$ and $n = 0$.

INDUCTION STEP.   Assume the theorem true for $2, 3, \ldots, a - 1$. Since $g > 1$, the numbers $g^0, g^1, g^2, \ldots$ form an increasing sequence. Any positive integer lies between two terms of the sequence (cf. Axiom 2.2). This means that there is a unique n such that

$$g^n \le a < g^{n+1}$$

By Theorem 8.5

$$a = c_n g^n + r \qquad 0 \le r < g^n$$
$$c_n g^n = a - r > g^n - g^n = 0$$

so that

$$c_n > 0 \qquad c_n g^n \le a < g^{n+1}$$

so

$$c_n g^n < g^{n+1} \qquad \text{or} \qquad c_n < g$$

It has now been established that $0 < c_n < g$. If $r = 0$,

$$a = 0 + 0 \cdot g + \cdots + 0 \cdot g^{n-1} + c_n g^n$$

If $r > 0$, note $r < g^n \le a$. Thus the induction hypothesis applies to r, and r can be expressed in the form

$$r = b_0 + b_1 g + \cdots + b_t g^t$$

where $0 \le b_i < g$ for $i = 0, \ldots, t$. Of course $t < n$, since $r < g^n$.

With $r > 0$, we have

$$a = b_0 + b_1 g + \cdots + b_t g^t + 0 \cdot g^{t+1} + \cdots + 0 \cdot g^{n-1} + c_n g^n$$

a now has the desired representation, and the theorem follows from the induction principle. To show uniqueness, assume

$$a = c_0 + c_1 g + \cdots + c_n g^n = d_0 + d_1 g + \cdots + d_r g^r$$

with

$$0 \le c_m < g \qquad \text{for } m = 0, \ldots, n$$
$$0 \le d_m < g \qquad \text{for } m = 0, \ldots, r$$

Subtract the two representations of a.

$$0 = e_0 + e_1g + \cdots + e_sg^s$$

where

$$e_m = c_m - d_m \quad \text{for } m = 0, \ldots, s$$

s is the largest value of m for which $c_m \neq d_m$.

If $s = 0$, the $c_0 \neq d_0$ is a contradiction. If $s > 0$, $e_s \neq 0$ and $|e_m| = |c_m - d_m| < g$, that is,

$$|e_m| \leq g - 1$$
$$e_sg^s = -(e_0 + e_1g + \cdots + e_{s-1}g^{s-1})$$
$$g^s \leq |e_sg^s| = |e_0 + e_1g + \cdots + e_{s-1}g^{s-1}|$$

Since

$$e_i \leq g - 1 \quad \text{for } i = 0, \ldots, s - 1$$

$$g^s \leq (g - 1)(1 + g + \cdots + g^{s-1}) = (g - 1)\frac{g^s - 1}{g - 1} = g^s - 1$$

which is a contradiction. ∎

If $g = 2$, the representation is called *binary* or *dyadic*.

If $g = 3$, the representation is called *ternary* or *triadic*.

If $g = 8$, the representation is called *octal*.

If $g = 10$, the representation is called *decimal*.

If $g = 12$, the representation is called *duodecimal*.

If $g = 16$, the representation is called *hexadecimal*.

For applications in switching theory, binary representations are very useful. Binary representations are also important for theoretical work in the foundations of mathematics.

A formal procedure is now presented for converting a given number N to a base g representation for N.

Algorithm 2. Given a number N and a base g such that $g > 1$,

(1) Let $q_0 = N$ and $i = 1$.

(2) Compute q_i and c_{i-1} by Theorem 8.5, that is

$$q_{i-1} = q_ig + c_{i-1}$$

(3) If $q_i = 0$, go to step 5.

(4) If $q_i \neq 0$, replace i by $i + 1$ and go to step 2.

(5) The unique representation is

$$N = \sum_{i=0}^{n} c_ig^i$$

The algorithm assumes that N is "given." If a person is using the algorithm, then N is "given" in decimal. If a computer is used, then the representation will be in the computer's natural representation.

It is necessary to show that the algorithm halts.

Lemma 3. There exists an index i such that $q_i = 0$.

PROOF. Upon examination of the proof of Theorem 8.5, it is noticed that

$$0 \leq q_i = \left[\frac{q_{i-1}}{g}\right] \leq \frac{q_{i-1}}{g} < q_{i-1}$$

because $g > 1$. Thus, we have

$$0 \leq \cdots < q_2 < q_1 < q_0 = N$$

By Axiom 2.1, there must be an index h such that $q_h = 0$. ∎

Next it will be shown that the algorithm actually computes the representation of N.

Lemma 4. $N = \sum\limits_{i=0}^{n} c_i g^i$, where $0 \leq c_i < g$ and the c_i are as computed in Algorithm 2.

PROOF. Note that $c_i = q_i - g q_{i+1}$ for $i = 0, \ldots, n - 1$ and that $c_n = q_n$. Thus

$$\sum_{i=0}^{n} c_i g^i = \sum_{i=0}^{n-1} g^i (q_i - q_{i+1} g) + q_n g^n = q_0 = N \quad \blacksquare$$

The procedure just given is an example of the way we shall prescribe algorithms. The methods will be formulated precisely enough that it will be easy to convert them to digital computer programs. Computational shortcuts will be indicated whenever possible.

EXAMPLE. Convert the decimal integer 219 to a base 6 representation.

$$219 = 36(6) + 3$$
$$36 = 6(6) + 0$$
$$6 = 1(6) + 0$$
$$1 = 0(6) + 1$$

Thus the base 6 representation is 1003. To avoid confusion, we enclose the number in parentheses and list the radix as a subscript, that is, $(219)_{10} = (1003)_6$.

The procedure for recovering a number from a base g representation is so simple that no formal procedure is required.

Algorithm 5. Given a number in base g notation $(c_n, \ldots, c_0)_g$, the number is converted to decimal by forming the weighted sum

$$(c_n, \ldots, c_0)_g = \sum_{i=0}^{n} c_i g^i$$

EXAMPLE. $(2322)_8 = 2 + 2 \cdot 8 + 3 \cdot 8^2 + 2 \cdot 8^3$
$$= 2 + 16 + 192 + 1024 = (1234)_{10}$$

The calculations are easier to perform if the following regrouping is performed.

$$(2322)_8 = 2 + 8(2 + 8(3 + 8(2))) = 2 + 8(2 + 152)$$
$$= 2 + 1232 = 1234$$

Lastly, the problem of converting from one arbitrary system to another is considered.

Algorithm 6.   To convert an integer from base g_1 to base g_2, perform the following computations:

(1)   Convert from base g_1 to decimal by Algorithm 5.
(2)   Convert from decimal to base g_2 by Algorithm 2.

Certain specific radices are particularly easy to manipulate.   To convert from binary to octal, merely group the binary digits into triples from the right and convert each triple to its octal equivalent.   This technique works because $8 = 2^3$.

EXAMPLE.   Convert $(1101101101110)_2$ into octal.
$$((001)(101)(101)(101)(110))_2 = (15556)_8$$

PROBLEMS

1.   Devise an algorithm for the conversion of decimal fractions into a base g system.   HINT: Use [ ] and { } notation.

2.   Is the radix representation of every real number unique?   Explain.

3.   Convert the following integers into base 2 and base 8.
(*a*) 19   (*c*) 42   (*e*) 126
(*b*) 17   (*d*) 147   (*f*) 1023

4.   Convert the following three numbers to the binary system.   Do not use more than 10 binary digits.   Is it necessary to use all of the decimal digits that are given to produce these expansions?

$\pi = 3.141592654 \cdots$ $e = 2.718281828 \cdots$ $\gamma = 0.5772156649 \cdots$

5.   Convert the following octal numbers to binary and to decimal: 721, 654, and 1472365.

6.   Expand the integer 42 to a representation using radix -3, where $0 \le c_i < 3$.

7.   Can you state and prove a theorem analgous to Theorem 9.1 for negative radices?

8.   What is the largest number representable with n digits in a radix g system?

9.   What is the largest number representable with n digits in a radix $-g$ system?

10   GRAPH THEORY

When switching networks are considered, it will be seen that a variety of properties of the networks are independent of the switching elements themselves and depend entirely on the interconnections of the elements, i.e., the associated graph.   For this reason the elements of graph theory are mentioned now, although most of the concepts are familiar to engineers.

Definition 1.   A *graph* is a system $V = \langle V, I \rangle$, where V is called the sets of *vertices* and I is a binary relation on V, the *incidence relation*.

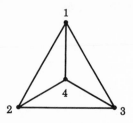

FIG. 1

For *undirected* (*directed*) graphs we think of aIb just in case there is an undirected (directed) line from a to b. Since I would be a symmetric relation for undirected graphs, we write (a,b) ϵI but omit (b,a) from I.

EXAMPLE. $V = \langle\{1,2,3,4\}, \{(1,2),(2,3),(1,3),(1,4),(2,4),(3,4)\}\rangle$.   The pictorial representation is given in Fig. 1.

Definition 2.   Two graphs V_1 and V_2 are *isomorphic* iff there is a one-to-one onto mapping α from V_1 to V_2 such that $aI_1b \Leftrightarrow \alpha(a)I_2\alpha(b)$.

EXAMPLE. V_1 and V_2 are shown in Fig. 2.   The graphs are isomorphic under the correspondence α.

Definition 3.   The number of edges incident at a vertex is called the *degree* of the vertex.   For a directed graph, the *in degree* of a vertex is the number of edges coming in to the vertex.   The *out degree* is defined similarly.

EXAMPLE.   In Fig. 3 the graph G_1 is directed and G_2 is undirected.   In G_1 the in degree of node 3 is 1 and the out degree is 1.   At node 2 of G_1 the in degree is 2 and the out degree 0.   In G_2 the degree of all nodes is 2.

Definition 4.   A *path* is any finite non-void sequence of edges of the form $((a_0,a_1), (a_1,a_2), (a_2,a_3), \ldots, (a_{n-1},a_n))$ where a_iIa_{i+1} for $0 \le i < n$. A graph is *connected* iff there exists a path between any two of its vertices.

If a graph is not connected, one can uniquely decompose the graph into maximal connected subgraphs called *components*.

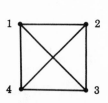

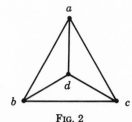

v	$\alpha(v)$
1	a
2	b
3	c
4	d

FIG. 2

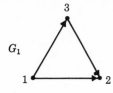

G_1

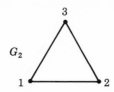

G_2

FIG. 3

Definition 5. A *circuit* is a finite path in which the initial vertex and final vertex coincide. That is, a circuit is a path with the form $((a_1,b_1),$ $(b_1b_2),\ \ldots\ ,(b_k,a_1))$.

EXAMPLE. Let V be as shown in Fig. 4. The set $C = ((1,2),(2,3),(3,5),(5,1))$ is a circuit of V. Note that $D = ((1,2),(2,3),(3,5),(5,2))$ is not a circuit of V.

Definition 6. Let V be a graph with e edges, v vertices, and p components. The *rank* of V, written $\rho(V)$, is defined as $v - p$. The *nullity* of V, written $\mu(V)$, is defined as $e - v + p$. (Note that $\mu + \rho = e$.)

EXAMPLE. For the graph in the above example, $p = 1$, so that $\rho = 4$ and $\mu = 6$.

Definition 7. A *cut set* C of a connected graph V is a set of edges of the graph such that removal of C reduces the rank of V by 1, but no proper subset of C would reduce the rank.†

In other words, the removal of a cut set from a connected graph results in a disconnected graph.

EXAMPLE. Referring to the preceding example, the set $C = \{(1,2),(1,3),(1,4),(1,5)\}$ is a cut set.

To a mathematician, isomorphism of graphs means that the graphs have essentially the same structure. To an engineer, this concept is too restrictive, since the graphs shown in Fig. 5 are not isomorphic yet would possess the same engineering attributes if the graphs represented networks. This type of reasoning led H. Whitney[4] to define the concept of two-isomorphic graphs.

† It is understood that when an edge (a_i,a_j) is removed, the vertices a_i and a_j remain in the graph.

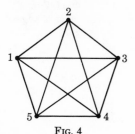

FIG. 4

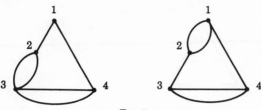

FIG. 5

Definition 8. Two graphs V_1 and V_2 are *two-isomorphic* iff they are isomorphic or become isomorphic under the following operations:

(a) If a graph has a vertex v which is contained in a subgraph W and in $\bar{W}$ (i.e., a *cut point*), then v is split into two vertices v' and v'' while the graph is split into two graphs, W containing v' and $\bar{W}$ containing v''. We call this operation *splitting*.

(b) If the graph consists of two subgraphs W_1 and W_2 which have only two vertices a and b in common, the interchange of their terminals in one of the subgraphs.

Definition 9. A graph V is *planar* iff there exists a mapping of V onto a plane such that no two branches of V have a point in common which is not a vertex.

It is necessary to introduce the concept of duality of graphs. The definition to be given is a combinatorial one which may appear to have little to do with the usual geometric concept. The connection will become apparent shortly.

Definition 10. V_2 is a *dual graph* of V_1 iff there exists a one-to-one mapping α from the edges of V_1 onto the edges of V_2 such that if W_1 is any subgraph of V_1 and W_2 is the *complement* of the corresponding subgraph of V_2, then

$$\rho(W_2) = \rho(V_2) - \mu(W_1)$$

Proposition 11. If V_2 is a dual of V_1, then

$$\rho_1 = \mu_2 \quad \text{and} \quad \rho_2 = \mu_1$$

PROOF. Let $W_1 = V_1$, then $\alpha(V_1) = V_2$ so that $W_2 = \emptyset$, the null graph (cf. Prob. 5). By the definition, $0 = \rho(\emptyset) = \rho_2 - \mu_1$. Since $\rho_1 + \mu_1 = \rho_2 + \mu_2 =$ number of edges, then $\rho_1 = \mu_2$. $\blacksquare$

G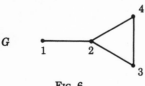

FIG. 6

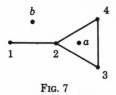

FIG. 7

Lemma 12.   If V_2 is a dual of V_1, then V_1 is a dual of V_2.

PROOF.   Let V_1 and V_2 have e edges.   Let W_2 be any subgraph of V_2 and W_1 be the complement of the subgraph of V_1.

$$\rho(W_2) = \rho(V_2) - \mu(W_1) \qquad \text{and} \qquad \rho(V_2) = \mu(V_1)$$

If W_1 and W_2 have e_1 and e_2 edges, respectively, then

$$\begin{aligned}\rho(W_1) &= e_1 - \mu(W_1) = e_1 - (\rho(W_2) - \rho(W_2)) = e_1 - \mu(V_1) + \rho(W_2)\\&= e_1 - \mu(V_1) + e_2 - \mu(W_2) = e - \mu(V_1) - \mu(W_2)\\&= \rho(V_1) - \mu(W_2) \quad \blacksquare\end{aligned}$$

The preceding theorems use the phrase "a dual of." It is appropriate to ask if all graphs have duals and also if the dual of a graph is unique if it exists at all.

Theorem 13.   (Whitney) If V_1 and V_2 are dual graphs of V, then V_1 is two-isomorphic to V_2.

PROOF.   This theorem depends on some involved results about two-isomorphism of graphs and cannot be proved here.   See the original paper by Whitney[4]. $\blacksquare$

Theorem 14.   A graph V has a dual iff V is planar.

PROOF.   See Seshu and Reed for a reproduction of Whitney's original proof. $\blacksquare$

EXAMPLE.   The usual method of construction of the dual is illustrated by the graph of Fig. 6.   Place a point in every region of the graph.   For the present case, we call them a and b, Fig. 7.   Draw all lines connecting adjacent points through one branch of the graph.   We draw these in with dotted lines, Fig. 8.   The dual graph consists of the dotted lines, Fig. 9.

For engineering purposes, it is often necessary to fix a pair of vertices and call them the terminals of the network.

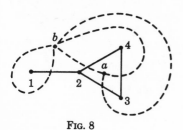

FIG. 8

G^D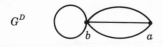

FIG. 9

Definition 15.   A *two-terminal graph* with terminals 1 and 1' is a system

$$V = \langle V, I, 1, 1' \rangle \qquad 1, 1' \in V$$

Two-terminal series-parallel graphs (or networks) are of special importance.   The formal definition of such networks is given inductively.

Definition 16.   Two two-terminal graphs are joined in a *series connection* iff they have exactly one vertex of degree 2 in common.   Two two-terminal graphs are in *parallel* iff they are incident at the same two vertices.

Definition 17. V is called a *two-terminal series-parallel graph* iff V consists of a single edge or is obtained from single edges by a finite number of series and parallel connections.

It is essential to understand that the terminals must be specified in order to know if a graph is series-parallel or not.   Figure 10 shows two graphs.   One is series-parallel with respect to the marked terminals, and the other is non-series-parallel.

Definition 18.   A two-terminal graph is *planar* iff the graph with an additional branch added between the terminals is planar.

In Fig. 11, is shown a planar graph which is not planar as a two-terminal graph with terminals 1 and 1'.

Definition 19.   A pair of two-terminal graphs are called *duals* iff the graphs obtained by adding edges between the terminals are duals in the sense of Definition 10 and the additional edges correspond.

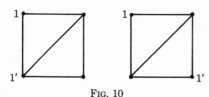

FIG. 10

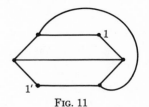

FIG. 11

This section is concluded with the proof of two propositions which will be required for future work.

Theorem 20. If V_1 and V_2 are dual graphs, there is a one-to-one map from circuits in one to cut sets of the other.

PROOF. Let $\{C_1, \ldots, C_l\}$ be the set of circuits of V. Let α be the correspondence between the edges of V_1 and V_2 which is caused by duality. Consider a particular circuit of V_1, say, C. It is claimed that $\alpha(C)$ is a cut set of V_2. Since V_2 is a dual of V_1,

$$\rho(G_2) - \mu(\alpha(C)) = \rho(V_2) - \mu(C)$$

The nullity of any circuit is 1 (Prob. 8), so that

$$\rho(G_2) - \mu(\alpha(C)) = \rho(V_2) - 1$$

Thus removal of $\alpha(C)$ lowers the rank of V_2 by 1. No proper subset of $\alpha(C)$ could lower the rank by 1, because if it did, a proper subset of C would be a circuit, and that would contradict property a in Prob. 9. Thus $\alpha(C)$ is a cutset of V_2. ▌

Theorem 21. Let V_1 and V_2 be two-terminal dual graphs with terminals 1-1′ and 2-2′. Paths between the terminals of either graph correspond in a one-to-one fashion with cut sets which place the terminals in different sets.

PROOF. Connect 1 and 1′ by an edge. Now every path between 1 and 1′ is a circuit. By Theorem 20, this circuit maps into a cut set and it remains only to show that this cut set places the terminals in different sets. Since the edge corresponding to 1-1′ must correspond to the edge 2-2′, the terminals are indeed separated by removal of this set. ▌

EXAMPLE. Consider the graph G shown in Fig. 12. The dual two-terminal graph is given in Fig. 13. Under the duality map α we have

$$\alpha: (1,3) \to (a,a')$$
$$(3,2) \to (a,b)$$
$$(2,1') \to (a,b)$$
$$(3,1') \to (b,a')$$

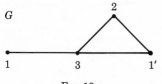

G

2

1   3   1′

FIG. 12

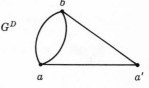

G^D

b

a a'

FIG. 13

In G the path $(1,3)$, $(3,2)$, $(2,1')$ takes us from 1 to $1'$. The corresponding set in G^D, the dual graph of G, is $\{(a,a'),(a,b),(a,b)\}$, which is a cut set that separates a and a'.

PROBLEMS

1. Let V be a finite graph. Show that there are an even number of vertices of odd degree.

2. Show that a graph V is planar iff V can be mapped onto a sphere as in Definition 9.

3. Define the *complete graph on n points* to be $K_n = \langle V_n,1 \rangle$, where V_n is a set of n elements and 1 denotes the universal relation on V_n, that is, $1 = V_n \times V_n$. Show that, for the complete graph K_n, $\rho = n - 1$ and $\mu = (n - 2)(n - 1)/2$.

4. Show that there are P_n paths between any pair of vertices in K_n $(n \geq 2)$ where

$$P_n = (n - 2)! \sum_{j=0}^{n-2} \frac{1}{j!}$$

5. Let V be a set with n elements. $\emptyset$ denotes the empty graph $\emptyset = \langle V,\emptyset \rangle$. Show that $\rho(\emptyset) = 0$ and $\mu(\emptyset) = 0$.

6. Construct an algorithm for determining if a given two-terminal graph is series-parallel.

7. Give an example of two graphs which are duals but are not isomorphic.

8. Show that a subgraph W of a graph V is a circuit iff $\mu(W) = 1$.

9. Show that the circuits C of a graph V satisfy the following three conditions:
 (a) No proper subset of C is a circuit.
 (b) If C_1, $C_2 \in C$ and if an edge e is in C_1 and C_2 while an edge $e_2 \in C_1$ and $e_2 \notin C_2$, then there exists a circuit in $C_1 \cup C_2$ such that $e_2 \in C_1 \cup C_2$ but $e_1 \notin C_1 \cup C_2$.
 (c) If $C_1 \cap C_2 = \{e\}$, then $C_1 \cup C_2 - \{e\} = \bigcup_j C_j$, where the C_j are circuits.

10. (Elgot-Wright) If x and y are nodes of a graph, define $x \leq y \Leftrightarrow (x = y)$ or (there is a chain containing x and y such that x precedes y in the chain).
 (a) Show that $\leq$ is a partial ordering on the set of nodes of the network.
 (b) Show that if the graph is series-parallel, then $\leq$ determines a lattice.

11. Let V be an undirected graph and let a and b be vertices. Let the ith path from a to b be denoted by $S_i(a,b)$. The *distance from a to b* is defined to be

$$d(a,b) = \min_i \, (\text{length } (S_i(a,b)))$$

where the length of a path is the number of edges in it.
Show that
$$d(a,b) \geq 0$$
$$d(a,b) = 0 \qquad \text{iff } a = b$$
$$d(a,b) = d(b,a)$$
$$d(a,b) + d(b,c) \geq d(a,c)$$

12. Does the formal definition of a graph $V = \langle V,I \rangle$ allow for edges in parallel? Give a more general definition.

11 SUMMARY

Two general references for the mathematics used in this book are Birkhoff and MacLane and Mostow, Sampson, and Meyer. Chevalley's book is also a good source, but it is somewhat less of a survey book. Birkhoff's *Lattice Theory*[1] is also an excellent reference, but it is more advanced. The material on abstract algebras in this chapter follows Birkhoff's forward on algebra.[1]

There are now several excellent books on graph theory; Seshu and Reed is best oriented toward the applications to engineering and is the least sophisticated reference. The more advanced reader will wish to read the books by Berge, König, or Ore.

CHAPTER 2 *boolean algebra and an application*

1 INTRODUCTION

Two kinds of networks will concern us. The first kind, called a *combinational switching network*, is a device whose output depends only on the input at the present time. The second kind, the *sequential machine*, has an output which is a function of the present input and the entire past history of inputs. Naturally, sequential machines are more complicated than combinational circuits, so we shall postpone their study until Chap. 9.

Historically, the theory of switching networks started in 1938 with Shannon's thesis[1] and a similar, but independent, thesis of Shestakoff. In retrospect, it is possible to trace the basic idea back to P. Ehrenfest in 1910. The basic idea, suggested by Ehrenfest and developed by Shannon and Shestakoff, was to construct a mathematical system which enables one to systematically represent and analyze switching circuits.

Although Shannon applied the classical propositional calculus to relay circuits, there is an algebraic system known as boolean algebra which is in a certain sense, equivalent to the propositional calculus. We shall develop boolean algebra in this chapter in order to have a technique for the study (and synthesis) of switching networks. We shall develop boolean algebra abstractly as a mathematical system, and the intended interpretation will be given in Chap. 3.

2 AN AXIOMATIC DESCRIPTION OF BOOLEAN ALGEBRAS

The first approach that will be taken is to characterize boolean algebras by a set of axioms.

Definition 1.   A *boolean algebra* is a system $B = \langle B,+,\cdot,0,1 \rangle$, where B has at least two distinct elements and satisfies the following axioms.

1.	$(\forall a)(\forall b)(\forall c)$	$(a + b) + c = a + (b + c)$	associativity of $+$
2.	$(\forall a)(\forall b)(\forall c)$	$(ab)c = a(bc)$	associativity of $\cdot$
3.	$(\forall a)(\forall b)$	$a + b = b + a$	commutativity of $+$
4.	$(\forall a)(\forall b)$	$ab = ba$	commutativity of $\cdot$
5.	$(\exists !0)(\forall a)$	$a + 0 = 0 + a = a$	existence of a unique identity under $+$
6.	$(\exists !1)(\forall a)$	$a1 = 1a = a$	existence of a unique identity under $\cdot$
7.	$(\forall a)(\forall b)(\forall c)$	$a + (bc) = (a + b)(a + c)$	distributively of $+$ over $\cdot$
8.	$(\forall a)(\forall b)(\forall c)$	$a(b + c) = (ab) + (ac)$	distributively of $\cdot$ over $+$
9.	$(\forall a)(\exists \bar{a})$	$a\bar{a} = 0$ and $a + \bar{a} = 1$	existence of a complement

Note that the usual abbreviation of writing ab for $a \cdot b$ has been followed.   It is now possible to prove theorems directly from the axioms. A few such theorems are derived so that the reader can gain familiarity with the operations of boolean algebra.   It will be shown shortly that there is a better method of proof than deduction from the axioms for finite boolean algebras.

Theorem 2. $a + a = a$

PROOF.
$a + a = (a + a) \cdot 1$	Axiom 6
$= (a + a)(a + \bar{a})$	Axiom 9
$= a + (a\bar{a})$	Axiom 7
$= a + 0$	Axiom 9
$= a$	Axiom 5 |

Theorem 3. $aa = a$

PROOF.
$aa = aa + 0$	Axiom 5
$= aa + a\bar{a}$	Axiom 9
$= a(a + \bar{a})$	Axiom 8
$= a1$	Axiom 9
$= a$	Axiom 6 |

Theorem 4. $a + 1 = 1$

PROOF. $a + 1 = (a + 1) \cdot 1$ Axiom 6
$= (a + 1)(a + \bar{a})$ Axiom 9
$= a + (1\bar{a})$ Axiom 7
$= a + \bar{a}$ Axiom 6
$= 1$ Axiom 9 |

Theorem 5. $a0 = 0$

PROOF. $a0 = (a0) + 0$ Axiom 5
$= a0 + a\bar{a}$ Axiom 9
$= a(0 + \bar{a})$ Axiom 8
$= a(\bar{a})$ Axiom 5
$= 0$ Axiom 9 |

Theorem 6. $a + ab = a$

PROOF. $a + ab = a1 + ab$ Axiom 6
$= a(1 + b)$ Axiom 8
$= a(b + 1)$ Axiom 3
$= a1$ Theorem 4
$= a$ Axiom 6 |

Theorem 7. $a(a + b) = a$

PROOF. $a(a + b) = aa + ab$ Axiom 8
$= a + ab$ Theorem 3
$= a$ Theorem 6 |

Theorem 8. $\bar{a}$ is unique.

PROOF.   Suppose a has two complements $\bar{a}_1$ and $\bar{a}_2$.
By Axiom 9

$$a + \bar{a}_1 = 1 \qquad a + \bar{a}_2 = 1$$
and $a\bar{a}_1 = 0 \qquad a\bar{a}_2 = 0$ (1)
then $\bar{a}_2 = 1\bar{a}_2$ Axiom 6
$= (a + \bar{a}_1)\bar{a}_2$ Eqs. (1)
$= \bar{a}_2(a + \bar{a}_1)$ Axiom 4
$= \bar{a}_2 a + \bar{a}_2\bar{a}_1$ Axiom 8
$= a\bar{a}_2 + \bar{a}_1\bar{a}_2$ Axiom 4
$= 0 + \bar{a}_1\bar{a}_2$ Eqs. (1)
$= a\bar{a}_1 + \bar{a}_1\bar{a}_2$ Eqs. (1)
$= \bar{a}_1 a + \bar{a}_1\bar{a}_2$ Axiom 4
$= \bar{a}_1(a + \bar{a}_2)$ Axiom 8
$= \bar{a}_1 1$ Eqs. (1)
$= \bar{a}_1$ Axiom 6 |

Theorem 9. $\bar{\bar{a}} = a$

PROOF.   We are now attempting to find the complement of $\bar{a}$, but

$$\bar{a} + a = 1 \qquad a\bar{a} = 0$$

a is one complement of $\bar{a}$. By Theorem 8, a is the unique complement of $\bar{a}$; hence

$$\bar{\bar{a}} = a \quad \blacksquare$$

Theorem 10. $\overline{(a + b)} = \bar{a}\bar{b}$

PROOF. The method of attack will be to show that $(a + b) + \bar{a}\bar{b} = 1$ and $(a + b)\bar{a}\bar{b} = 0$. This shows that $(a + b)$ and $\bar{a}\bar{b}$ are complements. Theorem 8 guarantees that the complement is unique. First,

$$
\begin{aligned}
(a + b) + \bar{a}\bar{b} &= ((a + b) + \bar{a})((a + b) + \bar{b}) && \text{Axiom 7}\\
&= ((b + a) + \bar{a})(a + (b + \bar{b})) && \text{Axioms 3 and 1}\\
&= (b + (a + \bar{a}))(a + 1) && \text{Axioms 1 and 9}\\
&= (b + 1)1 && \text{Axiom 9 and}\\
& && \text{Theorem 4}\\
&= 1 && \text{Theorem 4}
\end{aligned}
$$

Second,

$$
\begin{aligned}
(a + b)\bar{a}\bar{b} &= a(\bar{a}\bar{b}) + b(\bar{a}\bar{b}) && \text{Axiom 8}\\
&= (a\bar{a})\bar{b} + b(\bar{b}\bar{a}) && \text{Axioms 2 and 4}\\
&= 0 + (bb)\bar{a} && \text{Axioms 9 and 2}\\
&= 0 && \text{Axiom 9} \quad \blacksquare
\end{aligned}
$$

Theorem 11. $\overline{ab} = \bar{a} + \bar{b}$

PROOF. The method of proof is exactly like that of the preceding theorem. We shall show that

$$(\bar{a} + \bar{b}) + (ab) = 1 \quad \text{and} \quad (\bar{a} + \bar{b})ab = 0$$

First,

$$
\begin{aligned}
(\bar{a} + \bar{b}) + ab &= ((\bar{a} + \bar{b}) + a)((\bar{a} + \bar{b}) + b) && \text{Axiom 7}\\
&= ((\bar{b} + \bar{a}) + a)(\bar{a} + (\bar{b} + b)) && \text{Axioms 3 and 1}\\
&= (\bar{b} + (\bar{a} + a))(\bar{a} + 1) && \text{Axioms 1 and 9}\\
&= (\bar{b} + 1)1 && \text{Axiom 9 and}\\
& && \text{Theorem 4}\\
&= 1 && \text{Theorem 4}
\end{aligned}
$$

Finally,

$$
\begin{aligned}
(\bar{a} + \bar{b})ab &= \bar{a}(ab) + \bar{b}(ab) && \text{Axiom 8}\\
&= (\bar{a}a)b + \bar{b}(ba) && \text{Axioms 2 and 4}\\
&= 0 + (\bar{b}b)a && \text{Axioms 9 and 2}\\
&= 0 && \text{Axiom 9} \quad \blacksquare
\end{aligned}
$$

By this time the reader should have gained enough familiarity with the axioms and theorems that it should not be necessary to proceed only one step per line in the proofs.

Theorem 12. $a + \bar{a}b = a + b$

PROOF. $a + \bar{a}b = (a + \bar{a})(a + b) = a + b \quad \blacksquare$

Theorem 13. $a(\bar{a} + b) = ab$

PROOF. $\bar{a} + (\bar{a}\bar{b}) = \bar{a} + \bar{b} \quad$ by Theorem 12

$a(\bar{a} + b) = ab \quad$ by Theorems 10 and 11 $\quad \blacksquare$

Several interesting results have now been derived. Theorem 8 along with the axioms implies that $(\bar{})$ is a mapping from B into B. Theorems 10 and 11 are called the De Morgan theorems.

A number of other important concepts are introduced in the problems and will be used throughout the rest of this book.

PROBLEMS

1. Define $x \leq y$ iff $x + y = y$ in the boolean algebra $B = \langle B, +, \cdot, 0, 1 \rangle$. Show $\leq$ is a partial ordering on B.

2. Show that $x \leq y$ iff $x = xy$ iff $\bar{y} \leq \bar{x}$.

3. Show that $x \leq x + y$ and $x \geq xy$.

4. Show that if $x_1 \leq y_1$ and $x_2 \leq y_2$, then $x_1 + x_2 \leq y_1 + y_2$ and $x_1 x_2 \leq y_1 y_2$.

5. Show that $x \leq y$ iff $x\bar{y} = 0$ iff $\bar{x} + y = 1$.

6. Show that $x \leq y + z$ if $x \leq y$ or $x \leq z$ and that $x \leq yz$ iff $x \leq y$ and $x \leq z$.

7. Define $x \oplus y = x\bar{y} + \bar{x}y$ in the boolean algebra B. Show that $0 \oplus 0 = 1 \oplus 1 = 0$ and that $0 \oplus 1 = 1 \oplus 0 = 1$.

8. Show that $x \oplus 0 = x$ and that $x \oplus 1 = \bar{x}$.

9. Show that $x \oplus x = 0$ and that $x \oplus \bar{x} = 1$.

10. Show that $x \oplus y = y \oplus x$.

11. Show that $(x \oplus y) \oplus z = x \oplus (y \oplus z)$.

12. Show that $x \oplus y = z \Rightarrow x \oplus z = y$.

13. Show that $x \oplus y = z \Rightarrow x \oplus y \oplus z = 0$.

14. Show that $x(y \oplus z) = xy \oplus xz$.

15. Let S be any set with n elements. Show that the set of all subsets of S forms a boolean algebra where $+$ is interpreted as set union and $\cdot$ is interpreted as set intersection. Naturally, 0 is $\emptyset$ and 1 is S. Note that this boolean algebra has 2^n elements (cf. Prob. 1-2.2).

3 BOOLEAN FUNCTIONS

The central concept of switching theory is the *boolean function*. Because of the intended application, boolean functions are also called *switching functions*.

Definition 1. The system $A = \langle \{0,1\}, +, \cdot, 0, 1 \rangle$ is a boolean algebra. The operations $+$ and $\cdot$ are defined as

$$0 + 0 = 0$$
$$0 + 1 = 1 + 0 = 1 + 1 = 1 \qquad (1)$$
$$\bar{0} = 1$$
$$\bar{1} = 0$$

The reader can easily verify that all the axioms of a boolean algebra are satisfied for A.

Definition 2. A *boolean function* or *switching function* $f(x_1, \ldots, x_n)$ is defined to be a mapping from $\underset{i=1}{\overset{n}{\times}} \{0,1\} = \{0,1\}^n$ into $\{0,1\}$.

Since there are 2^n elements in $\{0,1\}^n$ and 2 elements in $\{0,1\}$, the following result is immediate (cf. Prob. 1-5.1).

Proposition 3. There are 2^{2^n} switching functions of n variables.

The next problem is to decide how to define $+$, $\cdot$, and $^-$ for switching functions. The answer is given in the following definition.

Definition 4. Let f, g, and h denote switching functions of n variables. Define

$$f + g = h \qquad \text{iff } f(x_1, \ldots ,x_n) + g(x_1, \ldots ,x_n) = h(x_1, \ldots ,x_n)$$

where all the x_i vary over 0, 1 and the functional values are combined according to the rules of (1). $fg = h$ is defined similarly.

$$\bar{f} = g \qquad \text{iff } \bar{f}(x_1, \ldots ,x_n) = g(x_1, \ldots ,x_n)$$

as every x_i varies over 0, 1.

EXAMPLE. $n = 2$. Suppose f maps $(0,1)$ and $(1,1)$ into 1 and everything else into 0; suppose g maps $(1,1)$ into 1 and everything else into 0. $f + g$ maps $(0,1)$ and $(1,1)$ into 1 and everything else into 0. fg maps $(1,1)$ into 1 and everything else into 0. $\bar{f}$ maps $(1,0)$ and $(0,0)$ into 1 and $(0,1)$, $(1,1)$ into 0. These statements may be expressed in a tabular form.

x_1	x_2	f	g	$f+g$	$f \cdot g$	$\bar{f}$	$\bar{g}$
0	0	0	0	0	0	1	1
0	1	1	0	1	0	0	1
1	0	0	0	0	0	1	1
1	1	1	1	1	1	0	0

Thus the operations on the functions are defined "pointwise" on the range on the functions. The tabular representation, or "truth table," is a convenient way to compute, since one writes out f and g and proceeds through the table row by row computing by the rules given in (1).

Proposition 5. Let F_n be the set of all switching functions of n variables. The system $F_n = \langle F_n, +, \cdot, 0, 1 \rangle$ is a boolean algebra of the 2^{2^n} functions of n variables, called the *free boolean algebra on n generators*.

The constant 0 in F_n is the function which maps every n-tuple into 0. Similarly, 1 is the function which maps every n-tuple into 1. The same symbol is being used for two different objects, but there is scarcely any danger of confusion.

Definition 6. The *weight*† of a switching function f is defined to be the number of elements of $\{0,1\}^n$ which are mapped into 1, that is, the cardinality of $f^{-1}(1)$. The weight of f is denoted by $w(f)$.

† The term *measure* is sometimes used for this concept.

Proposition 7

$$w(\bar{f}) = 2^n - w(f)$$
$$w(f + g) = w(f) + w(g) - w(fg)$$
$$w(fg) = w(f) + w(g) - w(f + g)$$

There are a variety of ways to represent boolean functions which are useful in switching theory. The elements of the domain are put into a one-to-one correspondence with the integers $0, 1, \ldots, 2^n - 1$ by imagining that each n-tuple of zeroes and ones is the binary representation of the corresponding integer. This map is one-to-one by Theorem 1-9.1.

Definition 8. If i is any integer such that $0 \leq i \leq 2^n - 1$ and if the binary representation of i is $(i_1, \ldots, i_n)$, $i_j \epsilon \{0,1\}$ for $j = 1, \ldots, n$, then the *minterm function* $m_i(x_1, \ldots, x_n)$ is defined by

$$m_i(x_1, \ldots, x_n) = \begin{cases} 1 & \text{if } x_1 = i_1, \ldots, x_n = i_n \\ 0 & \text{otherwise} \end{cases}$$

Note that $m_i m_j = 0$ if $i \neq j$.

Theorem 9. Every switching function can be uniquely written as a sum of minterm functions.

PROOF. The argument is an induction on the weight of f.
BASIS. $k = 0$; the theorem is trivially true. $k = 1$; every such function is a minterm function.

INDUCTION STEP. Suppose f is a function with weight k. Choose some element $i = (i_1, \ldots, i_n)_2$ such that $f(i_1, \ldots, i_n) = 1$. Clearly, such an i must exist because f has weight k and $k \geq 1$. Then $f = m_i(x_1, \ldots, x_n) + g(x_1, \ldots, x_n)$, where g has weight at most $k - 1$, by Proposition 7. The proof is complete by the induction principle. Uniqueness is also easy to show. ▌

Corollary 10. Any switching function of n variables can be written

$$f(x_1, \ldots, x_n) = \sum_{i \epsilon I} m_i(x_1, \ldots, x_n)$$

where I is some subset of the integers $0, 1, \ldots, 2^n - 1$.

Corollary 11. If

$$f(x_1, \ldots, x_n) = \sum_{i \epsilon I} m_i(x_1, \ldots, x_n)$$

and

$$g(x_1, \ldots, x_n) = \sum_{j \epsilon J} m_j(x_1, \ldots, x_n)$$

then

$$f(x_1, \ldots, x_n)g(x_1, \ldots, x_n) = \sum_{i \epsilon I \cap J} m_i(x_1, \ldots, x_n)$$

$$f(x_1, \ldots, x_n) + g(x_1, \ldots, x_n) = \sum_{i \epsilon I \cup J} m_i(x_1, \ldots, x_n)$$

and

$$\bar{f}(x_1, \ldots, x_n) = \sum_{i \notin I} m_i(x_1, \ldots, x_n)$$

Considerably more will be said about this representation at a later time, but for the present, an example is worked.

EXAMPLE.   The minterm functions of two variables, along with a typical function and its expansion, are given in Table 1.

TABLE 1

$$f(x_1,x_2) = m_0(x_1,x_2) + m_2(x_1,x_2) + m_3(x_1,x_2)$$

x_1	x_2	$m_0(x_1,x_2)$	$m_1(x_1,x_2)$	$m_2(x_1,x_2)$	$m_3(x_1,x_2)$	f
0	0	1	0	0	0	1
0	1	0	1	0	0	0
1	0	0	0	1	0	1
1	1	0	0	0	1	1

Theorem 9 has a geometric interpretation which is very useful and gives insight into some properties of switching functions.   It is assumed that the reader is familiar with cubes and their n-dimensional versions, hypercubes.   The n-dimensional cube has 2^n vertices with n lines emanating from each vertex.   The vertices of the n-cube are labeled with n-tuples of zeroes and ones such that two vertices are connected by a line iff the labels differ in one and only one position (cf. Prob. 8).   As examples, the n cubes ($n = 1, \ldots , 4$) are shown in Figs. 1 to 4.

Theorem 12.   Every switching function can be uniquely represented as a subset of vertices of the n-cube.

PROOF.   The minterm functions correspond in a one-to-one fashion to the vertices, i.e., the map φ is given explicitly by

$$\varphi: m_i(x_1, \ldots ,x_n) \leftrightarrow (i_1, \ldots ,i_n)_2 = i$$

Thus, Theorem 9 guarantees a unique representation. |

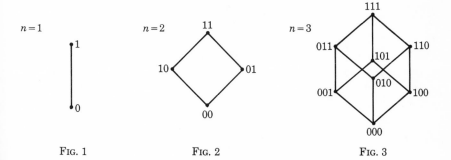

FIG. 1   FIG. 2   FIG. 3

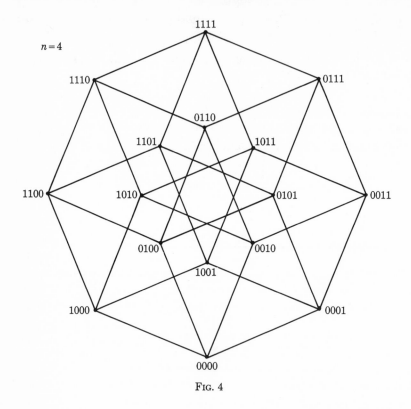

FIG. 4

EXAMPLE.   Let

$$f(x_1,x_2,x_3) = m_0(x_1,x_2,x_3) + m_2(x_1,x_2,x_3) + m_4(x_1,x_2,x_3) + m_6(x_1,x_2,x_3) + m_7(x_1,x_2,x_3).$$

More compactly, $f(x_1,x_2,x_3) = \Sigma(0,2,4,6,7)$, or $f(x_1,x_2, x_3)$ has index set $I = \{0,2,4,6,7\}$. The geometric representation is shown in Fig. 5, where the designated vertices are marked by heavy circles.

It is convenient to have a distance function defined on the hypercube.

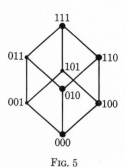

FIG. 5

Definition 13. Let $i = (i_1, \ldots, i_n)$ and $j = (j_1, \ldots, j_n)$, $i_k, j_k \in \{0,1\}$ for $k = 1, \ldots, n$, be two vertices of the n cube. The *distance between* i *and* j is defined as follows and denoted by $d(i,j)$.

$$d(i,j) = \sum_{k=1}^{n} (i_k \oplus j_k)$$

The expression $i_k \oplus j_k$ has the value 0 or 1 according as i_k and j_k are the same or not, and the summation is to be interpreted as the sum of natural numbers. Thus, $d(i,j)$ is the number of places where i and j disagree.

EXAMPLE. The distance between the points $i = (0,1,0,1)$ and $j = (1,0,0,1)$ on the four cube is

$$d(i,j) = 1 + 1 + 0 + 0 = 2$$

This distance function has the following properties, the proofs of which are left to the reader.

Proposition 14

$d(i,j) \geq 0$	nonnegative function
$d(i,j) = d(j,i)$	symmetric function
$d(i,j) = 0$ iff $i = j$	
$d(i,k) \leq d(i,j) + d(j,k)$	triangle inequality

PROBLEMS

1. Prove the properties of $d(i,j)$ stated in Proposition 14.

2. We define a *sphere of radius r and center c on the n cube* as follows:

$$K_r^c = \{i \mid d(i,c) = r\}$$

Show that these spheres have two centers. What is the relation between the centers? Does every ordinary sphere in extended euclidean n space have two centers?

3. Show that K_r^c has $\binom{n}{r}$ points.

4. Show that there exist at most $[2^n/(n + 1)]$ solid spheres of radius 1 in the n cube which are disjoint. A *solid sphere* is a sphere union its center.

5. Show that the n cube has $2^{n-k} \binom{n}{k}$ subcubes of dimension k. HINT: Let $N(k,n)$ be the desired number of subcubes. Show that $N(k,n) = N(k - 1, n - 1) + 2N(k, n - 1)$. Verify by induction that $2^{n-k} \binom{n}{k}$ is the solution of this difference equation.

6. Show that the following algorithm actually produces a drawing of an n cube. (In order to give a proof for this problem, a precise definition of an n cube is needed.)

    (a) Draw $n + 1$ horizontal lines across a sheet of paper and label them $0, \ldots, n$.

(b) Lay off $\binom{n}{k}$ points on the kth line $(k = 0, \ldots, n)$. $\Big[$ It does not matter if k is counted from the top or bottom, since $\binom{n}{k} = \binom{n}{n-k}.\Big]$

(c) Label the $\binom{n}{k}$ points on the kth line by the n-tuples of zeroes and ones that have k ones in a one-to-one fashion for $k = 0, \ldots, n$.

(d) Connect points in the kth line to points in the $k + 1$ line iff the distance between two points is exactly 1 for $k = 0, \ldots, n$.

(e) The resulting figure is an n cube.

7. Construct a representation for switching functions by associating with every function f an integer i, where $0 \le i \le 2^{2^n} - 1$, by considering the truth table representation of f as a number. Derive some properties of these *characteristic numbers*, as they are sometimes known.

8. Explain how to convert between the characteristic numbers of Prob. 9 and the representations studied in this section.

9. Let $Z_m = \{0, \ldots, m - 1\}$ and define a *Post function* to be any mapping from Z_m^n into Z_m, where $Z_m^n = Z_m \times \cdots \times Z_m$ (n times). Give a geometric interpretation of Post functions.

4 BOOLEAN FORMS

We now define the boolean formulas, or forms, by the following inductive definition. Further analysis will be required to relate these forms to the functions.

Definition 1.   The *boolean formulas* generated by $x_1, \ldots, x_n$ are given by the following statements, where we shorten the word formula to form:

(1) 0 and 1 are boolean forms.

(2) If x_i is a variable, then x_i for $i = 1, \ldots, n$ is a boolean form.

(3) If A is a boolean form, then $\bar{A}$ is a boolean form.

(4) If A and B are boolean forms, then $A + B$ is a boolean form.

(5) If A and B are boolean forms, then AB is a boolean form.

(6) The only boolean forms are given by (1)–(5).

Definition 1 gives a test for telling if a given collection of symbols is a boolean form.

EXAMPLE.   Test $A = x_1(\overline{x_2 + \bar{x}_3})$ to see if A is a boolean form. A is a product of two terms and is a boolean form by (5) if x_1 and $(\overline{x_2 + \bar{x}_3})$ are boolean forms. x_1 is a boolean form by (2), and $\overline{x_2 + \bar{x}_3}$ is a boolean form if $x_2 + \bar{x}_3$ is by (3). By (4), $x_2 + \bar{x}_3$ is a boolean form if x_2 is [and it is by (2)] and if $\bar{x}_3$ is. $\bar{x}_3$ is a boolean form by (3) and (2).

It is very easy to recognize the boolean forms by inspection, and so a formal procedure is not usually written out. It is another matter for a digital computer to recognize boolean forms, and this is why the method has been elaborated upon.

It is clear that there are infinitely many boolean forms (even when $n = 0$). For instance

$$x_1$$
$$x_1 x_1$$
$$x_1 x_1 x_1$$
$$\cdots$$

It seems plausible to impose an equivalence relation on the forms so that there are a finite number of equivalence classes. We shall do this and, in doing so, discover the intimate connection between boolean functions and boolean forms.

Definition 2. The *assignment mapping* α is a function defined from the set of variables into $\{0,1\}$.

The assignment is a function from the boolean forms which are variables into $\{0,1\}$. It is desirable to construct a function from arbitrary boolean forms to $\{0,1\}$, relative to a particular assignment. This, a familiar situation in logic, is accomplished by the following definition.

Definition 3. Relative to the assignment α, we define the *valuation* mapping of a form A, denoted as $|A|_\alpha$, by the following recursive definition.

(1) $|0|_\alpha = 0$, $|1|_\alpha = 1$
(2) If x_i is a variable, $|x_i|_\alpha = \alpha(x_i)$ for $i = 1, \ldots, n$.
(3) If A is a form, $|\bar{A}|_\alpha = 1$ iff $|A|_\alpha = 0$.
(4) If A and B are forms, $|A + B|_\alpha = 1$ iff $|A|_\alpha = 1$ or $|B|_\alpha = 1$.
(5) If A and B are forms, $|AB|_\alpha = 1$ iff $|A|_\alpha = 1$ and $|B|_\alpha = 1$.

The mechanics of using the valuation mapping are important and are illustrated by the following example.

EXAMPLE. Consider the form $x + (\bar{y}z)$. Let α be the assignment $\alpha(x) = 0$, $\alpha(y) = 0$, $\alpha(z) = 1$. Then

$$|x + (\bar{y}z)|_\alpha = 1 \qquad \text{iff } |\bar{y}z|_\alpha = 1 \quad \text{or} \quad |x|_\alpha = 0$$

But $|x|_\alpha = \alpha(x) = 0$, so that $|x + (\bar{y}z)|_\alpha = 1$ iff $|\bar{y}z|_\alpha = 1$. $|\bar{y}z|_\alpha = 1$ iff $|\bar{y}|_\alpha = 1$, and $|z|_\alpha = 1 = \alpha(z)$. Since $\alpha(z) = 1$, we have the situation that

$$|x + (\bar{y}z)|_\alpha = 1 \qquad \text{iff } |\bar{y}|_\alpha = 1$$

However $|\bar{y}|_\alpha = 1$ iff $|y|_\alpha = 0$ and, since $|y|_\alpha = \alpha(y) = 0$, therefore

$$|x + (\bar{y}z)|_\alpha = 1$$

Thus, given any finite boolean form and any assignment α, there is a method for determining $|A|_\alpha$.

Definition 4. Two boolean forms A and B are said to be *equivalent*, written $A \equiv B$, iff for every assignment α, $|A|_\alpha = |B|_\alpha$.

Proposition 5.   Equivalence of boolean forms is an equivalence relation, and the rank of the relation is 2^{2^n}.

PROOF.   The first statement is trivial to verify.   The number of different equivalence classes may be counted as follows.   Since there are 2^n possible α mappings, in general there are $\binom{2^n}{i}$ possible valuation functions with i ones in their graph for $i = 0, \ldots, n$.   The total number of graphs of valuation functions, which is the same as the number of equivalence classes, is

$$\sum_{i=0}^{2^n} \binom{2^n}{i} = (1 + 1)^{2^n} \quad \blacksquare$$

The connection between the boolean forms and the boolean functions will now be developed.   This relation is important; for an understanding of combinational switching theory.

Theorem 6.   There is a one-to-one mapping $| \ |$ from B_n, the boolean algebra of formulas, into F_n, the free boolean algebra of functions, such that

(1) Equivalent forms map into the same function.
(2) $|A + B| = |A| + |B|$
(3) $|AB| = |A| \, |B|$
(4) $|\bar{A}| = \overline{|A|}$

PROOF.   If A is a boolean form, the mapping $| \ |$ is defined by

$$| \ |: A \rightarrow |A| = \bigcup_\alpha (\alpha, |A|_\alpha)$$

where α ranges over all n-tuples of zeros and ones.   Suppose that $A \equiv B$; then, for all α, $|A|_\alpha = |B|_\alpha$ so

$$|A| = \bigcup_\alpha (\alpha, |A|_\alpha) = \bigcup_\alpha (\alpha, |B|_\alpha) = |B|$$

Thus, equivalent forms map into the same function.
Note that

$$|A| = \bigcup_\alpha (\alpha, |A|_\alpha) = \sum_{|A|_\alpha = 1} m_\alpha(x_1, \ldots, x_n)$$

Thus by Corollary 3.11,

$$|A + B| = |A| + |B|$$
$$|AB| = |A| \, |B|$$
$$|\bar{A}| = \overline{|A|} \qquad \blacksquare$$

The question that arises is whether the map $| \ |$ is *onto*.   The answer is yes, but a proof is postponed until the next section, where the fundamental properties of canonical forms are given.

Consider the problem of determining if A and B are equivalent in the finite case. $A \equiv B$ iff for every α, $|A|_\alpha = |B|_\alpha$.   There are only a finite number of assignments α, namely, 2^n, so that there is an algorithm for deciding if two forms are equivalent.   Since the theorems that were established in Sec. 2 were a matter of establishing equivalence between formulas, there is now a mechanical procedure for proving theorems of this type in *finite* boolean algebras.   This *decision procedure* is in no way a substitute for the axiomatic development of Sec. 2 since it only applies to finite boolean algebras.   Infinite boolean algebras occur in our development in Chap. 12.

EXAMPLE.   Is $\overline{(a + b)} \equiv \bar{a}\bar{b}$?   It is most convenient to set up a table where a and b are allowed to range over $\{0,1\}$ independently.

a	b	$(a + b)$	$\overline{(a + b)}$	$\bar{a}$	$\bar{b}$	$\bar{a}\bar{b}$
0	0	0	1	1	1	1
0	1	1	0	1	0	0
1	0	1	0	0	1	0
1	1	1	0	0	0	0

As an example, the calculation of the first row is carried out in detail.   Note that $\alpha(a) = \alpha(b) = 0$.   Therefore, $|a + b|_\alpha = 0$ and $|\overline{(a + b)}|_\alpha = 1$.   Note that $|\bar{a}|_\alpha = |\bar{b}|_\alpha = 1$, so that $|\bar{a}\bar{b}|_\alpha = 1$.   Thus for the α given in the first row, $|\overline{(a + b)}|_\alpha = |\bar{a}\bar{b}|_\alpha$.   The remainder of the table is filled in similarly; and by comparing the column labeled $\overline{a + b}$ and $\bar{a}\bar{b}$, one concludes that $\overline{(a + b)} = \bar{a}\bar{b}$.

A careful examination of the axioms of Sec. 2 suggests that they may be grouped into dual pairs, axiom k paired with axiom $k + 1$ for $k = 1, \ldots, 8$, and axiom 9 paired with itself.   A similar observation about the theorems of Sec. 2 is also valid and suggests a duality between $+$ and $\cdot$ in boolean algebras.

For example,

$$\overline{(a + b)} = \bar{a}\bar{b}$$
$$\overline{(ab)} = \bar{a} + \bar{b}$$

are two theorems which appear to have a close relation to one another. The precise definition of the dual formula is now given.

Definition 7.   The *dual* of a form A, written A^D, is inductively defined as follows:

(1) $0^D = 1$
(2) $1^D = 0$
(3) If x_i is a variable, then $x_i{}^D = x_i$ for $i = 1, \ldots, n$.
(4) If A, B, and C are boolean forms and $A = B + C$, then

$$A^D = B^D C^D$$

(5) If A, B, and C are boolean forms and $A = BC$, then

$$A^D = B^D + C^D$$

(6) If A and B are boolean forms and $A = \bar{B}$, then $A^D = (\overline{B^D})$.

What is the relation between $|A^D|$ and $|A|$? The following theorem gives us the answer and illustrates an important type of inductive proof.

Theorem 8. If A is a boolean form constructed from x_i for $i = 1$, . . . , n and $f_A(x_1, . . . ,x_n)$ is the associated function $(f_A = |A|)$, then

$$f_{A^D}(x_1, . . . ,x_n) = \bar{f}_A(\bar{x}_1, . . . ,\bar{x}_n)$$

We often write $f^D(x_1, . . . ,x_n) = \bar{f}(\bar{x}_1, . . . ,\bar{x}_n)$.

PROOF.   The argument is an induction on the shape of the boolean form A.

BASIS.   If $A = 0$, then $f_A(x_1, . . . ,x_n) = 0$ and $\bar{f}_A(\bar{x}_1, . . . ,\bar{x}_n) = 1$, and similarly for $A = 1$. If $A = x_i$, then $\bar{f}_A(\bar{x}_1, . . . ,\bar{x}_n) = x_i$.

INDUCTION STEP.   Suppose $A = B + C$; then $A^D = B^D C^D$. Thus

$$f_A(x_1, . . . ,x_n) = f_B(x_1, . . . ,x_n) + f_C(x_1, . . . ,x_n)$$

and $\bar{f}_A(\bar{x}_1, . . . ,\bar{x}_n) = \overline{(f_B(\bar{x}_1, . . . ,\bar{x}_n) + f_C(\bar{x}_1, . . . ,\bar{x}_n)}$

$$= \bar{f}_B(\bar{x}_1, . . . ,\bar{x}_n)\bar{f}_C(\bar{x}_1, . . . ,\bar{x}_n)$$

$$= f_{B^D}(x_1, . . . ,x_n)f_{C^D}(x_1, . . . ,x_n) = f_{A^D}(x_1, . . . ,x_n)$$

The proof is similar for $A = BC$.

Suppose $A = \bar{B}$; then $f_A(x_1, . . . ,x_n) = \bar{f}_B(x_1, . . . ,x_n)$ and $A^D = (\overline{B^D})$
$f_{A^D} = \bar{f}_{B^D}(x_1, . . . ,x_n) = \bar{\bar{f}}_B(\bar{x}_1, . . . ,\bar{x}_n) = f_B(\bar{x}_1, . . . ,\bar{x}_n)$
$$= \bar{f}_A(\bar{x}_1, . . . ,\bar{x}_n) \quad \blacksquare$$

It should be clear to the reader that Definition 7 can be used to construct the dual of a boolean form directly.

EXAMPLE.   Let $A = x + \bar{y}z$
$$A^D = (x + \bar{y}z)^D = (x^D)(\bar{y}z)^D = x((\bar{y})^D + z^D)$$
$$= x(\bar{y} + z)$$

Corollary 9.   *If $A \equiv B$, then $A^D \equiv B^D$.*
The significance of Corollary 9 is that it was only necessary to prove the odd-numbered theorems of Sec. 2. The even-numbered theorems followed by duality.

We have elaborated on the distinction between forms and functions by the use of the valuation mapping and the use of two equivalence relations, $=$ and $\equiv$. From this point on, it is assumed that the reader understands this distinction. We shall henceforth write expressions like

$$f(x,y) = x + \bar{y} = (\overline{\bar{x}y})$$

and leave the reader the task of supplying the proper interpretation.

PROBLEMS

1. Show that an induction on the shape of a formula, as done in Theorem 8, is not a new principle but follows from the induction principles stated in Sec. 1-2.

2. A form A (function f_A) is *self-dual* iff $A = A^D$ ($f_{A^D} = f_A$). Show that there are $2^{2^{n-1}}$ self-dual boolean functions of n variables.

3. A boolean function f of n variables is called a *neutral function* iff $w(f) = 2^{n-1}$, that is, there are as many zeros as ones in the graph of f. How many neutral functions are there?

4. Let $f(x_1, \ldots ,x_{n-1})$ be any function of $n - 1$ variables. Construct a function

$$h_f(x_1, \ldots ,x_n) = \bar{x}_n f(x_1, \ldots ,x_{n-1}) + x_n \bar{f}(\bar{x}_1, \ldots ,\bar{x}_{n-1})$$

Show that the mapping $h: f(x_1, \ldots ,x_{n-1}) \to h_f(x_1, \ldots ,x_n)$ is a one-to-one map from the switching functions of $n - 1$ variables onto the class of self-dual switching functions of n variables.

5. Does the mapping h of Prob. 4 preserve $+$ and $\cdot$? That is,

$$h_{f+g} = h_f + h_g \qquad \text{and} \qquad h_{fg} = h_f h_g$$

Does the mapping h preserve complements; is $h_{\bar{f}} = \bar{h}_f$?

6. The formulas of m-value logic are built up in the usual way by induction.

(*a*) $0, \ldots , m - 1$ are Post formulas.

(*b*) $x_i (1 = 1, \ldots ,n)$ is a Post formula.

(*c*) If A is a Post formula, then $\sim A$ is a Post formula.

(*d*) If A is a Post formula, then $\neg A$ is a Post formula.

(*e*) If A, B are Post formulas, then AB is a Post formula.

(*f*) If A and B are Post formulas, then $A \vee B$ is a Post formula.

(*g*) The only Post formulas are as given in (*a*) to (*f*).

As usual, the interpretation is given by a mapping from the formulas into the truth values.

As *assignment* is defined as a mapping from $X = \{x_1, \ldots ,x_n\}$ into Z_m. The *valuation mapping with respect to an assignment* is defined as a mapping $|\ |_\alpha$ recursively as follows:

(*a*) $|0|_\alpha = 0, \ldots , |m - 1|_\alpha = m - 1$

(*b*) $|x_i|_\alpha = \alpha(x_i)$ for $i = 1, \ldots , n$

(*c*) $|\sim A|_\alpha = m - 1 - |A|_\alpha$

(*d*) $|\neg A|_\alpha = \begin{cases} |A|_\alpha + 1 & \text{if } |A_\alpha| \neq m - 1 \\ 0 & \text{if } |A_\alpha| = m - 1 \end{cases}$

(*e*) $|AB|_\alpha = \min (|A|_\alpha, |B|_\alpha)$

(*f*) $|A \vee B|_\alpha = \max (|A|_\alpha, |B|_\alpha)$

Thus two Post formulas P and Q are called *equivalent*, written $P \equiv Q$, if and only if for every assignment α, $|P|_\alpha = |Q|_\alpha$. Define operations on the functions so that one can prove a result analogous to Theorem 6.

5 CANONICAL FORMS

The main result of this section is that for any given function f, there is a unique canonical form associated with f. An expression is given for computing this form in Theorem 5.

The unique form corresponding to f is called the *canonical form of f* or *expanded normal form of f* or *the disjunctive normal form of f*. It will be shown that two forms are equivalent iff they have the same canonical form, which, provides a method for deciding the equivalence of forms without resorting to the enumeration of assignments.

In combinational switching theory (both theoretical and practical), a complete understanding of canonical forms is essential.

Definition 1. A *literal* is defined to be a variable or its complement.

Definition 2. A form A is called a *minterm* or *fundamental product* in B_n iff A is the concatenation of n distinct literals.

It is clear that there are always 2^n minterms in B_n.

EXAMPLE. The eight minterms of B_3 are

$$\bar{x}_1\bar{x}_2\bar{x}_3 \qquad \bar{x}_1 x_2 \bar{x}_3 \qquad x_1\bar{x}_2\bar{x}_3 \qquad x_1 x_2 \bar{x}_3$$
$$\bar{x}_1\bar{x}_2 x_3 \qquad \bar{x}_1 x_2 x_3 \qquad x_1\bar{x}_2 x_3 \qquad x_1 x_2 x_3$$

The minterms can be denoted in the following way. If $(i_1, \ldots, i_n)$ is an n-tuple of zeroes and ones, then

$$x_1^{i_1} \cdots x_n^{i_n}$$

is a typical minterm, where

$$x_j^{i_j} = \begin{cases} \bar{x}_j & \text{if } i_j = 0 \\ x_j & \text{if } i_j = 1 \end{cases} \quad \text{for } j = 1, \ldots, n$$

EXAMPLE. $x_1^0 x_2^1 x_3^1 = \bar{x}_1 x_2 x_3$

Proposition 3. A minterm $x_1^{i_1} \cdots x_n^{i_n}$ denotes the function

$$m_i(x_1, \ldots, x_n)$$

where $i = (i_1 \cdots i_n)_2$.

The following theorem shows how to associate a form with any function of one variable. This theorem is useful in many calculations which follow.

Theorem 4. If f is a boolean function of one variable, then

$$f(a) = af(1) + \bar{a}f(0)$$

PROOF. Suppose $\alpha(a) = 1$, then

$$f(1) = |a|_\alpha |f(1)|_\alpha + |\bar{a}|_\alpha |f(0)|_\alpha$$
$$= |f(1)|_\alpha = f(1)$$

and similarly if $\alpha(a) = 0$. Thus the theorem is true for all assignments. ∎

See the problems at the end of this chapter for a different interpretation of boolean functions which requires a more involved proof of Theorem 4.

The next theorem gives the canonical form for any boolean function of n variables.

Theorem 5.   If f is a boolean function of n variables, then

$$f(x_1, \ldots ,x_n) = \sum_{i_1=0}^{1} \cdots \sum_{i_n=0}^{1} f(i_1, \ldots ,i_n)x_1^{i_1} \cdots x_n^{i_n}$$

PROOF

BASIS.   If $n = 1$, the result reduces to Theorem 4.

INDUCTION STEP.   Assume Theorem 5 true for $n - 1$ variables.

$$f(x_1, \ldots ,x_n) = \sum_{i_2=0}^{1} \cdots \sum_{i_n=0}^{1} f(x_1,i_2, \ldots ,i_n)x_2^{i_2} \cdots x_n^{i_n}$$

However,

$$f(x_1,i_2, \ldots ,i_n) = x_1^0 f(0,i_2, \ldots ,i_n) + x_1^1 f(1,i_2, \ldots ,i_n)$$

$$f(x_1, \ldots ,x_n) = \sum_{i_2=0}^{1} \cdots \sum_{i_n=0}^{1} (x_1^0 f(0,i_2, \ldots ,i_n) + x_1^1 f(1, \ldots ,i_n))x_2^{i_2} \cdots x_n^{i_n}$$

$$= \sum_{i_1=0}^{1} \cdots \sum_{i_n=0}^{1} f(i_1, \ldots ,i_n)(x_1^{i_1} \cdots x_n^{i_n}) \quad \blacksquare$$

It should be clear that there are many forms corresponding to a given boolean function f. The following corollary shows that there is only one expanded normal form for f and that is given in Theorem 5.

Corollary 6.   The expanded normal form of a boolean function is unique.

PROOF.   Suppose that there were two different expanded forms corresponding to f. Since the forms are different, there must exist a set of indices $(i_1, \ldots ,i_n)$ such that one coefficient is 0 and the coefficient in the other form is 1. Let an assignment α be defined such that $\alpha(x_1) = i_1, \ldots , \alpha(x_n) = i_n$. Then according to the first form, $f(i_1, \ldots ,i_n) = 1(0)$; and the second form implies that $f(i_1, \ldots ,i_n) = 0(1)$, which contradicts that both forms represent f. $\blacksquare$

It is necessary to be able to write the canonical form for a given function. The general method is illustrated by a detailed example.

EXAMPLE.   Suppose $f(x_1,x_2,x_3)$ is given by its graph as in Table 1. To write the expanded form for f, one starts down the column under f. In the first row, there is a zero in the f column; so the corresponding term is

$$f(0,0,0)x_1^0 x_2^0 x_3^0 = 0 \cdot \bar{x}_1 \bar{x}_2 \bar{x}_3 = 0$$

Since for any a, $a + 0 = a$, the contribution of any row for which the entry under f is zero can be ignored. When the entry under f is 1, the term is included. Thus

$$f(x_1, x_2, x_3) = x_1{}^0 x_2{}^0 x_3{}^1 + x_1{}^0 x_2{}^1 x_3{}^1 + x_1{}^1 x_2{}^0 x_3{}^1 + x_1{}^1 x_2{}^1 x_3{}^1$$
$$= \bar{x}_1 \bar{x}_2 x_3 + \bar{x}_1 x_2 x_3 + x_1 \bar{x}_2 x_3 + x_1 x_2 x_3$$

TABLE 1

x_1	x_2	x_3	f
0	0	0	0
0	0	1	1
0	1	0	0
0	1	1	1
1	0	0	0
1	0	1	1
1	1	0	0
1	1	1	1

Corollary 7. Two boolean forms are equivalent iff they have the same canonical forms.

Corollary 7 suggests that it would be desirable to have a method for converting any boolean form to an equivalent canonical form. Such a method is sketched below. It is instructive to write out a formal algorithm for this process.

Algorithm 8. Given a boolean form A.

(1) Write A as a sum of products of literals.
(2) Delete repeated products in the sum-of-products representation.
(3) Examine each product. If a product is a fundamental product, continue to the next product.
(4) If a product is not a minterm, it is missing some literals, say, $x_{i_1}, \ldots, x_{i_k}$. Multiply this product by

$$(x_{i_1} + \bar{x}_{i_1}) \cdots (x_{i_k} + \bar{x}_{i_k})$$

(5) After steps 3 and 4 have been performed on all products, multiply out each term and remove redundant terms.
(6) The resulting form is the unique canonical form which is equivalent to A.

PROOF. The formal argument is left to the reader. ∎

EXAMPLE. Let $A = (x_1 + x_2)(x_1 + \bar{x}_3)$. First A is written as a sum of products

$$A = x_1 + x_2 \bar{x}_3$$
By 4, $\quad A = x_1(x_2 + \bar{x}_2)(x_3 + \bar{x}_3) + x_2 \bar{x}_3(x_1 + \bar{x}_1)$
By 5, $\quad A = x_1 x_2 x_3 + x_1 x_2 \bar{x}_3 + x_1 \bar{x}_2 x_3 + x_1 \bar{x}_2 \bar{x}_3 + x_1 x_2 \bar{x}_3 + \bar{x}_1 x_2 \bar{x}_3$
$\quad\quad A = x_1 x_2 x_3 + x_1 x_2 \bar{x}_3 + x_1 \bar{x}_2 x_3 + x_1 \bar{x}_2 \bar{x}_3 + \bar{x}_1 x_2 \bar{x}_3$

PROBLEMS

1. Let $B = \langle B, +, \cdot, 0, 1 \rangle$ be an arbitrary boolean algebra. A boolean function from B into B is defined inductively as follows:

(a) $f(a) = 0$ is a boolean function.⎱ (Constant functions.)
(b) $f(a) = 1$ is a boolean function.⎰
(c) $f(a) = a$ is a boolean function. (Identity function.)
(d) If f and g are boolean functions, then if $f(a) + g(a) = h(a)$ for every a, then h is a boolean function.
(e) If f and g are boolean functions, then if $f(a)g(a) = h(a)$ for every a, then h is a boolean function.
(f) If f is a boolean function, then if $h(a) = \bar{f}(a)$ for every a, then h is a boolean function.
(g) Nothing is a boolean function except as given in (a) to (f).

Discuss the relation of this definition to Definition 3.2.

2. Prove Theorem 4 if the definition of Prob. 1 is employed. (HINT: Follow the inductive definition of boolean function.)

3. Show that $f(x_1, \ldots, x_n) = (x_1 + f(0, x_2, \ldots, x_n))(\bar{x}_1 + f(1, x_2, \ldots, x_n))$.

4. Show that

$$f(x_1, \ldots, x_n) = \prod_{i_1 = 0}^{1} \cdots \prod_{i_1 = 0}^{1} (f(i_1, \ldots, i_n) + x_1^{i_1} + \cdots + x_n^{i_n})$$

where $x_j{}^{i_j} = \begin{cases} x_j & \text{if } i_j = 0 \\ \bar{x}_j & \text{if } i_j = 1 \end{cases}$ for $j = 1, \ldots, n$

This problem provides another canonical form as a product of sums.

5. Let f be a boolean function of n variables. We write $f = f_1 + \cdots + f_k$ for the expanded normal form of f $(0 \leq k \leq 2^n)$. Show that $i \neq j$ implies $f_i f_j = 0$. This relation will become more apparent when we study the atoms of a boolean algebra. Note also that $f = f_1 \oplus \cdots \oplus f_k$.

6. Show that any function may be expressed in the form $f(x_1, \ldots, x_n) = g_0 \oplus g_1 x_1 \oplus \cdots \oplus g_n x_n \oplus g_{n+1} x_1 x_2 \oplus \cdots \oplus g_{2^n - 1} x_1 \cdots x_n$, where $g_i \in \{0, 1\}$ for $i = 0, \ldots, 2^n - 1$. (HINT: $\bar{x}_k = x_k \oplus 1$) This canonical normal form has no complements occurring among the variables.

7. Develop rules for transforming from the form given in Theorem 5 to the forms given in Probs. 4 and 6 and conversely.

8. Derive a canonical form theorem for Post functions.

6 FUNCTIONAL COMPLETENESS

In the study of B_n there were three functions defined on the elements of the domain, namely, $+$, $\cdot$, and $^-$. Enough forms could be constructed from the variables by a finite number of applications of $+$, $\cdot$, and $^-$, so that any function f can be represented by a form constructed from $x_1, \ldots, x_n$, $+$, $\cdot$, and $^-$.

Definition 1. A set of operations $\{o_1, \ldots, o_k\}$ on B_n is *functionally complete* iff for every boolean function f there exists a form A constructed from $x_1, \ldots, x_n, o_1, \ldots, o_k$ such that A denotes f.

EXAMPLE. The set $\{+, \cdot, ^-\}$ is functionally complete by virtue of Theorem 5.5.

EXAMPLE. Consider the set $\{+, \cdot\}$ on B_2. One generates the forms x, y, xy, $x + y$. The functions corresponding to these forms consist of only a proper subset of F_2. It is interesting to carry the example one step further and note that both

$$\{+, ^-\} \quad \text{and} \quad \{\cdot, ^-\}$$

are functionally complete, since $\cdot$ $(+)$ can be obtained by the use of the De Morgan laws.

It is, of course, necessary to have a way to test if a given set of operations is functionally complete. The usual one is to attempt to generate $\{+, ^-\}$ (or $\{\cdot, ^-\}$) from the given set.

EXAMPLE. The *stroke function* $x|y$ is functionally complete where $x|y = \overline{(xy)}$ because

$$x|x = \overline{(xx)} = \bar{x}$$
$$(x|x)|(y|y) = \bar{x}|\bar{y} = \overline{(\bar{x}\bar{y})} = x + y$$

Functional completeness is considered in trying to select a primitive set of components for the design of, say, a computer. We certainly want to be able to realize any possible boolean function, but we would like to have as few primitive components as necessary. We have seen by the preceding example that any function may be realized by using the stroke function alone. This means a considerable reduction in the manufacturing cost of producing a computer using this one type of component. The stroke function can be realized quite inexpensively, as will be seen shortly.

PROBLEMS

1. Show that the following set of connectives are functionally complete.
   (a) The dagger function $\{\downarrow\}$, where $p \downarrow q = \overline{(p + q)}$
   (b) $\{^-, \supset\}$, where $p \supset q = \bar{p} + q$
   (c) $\{\supset, \not\subset\}$, where $p \not\subset q = \bar{p}q$
2. Show that the ternary median operation (x,y,z), or *majority function*, complementation, and 0 have the property of being functionally complete. The operation may be defined in the following two forms: $(x,y,z) = (xy + yz + xz) = (x + y)(y + z)(x + z)$. Show that $(a,b,(c,d,e)) = ((a,b,c),d,(a,b,e))$.

3. The use of the constants 0 and 1 materially increases the number of functions which can be generated. Show that $\{0, \supset\}$ is functionally complete.

4. A function f is called *linearly separable* iff there exist real numbers $a_1, \ldots,$

a_n, T such that

$$f(x_1, \ldots, x_n) = \begin{cases} 1 & \text{if } \sum_{i=1}^{n} a_i x_i \geq T \\ 0 & \text{if } \sum_{i=1}^{n} a_i x_i < T \end{cases}$$

Show that the class of linearly separable functions is complete.

7 REPRESENTATION OF BOOLEAN ALGEBRAS

In this section we shall derive some slightly deeper results about boolean algebras.   In particular, some of the results will indicate the mathematical structure of boolean algebras.   Boolean algebra is of interest to us only in the case where the domain of the system is finite.   Many of our results in this section can also be obtained for infinite algebras, but the proofs become more complicated.   Boolean algebra is intimately related to topology and measure theory.   Readers interested in this relationship should consult the excellent book of Sikorski.

Definition 1.   An element a in a boolean algebra is an *atom* iff $a \neq 0$ and for every x,

$$xa = a \quad \text{or} \quad xa = 0$$

Proposition 2.   If a and b are atoms and $ab \neq 0$, then $a = b$.

Theorem 3.   Let a, a_1, $\ldots$, a_n be atoms in a boolean algebra.   If $x = a_1 + \cdots + a_n$ and $a \leq x$, then there exists $1 \leq i \leq n$ such that $a = a_i$.   ($\leq$ is defined in Prob. 2.1.)

PROOF.   Since a is an atom,

$$xa = 0 \quad \text{or} \quad xa = a$$

The case $xa = 0$ is trivial and is left to the reader.   Suppose

$$xa = a$$
$$a(a_1 + \cdots + a_n) = a$$
$$aa_1 + \cdots + aa_n = a$$

Using Proposition 2, there must exist at least one i such that $aa_i \neq 0$, and therefore

$$a = a_i \quad \blacksquare$$

Theorem 4.   In a finite boolean algebra, any element x is the sum of all atoms a such that $a \leq x$.

PROOF.   Let a_1, $\ldots$, a_n be the atoms less than or equal to x.   Let $y = a_1 + \cdots + a_n$.   We must show that $x = y$.   We immediately note that $y \leq x$ by Prob. 2.4.   All that remains is to show that $x \leq y$.   This is equivalent to showing $x\bar{y} = 0$ by

Prob. 2.5.   Suppose $x\bar{y} \neq 0$; then there exists an atom a such that $a \leq x\bar{y}$, from which $a \leq x$ and $a \leq \bar{y}$.   The existence of a is guaranteed by Prob. 2 of this section, and the second clause of the preceding sentence is true because of Prob. 2.6.

$a \leq x$ implies $a = a_i$ for some i, since a is an atom contained in x.   Thus $a \leq y$. $a \leq y$ and $a \leq \bar{y}$ implies $a \leq y\bar{y} = 0$, which is a contradiction, since a was chosen to be an atom.   ▌

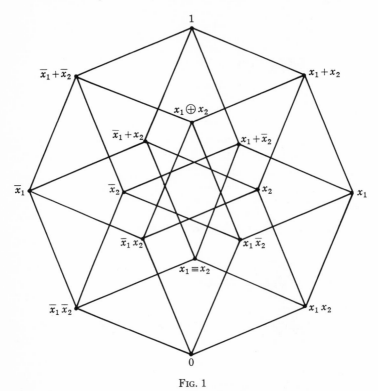

FIG. 1

Theorem 5.   Let $B = \langle B,+,\cdot,0,1 \rangle$ be any finite boolean algebra.   Let C be the set of all subsets of the atoms of B.   Then the system

$$C = \langle C,\cup,\cap,\emptyset,C \rangle$$

is a boolean algebra isomorphic to B.†

PROOF.   Let α be a function which maps $x \in B$ into the set of atoms in B which are $\leq x$.   Clearly, α is a mapping from B into C.   The mapping is onto since given any set of atoms C, the union of all the elements in C is an element which maps into C.   It is also one-to-one, since the representation of an element of B as a sum of atoms is

† The operation-preserving properties of an isomorphism α of boolean algebras are

$$\alpha(a + b) = \alpha(a) + \alpha(b) \qquad \alpha(ab) = \alpha(a)\alpha(b) \qquad \text{and} \qquad \alpha(\bar{a}) = \overline{\alpha(a)}$$

unique by Theorem 4. The reader should show that if

$$\alpha(a) = C_1 \quad \text{and} \quad \alpha(b) = C_2$$
then $\quad \alpha(a + b) = C_1 \cup C_2 \quad$ and $\quad \alpha(ab) = C_1 \cap C_2 \quad |$

Corollary 6. The number of elements in a finite boolean algebra is 2^k for some k. Two finite boolean algebras are isomorphic iff they have the same number of elements.

EXAMPLE. The diagram shown in Fig. 1 represents the boolean algebra of switching functions of two variables. The atoms of this algebra are $\bar{x}_1\bar{x}_2$, $\bar{x}_1x_2$, $x_1\bar{x}_2$, and x_1x_2. The mapping α is explicitly given below:

$$\alpha(0) = \emptyset \qquad\qquad \alpha(x_1 \equiv x_2) = \{\bar{x}_1\bar{x}_2, x_1x_2\}$$
$$\alpha(\bar{x}_1\bar{x}_2) = \{\bar{x}_1\bar{x}_2\} \qquad \alpha(\bar{x}_1) = \{\bar{x}_1\bar{x}_2, \bar{x}_1x_2\}$$
$$\alpha(\bar{x}_1x_2) = \{\bar{x}_1x_2\} \qquad \alpha(\bar{x}_2) = \{\bar{x}_1\bar{x}_2, x_1\bar{x}_2\}$$
$$\alpha(x_1\bar{x}_2) = \{x_1\bar{x}_2\} \qquad \alpha(\bar{x}_1 + x_2) = \{\bar{x}_1\bar{x}_2, \bar{x}_1x_2, x_1x_2\}$$
$$\alpha(x_1x_2) = \{x_1x_2\} \qquad \alpha(x_1 + \bar{x}_2) = \{\bar{x}_1\bar{x}_2, x_1\bar{x}_2, x_1x_2\}$$
$$\alpha(x_1) = \{x_1\bar{x}_2, x_1x_2\} \qquad \alpha(\bar{x}_1 + \bar{x}_2) = \{\bar{x}_1\bar{x}_2, \bar{x}_1x_2, x_1\bar{x}_2\}$$
$$\alpha(x_2) = \{\bar{x}_1x_2, x_1x_2\} \qquad \alpha(x_1 + x_2) = \{\bar{x}_1x_2, x_1\bar{x}_2, x_1x_2\}$$
$$\alpha(x_1 \oplus x_2) = \{\bar{x}_1x_2, x_1\bar{x}_2\} \qquad \alpha(1) = \{\bar{x}_1\bar{x}_2, x_1x_2, \bar{x}_1x_2, x_1\bar{x}_2\}$$

A boolean algebra is a special type of lattice. The drawing that we have used, Fig. 1, is the lattice diagram for F_2, the set of switching functions of two variables.

PROBLEMS

1. An element a in a boolean algebra is *minimal* iff $a \neq 0$ and for every x if $x \leq a$, then $x = a$ or $x = 0$. Show that a is an atom iff a is minimal.

2. In a finite boolean algebra, for any element $x \neq 0$, there exists an atom a such that $a \leq x$.

3. Show that a finite boolean algebra having 2^k elements has k atoms.

4. Discuss the connection (if any) between the mapping constructed in Theorem 5, the expanded normal form theorem, and Theorem 3.9.

5. A boolean function f is said to be *linear* iff $f(x \oplus y) = f(x) \oplus f(y) \oplus f(0, \ldots, 0)$ for x, $y \in \{0,1\}^n$. Prove that there are 2^{n+1} linear functions of n variables. Show that every linear boolean function except 0 and 1 has weight 2^{n-1}.

6. Discuss boolean algebras as lattices. That is, what is the least set of axioms which must be added to the lattice axioms to characterize boolean algebras?

8 ALGEBRAIC STRUCTURE OF BOOLEAN ALGEBRAS

We shall now derive a few algebraic properties of boolean algebra. If the reader is familiar with the ordinary theory of commutative rings, the results presented in this section will be especially familiar. In fact, one can subsume the theory of boolean algebras under the theory of rings of characteristic 2. We shall not follow this course of action, because we wish to keep our treatment self-contained.

Let us work with an arbitrary boolean algebra $B = \langle B, +, \cdot, 0, 1 \rangle$. We come first to the concept of an ideal.

Definition 1. I is an *ideal* of B iff I is a nonempty subset of B such that

(1) If $a, b \in I$, then $a + b \in I$.

(2) If $b \in I$ and $a \leq b$, then $a \in I$.

EXAMPLES

(1) Let $I_a = \{x \in B | x \leq a\}$. Clearly, I_a is an ideal. An ideal of this form is called the *principal ideal* determined by a.

(2) The set $\{0\}$ is an ideal.

(3) B is an ideal.

(4) If A and C are ideals, $A \cap C$ is an ideal.

Let $B_1 = \langle B_1, +, \cdot, 0, 1 \rangle$ and $B_2 = \langle B_2, +, \cdot, 0, 1 \rangle$. We can now define the important concept of a homomorphism, implicitly used in the last section.

Definition 2. α is said to be a homomorphism from B_1 into (onto) B_2 if α is a mapping from B_1 into (onto) B_2 and in addition if

$$\alpha(a + b) = \alpha(a) + \alpha(b)$$
$$\alpha(ab) = \alpha(a)\alpha(b)$$
$$\alpha(\bar{a}) = \overline{(\alpha(a))}$$

α is called an *isomorphism* if α is a homomorphism onto B_2 and α is one-to-one.

Quotient algebras will now be introduced by following the method of Chap. 1.

Definition 3.   If I is an ideal on B, the *equivalence relation induced by* I, written R_I, is defined by

$$aR_I b \Leftrightarrow a\bar{b} \in I \wedge \bar{a}b \in I$$

Proposition 4.   If I is an ideal of B, then R_I is an equivalence relation.

PROOF $\qquad\qquad\qquad\qquad aR_I a \Leftrightarrow 0 \in I$

Zero is in every ideal by (2) of Definition 1. The symmetric condition is obvious. Suppose $aR_I b \wedge bR_I c$, then $a\bar{b} \in I$, and by property (2) of Definition 1, $a\bar{b}\bar{c} \in I$. Similarly, $ab\bar{c} \in I$ because $b\bar{c} \in I$. Thus by property (1) of the definition,

$$ab\bar{c} + a\bar{b}\bar{c} = a\bar{c} \in I$$

Similarly, $\bar{a}c \in I$ and $aR_I c$.   ∎

Definition 5.   If I is an ideal of B, the *quotient of B modulo I*, written B/I, is defined as

$$B/I = \langle C, +, \cdot, 0, 1 \rangle$$

where
$$C = \{R_I[b] | b \in B\}$$
$$R_I[a] + R_I[b] = R_I[a + b]$$
$$R_I[a] \cdot R_I[b] = R_I[ab]$$
$$\overline{R_I[a]} = R_I[\bar{a}]$$
$$0 = R_I[0]$$
$$1 = R_I[1]$$

Proposition 6. B/I is well defined.

PROOF. It must be shown that the definitions of the operations of the quotient algebra do not depend on the representatives of the equivalence classes. Suppose that $a_1 R_I a_2$ and $b_1 R_I b_2$; then

$$\overline{(a_1 + b_1)}(a_2 + b_2) = \bar{a}_1\bar{b}_1(a_2 + b_2) = \bar{a}_1 a_2 \bar{b}_1 + \bar{a}_1 \bar{b}_1 b_2$$
$$\leq \bar{a}_1 a_2 + \bar{b}_1 b_2 \; \epsilon \; I$$

Similarly, $(a_1 + b_1)\overline{(a_2 + b_2)} \; \epsilon \; I$

Thus $(a_1 + b_1)R_I(a_2 + b_2)$

which is the equivalent of

$$R_I[a_1 + b_1] = R_I[a_2 + b_2]$$

For $\cdot$, the argument proceeds in the following way:

$$\overline{(a_1 b_1)}(a_2 b_2) = (\bar{a}_1 + \bar{b}_1)(a_2 b_2) = \bar{a}_1 a_2 b_2 + a_2 \bar{b}_1 b_2$$
$$\leq \bar{a}_1 a_2 + \bar{b}_1 b_2 \; \epsilon \; I$$

Similarly, $(a_1 b_1)\overline{(a_2 b_2)} \; \epsilon \; I$

so that $a_1 b_1 R_I a_2 b_2$

or $R_I[a_1 b_1] = R_I[a_2 b_2]$

For $^-$, we must show $a_1 R_I a_2$ implies $\bar{a}_1 R_I \bar{a}_2$

$$\bar{a}_1 \bar{\bar{a}}_2 = \bar{a}_1 a_2 \; \epsilon \; I$$

Similarly, $a_1 \bar{a}_2 \; \epsilon \; I$

so that $R_I[\bar{a}_1] = R_I[\bar{a}_2]$ ∎

We immediately infer the important homomorphism theorems for boolean algebras.

Theorem 7. The quotient algebra B/I is a homomorphic image of B.

PROOF. Clearly, the mapping $\alpha(a) = R_I[a]$ is a function defined from B into B/I. The mapping is onto B/I, since every equivalence class is nonempty. α is clearly a homomorphism by the proof of Proposition 6. The mapping α is called the *natural* or *canonical homomorphism*. ∎

Theorem 8. Suppose α is a homomorphism from B_1 onto B_2. Let the kernel K be the ideal of all $x \; \epsilon \; B_1$ such that $\alpha(x) = 0$. Then B_1/K is isomorphic to B_2.

PROOF. K is an ideal because if $k_1, k_2 \; \epsilon \; K$, then

$$\alpha(k_1 + k_2) = \alpha(k_1) + \alpha(k_2) = 0 + 0 = 0$$

Thus $k_1 + k_2 \; \epsilon \; K$. Suppose $k \; \epsilon \; K$, $a \leq k$, then

$$a \leq k \Rightarrow \alpha(a) \leq \alpha(k) = 0 \qquad \text{so} \qquad \alpha(a) = 0$$

Thus $a \; \epsilon \; K$. Since K is an ideal, we form B_1/K. We shall show that the mapping β defined below is an isomorphism of B_1/K onto B_2. Take

$$\beta(R_K[a]) = \alpha(a)$$

Clearly, β is a homomorphism of B_1/K onto B_2.   To show that β is one to one, assume that

$$\alpha(a) = \alpha(b)$$

then $\alpha(a\bar{b}) = \alpha(a)\overline{\alpha(b)} = 0$ also $\alpha(\bar{a}b) = 0$
Thus aR_Kb and $R_K[a] = R_K[b]$ $\blacksquare$

EXAMPLE.   Let $I = \{0,ab\}$ on F_2.   Then $R_I = \{[0,ab], [\bar{a}\bar{b}, a \equiv b], [a\bar{b},a][\bar{a}b,b][a \oplus b,$ $a + b], [\bar{b}, a + \bar{b}], [\bar{a} + b, \bar{a}], [\bar{a} + \bar{b}, 1]\}$. B/I is a boolean algebra of eight elements, and $\alpha(x) = R_I[\alpha]$ is a homomorphism with kernel I.

PROBLEMS

1.   Let S be any set of elements in the boolean algebra $B = \langle B, +, \cdot, 0, 1 \rangle$.   There exist ideals containing S, namely, B itself.   Show that the intersection of all the ideals containing S is the least ideal containing S.   We say that this ideal, call it I, is *generated by* S.   Show that the elements of I consist of those elements a such that there exist elements $a_1, \ldots, a_n$ of S such that

$$a \le a_1 + \cdots + a_n$$

2.   Show that any homomorphism of B into itself must take 0 into 0 and 1 into 1.

3.   Let α be a homomorphism from B_1 onto B_2.   Show that $a \le b$ implies $\alpha(a) \le \alpha(b)$.   Can you generalize when α is an isomorphism?

4.   Let α be a homomorphism from B_1 onto B_2 having kernel K.   Show that α is an isomorphism iff $K = \{0\}$.

5.   Let B be a boolean algebra having 2^k elements.   Show that the automorphism group of B is isomorphic to the symmetric group on k letters.   (HINT: Atoms must be mapped onto atoms under an automorphism).

6.   Let A and B be boolean algebras with atoms $\{a_1, \ldots, a_j\}$ and $\{b_1, \ldots, b_k\}$, respectively.   Define a new boolean algebra $A \otimes B$ whose jk atoms are $a_r \otimes b_s$ for $i = 1, \ldots, j; s = 1, \ldots, k$. $A \otimes B$ is the *tensor product* of A and B.   Deduce some properties of $A \otimes B$ and relate $A \otimes B$ to A and B.

9   APPLICATION OF BOOLEAN ALGEBRA

A sizable portion of the remainder of this book will be devoted to the applications of boolean algebra to the analysis and design of switching circuits.   In this section, another application of boolean algebra will be sketched.

Let $p, q, r, \ldots$ be variables ranging over simple declarative sentences.   Let the letter 1 indicate truth and 0 indicate falsehood.   An assignment α associates with every simple declarative sentence its truth value. $p + q$ denotes the sentence "p is true or q is true." pq denotes the compound sentence "p is true and q is true." $\bar{p}$ means "$\bar{p}$ is true iff p is false" and $p \supset q$ means "if p, then q." $p \equiv q$ means "$(p \supset q)$ and $(q \supset p)$."

We call a formula S a *tautology* (*contradiction*) iff S is true (false) for all possible assignments of truth values to the variables of S.

EXAMPLE. $p(p \supset q) \supset q$ is a tautology, since

p	q	$(p \supset q)$	$p(p \supset q)$	$p(p \supset q) \supset q$
0	0	1	0	1
0	1	1	0	1
1	0	0	0	1
1	1	1	1	1

EXAMPLE. Is the following sentence a tautology? If San Francisco is southwest of Berkeley and if it is not smoggy in Los Angeles, then pigs can fly. Let s denote "San Francisco is southwest of Berkeley"; let l denote "it is smoggy in Los Angeles"; and let p denote "pigs can fly." The sentence is represented as

$$s\bar{l} \supset p$$

s	l	p	$s\bar{l}$	$s\bar{l} \supset p$
0	0	0	0	1
0	0	1	0	1
0	1	0	0	1
0	1	1	0	1
1	0	0	1	0
1	0	1	1	1
1	1	0	0	1
1	1	1	0	1

Thus the sentence is not a tautology but depends on the weather in Los Angeles.

We now give an example (due to Birkhoff and MacLane) of an application of boolean algebra.

EXAMPLE. Would you accept the results of the following survey? A thousand children were sampled and 900 liked candy, 650 liked ice cream, 719 liked cake, 458 liked both candy and ice cream, 575 liked candy and cake, 460 liked both ice cream and cake, and 307 liked all three.

ANSWER. If No. (A) denotes the number of children who prefer A, then

$$\text{No. } (A \cup B) = \text{No. } (A) + \text{No. } (B) - \text{No. } (A \cap B)$$

by the definitions of union and intersection. Note that

$$\text{No. } (A \cup B \cup C) = \text{No. } (A) \cup \text{No. } (B) \cup \text{No. } (C) - \text{No. } (A \cap B) - \text{No. } (A \cap C)$$
$$- \text{No. } (B \cap C) + \text{No. } (A \cap B \cap C)$$

Thus the number of children who like ice cream, candy, or cake is

$$900 + 650 + 719 - 458 - 575 - 460 + 307 = 1{,}083$$

which is larger than the number of children sampled.

PROBLEMS

1. Decide if the following sentence is a tautology or a contradiction or if it depends on the weather: Either it is raining in Boston, but not raining in Chicago, or it isn't raining in Boston or in Denver, or it is raining in Chicago or in Denver. Use the following notation: Let b be the proposition "it is raining in Boston"; let c be the proposition "it is raining in Chicago"; and let d be the proposition "it is raining in Denver."

2. Use truth tables to determine if the following equivalences are tautologies:

(a) $(p + q) \equiv ((p \supset q) \supset q)$

(b) $(a \oplus b) \equiv \overline{(a \equiv b)}$

(c) $((p \wedge q) \supset r) \equiv (p \supset (q \supset r))$

10 SUMMARY

This chapter has presented a theory of finite boolean algebras in just the form necessary for our future applications to switching theory.

Additional references are Stoll, and Birkhoff and MacLane for an elementary exposition. The more advanced reader should consult Birkhoff[1] or Sikorski. The classical propositional calculus is treated very nicely by Kleene[1] and by Church.[1]

CHAPTER *3* *combinational switching circuits*

1 INTRODUCTION

In this chapter combinational switching theory will be studied by first indicating some physical components which can be used as switching elements. The theory of boolean algebra will then be applied to give methods for the analysis and synthesis of switching circuits.

Definition 1. A *combinational network* is a network in which the outputs at time t depend only upon the inputs at time t.

Definition 2. A *sequential machine* (*circuit or network*) is a device whose output at time t depends on all inputs at times p, where $0 \leq p \leq t$.†

Thus sequential machines, like human beings, react to a given situation (input) in a manner dependent on their past histories. In Chaps. 3 to 8, combinational switching theory will be presented. In the remainder of the book, sequential machines will be studied.

2 SWITCHING COMPONENTS (BRANCH TYPE)

Components which possess useful switching properties are discussed in this section. Techniques for design using these components are given in later sections.

An *electromagnetic relay* consists of two parts: (1) an electromagnet which is energized by an electrical signal and (2) a collection of contacts.

---

† $p \leq t$ is sometimes called the *causal condition*. Intuitively, the machine is not clairvoyant and will not respond to events which have not yet happened.

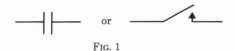

FIG. 1

The operation of the magnet causes the relay contacts to operate.   Three kinds of relay contacts will be discussed.   A contact is *normally open* (*closed*) if there is a (no) closed path between its terminals when and only when the relay coil is energized.   A *transfer contact* is a particular combination of a normally open and a normally closed contact on the same relay (cf. example below).

A normally open contact is denoted by Fig. 1, and a normally closed contact is denoted by Fig. 2.   A transfer contact is usually denoted by Fig. 3.   It is clear that both a normally open contact (sometimes called a *make* contact) and a normally closed contact (often called a *break* contact) require two springs in the construction of the relay.   On the other hand, a transfer contact is really two contacts, but merely requires three springs. Thus it is advantageous to use transfer contacts wherever possible. Other advantages of transfer contacts will appear later.

Of course, there are practical constraints applicable to real relays. One cannot have too many contacts on a relay, because this entails a more powerful magnet for the coil; hence the relay is slower and more expensive.   Connecting two coils in parallel may involve difficulty if contacts on the different relays operate at different speeds.

EXAMPLE.   A typical combinational relay circuit is shown in Fig. 4.   The coils receive the inputs, but it is clear that we may forget the coils and study only the

FIG. 2   FIG. 3

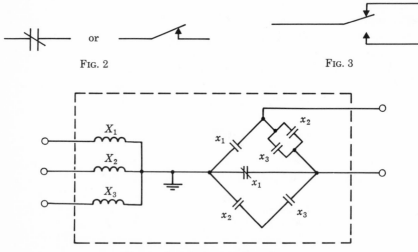

FIG. 4   A typical relay network.

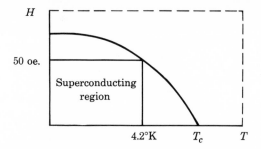

FIG. 5   *H-T* curve for tantalum.

contact network as long as the entire network has the general form shown in Fig. 4. Note the convention of using capital letters for the relay coils and the corresponding small letters for the contacts.

Another device, the *cryotron*, which bears a decided resemblance to relay contacts, avoids the inherent limitation present with relays, namely, that they are big and slow. The cryotron utilizes some special properties of certain elements (niobium, lead, and tantalum) at very low temperatures. At very low temperatures, these elements become *superconducting;* i.e., they have essentially no resistance to the flow of current. Figure 5 illustrates the behavior of tantalum, i.e., the plot of the magnetic field H versus the temperature T.

A typical cryotron is shown in Fig. 6; the operation of the device is as follows: The resistance of the straight wire is controlled by the magnetic field induced by the current I_c in the coil. The device is operated at a temperature such that the control wire is superconducting at all times and the amount of current in I_c controls whether or not current I_g can pass through the device, i.e., whether the tantalum is superconducting. The low temperatures required for the cryotron ($<10°K$) require that the circuits be kept in liquid helium for cooling.

The transistor is an electronic device with three terminals called the emitter, collector, and base. Most of our applications will involve grounding the emitter and using the base as the input and the collector

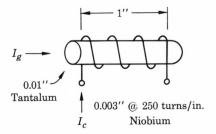

FIG. 6   A wire-wound cryotron.

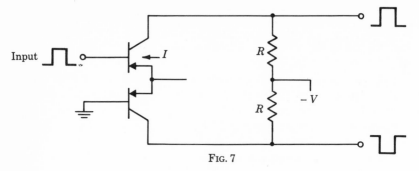

FIG. 7

as the output. Thus one may consider the action of a npn transistor to be analogous to that of a triode, and the behavior of the pnp transistor can be predicted from the behavior of the npn by imagining the signs of all voltages to be reversed.

It is possible to use transistors for switching devices in a manner closely related to relays or cryotrons. This method, called *direct-coupled transistor logic*, or DCTL, involves connecting transistors in series and causing one or the other to pass current. In Figure 7 a constant current I flows into both emitters. The input causes the top transistor to be either conducting or cut off. If the top transistor is conducting, current flow is through top resistor R to the supply while the lower transistor is cut off. The top output terminal is high while the bottom output terminal is low. Now suppose that the top transistor is off, then the (constant) current flow is through the bottom transistor and the analysis is trivial to complete.

All the components discussed in this section have the following attributes in common, namely, that all the devices switch a path. That is, at a given time, there is a closed path between certain terminals or there is not such a path; such components are called *branch-type* elements. In the next section, some devices of a different character are introduced.

PROBLEMS

1. Consider a relay contact network and let C be the number of contacts and S the number of springs. Show that

$$S \geq \left[\frac{3C + 1}{2} \right]$$

where $[x]$ means the integer part of x.

2. In Fig. 6 note that as I_g is increased, the amount of current needed for I_c is lower, since I_g itself produces a magnetic field, called the *self-field*. The *current gain* G is defined as the ratio of the magnetic field produced by I_c to the self-field induced by a current in the tantalum which is equal to I_c. Show that if one cryotron is expected to drive another cryotron, then $G \geq 1$.

3 SWITCHING COMPONENTS (GATE TYPE)

The circuits to be examined in this section differ radically from the branch-type circuits of the preceding section. We shall assume that all the units to be considered in this section are electronic in nature. The units receive voltages as inputs and produce an output voltage. We shall assume that combinational networks of these units are defined as "feedback-free" connections of external inputs to the units and connections from the outputs of some units to the inputs of other units.

A typical combinational network of the type to be described is shown in Fig. 1. We shall indicate methods of construction for realizing AND, OR, and NOT functions. By an AND (OR) circuit, one means a two-input one-output device such that the output voltage is positive (denoted by 1) iff both (at least one) of the inputs are positive voltages. A NOT circuit produces a positive output voltage iff a negative input voltage is applied.

The realization of these circuits with diodes and vacuum tubes is presented first. Let a and b be input signals, and assume that the signals are to range between $+e$ volts and 0 volts or ground. The circuit of Fig. 2 realizes the AND network. If both a and b are at ground potential, both diodes are drawing current and f is at ground potential. If a is at $+e$ volts and b is at ground, then the diode at b is drawing current which brings f to 0 volts while back-biasing the diode at a. If both inputs are at $+e$, f is at $+e$ volts and both diodes are conducting. Considering a and b to be continuous voltages with respect to time, this circuit actually realizes min (a,b).

Reversing the direction of the diodes and the supply voltage produces the circuit which realizes the OR network, Fig. 3. If both a and b are at

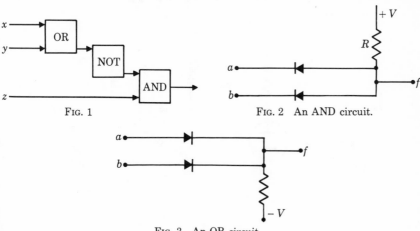

Fig. 1

Fig. 2   An AND circuit.

Fig. 3   An OR circuit.

ground potential, then both diodes conduct and f is at zero volts.   If a is at $+e$ volts while b is at ground, then the diode at a conducts to bring f to $+e$ volts while the diode at b is back-biased, causing no current flow. If both diodes are at $+e$ volts, then both diodes conduct and f is at $+e$ volts.   Considering a and b to be continuous signals, this circuit realizes max (a,b).

The salient characteristic of diode logic circuits as opposed to, say, analog computer diode circuits is that the diodes are forward-biased in digital circuits.

Given a signal a between zero and e volts, we use a single inverter to obtain the NOT circuit, Fig. 4.   The tube is biased so that it is normally nonconducting with the input a at ground potential.   Then f would be at the supply voltage except that the diode clamps f to $+e$ volts.   When a is at $+e$ volts, the tube conducts and the plate voltage falls.   The cathode is biased so that the plate voltage would drop below ground except that it is clamped at zero volts.

Transistors are used in electronic switching circuits in a way analogous to that in which vacuum tubes are used.   Since certain transistors are as cheap as diodes, a homogeneous sort of technology is often used, with the same type of transistor employed for negation as well as AND and OR circuits.

A rather special transistor circuit is shown in Fig. 5.   This device is called a NOR circuit, since the output as a logical function of inputs is $(\overline{a + b})$.   Thus the NOR circuit realizes the dagger function of Sec. 2-6, which is functionally complete.   Thus any boolean function can be implemented by using only the circuit of Fig. 5.   The analysis of the NOR circuit behavior is left to the reader.

The general class of circuits of this section is given the name *gate* circuits, because it is the presence or absence of a voltage level which transmits information.

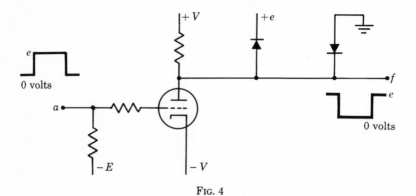

FIG. 4

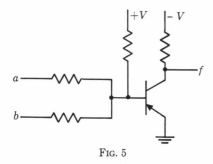

FIG. 5

In a remarkable paper Löfgren† has argued that *every switching component is of either the gate type or the branch type.* Löfgren's result depends upon some involved assumptions and precise definitions of gate and branch circuits. We shall not go into the details of his work, but two points should be emphasized. Löfgren's result is controversial and not universally accepted, because his assumptions and methods are questioned by some people. On the other hand, no switching components which do not fall into his dichotomy are now known.

In this book, techniques of analysis and synthesis for both types of circuits will be given. In the study of branch-type components, relays will be the usual example. For gate-type networks, AND, OR, and NOT components will be used. The details of using other components may be found in the references.

It is important to realize that changing components will make the realization of some functions harder or easier; but for the overwhelming majority of functions, the cost of realization does not change much. These considerations imply that future results in switching theory will come from more knowledge of the structure of boolean functions rather than from an improved component. Our emphasis will be on those considerations which are independent of technology.

PROBLEMS

1. Let us represent $a = 0$ by zero volts and $a = 1$ by $-e$ volts. Construct AND, OR, and NOT circuits in this *negative logic.* Discuss the meaning of this in terms of duality and De Morgan's laws.

2. If $a = 0$ is represented by zero volts and $a = 1$ by $+e$ volts, what logical functions are realized by the circuits of Fig. P2?

† A Theory of Uniform Switching Nets," *Elec. Eng. Res. Lab. Tech. Rept.* 6, University of Illinois, 1962.

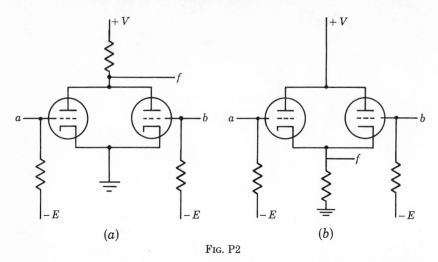

FIG. P2

3. In the circuits of Fig. P3 the pentode is to be of the suppressor cutoff variety (i.e., 5915). A negative voltage on the suppressor cuts off plate current. What logical functions do the circuits of Fig. P3 realize?

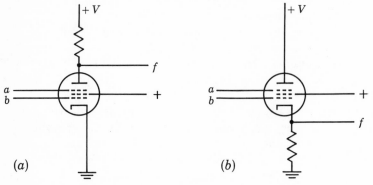

FIG. P3

4. What logical function is realized by the circuit of Fig. P4?

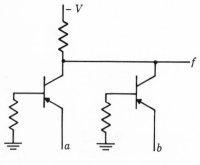

FIG. P4

5. (Ditman) Digital circuits have applications in analog computers. Show that the circuit of Fig. P5 realizes the absolute value of the input voltage. Note that we have an OR circuit in the diagram.

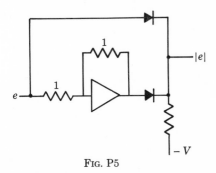

FIG. P5

6. State a duality principle for transistor logic circuits.

4 APPLICATIONS OF BOOLEAN ALGEBRA TO BRANCH - TYPE NETWORKS

The relation between boolean algebra and branch-type switching components is now indicated. The details will be written out for relay contact networks, although any branch-type component could be substituted.

First we define a mapping from certain boolean forms into a special class of two-terminal networks.

Definition 1. The mapping φ is defined from boolean forms in which *negation appears only over variables* into two-terminal series-parallel networks as follows:

(1) $\varphi(0)$ is ·

(2) $\varphi(1)$ is ────────·

(3) If x_i is a variable, then $\varphi(x_i)$ is ───┤├───

(4) If x_i is a variable, then $\varphi(\bar{x}_i)$ is ───╫┤───

(5) If A and B are boolean forms in which negation appears only over variables, then $\varphi(A + B)$ is as shown in Fig. 1.

(6) If A and B are boolean forms in which negation appears only over variables, then $\varphi(AB)$ is as shown in Fig. 2.

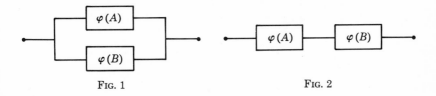

FIG. 1   FIG. 2

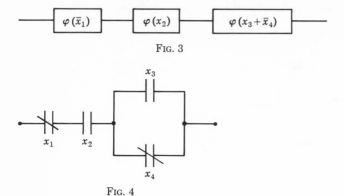

FIG. 3

FIG. 4

EXAMPLE.   Consider $A = \bar{x}_1 x_2 (x_3 + \bar{x}_4)$.   The circuit of $\varphi(A)$ can be constructed from Definition 1.   Since A is a product of three terms, the network will be as shown in Fig. 3.   Reapplying Definition 1, $\varphi(A)$ is as shown in Fig. 4.   Note that the network associated with a form by φ is essentially *unique*.

Proposition 2. φ is onto.   That is, given any two-terminal series-parallel contact network N constructed from make and break contacts labeled $x_1, \ldots, x_n$, there is a boolean form A in which negation appears only over the x_i $(i = 1, \ldots, n)$ such that $\varphi(A) = N$.

PROOF.   One reverses Definition 1.   The technique is more fully explained by the following example. **|**

EXAMPLE.   Given the network N, Fig. 5.   Since the network is essentially a series connection of three networks, one gets

$$(x_1\bar{x}_2 + x_3)x_4(\bar{x}_1 + x_3)$$

Given a network with associated form A and, if relay (coil) X_i is operated, then assign 1 to all contacts x_i and 0 to $\bar{x}_i$ for $i = 1, \ldots, n$. This is a typical assignment α, and $|A|_\alpha = 1$ iff there is a closed path between the terminals.   This suggests the following definition.

Definition 3.   If N is a two-terminal network constructed from branch-type elements x_i $(i = 1, \ldots, n)$, then the *transmission function of N*,

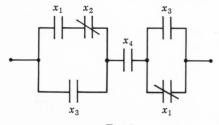

FIG. 5

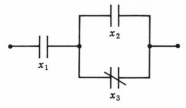

FIG. 6 Network N.

f_N is a boolean function which is 1 iff there is a closed path between the terminals of the network.

Proposition 4. If N is a two-terminal series-parallel network with associated form A_N, then the boolean function associated with A_N is the transmission function of N.

PROOF. Induction on the shape of N. |

Definition 5. Two networks N_1 and N_2 are *equivalent*, written $N_1 \equiv N_2$, iff $f_{N_1} = f_{N_2}$.

Proposition 6. Networks N_1 and N_2 are equivalent iff the associated boolean forms are equivalent, that is, $N_1 \equiv N_2 \Leftrightarrow A_{N_1} = A_{N_2}$.

EXAMPLE. The network N is given in Fig. 6. $A_N = x_1(x_2 + \bar{x}_3)$. If coils X_1 and X_3 are energized and X_2 is not energized, then $\alpha(x_1) = 1$, $\alpha(x_3) = 1$, and $\alpha(x_2) = 0$. By the methods of Sec. 2-4, $|x_1(x_2 + \bar{x}_3)|_\alpha = 0$; that is, if the coils are in the given state, then there is an open path between the terminals. The reader should construct the entire table for $x_1(x_2 + \bar{x}_3)$ and check to see the relation between the function and closed paths between the terminals.

EXAMPLE. Note in Fig. 7 that $A_{N_1} = \bar{a}b + c(a + b)$ and $A_{N_2} = \bar{a}b + ac$; however, N_1 and N_2 are equivalent, since $A_{N_1} = A_{N_2}$. It is clear that N_2 is cheaper than N_1, since N_2 uses four contacts and seven springs, whereas N_1 uses five contacts and ten springs.

We summarize our initial presentation of the application of boolean algebra to switching theory by Fig. 8. Note that the transmission func-

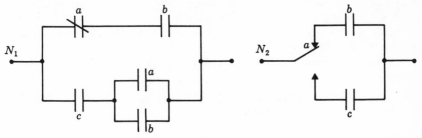

FIG. 7

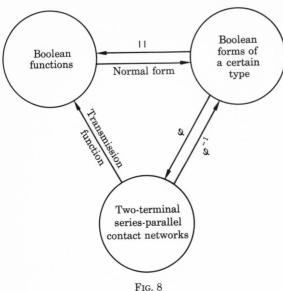

FIG. 8

tion gives the terminal behavior of the network and the boolean form "looks like" the network with respect to interconnections, etc.

PROBLEMS

1. Let f be a function of n variables represented on the n cube as in Sec. 2-3. Show that if the points of f [really $f^{-1}(1)$] form an r-dimensional subcube for $0 \le r \le n$, then f is realizable by a series connection of $n - r$ relay contacts.

2. Define the *cost* of realizing a function with branch-type elements as the number of the components required. Show that the cost of realizing a switching function f of n variables with branch-type elements in a series-parallel network is at most

$$\sum_{k=0}^{n} q_k(n - k)$$

where q_k is the number of cubes of dimension k in the geometric representation of f. Why is the result an inequality and not equality?

3. Why is the mapping φ restricted to forms which have negation over individual variables only?   (HINT: Look at $\overline{x_1 + x_2}$.)

4. Are there non-series-parallel contact nets?   What does this imply about φ?

5   APPLICATIONS OF BOOLEAN ALGEBRA TO GATE - TYPE NETWORKS

For gate-type elements, the application of boolean algebra is somewhat different.   We shall assume the existence of three primitive ele-

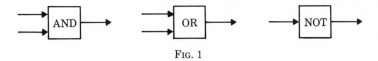

FIG. 1

ments as shown in Fig. 1: an AND circuit, an OR circuit, and a NOT circuit.

Informally, a *gate-type combinational switching network* is any finite number of AND, OR, or NOT units so interconnected that the output of any element may not be connected to the input of another element to form a closed loop.†

EXAMPLE. A circuit of the form shown in Fig. 2 is meant to be excluded because the device is inherently sequential in behavior.

Given any gate-type network, one can immediately write down the associated boolean form, as will be seen by the following example.

EXAMPLE. The network is N, Fig. 3. With the output of the OR circuit, we associate the form $x_1 + x_2$. With the first AND circuit, we associate x_2x_3. Similarly, the output of the entire circuit is associated with

$$A_N = x_2x_3(\overline{x_1 + x_2})$$

Definition 1. The *transmission function* of a gate-type combinational switching network is a boolean function which is 1 iff the output node is positive.

Note that $A = x_2x_3(\overline{x_1 + x_2}) = x_2x_3\bar{x}_1\bar{x}_2 = 0$, so that the example chosen in Fig. 3 has a transmission function which is never 1.

† An inductive definition of a well-formed gate-type network should be given by the reader.

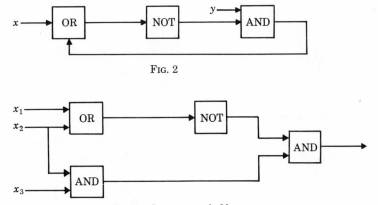

FIG. 2

FIG. 3   Gate network N.

Proposition 2. Given a combinational network of the gate type with associated form A_N, the boolean function associated with A_N is the transmission function of N.

PROBLEMS

   1. Give a formal inductive definition of a gate-type combinational circuit.

   2. (Misek) The circuit of Fig. P2 actually does something useful. The input is a single positive pulse. What does the circuit do?

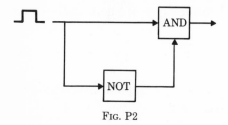

FIG. P2

   3. Give examples which show that the gate-type network associated with a boolean form is not unique.

6 BRANCH - TYPE NETWORKS REVISITED

The preceding section indicates that there is a boolean form associated with every gate-type switching network. Branch-type networks will now be examined in more detail in an attempt to generalize to non-series-parallel networks, etc.

A bridge-type network N is shown in Fig. 1. It is desirable to associate a boolean form A with N such that A denotes f_N, the transmission function of N. One way to do this is to associate a product of literals with every path between the input-output terminals and sum over all paths. For N, this yields

$$A = x_1x_2 + x_1x_5x_3 + x_4x_3 + x_4x_5x_2$$

The form A is written as a sum of products which corresponds by the methods of Sec. 4 to a series-parallel network as shown in Fig. 2. Note that the series-parallel network involves 10 contacts as compared to 5 in the original network.

To formalize this approach, we have the following definition.

Definition 1. Let N be a two-terminal branch-type network and define the *path product* to be the concatenation of all the labels on a path between the terminals, where the branches are labeled as shown in Fig. 3.

EXAMPLE. For the network shown in Fig. 4 the path products between the terminals are $x_1\bar{x}_2$ and x_1x_3.

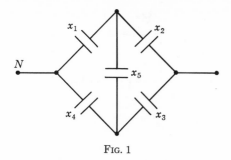

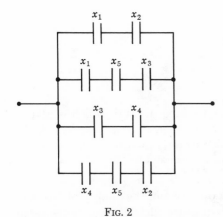

FIG. 1

FIG. 2

Definition 2. Let N be any two-terminal branch-type network and let P_i be the path product associated with path i. Then *the boolean form associated with N* is

$$\sum_i P_i$$

where the sum is over all paths between the terminals.

Proposition 3. If N is any branch-type network and A_N is the form associated with N by Definition 2, then the transmission function of N is the boolean function denoted by A_N.

Next we wish to discuss duality for branch-type networks.

FIG. 3

FIG. 4

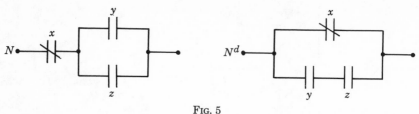

FIG. 5

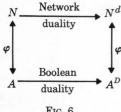

FIG. 6

Definition 4. If N is a two-terminal switching network which is planar when considered as a two-terminal graph, then the *dual network* of N, written N^d, is defined to be the graph theoretic dual of N (cf. 1-10.19).

EXAMPLE.   A network N and its dual are shown in Fig. 5.

The connection between network duality and the duality of Boolean forms is now developed. The case of series-parallel networks is discussed first.

Theorem 5. Let N be a two-terminal series-parallel network with boolean form A. The boolean form associated with N^d is A^D. The theorem is summarized in Fig. 6.

PROOF.   The argument is an induction on the shape of series-parallel networks. The result is trivial for unit networks.

INDUCTION STEP.   Suppose the network is as shown in Fig. 7, with associated boolean form $A_N = A_{N_1} A_{N_2}$. The network dual is as shown in Fig. 8. The new boolean form associated with the network is $A_{N^d} = A_{N_1^d} + A_{N_2^d}$, but by the induction

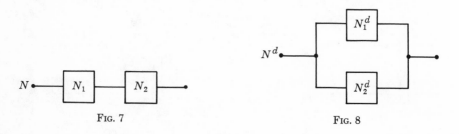

FIG. 7   FIG. 8

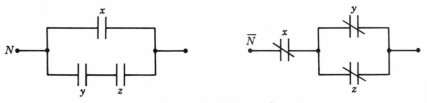

FIG. 9   A network and its complement.

hypothesis $A_{N_i d} = A_{N_i}^D$ for $i = 1, 2$.   Therefore,

$$A_{N^d} = A_{N_1}^D + A_{N_2}^D = A_N^D$$

The remaining case is similar. |

The analysis for non-series-parallel networks is slightly more involved.

Theorem 6.   Let N be a planar two-terminal network with associated boolean form A_N and transmission function f_N.   The form associated with N^d, called A_{N^d}, has the property†

$$A_{N^d} \equiv A_N^D$$

PROOF.   The argument will show that $f_{N^d} = \bar{f}_N(\bar{x}_1, \ldots, \bar{x}_n) = f_N^D$ (cf. Theorem 2-4.8). $f_{N^d} = 1$ iff there is a path product P_i and an assignment α in N^d such that $|P_i|_\alpha = 1$.   By Theorem 1-10.21, the set of branches in N, corresponding to the path product in N^d, is a cut set (and conversely).   Thus by reversing the assignment α, [replace 1(0) by 0(1)] those branches in the cut set are effectively removed and the terminals of the network are separated.   Thus $f_N(\alpha(\bar{x}_1), \ldots, \alpha(\bar{x}_n)) = 0$, or $f_N^D = 1$.   We have shown $f_{N^d} = 1$ iff $f_N^D = 1$, that is, that $f_{N^d} = f_N^D$ and therefore $A_{N^d} = A_N^D$. |

The reason for requiring that the domain of the φ mapping of Sec. 4 be only forms with negation over individual variables is now given.

Definition 7.   Given a two-terminal network N with boolean form A_N, *a complementary network for N*, denoted by $\bar{N}$, is a two-terminal network with boolean form A such that $A = \bar{A}_N$.

Figure 9 illustrates a network for the form $x + yz$.   One cannot associate a branch-type network with $(\overline{x + yz})$ immediately, but one can note $(\overline{x + yz}) = \bar{x}(\bar{y} + \bar{z})$.   A complementary network does exist; it is shown in Fig. 9.   The following theorem tells how to construct the complementary network for planar networks.

Theorem 8.   If N is a planar two-terminal network, then $\bar{N}$ can be constructed by forming N^d and then replacing every make (break) contact by a break (make) contact.

† For series-parallel networks, the forms are identical; the best that one can say in general is that the forms are equivalent.

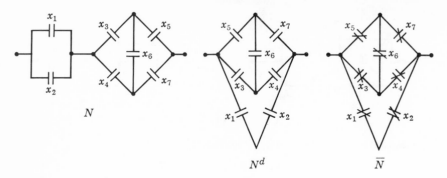

$$N \qquad\qquad N^d \qquad\qquad \bar{N}$$

FIG. 10

PROOF. $f_{N^d}(x_1, \ldots, x_n) = \bar{f}_N(\bar{x}_1, \ldots, \bar{x}_n)$, so $\bar{f}_N(x_1, \ldots, x_n) = f_{N^d}(\bar{x}_1, \ldots, \bar{x}_n)$. ∎

EXAMPLE. N, N^d, and $\bar{N}$ are shown in Fig. 10.

PROBLEMS

1. Show that every series-parallel network is either *essentially series* (e.s.) or *essentially parallel* (e.p.).   The idea is that an e.s. network is a series connection of e.p. networks, and vice versa.   Show that the dual of an e.s. network is an e.p. network.

2. Write out the details for extending the results of this section to gate-type networks when possible.

3. Show that branch-type complementary networks always exist.   Is there always a complementary network which is series-parallel?

4. Find a complementary network for N as given in Fig. P4.

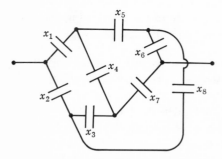

FIG. P4

7 ANALYSIS AND SYNTHESIS OF SWITCHING NETWORKS

The analysis problem for a switching circuit is to take a given finite network and construct the transmission function for the circuit.   There are, of course, a variety of ways to express the function.   By far the

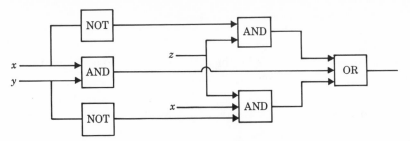

FIG. 1   Network N.

most advantageous way to analyze the circuit is to find the boolean form associated with the circuit.   This is easy to do, and one can then manipulate the form by the identities of boolean algebra to try to find an equivalent but cheaper form.

EXAMPLE.   Given the network N, as shown in Fig. 1, the associated boolean form is

$$A_N = x\bar{y}z + xy + \bar{x}z$$

Note that

$$A_N = xy + z(\bar{x} + x\bar{y}) = xy + z(\bar{x} + \bar{y})$$
$$A_N = xy + z(\overline{xy}) = (xy + z)(xy + (\overline{xy})) = xy + z$$

Thus network N may be replaced by the equivalent network M, as shown in Fig. 2, and network M is cheaper:

$$A_M = xy + z$$

We shall shortly learn an important special technique for analysis of branch-type networks which makes the computations very simple.   Note that we have indicated an algorithm for the analysis of any finite switching network.

Algorithm 1.   Given any finite network N, the analysis of N can be carried out by the following steps:

(1) For two-terminal branch-type networks, associate a boolean form with the network by the φ mapping of Sec. 4.   Go to step 4.

(2) If the branch-type network has k terminals, use the φ map to associate a boolean form with every one of $k(k-1)/2$ pairs of terminals.   Go to step 4.

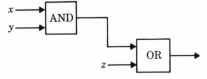

FIG. 2   Network M.

(3) For k output gate-type networks, associate a boolean form with every one of the k outputs as indicated in Sec. 5. Go to step 4.

(4) Recover the transmission functions from the constructed forms by the valuation function.

EXAMPLE.   Given the four-output relay circuit shown in Fig. 3, the boolean form associated with pairs of nodes i, j is written as A_{ij}.   An easy computation shows that

$$A_{12} = x_1 + \bar{x}_2$$
$$A_{13} = (x_1 + \bar{x}_2)(x_1 x_2 + x_3) = x_1 x_2 + \bar{x}_2 x_3$$
$$A_{14} = (x_1 + \bar{x}_2)(x_1 + x_2 x_3) = x_1$$
$$A_{23} = x_3 + x_1 x_2$$
$$A_{24} = x_1 + x_2 x_3$$
$$A_{34} = x_2 + x_1 x_3$$

If the actual transmission function is needed, it is recovered by the valuation map. As an example, we compute the functions denoted by A_{12} and A_{13}.

x_1	x_2	x_3	$f_{A_{12}}$	$f_{A_{13}}$
0	0	0	1	0
0	0	1	1	1
0	1	0	0	0
0	1	1	0	0
1	0	0	1	0
1	0	1	1	1
1	1	0	1	1
1	1	1	1	1

The synthesis of switching circuits is accomplished in the following way. One is given the requirements of a network and asked to design the network. For the moment, we are not concerned with minimality or even economy. Our only concern is the realization of at least one network. We shall assume that the network specifications are given by listing the transmission functions to be realized. Synthesis can be accomplished by associating a boolean form with the function by using the canonical form theorem 2-5.5. Then the network is constructed by associating a circuit with the form, as done in this chapter.

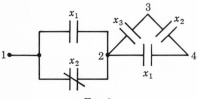

Fig. 3

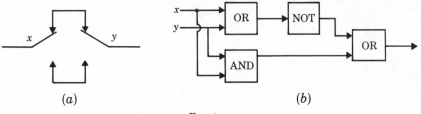

(a) (b)

FIG. 4

EXAMPLE.   Design a network whose transmission function is given by the table:

x	y	$f(x,y)$
0	0	1
0	1	0
1	0	0
1	1	1

We now apply Theorem 2-5.5 for $n = 2$.

$$f(x,y) = \bar{x}\bar{y}f(0,0) + \bar{x}yf(0,1) + x\bar{y}f(1,0) + xyf(1,1)$$

The table tells us that

$$f(0,0) = f(1,1) = 1 \quad \text{and} \quad f(0,1) = f(1,0) = 0$$

Thus
$$f(x,y) = \bar{x} \cdot \bar{y} \cdot 1 + \bar{x} \cdot y \cdot 0 + x \cdot \bar{y} \cdot 0 + x \cdot y \cdot 1$$
$$= \bar{x}\bar{y} + xy$$

A contact network realization is shown in Fig. 4a, and an electronic realization is shown in Fig. 4b.

EXAMPLE.   A man wishes to illuminate his garage and be able to turn the light off and on from both the house and the garage.   Design a circuit for the customer.

Let g denote the switch in the garage and h the switch in the house.   Let k represent the light such that

$$k = \begin{cases} 1 & \text{if the light is on} \\ 0 & \text{if the light is off} \end{cases}$$

Then $k = 1$ iff the switch in the house is activated while the garage switch is untouched, or vice versa.   In tabular form,

h	g	$k(h,g)$
0	0	0
0	1	1
1	0	1
1	1	0

$$k(h,g) = h\bar{g} + \bar{h}g$$

The circuit is given in Fig. 5.

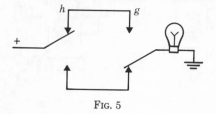

FIG. 5

EXAMPLE.   Consider the network having two inputs and two outputs given by the following table.   This example is a *binary half adder;* i.e., interpret x and y to be the binary digits to be added. s is their sum and c is the carry.

x	y	s	c
0	0	0	0
0	1	1	0
1	0	1	0
1	1	0	1

$$s = x\bar{y} + \bar{x}y$$
$$c = xy$$

EXAMPLE.   We generalize to the *full adder.* x and y are the binary digits to be added, and c_{i-1} is the carry from the next lowest position. s_i is the sum and c_i is the

x	y	c_{i-1}	s_i	c_i
0	0	0	0	0
0	0	1	1	0
0	1	0	1	0
0	1	1	0	1
1	0	0	1	0
1	0	1	0	1
1	1	0	0	1
1	1	1	1	1

$$s_i = \bar{x}\bar{y}c_{i-1} + \bar{x}y\bar{c}_{i-1} + x\bar{y}\bar{c}_{i-1} + xyc_{i-1}$$
$$c_i = \bar{x}yc_{i-1} + x\bar{y}c_{i-1} + xy\bar{c}_{i-1} + xyc_{i-1}$$

carry.   These expressions are not the simplest possible forms which have the same graph, but they will suffice in the present discussion.

EXAMPLE.   A binary adder which adds two n-bit numbers has the form shown in Fig. 6,   where the two numbers to be added are

$$X = x_n 2^{n-1} + \cdots + x_1 = (x_n, \ldots, x_1)_2$$
and
$$Y = y_n 2^{n-1} + \cdots + y_1 = (y_n, \ldots, y_1)_2$$

The desired network is given in Fig. 6.

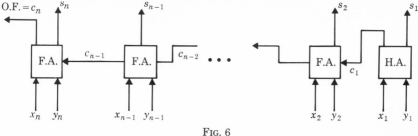

FIG. 6

Their sum is $S = (s_n, \ldots, s_1)_2$ and O.F. indicates overflow, i.e., that the sum has more than n bits. H.A. stands for the half adder designed earlier, and F.A. denotes the full adder designed in the preceding example.

PROBLEMS

1. Design relay and electronic circuits for realizing the following function.

x	y	z	$f(x,y,z)$
0	0	0	0
0	0	1	1
0	1	0	1
0	1	1	1
1	0	0	1
1	0	1	1
1	1	0	0
1	1	1	1

(HINT: Use Prob. 2-5.4.)

2. Suppose a design problem is specified by the graph of the function to be synthesized as in Prob. 1.   When should one use Prob. 2-5.4, and when should one use Theorem 2-5.5?

3. Roughly speaking, the *level* of a logical formula is the number of stages of circuitry in the realization of the formula.   Theorem 2-5.5 says that every formula is equivalent to a two-level formula.   It is sometimes advantageous to consider formulas with more than two levels.   Give a precise definition of the level of a formula by induction on the shape of a boolean formula generated from the $2n + 2$ primitive forms $0, 1, x_1, \bar{x}_1, \ldots, x_n, \bar{x}_n$ with operations $+$ and $\cdot$

4. There is a convenient way to write formulas, called *Polish notation*, in which parentheses are not needed.   Incidentally, this notation is used in the construction of compilers for digital computers.   For boolean formulas, one writes

$$0 \to 0$$
$$1 \to 1$$
$$x_i \to x_i$$
$$A + B \to + AB$$
$$A \cdot B \to \cdot AB$$
$$\bar{A} \to - A$$

As an example, $(xy + yz) + x\bar{z}$ is written $+ + \cdot xy \cdot yz \cdot x - z$. Write out the following formulas in Polish notation:

$$(ab) + (ac) \qquad (a(ba)) + c$$

5. How can the level of a form be determined from its representation in Polish notation?

6. Frequently, a boolean function is specified as being 1 for certain inputs, 0 for others, and for the remainder of the input, one doesn't care whether the function is 0 or 1. Thus a *don't care function* is a mapping from $\{0,1\}^n$ into $\{0,1,D\}$. How many don't care functions of n variables are there?

7. If f and g are don't care functions, define $f + g, fg, \bar{f}$ by pointwise operations on the range $\{0,1,D\}$ as follows

$$
\begin{aligned}
&0 + 1 = 1 + 0 = 1 \\
&1 + D = D + 1 = 1 \\
&0 + D = D + 0 = D \\
&1 \cdot 0 = 0 \cdot 1 = 0 \cdot D = D \cdot 0 = 0 \\
&1 \cdot 1 = 1 \\
&1 \cdot D = D \cdot 1 = D \\
&\bar{1} = 0, \bar{0} = 1 \\
&\bar{D} = D
\end{aligned}
$$

What sort of mathematical system does the class of don't care functions together with these operations form?

8. Let f be a don't care function. Define f_0 to be a boolean function obtained from f by replacing every D in the graph of f by 0. Similarly, define f_1 as the function obtained from f by substituting 1 for every D. Define the *interval between f_0 and f_1* to be $[f_0, f_1] = \{g | f_0 \leq g \leq f_1\}$, where $\leq$ is the partial order of the boolean function algebra. Prove that the mapping $\varphi \colon f \to [f_0, f_1]$ is a one-to-one map from don't care functions onto intervals of the boolean function algebra.

9. Define operations $+$, $\cdot$, and $^-$ on intervals of the boolean algebra of functions such that

$$\varphi(f) + \varphi(g) = \varphi(f + g) \qquad \varphi(f)\varphi(g) = \varphi(fg) \qquad \varphi(\bar{f}) = \overline{\varphi(f)}$$

where φ is defined in Prob. 8.

10. Define the *weight of a don't care function* to be (a,b), where a is the number of domain elements which map into 1 and b is the number of domain elements which map into D. Show that the number of elements in $[f_0, f_1]$ is 2^b.

8 ANALYSIS BY BOOLEAN MATRICES

Chapter 3 is concluded by considering a technique of analysis which is more efficient than the methods of the preceding section. The technique involves calculations with boolean matrices which are also useful in the analysis of sequential machines.

The methods of this section are explained in terms of branch-type networks, and a generalization to gate-type networks can be given, but we shall not do so. (Cf. Seshu and Reed.)

Definition 1. A *switching matrix* $A = (a_{ij})$ is defined as a $k \times k$ ($k > 1$) symmetric matrix whose diagonal elements are all 1's and whose entries are switching functions.

It is necessary to define operations on the matrices. The following definition gives the operations in terms of the corresponding operations on the matrix elements.

Definition 2. If $A = (a_{ij})$, $B = (b_{ij})$ are $k \times k$ switching matrices, we define the following matrix operations:

$$A = B \qquad \text{iff} \quad a_{ij} = b_{ij} \qquad \text{for } i, j = 1, \ldots, k$$

$$A + B = C \qquad \text{iff} \quad c_{ij} = a_{ij} + b_{ij} \qquad \text{for } i, j = 1, \ldots, k$$

$$A * B = C \qquad \text{iff} \quad c_{ij} = a_{ij}b_{ij} \qquad \text{for } i, j = 1, \ldots, k$$

$$\bar{A} = C \qquad \text{iff} \begin{cases} c_{ij} = \bar{a}_{ij} & \text{for } i, j = 1, \ldots, k, \text{ where } i \neq j \\ c_{ii} = 1 & \text{for } i = 1, \ldots, k \end{cases}$$

$$A \leq B \qquad \text{iff} \quad a_{ij} \leq b_{ij} \qquad \text{for } i, j = 1, \ldots, k$$

Let $B_{k,n}$ be the set of all $k \times k$ ($k > 1$) switching matrices with elements from a free boolean algebra on n generators. The following result is immediate.

Theorem 3. The system $B_{k,n} = \langle B_{k,n}, +, *, 0, 1 \rangle$ is a boolean algebra.

PROOF. We shall leave the proof to the reader, but in passing, we note the 0 element and the 1 element.

$$0 = \begin{bmatrix} 1 & 0 & 0 & \cdots & 0 \\ 0 & 1 & 0 & \cdots & 0 \\ 0 & 0 & 1 & \cdots & 0 \\ \cdot & \cdot & \cdot & \cdots & 0 \\ 0 & 0 & 0 & \cdots & 1 \end{bmatrix} \qquad 1 = \begin{bmatrix} 1 & 1 & 1 & \cdots & 1 \\ 1 & 1 & 1 & \cdots & \cdot \\ 1 & 1 & 1 & \cdots & \cdot \\ \cdot & \cdot & \cdot & \cdots & 1 \\ 1 & 1 & 1 & \cdots & 1 \end{bmatrix} \quad \blacksquare$$

It is useful to associate a boolean matrix with *any* branch-type switching network.† It is assumed that the nodes of the network are labeled with the integers $1, \ldots, k$.

Definition 4. A *connection matrix* is defined to be a switching matrix whose i-j entry is the transmission function of the two-terminal network connecting nodes i and j and not containing any intermediate labeled nodes.

Thus, given any network with certain nodes labeled, we can construct its connection matrix, and, conversely, for any switching matrix we can associate a switching circuit.

† Any switching network means any finite network, i.e., no restrictions to series-parallel networks, planar networks, etc.

EXAMPLE. We find the connection matrix for the circuit shown in Fig. 1. The matrix C is given by

$$C = \begin{bmatrix} 1 & x_1 & 0 & x_4 & \bar{x}_1 & 0 & 0 & \bar{x}_1 \\ x_1 & 1 & x_3 & 0 & 0 & 0 & \bar{x}_2 & 0 \\ 0 & x_3 & 1 & \bar{x}_4 & 0 & \bar{x}_3 & 0 & x_3 \\ x_4 & 0 & \bar{x}_4 & 1 & \bar{x}_4 & 0 & 0 & 0 \\ \bar{x}_1 & 0 & 0 & \bar{x}_4 & 1 & x_3 & 0 & x_1 \\ 0 & 0 & \bar{x}_3 & 0 & x_3 & 1 & x_2 & 0 \\ 0 & \bar{x}_2 & 0 & 0 & 0 & x_2 & 1 & \bar{x}_2 \\ \bar{x}_1 & 0 & x_3 & 0 & x_1 & 0 & \bar{x}_2 & 1 \end{bmatrix}$$

To completely analyze a circuit, one would desire a $k \times k$ matrix whose i-j entry is the transmission function of the network with terminals i and j. This suggests the following definition.

Definition 5. For any connection matrix A, we define the *characteristic matrix or transmission matrix* $\chi(A) = (t_{ij})$ such that t_{ij} is the transmission function of the two-terminal network connecting node i to j. Clearly, $\chi(A)$ will be a symmetric matrix, since $t_{ij} = t_{ji}$.

EXAMPLE. Given the network shown in Fig. 2, the connection matrix A and the transmission matrix $\chi(A)$ are as shown. The reader should verify that $\chi(A)$ is correct.

$$A = \begin{bmatrix} 1 & x_1 & \bar{x}_2 & \bar{x}_1 \\ x_1 & 1 & x_2 & x_2 + \bar{x}_3 \\ \bar{x}_2 & x_2 & 1 & x_3 \\ \bar{x}_1 & x_2 + \bar{x}_3 & x_3 & 1 \end{bmatrix}$$

$$\chi(A) = \begin{bmatrix} 1 & (x_1 + x_2 + \bar{x}_3) & 1 & 1 \\ (x_1 + x_2 + \bar{x}_3) & 1 & (x_1 + x_2 + \bar{x}_3) & (x_1 + x_2 + \bar{x}_3) \\ 1 & (x_1 + x_2 + \bar{x}_3) & 1 & 1 \\ 1 & (x_1 + x_2 + \bar{x}_3) & 1 & 1 \end{bmatrix}$$

A systematic method for computing the transmission matrix $\chi(A)$ will be presented in the next section. The following definition will be the foundation of the method.

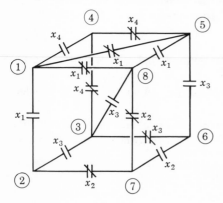

FIG. 1

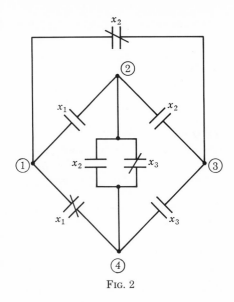

FIG. 2

Definition 6. Let $A = (a_{ij})$ and $B = (b_{ij})$ be two $k \times k$ switching matrices, and define the *matrix product* $C = A \cdot B$ iff $c_{ij} = \sum_{l=1}^{k} a_{il} b_{lj}$. The sum is the sum of the boolean algebra, and $a_{il} b_{lj}$ denotes the product of two elements of the boolean algebra.

EXAMPLE.   Consider the network of Fig. 3, with matrix A:

$$A = \begin{bmatrix} 1 & x_1 & 0 & 0 \\ x_1 & 1 & x_2 & 0 \\ 0 & x_2 & 1 & x_3 \\ 0 & 0 & x_3 & 1 \end{bmatrix}$$

We compute A^2

$$A^2 = \begin{bmatrix} 1 & x_1 & x_1 x_2 & 0 \\ x_1 & 1 & x_2 & x_2 x_3 \\ x_1 x_2 & x_2 & 1 & x_3 \\ 0 & x_2 x_3 & x_3 & 1 \end{bmatrix} \qquad A^3 = \begin{bmatrix} 1 & x_1 & x_1 x_2 & x_1 x_2 x_3 \\ x_1 & 1 & x_2 & x_2 x_3 \\ x_1 x_2 & x_2 & 1 & x_3 \\ x_1 x_2 x_3 & x_2 x_3 & x_3 & 1 \end{bmatrix}$$

Another multiplication indicates that $A^4 = A^3$, and it is trivial to verify that $A^3 = \chi(A)$.   This is not an accident.

$$
\begin{array}{cccc}
x_1 & x_2 & x_3 \\
\end{array}
$$

① ② ③ ④

FIG. 3

PROBLEMS

1. Construct an example to show that the product of two switching matrices of order k is not necessarily a switching matrix.

2. Let A, B, and C be switching matrices. Show that

$$A(B + C) = AB + AC \qquad A(BC) = (AB)C$$

3. In the definition of $B_{k,n}$, it is assumed that $k > 1$. Why?

4. Compute $\chi(C)$ for the matrix C constructed in the example following Definition 4.

5. If A, B, C, and D are switching matrices of order n and if $A \leq C$ and $B \leq D$, show that $AB \leq CD$.

6. Construct an algebra of relations and relate it to switching matrices. HINT: Let $G = \{a_1, a_2, \ldots\}$ be any set. Define any relation R on G. Construct relation matrices (r_{ij}) such that

$$r_{ij} = \begin{cases} 1 & \text{if } a_i R a_j \\ 0 & \text{otherwise} \end{cases}$$

7. Discuss the system $B_{k,0}$ and relate it to the Prob. 6 and the theory of graphs.

8. Discuss the case $B_{2,n}$.

9. Given a two-terminal network of k nodes constructed from elements $x_1, \ldots, x_n$ and their complements. Show that one can obtain the transmission function of the network by the process of *node removal* as given below.

(a) Construct the $k \times k$ connection matrix A of the given network and assume that the terminals are labeled 1 through k, respectively.

(b) Construct a matrix $(a_{ij} + a_{i2}a_{2j})$ and then delete the second row and column.

(c) If the new matrix has order 2, go to step d; otherwise, go to step b and call the new matrix $A = (a_{ij})$.

(d) Stop. The reduced matrix is of the form $\begin{bmatrix} 1 & F \\ F & 1 \end{bmatrix}$, where F is a boolean form whose associated function is the transmission function of the original network.

EXAMPLE. Using a previous example, Fig. P9, we have,

$$A = \begin{bmatrix} 1 & x_1 & 0 & 0 \\ x_1 & 1 & x_2 & 0 \\ 0 & x_2 & 1 & x_3 \\ 0 & 0 & x_3 & 1 \end{bmatrix}$$

Removing node 2,

$$\begin{bmatrix} 1 & x_1 x_2 & 0 \\ x_1 x_2 & 1 & x_3 \\ 0 & x_3 & 1 \end{bmatrix}$$

Finally,

$$\begin{bmatrix} 1 & x_1 x_2 x_3 \\ x_1 x_2 x_3 & 1 \end{bmatrix}$$

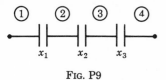

FIG. P9

9 ANALYSIS THEOREMS

We can now prove the theorems which will enable us to compute $\chi(A)$ for any switching matrix A.

Theorem 1. If A is any switching matrix of order n, then there exists an integer $q \leq n - 1$ such that

$$A \leq A^2 \leq \cdots \leq A^q = A^{q+1} = \cdots$$

PROOF. Let $A = (a_{ij})$ and $A^h = (b_{ij})$. Then

$$A^{h+1} = \left(\sum_{k=1}^{n} b_{ik} a_{kj} \right) = \left(b_{ij} + \sum_{k=1}^{n} b_{ik} a_{kj} \right)$$

since $a_{jj} = 1$. Thus,

$$b_{ij} \leq \sum_{k=1}^{n} b_{ik} a_{kj} \quad \text{and} \quad A^h \leq A^{h+1}$$

This shows $A \leq A^2 \leq \cdots$. We must show that this chain does not strictly increase indefinitely. It will be sufficient to show that

$$A^{n-1} = A^n$$

Since we already know $A^{n-1} \leq A^n$, we need only show $A^n \leq A^{n-1}$. We are using the fact that $\leq$ is a partial ordering and hence antisymmetric.

Consider an off-diagonal element of A^n. It is of the form

$$\sum_{k_{n-1}=1}^{n} \sum_{k_{n-2}=1}^{n} \cdots \sum_{k_1=1}^{n} a_{ik_1} a_{k_1 k_2} \cdots a_{k_{n-2}k_{n-1}} a_{k_{n-1}j}$$

Note that there are $n - 1 + 2 = n + 1$ subscripts, so not all of them can be distinct (Dirichlet's principle). Consider a term of the above sum, and suppose there exists an integer s such that $j = k_s$. The term is of the form

$$a_{ik_1} a_{k_1 k_2} \cdots a_{k_{s-1}j} a_{jk_{s+1}} \cdots a_{k_{n-1}j}$$

but since $ab \leq a$. this is contained in the term

$$a_{ik_1} \cdots a_{k_{s-1}j}$$

which is the i-j entry of A^s and is contained in the i-j entry of A^{n-1}. The previous argument is symmetric if $i = k_s$ for some integer s.

The remaining case occurs if there exist integers r and s such that $k_s = k_r$. The generic term becomes (assuming $s < r$)

$$a_{ik_1} \cdots a_{k_{s-1}k_r} a_{k_r k_{s+1}} \cdots a_{k_{r-1}k_r} a_{k_r k_{r+1}} \cdots a_{k_{n-1}j}$$

which is contained in

$$a_{ik_1} \cdots a_{k_{s-1}k_r} a_{k_r k_{r+1}} a_{k_r k_{r+1}} \cdots a_{k_{n-1}j}$$

This term is contained in the i-j entry of A^{n-1}. Therefore,

$$A^n \leq A^{n-1} \quad \text{and} \quad A^n = A^{n-1} \quad \blacksquare$$

Corollary 2. $A^q = A^{q+1} = \cdots = \chi(A)$

PROOF.   Let $A^q = (a_{ij})$. It will be sufficient to show $A^{n-1} = \chi(A)$. The i-j entry of A^2 is

$$\sum_{k=1}^{n} a_{ik} a_{kj}$$

This term is 1 when and only when there is a path directly between nodes i and j or there is a path from i to j through one intermediate node.

The i-j term of A^3 is 1 when and only when there is a path from i directly to j, there is a path from i to j through one intermediate node, or there is a path from i to j through two intermediate nodes.

The argument is repeated. No path requires more than $n - 2$ intermediate nodes, since there are only n nodes. The i-j entry of A^{n-1} is 1 when and only when i and j are connected, that is, $A^{n-1} = \chi(A)$. $\blacksquare$

Theorem 3.   Let A be a switching matrix. $A = \chi(A)$ iff $A = A^2$.

PROOF.   Assume $A = A^2$. By induction, $A = A^{n-1}$ and $A^{n-1} = \chi(A)$. Conversely, if

$$A = \chi(A) \quad \text{then} \quad A = A^{n-1}$$
$$A^2 = A^n = \chi(A) = A$$

so

$$A = A^2 \quad \blacksquare$$

The results of the previous theorems are combined to give a formal algorithm for the analysis of any finite combinational branch-type switching network.

Algorithm 4.   Given any finite network with k nodes and constructed from branch-type elements $x_1, \ldots, x_n$ and their complements.

(1) Label all the nodes by the integers $1, \ldots, k$.
(2) Write a connection matrix A whose i-j entry is a boolean form denoting the transmission function of the two-terminal network connecting nodes i and j without passing through any intermediate nodes.
(3) Let $i = 1$.
(4) Construct $A A^i = B$.
(5) If $B = A^i$, go to step 7.
(6) If $B \neq A^i$, replace A^i by B and go to step 4.
(7) Halt. B is the transmission matrix $\chi(A)$.

Proof.   Theorem 1 shows that the algorithm stops, and Theorem 2 says that the algorithm computes $\chi(A)$. $\blacksquare$

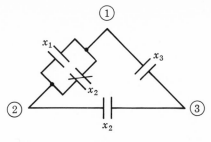

FIG. 1

EXAMPLE. The analysis of the network shown in Fig. 1 is easily carried out by this procedure.

$$A = \begin{bmatrix} 1 & x_1 + \bar{x}_2 & x_3 \\ x_1 + \bar{x}_2 & 1 & x_2 \\ x_3 & x_2 & 1 \end{bmatrix}$$

$$A^2 = \chi(A) = \begin{bmatrix} 1 & x_1 + \bar{x}_2 + x_3 & x_3 + x_1 x_2 \\ x_1 + \bar{x}_2 + x_3 & 1 & x_2 + x_3 \\ x_3 + x_1 x_2 & x_2 + x_3 & 1 \end{bmatrix}$$

PROBLEMS

1. Analyze the bridge circuit of Fig. P1.

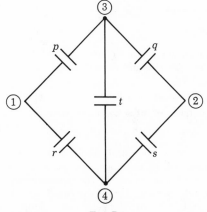

FIG. P1

2. Let A be a switching matrix of order n. Prove

$$A + A^2 + \cdots + A^n = A + A^2 + \cdots + A^{n+r}$$

for any $r \geq 0$.

3. Show that $\chi(\chi(A)) = \chi(A)$.

4. Show that $A \leq \chi(A)$.

5. Show that $\chi(A^2) = \chi(A)$. This is a special case of a more general result which will be proved later.

6. Compute $\chi(A)$ for the matrix A specified by the network of Fig. P6.

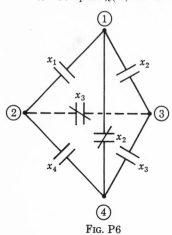

FIG. P6

7. Let S_k denote the symmetric group on $\{1, \ldots, k\}$ (cf. Sec. 1-6) and let A be any matrix of order k whose elements are in a boolean algebra. The *determinant of* A, written det (A), is defined as

$$\text{det } (A) = \sum_{\sigma \, \epsilon \, S_k} a_{1\sigma(1)} a_{2\sigma(2)} \cdots a_{k\sigma(k)}$$

Show that det (A) det $(B) \leq$ det (AB).

8. Let A be a connection matrix. Show that

$$\chi(A) = \text{adj}(A)$$

where $\text{adj}(A)$ is the *adjoint* of A defined as the matrix whose *i-j* entry is the determinant of the submatrix obtained by deleting the *j*th row and *i*th column. In other words, the *i-j* entry is the *cofactor* of a_{ji} in det (A).

9. Is the assumption that A is symmetric essential in Prob. 8?

10. (Yoeli) Let A and B be switching matrices of order k. Show that

$$\text{adj}(A)\text{adj}(\text{adj}(B)\text{adj}(A)) = \text{adj}(B)\text{adj}(\text{adj}(A)\text{adj}(B)) = \text{adj}(A + B)$$

11. There are many areas of interest in which long and involved sequences of operations must be analyzed. The situation can be complicated if some of the operations must be carried out before others. For instance, in the programming of a digital computer, the data must be read into memory before the computations start. Likewise, the computations must precede the output operations. Suppose that there are k steps in the procedure, and denote these steps by $a_1, \ldots, a_k$. One writes $a_i < a_j$ iff a_i *precedes* a_j. Thus, a *precedence relation* is a binary relation or, equivalently, a digraph on k points (Sec. 1-4). Consider a precedence relation $<$ and define the relation to be *consistent* if the relation contains no *contradictions*, where a contradiction takes the form $a < b$ and $b < a$. What graphical property does this condition imply?

12. (Marimont) Represent a precedence relation on k elements by a $k \times k$ matrix $R = (r_{ij})$ such that

$$r_{ij} = \begin{cases} 1 & \text{if } a_i < a_j \\ 0 & \text{otherwise} \end{cases}$$

The following algorithm tests for the consistency of the precedence matrix (relation). Prove that the algorithm works.

(a) Construct the precedence matrix $R = (r_{ij})$.

(b) If the ith row contains all zeroes, delete the ith row and column and form a smaller matrix. Continue until there are no nonzero columns.

(c) If the jth column contains all zeroes, delete the jth row and column and form a smaller matrix. Continue until there are no nonzero columns.

(d) If the remaining matrix has zero rows, go to step b.

(e) If the residual matrix is the empty matrix, then the relation is consistent. If not, the relation is inconsistent.

EXAMPLE.   The relation R is defined as

$$R = \begin{Bmatrix} (a_1,a_2) & (a_3,a_4) \\ (a_1,a_3) & (a_3,a_5) \\ (a_1,a_5) & (a_4,a_5) \\ (a_2,a_3) \end{Bmatrix}$$

The corresponding graph is shown in Fig. P12.

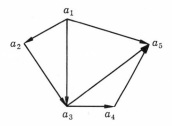

FIG. P12

The precedence matrix

$$R = \begin{bmatrix} 0 & 1 & 1 & 0 & 1 \\ 0 & 0 & 1 & 0 & 0 \\ 0 & 0 & 0 & 1 & 1 \\ 0 & 0 & 0 & 0 & 1 \\ 0 & 0 & 0 & 0 & 0 \end{bmatrix}$$

Applying the algorithm yields (deleting 1 and 5)

$$\begin{bmatrix} 0 & 1 & 0 \\ 0 & 0 & 1 \\ 0 & 0 & 0 \end{bmatrix}$$

Deleting 3 yields

$$\begin{bmatrix} 0 & 1 \\ 0 & 0 \end{bmatrix}$$

Deleting 2 gives

$$[0]$$

Deleting 1 gives ∅, the empty matrix; so R is consistent, which is easily seen from the graph (that is, once Prob. 11 is solved).

10 SUMMARY

In this chapter, techniques for the analysis and synthesis of any finite combinational switching circuit have been given. It might appear in light of these general results that our study of combinational switching theory should be finished. In fact, it is just begun.

The analysis techniques that have been given are quite general; and the use of matrix techniques leads to efficient computations, particularly for branch-type elements. The analysis techniques of this chapter suffice for most applications.

The synthesis method, on the other hand, is essentially the use of the canonical form theorem. This method is not efficient, because one may not "see" the structure of the function which permits more economical synthesis.

One aspect of the synthesis problem is minimization. Given a function f, what is the cheapest form A such that A denotes f? In the next chapter, some aspects of the minimization problem will be considered.

CHAPTER 4 *the minimization of boolean functions*

1 INTRODUCTION

In the synthesis method of Chap. 3 one derives a boolean form which corresponds to a given transmission function. This derived form should then be minimized to find an equivalent form which is cheaper with respect to some measure or other. It is the cheaper form which is realized.

In this chapter some minimization techniques are derived. Of course, it is possible to do minimization by algebraic manipulation. One takes the expanded normal form and applies the identities of boolean algebra to get cheaper forms. The difficulty with this approach is that it is not really an algorithm. The forms which can be derived depend on the designer's facility with boolean algebra and his experience. The methods to be presented here will be more systematic.

There is a graphical technique, generally called the *Karnaugh map method*, for minimization. This method is useful for the functions of up to five variables because the method is suitable for hand calculation.

The most important method that will be considered is Quine's algorithm. This is one of the original methods that was proposed, and an enormous body of literature has been based on it. Because of basic limitations in this method, only Quine's original algorithm is presented. After presenting the algorithm, we shall indicate the limitations.

While algorithms which produce minimal or near minimal solutions are known, most of these methods involve a considerable amount of exhaustive searching. The quest is for algorithms which are more efficient or which guarantee an absolutely minimal network.

2 THE PRECISE STATEMENT OF THE PROBLEM

The precise problem which will be posed here is the following: *Given a boolean function f represented as a normal form (sum of products), find a boolean form A which denotes f, A is also a sum of products, and A minimizes a suitable cost function.*

Of course, one can use products of sums in the obviously dual fashion. This problem, where the form A is required to be either a sum of products or a product of sums form, is called the *two-level minimization problem*. This restriction amounts to considering only a certain class of series-parallel networks. This is a severe restriction, since an example that was presented (a bridge network) is cheaper than any series-parallel representation of the same transmission function.

EXAMPLE.   Consider the function shown in the accompanying table. We now

x_1	x_2	f
0	0	0
0	1	1
1	0	0
1	1	1

list some of the infinitely many forms which denote f.

$$f(x_1,x_2) = \bar{x}_1 x_2 + x_1 x_2$$
$$= x_2$$
$$= x_2 x_2$$
$$= x_2 x_2 x_2$$
$$= x_2 + x_2$$
$$= x_2 x_2 + x_2$$

The example illustrates that a given function has infinitely many representations as a sum of products. If the following simple conditions are imposed on the form denoting the given function, then there will only be a finite number of forms. The rules are

$$x + x = x$$
$$xx = x$$
$$x\bar{x} = 0$$
$$x + \bar{x} = 1$$

In other words, by applying some of the theorems of boolean algebra, we can reduce the number of designated sums of products to a finite number.

EXAMPLE. Consider the function of three variables given by its graph. The expanded normal form of f is given, along with some forms which denote f and, finally, the minimal form.

x	y	z	$f(x,y,z)$
0	0	0	0
0	0	1	0
0	1	0	0
0	1	1	1
1	0	0	0
1	0	1	1
1	1	0	1
1	1	1	1

The forms are

1. $f(x,y,z) = \bar{x}yz + x\bar{y}z + xy\bar{z} + xyz$
2. $f(x,y,z) = \bar{x}yz + x\bar{y}z + xy + xz$
3. $f(x,y,z) = \bar{x}yz + xy\bar{z} + yz + xz$
4. $f(x,y,z) = x\bar{y}z + xy\bar{z} + xy + yz$
5. $f(x,y,z) = \bar{x}yz + x\bar{y}z + xy\bar{z} + xz$
6. $f(x,y,z) = \bar{x}yz + x\bar{y}z + xy\bar{z} + yz$
7. $f(x,y,z) = \bar{x}yz + x\bar{y}z + xy\bar{z} + xy$
8. $f(x,y,z) = xy + yz + xz$

The example indicates that the entire minimization problem is trivial in a mathematical sense, because the number of essentially different sums of products forms corresponding to f is finite and can be enumerated. Hence, the cheapest form can be selected from the enumeration. In practice, of course, the number of forms is too large to ever carry out the enumeration. Techniques for cutting down on the number of items to be enumerated are given in Chap. 5, but even these do not help very much.

Finally, the object of the minimization game is to lower the cost. This means that it will be necessary to specify a cost function. This function depends on the components to be used.

PROBLEMS

1. Given a function f of n variables with weight k, find an upper bound on the number of sums of products forms which correspond to f.

2. There are several possible choices for cost functions:
   (a) The form with fewest literals.
   (b) The form with the least number of terms, provided no expression with the same number of terms and fewer literals occurs.
   (c) The form which requires the least expensive hardware in its realization. When does the number of terms plus the number of literals equal the number of logical components required?

3 THE KARNAUGH MAP METHOD

The Karnaugh map method is presented in great detail in the book by Caldwell.[1]   A short discussion and two examples will be given here. The reader is asked to consult Caldwell's book for those details which he cannot supply himself.

The technique of the Karnaugh map is to represent a given switching function of the n cube as in Theorem 2-3.12.   The idea is to find a representation for the cube which makes it easy to "see" the subcubes of the cube.   In such a representation, it is essential to preserve the distance relationships between the domain elements.

For functions of two variables, map the four vertices of the square onto the quadrants of a sphere as in Fig. 1.   For functions of three variables, map the vertices onto the octants of a sphere as shown in Fig. 2. For functions of four variables, one must resort to a different geometric figure, the torus.   The regions are shown in Fig. 3.   Since it is inconvenient to construct three-dimensional figures on which to minimize functions, the surfaces are mapped into the plane.   The price which must be paid for working in the plane is that the corners of the figures are now adjacent.   The Karnaugh maps for $n = 1, \ldots, 4$ variables are shown in Fig. 4.

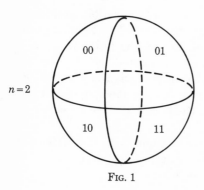

FIG. 1

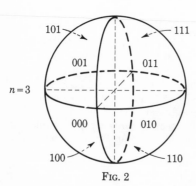

FIG. 2

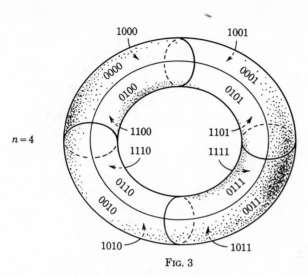

$n = 4$

Fig. 3

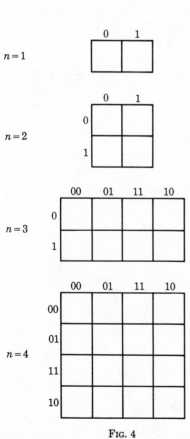

$n = 1$

$n = 2$

$n = 3$

$n = 4$

Fig. 4

Algorithm 1

(1) Given a function of n variables ($n \leq 4$), represent the function on the map by marking the appropriate squares with 1's.

(2) Select the largest possible subcubes which exactly cover the marked vertices. This can be done by exhaustion because $n \leq 4$.

(3) Read off the terms corresponding to the subcubes and call them $w_1, \ldots, w_k$.

(4) $f(x_1, \ldots, x_n) = \sum_{i=1}^{k} w_i(x_1, \ldots, x_n)$

The method is illustrated by two examples.

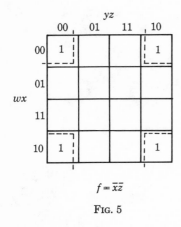

$$f = \bar{x}\bar{z}$$

Fig. 5

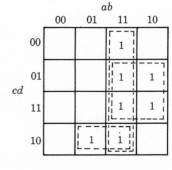

$$f = ad + ab + bc\bar{d}$$

Fig. 6

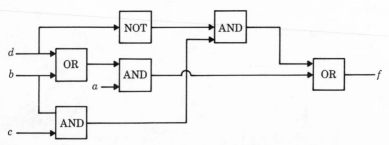

Fig. 7   A circuit realization for the function shown in Fig. 6.

EXAMPLE.   The function $f = \sum_{i \, \epsilon \, I} m_i$, where $I = \{0,2,8,10\}$, is shown on the map,
Fig. 5.   The four points form a two-dimensional subcube so that

$$f(w,x,y,z) = \bar{x}\bar{z}$$

EXAMPLE.   We minimize the function of Fig. 6 by using the map method.   The formula shown in Fig. 6 is the simplest disjunctive form; however, it can be slightly simplified algebraically:

$$f = a(b + d) + bc\bar{d}$$

The corresponding circuit is given in Fig. 7.

PROBLEMS

1.   Generalize the map method to functions of five variables by using two maps.

2.   Prove that the map method sketched in this section works.   [HINT: $x_1x_2 + \bar{x}_1x_2 = x_2$ occurs iff $d(x,y) = 1$, where $x = (x_1,x_2)$ and $y = (\bar{x}_1,x_2)$.   In general, $x_1\bar{x}_2 \cdots \bar{x}_n + x_1\bar{x}_2 \cdots \bar{x}_{n-1}x_n + \cdots + x_1x_2 \cdots x_n = x_1((\bar{x}_2 \cdots \bar{x}_n) + (\bar{x}_1 \cdots \bar{x}_{n-1}x_n) + (\bar{x}_2 \cdots x_{n-1}\bar{x}_n) + \cdots + (x_2 \cdots x_n)) = x_1$ holds iff the set of points involving $x_2, \ldots, x_n$ forms a subcube of dimension $n - 1$.]

3.   Minimize the following functions of four variables, where we write

$$f(x_1, \ldots, x_4) = \sum_{i \, \epsilon \, I} m_i(x_1, \ldots, x_4).$$

The functions are specified by writing down I.
   (a) $I = \{7,12,13\}$
   (b) $I = \{0,1,2,3,4,6,7,8,9,11,15\}$
   (c) $I = \{0,3,6,7,8,9,13,15\}$

4.   Generalize algorithm 1 to don't care functions.

5.   Generalize the map method to switching functions of six variables by using a three-dimensional map consisting of four maps each of which is the map for a function of four variables.

6.   Rework Prob. 1 using the method of Prob. 5.

7.   A switching function f is *symmetric* iff f is unchanged by any permutation of its variables.   What geometric properties does the class of symmetric switching functions exhibit on a Karnaugh map?

4   QUINE'S ALGORITHM

The algorithm of Quine[1] will now be presented.   The original paper by Quine was couched in terms of logic.   We choose to present a geometric formulation by Roth[1] in the hope of providing some intuitive insight into the process.   First, we introduce some convenient notation for subcubes.

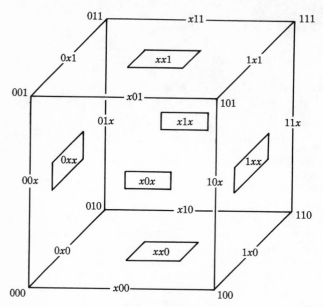

FIG. 1   The three-cube, (x, x, x).

Let W^k denote the k-dimensional cube.   Let us agree to call a single vertex a zero cube.   Then a pair of adjacent zero cubes will determine an *edge*, or a *one cube*.   If the two vertices are, say, $(1,0,1)$ and $(0,0,1)$, then we shall denote this one cube as $(x,0,1)$; as x ranges over $\{0,1\}$, this represents the points of the one cube.   In a similar way a two cube is made up of four one cubes.   For instance, $(0,0,1)$, $(0,1,1)$, $(1,0,1)$, $(1,1,1)$ make up the two cube $xx1$, where each x ranges over $\{0,1\}$ independently. The general situation should now be clear.   See Fig. 1 for the three cube with all possible subcubes drawn in.

We shall now introduce formal definitions for some simple geometric objects.   Given a function f, $K^0(f)$ will denote the vertices of the n cube which are mapped into 1 as in Sec. 2-3.   Thus $K^0(f)$ can be thought of as the set of zero cubes designated by f.   Likewise, $K^1(f)$ is to be the set of all one cubes generated by $K^0(f)$.   Inductively, $K^r(f)$ is to be all r cubes generated by the $r - 1$ cubes of f.   Thus, if f is a function of n variables,

$$K(f) = \bigcup_{i=0}^{n} K^i(f) \text{ is the family of all cubes which can be generated from } f.$$

It is clear that the cubes correspond to products of literals and that $K(f)$ corresponds to all possible product terms which could appear in a sum of products form for f.   We need to introduce some machinery for removing the unnecessary cubes.   Intuitively, it is desirable to keep only the largest cubes, since they correspond to terms with the fewest literals and will utilize fewer components.

To accomplish this computation, we introduce a mapping δ_i ($i = 1, \ldots, n$) which takes an r cube into a $(r + 1)$ cube. The δ_i, called *coface operators*, work as follows. If $(a_1, \ldots, a_n)$ is an r cube and if $a_i = x$, then $\delta_i(a_1, \ldots, a_n) = \emptyset$. This says that there is no $(r + 1)$-dimensional cube that $(a_1, \ldots, a_r)$ can be embedded into along the ith dimension. If $a_i \neq x$ and if

$$(a_1, \ldots, a_{i-1}, x, a_{i+1}, \ldots, a_n) = b \notin K(f)$$

then $\delta_i(a_1, \ldots, a_n) = \emptyset$, because embedding by the ith dimension gives a cube not generated by f. If $a_i \neq x$ and $b \in K(f)$, then $\delta_i(a_1, \ldots, a_n) = b$. This means that $\delta_i(a_1, \ldots, a_n)$ is the $(r + 1)$ cube generated by f and obtained from $(a_1, \ldots, a_n)$ by embedding along dimension i.

EXAMPLE. $f(x_1, x_2) = \bar{x}_1 \bar{x}_2 + \bar{x}_1 x_2 + x_1 \bar{x}_2$; see Fig. 2. Clearly,

$$K^0(f) = \{(0,0),(0,1),(1,0)\}$$
$$K^1(f) = \{(0,x),(x,0)\}$$
$$\delta_1(0,0) = (x,0)$$

but $\qquad \delta_2(1,0) = \emptyset \qquad$ since $(1,x) \notin K(f)$

Now these ideas are stated formally.

Definition 1. Let f be any boolean function of n variables. Define

$$K^0(f) = \{(x_1, \ldots, x_n) | f(x_1, \ldots, x_n) = 1\}$$

$K^r(f)$ is the set of all r cubes which are generated by $K^{r-1}(f)$. The *cubical complex of the function f* is defined to be $\langle \bigcup_{i=0}^{n} K^i(f), \delta_1, \ldots, \delta_n \rangle$, where the K^i are defined above. If $(a_1, \ldots, a_n)$ is an r cube with $a_i \in \{0,1,x\}$ for $i = 1, \ldots, n$, then

$$\delta_i(a_1, \ldots, a_n) = \begin{cases} \emptyset & \text{if } a_i = x \\ (a_1, \ldots, a_{i-1}, x, a_{i+1}, \ldots, a_n) = b & \text{if } a_i \neq x \\ \quad \text{and } b \in K(f) \text{ for } i = 1, \ldots, n \\ \emptyset & \text{if } a_i \neq x \\ \quad \text{and } b \notin K(f) \end{cases}$$

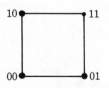

FIG. 2

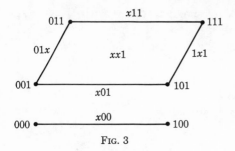

FIG. 3

where $\emptyset$ denotes the cube of dimension -1, the null cube.   The δ_i are called the *coface operators* and map $K^r \to K^{r+1}$.

We have discussed the computation of $K^r(f)$ from $K^{r-1}(f)$ in a heuristic way.   A more precise formulation will be given soon.

EXAMPLE.   Consider $f(x_1,x_2,x_3) = \bar{x}_1\bar{x}_2x_3 + \bar{x}_1x_2x_3 + x_1\bar{x}_2x_3 + x_1x_2x_3 + \bar{x}_1\bar{x}_2\bar{x}_3 + x_1\bar{x}_2\bar{x}_3$.

$$K^0 = \{(0,0,1),(0,1,1),(1,0,1),(1,1,1),(0,0,0),(1,0,0)\}$$

The reader should compute K^1 and K^2.   Note that

$$\delta_1(0,0,1) = (x,0,1) \qquad \delta_3(1,1,1) = \emptyset$$

A graphical picture representation of $K(f)$ is shown in Fig. 3.

EXAMPLE.   Let $f = \bar{x}_2 + x_3$.   Then $K(f)$ is given in Fig. 3.   This illustrates that it is not necessary to start from the expanded normal form.

PROBLEMS

1.   Show that $\delta_i\delta_j = \delta_j\delta_i$.

2.   Construct $K(f)$ for $f = \bar{x}_2x_1 + x_1x_3 + \bar{x}_2\bar{x}_3$.

3.   Show that the mapping $K: f \to K(f)$ is a one-to-one transformation of the switching functions *onto* the cubical complexes such that

$$K(f + g) = K(f) \cup K(g) \qquad K(fg) = K(f) \cap K(g)$$

4. Give a formal definition of a subcube $(a_1, \ldots, a_n)$ being contained in a subcube $(b_1, \ldots, b_n)$ where $a_i, b_j \in \{0,1,x\}$ for $i, j = 1, \ldots, n$.

5   PRIME SUBCUBES OR PRIME IMPLICANTS

The main idea of the Quine algorithm is to construct a special set of cubes which always contain the minimal cover.   Then this set of cubes will be refined until we get either the minimal cover or one which is close to it.

Definition 1.   A *cover* C of a complex $K(f)$ is the union of cubes such that every point in $K(f)$ is in C and conversely.

EXAMPLE.   Let $K(f) = \{(x,0),(0,x),(x,1)\}$, Fig. 1.   A cover of $K(f)$ is (x,x).

Definition 2.   The *cost of a cover* C of $K(f)$, written $\$(C)$, is defined to be

$$\$(C) = \sum_{k=0}^{n} q_k(n - k)$$

where q_k is the number of k cubes in C.   Cf. Prob. 3-4.2.

Definition 3.   A cube of dimension r, W^r, is said to be an *r-prime sub-cube†* iff $\delta_i W^r = \emptyset$ for every $i = 1, \ldots, n$. Z^r is the set of all r-prime subcubes, and the *space of all prime subcubes*, Z, is given as

$$Z = \bigcup_{r=0}^{n} Z^r$$

Geometrically, an elementary prime subcube is a cube which is not the face of a higher-dimensional cube.

The following theorem explains why the space Z of prime subcubes is so important.

Theorem 4.   If C is a minimal cover, then $C \subseteq Z$.

PROOF.   If $y \in C$ and $\delta_i y \neq \emptyset$, then we shall show that $C^* = (C - y) \cup \delta_i y$ is a cover having a lower cost than C.   Clearly, C^* is also a cover, since $\delta_i y \neq \emptyset$.   The cost of the two covers is the same except for the changes brought about by y.   Suppose dim $y = r$.   Then the terms of the cost function

$$q_r(n - r) + q_{r+1}(n - r - 1)$$

are replaced by

$$(q_r - 1)(n - r) + (q_{r+1} + 1)(n - r - 1) = q_r(n - r) + q_{r+1}(n - r - 1) - 1$$

and the cost is lowered, contradicting that C is the minimal cover. |

We shall need an algorithm to compute Z.   At first an algorithm which computes Z from the complex K^0 will be given.   That is, the algorithm uses no information about the higher-dimensional cubes of $K(f)$; in fact $K^i(f)$ for $i > 0$ are computed by the algorithm.

† Another term used for prime subcube is *prime implicant*.

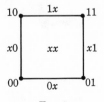

FIG. 1

Algorithm 5. Given the function $f(x_1, \ldots, x_n)$ expressed as K^0:

(1) Sort the zero cubes by weight and reorder the cubes in terms of increasing weight. Call the sets of cubes of weight i, S_i.

(2) Try to form all possible one cubes. Do this by adding every term of S_i with each term of S_{i+1}, $(i = 0, \ldots, n-1)$ componentwise modulo 2. If the sum has one 1 in it, then these cubes form a one cube. When the sum is being formed, the additions may be halted as soon as two 1's occur in the sum. Check every cube which enters into combination with another cube.

(3) The zero cubes which are not checked form Z^0.

(4) Let $i = 1$.

(5) Sort all the i cubes into columns such that all the members of each column have x's in the same positions. Sort every column by weight and repeat the componentwise additions modulo 2 as in step 2. Be sure to check all cubes which combine.

(6) The i cubes which are unchecked are Z^i.

(7) If there are no new $i + 1$ cubes, $Z^i = K^i$. Go to step 9.

(8) i is replaced by $i + 1$. Go to step 5.

(9) $Z = \bigcup\limits_{i=0}^{n} Z^i$

(10) Stop.

The algorithm may be illustrated by the following example. (Remember that we have not yet proved that this is an algorithm.)

EXAMPLE. K^0 is given below.

$$K^0 = \begin{cases} \begin{matrix} \checkmark0 & 0 & 0 & 0\} & S_0 \\ \checkmark0 & 1 & 0 & 0\} \\ \checkmark0 & 0 & 0 & 1\} & S_1 \\ \checkmark0 & 1 & 1 & 0\} \\ \checkmark1 & 1 & 0 & 0\} & S_2 \\ \checkmark1 & 1 & 1 & 0\} & S_3 \\ \checkmark1 & 1 & 1 & 1\} & S_4 \end{matrix} \end{cases}$$

The lines indicate the partition into $S_0, \ldots, S_4$. We compute K^1:

$$K^1 = \begin{cases} 0x00 & 000x & 01x0 & x100 \\ & 111x & 11x0 & x110 \end{cases}$$

In carrying out this computation, all terms of K^0 were checked, so that $Z^0 = \emptyset$. Now we compute K^2:

$$K^2 = \{x1x0\}$$

In this calculation the three unchecked terms are

$$Z^1 = \begin{cases} 0x00 & 000x \\ & 111x \end{cases}$$

The computation stops with K^2, so $Z^2 = \{x1x0\}$ and

$$Z = \left\{\begin{matrix} 0x00 \\ 000x \\ 111x \\ x1x0 \end{matrix}\right\}$$

Now we clean up the details in the following result.

Theorem 6.   The procedure of the preceding example is an algorithm which computes both $K^i(f)(i > 0)$ and Z.

PROOF.   Since n is finite, we have a finite number of vertices to be considered; so all the sorting operations are effective.   Clearly, the unchecked items are the prime implicants, since $\delta_i W = \emptyset$ for every i means just that W is not the face of a higher-dimensional cube.   The procedure terminates, since we always increase the dimension in each step, but the dimension is always less than or equal to n. $\mathbf{|}$

PROBLEMS

1.   Consider two infinite sequence of 0's and 1's with the probability of a 1 in any position of either word being $\frac{1}{2}$.   The two sequences are added sequentially and componentwise modulo 2.   If the addition is stopped as soon as two 1's appear in the sum, show that the expected number of additions is four.   HINT: Show the probability of obtaining two 1's in exactly k additions is $(k - 1)/2^k$.   Then show that

$$\sum_{k=2}^{\infty} \frac{k(k - 1)}{2^k} = 4$$

2.   Find Z for the following complex:

$$K^0 = \left\{\begin{matrix} 11001 & 11011 \\ 10011 & 10101 \\ 00110 & 10110 \\ 11000 & 10000 \\ 00000 & 11111 \\ 10001 & 00010 \\ 01101 & 00001 \\ 00111 & 00101 \end{matrix}\right\}$$

3. Show that the number of prime implicants of a function of n variables is not greater than 3^n.   Note that there can be more prime implicants than minterms.

4.   Show that the upper bound in Prob. 3 can be reduced to $3^n - 2^n$.

5.   (Karp) Show that if a function of n variables is chosen at random by labeling the vertices of the n cube with 0's and 1's such that the probability of a vertex being labeled 1 is $\frac{1}{2}$, then the expected number of prime implicants is

$$\sum_{k=0}^{n} \binom{n}{k} 2^{n-k-2^k}(1 - 2^{-2^k})^{n-k}$$

[HINT: Pr {a given k cube is a prime implicant} $= 2^{-2^k}(1 - 2^{-2^k})^{n-k}$]

6   ESSENTIAL PRIME SUBCUBES

For a given function f, the space of prime subcubes Z has now been constructed. It is known that the minimum cover is contained in Z. The first step in finding this cover is to select those cubes of the cover Z which must be included in a minimum cover. This gives rise to the following definition.

Definition 1.   A prime subcube e^k of dimension k in $K(f)$ is said to be an *essential prime subcube*† iff e^k contains a vertex which is not contained in any other prime subcube of K. The vertex is called a k-*distinguished* vertex. Let $E = \bigcup\limits_{j=0}^{n} e^j$.

The following theorem indicates the importance of the essential prime implicants.

Theorem 2.   If C is a minimum cover of the complex $K(f)$, then $E \subseteq C$.

PROOF.   Clearly, every vertex is contained in some cube of the cover. Assume that in the cover C, a k-distinguished vertex d is covered by a $(k-r)$-cube, $W^{k-r}(r > 0)$. The cost of this cover is then

$$\$(C) = A + q_{k-r}(n + r - k) + q_k(n - k)$$

where A is the cost of everything but the cubes of dimension k and $k - r$ under consideration.

Consider a new cover $D = (C - W^{k-r}) \cup e^k$, where e^k is the essential prime sub-cube corresponding to the vertex d. Clearly, D is also a cover. The cost of D is given by

$$\$(D) = A + (q_k + 1)(n - k) + (q_{k-r} - 1)(n + r - k) = \$(C) - r < \$(C)$$

since $r > 0$. This shows that C is not the minimum cover, which is a contradiction. Thus d must be covered by e^k; that is, the essential prime subcubes must be in a minimum cover.   **|**

Corollary 3.   If E, the space of essential prime subcubes, is a cover, then it is the unique minimum cover.

Unfortunately, the essential prime subcubes do not usually form a cover. An algorithm for obtaining the essential prime subcubes, assuming that Z was already computed by Algorithm 5.5, is now given.

Algorithm 4

(1) Construct a matrix having one row for each zero cube of $K(f)$ and one column for each prime subcube.
(2) If a zero cube is contained in a prime subcube, fill in a 1 in that position; otherwise, a 0. A zero cube $A = (a_1, \ldots, a_n)$,

---

† The term *essential prime implicant* is also used.

$a_i \in \{0,1\}$, is *contained* in a prime subcube $B = (b_1, \ldots ,b_n)$, $b_i \in \{0,1,x\}$, iff, for every $i = 1, \ldots , n$, $b_i = x$ or, if $b_i \neq x$, $a_i = b_i$.

(3) If a row has exactly one 1, then the column in which this 1 occurs has an essential prime subcube as its label.

EXAMPLE. The previous example is continued. The matrix is

	$0x00$	$000x$	$111x$	$x1x0$
0000	1	1	0	0
0100	1	0	0	1
0001	0	1	0	0
0110	0	0	0	1
1100	0	0	0	1
1110	0	0	1	1
1111	0	0	1	0

Thus the third, fourth, fifth, and seventh rows have exactly one 1 each. Therefore the essential prime subcubes are

$$E = \begin{cases} 000x \\ x1x0 \\ 111x \end{cases}$$

Theorem 5. The procedure given by Algorithm 4 is effective.

PROOF. We can surely form such a finite matrix. To check if a zero cube $(a_1, \ldots ,a_n)$ is covered by a prime subcube $(b_1, \ldots ,b_n)$, $b_i \in \{0,1,x\}$, check to see if a_i is covered by b_i for $i = 1, \ldots , n$. a_i is covered by b_i iff $b_i = x$ or $a_i = b_i$ when $b_i \neq x$. ∎

At this stage of the problem, there is generally more of the original complex to be covered. At the present time, there is no known non-exhaustive algorithm for selecting the remaining part of the cover to obtain a minimal result. The following procedure is a reasonably good one to follow with small problems.

Algorithm 6. Given the function f of n variables with Z and E already computed.

(1) Form $N^r = Z^r - E^r$ for $r = 0, \ldots , n$. Let $C = \emptyset$.

(2) Let N^m be the highest-dimensional nonvoid set of subcubes. Order the m cubes in any fashion and denote them by a_i.

(3) Let $i = 1$ and $N = \bigcup_0^n N^r$.

(4) $C' = C \cup \{a_i\}$.

(5) Delete all points of N contained in C'. If $C' - N = \emptyset$, go to step 8.

(6) Otherwise, i is replaced by $i + 1$, C is replaced by C', and if i does not exceed the number of m cubes, go to step 4.

(7) If i is larger than the number of m cubes, take $N^m = \emptyset$ and go to step 2.

(8) Stop. The cover is C'.

Intuitively, the algorithm removes the extremals and works on the remaining part of the problem. The method is to work on the higher-dimensional cubes first and hope to find a cover among them. If no cover is produced by the m-dimensional cubes, all possibilities are exhausted, since there must be a cover for N somewhere in the $\bigcup\limits_{r=0}^{n} N^r$.

EXAMPLE. We continue from the example following Algorithm 4. To carry out the calculations, we remove the essential prime subcubes and all elements of K^0 which they cover. We are left with only one prime subcube and no rows, indicating that the essential prime subcubes are the unique cover.

EXAMPLE. Consider the following problem.

	$xx00x$	$1x0x1$	$x00x1$	$01x01$	$011x1$	$0111x$	$x1111$	$11x11$
00000	1	0	0	0	0	0	0	0
00001	1	0	1	0	0	0	0	0
00011	0	0	1	0	0	0	0	0
01000	1	0	0	0	0	0	0	0
01001	1	0	0	1	0	0	0	0
01101	0	0	0	1	1	0	0	0
01110	0	0	0	0	0	1	0	0
10000	1	0	0	0	0	0	0	0
10001	1	1	1	0	0	0	0	0
10011	0	1	1	0	0	0	0	0
11000	1	0	0	0	0	0	0	0
11001	1	1	0	0	0	0	0	0
11011	0	1	0	0	0	0	0	1
11111	0	0	0	0	0	0	1	1
01111	0	0	0	0	1	1	1	0

We remove
$$E = \begin{Bmatrix} xx00x \\ x00x1 \\ 0111x \end{Bmatrix}$$

The simplified matrix is

	$1x0x1$	$01x01$	$011x1$	$x1111$	$11x11$
01101	0	1	1	0	0
11011	1	0	0	0	1
11111	0	0	0	1	1

One chooses $1x0x1$ first as a cover for N^2.   We reduce the matrix to find a cover for N^1.

	$01x01$	$011x1$	$x1111$	$11x11$
01101	1	1	0	0
11111	0	0	1	1

We choose $01x01$ and $x1111$ as our cover for N^1.   The complete cover C is given by

$$C = \begin{Bmatrix} xx00x & 1x0x1 \\ x00x1 & 01x01 \\ 0111x & x1111 \end{Bmatrix}$$

PROBLEMS

1. Prove that Algorithm 6 deserves its name; i.e., show that the procedure is an algorithm.   Note the exhaustive nature of the algorithm.

2. Work Prob. 3.4 by using Quine's algorithm.

7   GENERAL COMMENTS ON QUINE'S ALGORITHM

Quine's algorithm may be broken down into three steps, namely:

1. Compute the prime subcubes.
2. Remove the essential prime subcubes.
3. Find a cover of the remainder of the complex.

Of course, parts 1 and 2 are trivial to do.   Part 3 is the unsolved aspect of the problem.   The procedure given in Sec. 6 is exhaustive in nature and does not guarantee a minimal solution.   (Cf. previous example.)   Techniques for shortening part 3 by testing for isomorphic complexes will be given in Chap. 5.

It is interesting to note that part 3 of the Quine algorithm is a pattern-recognition problem.   It is very easy for humans to glance at a table and pick a good cover for the rows.   On the other hand, programming a digital computer for this task is not easy.

The Quine algorithm can be immediately extended to multiple-output networks, and it is not difficult to give an inefficient procedure for more than two-level minimization.   However, the previously mentioned difficulties are even more troublesome in the generalizations.

We have taken a very narrow point of view toward minimization problems.   The reader interested in these problems should read the more complete discussion given by Bartee, Lebow, and Reed.

PROBLEMS

1. (For those who know mathematical programming.) Show that the minimization problem can be recast as a problem in integer programming.

2. Rework Quine's algorithm for don't care functions.

3. Suppose f is denoted by a sum of products form. Find a systematic way to manipulate f to give a simpler form. (HINT: Make the sum of products into an irredundant sum of prime implicants. In other words, trade cost of the resulting form for shorter computations.)

4. Consider the minimization problem for multiple-output networks. The Quine algorithm can be immediately extended to work for n-input k-output networks if the proper definition of prime implicant is found. Carry out the extension. (HINT: A network with n inputs and k outputs is a function in a boolean algebra of 2^{k2^n} functions. The proper definition is the definition of prime implicant in this enlarged boolean algebra.)

5. Carry out the extension of Quine's algorithm to the multiple-level problem. (HINT: Replace the kth-level problem by a number of $(k-1)$-level problems and use induction.)

8 SUMMARY

The minimization problem for switching circuits has been discussed briefly. The methods available and the complexity involved in using them makes general minimization still a current research problem.

The presentation of the Quine[1] algorithm is based on the work of Roth,[1] although some of Quine's original terminology has been used.

CHAPTER 5 *transformation groups and group invariance*[†]

1 INTRODUCTION

The preceding chapters have indicated that there are so many switching functions that enumerative techniques are not particularly useful even with the help of digital computers. Some methods of reducing the number of functions to be considered in design algorithms will be given in this chapter. The technique to be used is to impose an equivalence relation on the family of functions; this will reduce the number of functions which must be checked to one member of each equivalence class.

The equivalence relation must be picked in a sensible way so that functions in the same class have similar structure, or nothing will be gained by this approach. For example, the relay network realization of functions

$$f(x_1,x_2,x_3) = x_1x_3 + \bar{x}_2 \quad \text{and} \quad g(x_1,x_2,x_3) = \bar{x}_2x_3 + x_1$$

are structurally identical, as can be seen in Fig. 1. This suggests that similarity of network realization is a useful equivalence relation. The precise definition of this kind of equivalence leads naturally to the theory of permutation groups defined on the domain of the boolean functions.

[†] The material in this chapter is advanced. The casual reader is advised to check Secs. 1 and 7 to 9 for the idea of equivalence under a group. Section 12 should be read to learn how to calculate invariants.

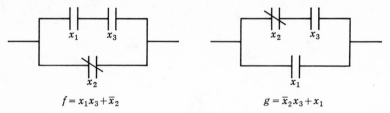

$$f = x_1 x_3 + \bar{x}_2 \qquad\qquad g = \bar{x}_2 x_3 + x_1$$

FIG. 1

Under the action of such a group, the functions are resolved into equivalence classes. It is natural to ask for the number of classes. The answer to such a question is difficult to derive.

In this chapter, counting techniques will be derived for the solution of this problem. Then the invariants for the most important group will be given.

2 PERMUTATION GROUPS

A brief mention of groups was made in Chap. 1. In this chapter the theory of permutation groups will be developed. Let G be a group of permutations on a set S. The group operation is composition, and the "one" element of G is the identity mapping. The product fg means that f is performed after g; that is, $fg(x) = f(g(x))$.

Definition 1. The number of elements in a group G is called the *order* of G. If G is a permutation group on a set S and S contains s elements, then s is said to be the *degree* of G.

EXAMPLE. The full symmetric group on $\{1, \ldots, n\}$, S_n, has degree n and order $n!$ (cf. Sec. 1-6).

Definition 2. Two elements of a group α and β are called *conjugate* iff there is a third element γ such that

$$\alpha = \gamma^{-1}\beta\gamma$$

Theorem 3. The relation of conjugacy is an equivalence relation in a group G.

PROOF. Clearly, $a = 1^{-1}a1$, where 1 is the identity in G. If $\alpha = \gamma^{-1}\beta\gamma$, then $\beta = \gamma\alpha\gamma^{-1} = (\gamma^{-1})^{-1}\alpha(\gamma^{-1})$. If $\alpha = \gamma_1^{-1}\beta\gamma_1$ and $\beta = \gamma_2^{-1}\delta\gamma_2$, then

$$\alpha = \gamma_1^{-1}\gamma_2^{-1}\,\delta\gamma_2\gamma_1 = (\gamma_2\gamma_1)^{-1}\,\delta\gamma_2\gamma_1 \quad \blacksquare$$

EXAMPLE. Let S_3 be the symmetric group on $\{1,2,3\}$. There are three conjugate classes given by

$$\begin{array}{ll} C_1 & \text{identity} \\ C_2 & [(1)(23),(2)(13),(3)(12)] \\ C_3 & [(123),(132)] \end{array}$$

where the notation (123) means 1 goes into 2, 2 goes into 3, and 3 goes into 1.

Next the important notion of equivalence under a group is introduced.

Definition 4. Let G be a permutation group on S. Two elements s_1, $s_2 \epsilon S$ are called *equivalent under* G iff there exists an $\alpha \epsilon G$ such that $s_1 = \alpha(s_2)$.

Proposition 5. Equivalence under a group is an equivalence relation.

Lemma 6. If G is a permutation group on S and $s \epsilon S$, then

$$H_s = \{\sigma | \sigma(s) = s\}$$

is a subgroup of G.

Definition 7. If H is a subgroup of a group G and if $\beta \epsilon G$, then

$$H\beta = \{\alpha\beta | \alpha \epsilon H\}$$

is called a *right coset* of H.

Left cosets can be defined in a similar way.

EXAMPLE. Let S_3 be the symmetric group on $\{1,2,3\}$ (cf. example following Theorem 3). Let A_3 be the subgroup

$$A_3 = \{1,(123),(132)\}$$

There are two cosets

$$A_3 1 = A_3$$
$$A_3(1)(23) = \{(1)(23),(2)(13),(3)(12)\}$$

Note that $S_3 = A_3 \cup A_3(1)(23)$.

Proposition 8. Two left (right) cosets of H in G are either disjoint or identical. The number of elements in a left (right) coset is the same as the order of H.

Definition 9. If H is a subgroup of a finite group G, then the number of right (left) cosets is called the *index* of H in G and is written $[G:H]$.

EXAMPLE. In the preceding example, it was seen that the index of A_3 in S_3 is 2.

Returning to a permutation group G on a set S, let H_s be the subgroup of G fixing a given $s \epsilon S$. The following result will be needed in the next section.

Lemma 10. The number of elements in the equivalence class containing s is the index of H_s in G.

PROOF. By Lemma 6, H_s is a subgroup of G. Let t_i be defined by

$$t_i = \sigma_i(s) \qquad i = 1, \ldots, g$$

where g is the order of G.   Define

$$\varphi_s : t_i \to \sigma_i H_s \qquad i = 1, \ldots, g$$

Thus φ_s is a map from elements of S which are equivalent to s onto left cosets. φ_s is one to one, since

$$\sigma_i \alpha = \sigma_j \beta \qquad a, \beta \, \epsilon \, H_s$$

That is, for every $x \, \epsilon \, S$, $\sigma_i \alpha(x) = \sigma_j \beta(x)$.   Choosing $x = s$

$$\sigma_i \alpha(s) = \sigma_j \beta(s) \qquad \text{or} \qquad t_i = \sigma_i(s) = \sigma_j(s) = t_j$$

Thus the number of elements equivalent to s is the same as $[G : H_s]$, the number of left cosets.   ▌

EXAMPLE.   Consider the group G acting on $\{1, \ldots, 4\}$, where

$$G = \{1, (12)(3)(4), (1)(2)(34), (12)(34)\}$$

The subgroup fixing 2 is $H_2 = \{1, (1)(2)(34)\}$.   The index of H_2 in G is 2, and the equivalence classes induced on $\{1, 2, 3, 4\}$ are

$$[1, 2] \qquad \text{and} \qquad [3, 4]$$

PROBLEMS

1. Show that if s is equivalent to t, then H_s is isomorphic to H_t.

2. Prove that the order of a group G is the product of the order of a subgroup H and the index of H in G.   This result is called Lagrange's theorem.

3. Show that any permutation can be written as a product of disjoint cycles.

4. (a) Show that any permutation can be written as a product of transpositions, where a *transposition* is defined as a cycle of length 2.   In other words, the symmetric group is generated by the $n(n-1)/2$ transpositions.

(b) Show that the symmetric group can be generated by the $n-1$ transpositions $(12), (13), \ldots, (1n)$.

5. Let $(a_1, \ldots, a_n) \, \epsilon \, S_n$, the symmetric group on $\{1, \ldots, n\}$. If σ is an arbitrary element of S_n, show that

$$\sigma(a_1, \ldots, a_k)\sigma^{-1} = (\sigma(a_1), \ldots, \sigma(a_k))$$

6. Show that the symmetric group S_n can be generated by $(1, 2, \ldots, n-1)$ and $(n-1, n)$.   (HINT: Use Probs. 4 and 5.)

7. Let S be a set of elements from the domain of a group G and let H be a subgroup of G.   Define the *normalizer of S in H* as

$$N_H(S) = \{\alpha \, \epsilon \, H \,|\, \alpha^{-1} S \alpha = S\}$$

Define the *centralizer of S in H* as

$$C_H(S) = \{\alpha \, \epsilon \, H \,|\, \alpha^{-1}\sigma\alpha = \sigma, \, \sigma \, \epsilon \, S\}$$

Show that $C_H(S) \subseteq N_H(S)$. Note that if S consists of a single element, $N_H(S) = C_H(S)$.

8. Show that the number of conjugates of an element $\alpha \epsilon G$ is the index of the normalizer (centralizer) $N_G(\{\alpha\})$ in G.

3 THEORY OF COUNTING

Having defined equivalence under a group, it is important to count the number of equivalence classes. The best answer that one could hope for would be a formula which, when the appropriate numbers were substituted, would yield the number of equivalence classes. Unfortunately, such a formula cannot usually be obtained. The next best thing to such a formula is a generating function. A *generating function* is a power series in an indeterminate x where the coefficient of, say, x^n is the desired number.

EXAMPLE. Suppose that one would like to count the number of *partitions* of n, that is, the number of nonnegative integral solutions (disregarding order) of

$$\sum_{i=1}^{n} a_i = n$$

Some values are listed in the accompanying table, where P_n is used to designate the desired number. No simple formula for P_n is known, but it is easy to show that P_n

n	1	2	3	4	5	6
P_n	1	2	3	5	7	11

is the coefficient of x^n in

$$\prod_{i=1}^{\infty} (1 - x^i)^{-1}$$

A solution to the problem of counting the number of equivalence classes will be given in terms of generating functions. First, a theorem of Froebenius which is itself a solution to the counting problem is derived.

Theorem 1. (Froebenius) The number of equivalence classes under a group G is given by $(1/g) \sum_{\alpha \epsilon G} I(\alpha)$, where $I(\alpha)$ is the number of elements of S left invariant under α and g is the order of G.

PROOF. Let

$$\delta_{\alpha(s),s} = \begin{cases} 1 & \text{if } \alpha(s) = s \\ 0 & \text{otherwise} \end{cases}$$

Then

$$I(\alpha) = \sum_{s \epsilon S} \delta_{\alpha(s),s}$$

We shall compute the right-hand side of the theorem and prove that it is equal to the number of equivalence classes.

$$\frac{1}{g} \sum_{\alpha \in G} I(\alpha) = \frac{1}{g} \sum_{\alpha \in G} \sum_{s \in S} \delta_{\alpha(s),s} = \frac{1}{g} \sum_{s \in S} \sum_{\alpha \in G} \delta_{\alpha(s),s} = \frac{1}{g} \sum_{s \in S} \sum_{\substack{\alpha \\ \alpha(s)=s}} 1 = \frac{1}{g} \sum_{s \in S} h_s$$

where h_s is the order of $H_s = \{\sigma | \sigma(s) = s\}$.

$$\frac{1}{g} \sum_{s \in S} h_s = \frac{1}{g} \sum_{[s] \subseteq S} \sum_{t \in [s]} h_s = \sum_{[s] \subseteq S} \frac{1}{g} \sum_{t \in [s]} h_t = \sum_{[s] \subseteq S} \frac{1}{g} h_s [G:H_s] = \sum_{[s] \subseteq S} 1$$

Lemma 2.10 and Prob. 2.1 were needed in the last line of this proof. |

The disadvantage of using the previous theorem to do the counting is that it requires one to compute $I(\alpha)$ for every $\alpha \in G$. Many of the groups to be considered have large orders, and this requires considerable calculation. An even more serious restriction is that the calculation of $I(\alpha)$ is time consuming for a set of large cardinality.

EXAMPLE.   Let V be Klein's four group acting on $\{1,2,3,4\}$

$$V = \{1,(12),(34),(12)(34)\}$$
$$I(1) = 4$$
$$I(12) = 2$$
$$I(34) = 2$$
$$I((12)(34)) = 0$$

The number of equivalence classes is

$$\tfrac{1}{4}(4 + 2 + 2) = 2$$

A straightforward calculation shows that V induces the partition

$$\{[1,2],[3,4]\}$$

One simplification that can be noted immediately reduces the enumeration of all elements of G to the enumeration of one element from each conjugate class of G.

Theorem 2.   If α and β are conjugates in G, then $I(\alpha) = I(\beta)$.

PROOF.   It is clearly sufficient to show that if $\alpha = \gamma^{-1}\beta\gamma$, then $\alpha(s) = s$ iff $\beta\gamma(s) = \gamma(s)$. Assuming $\alpha = \gamma^{-1}\beta\gamma$ and that $\alpha(s) = s$, then

$$\alpha(s) = s = \gamma^{-1}\beta\gamma(s)$$
$$\gamma(s) = \beta\gamma(s)$$

This set of relations shows that $I(\alpha) \leq I(\beta)$ and, by the symmetry of α and β, $I(\beta) \leq I(\alpha)$, which completes the proof. |

The most useful counting results will be given in terms of two generating functions. The most important definition is given now.

Definition 3. Let G be a permutation group of order g acting on S, where S contains s elements. Let $f_1, \ldots , f_s$ be s indeterminates and let $g_{j_1, \ldots , j_s} = g_{(j)}$ be the number of permutations of G having j_i cycles of length i for $i = 1, 2, \ldots , s$, so that

$$\sum_{i=1}^{s} i j_i = s \tag{1}$$

The *cycle index polynomial* is defined to be

$$Z_G(f_1, \ldots , f_s) = \frac{1}{g} \sum_{(j)} g_{j_1, j_2, \ldots , j_s} f_1^{j_1} f_2^{j_2} \cdots f_s^{j_s}$$

where the sum is taken over all partitions of s which satisfy (1).

EXAMPLE.   The cycle index of S_3 is

$$Z_{S_3}(f_1, f_2, f_3) = \tfrac{1}{6}(f_1^3 + 3 f_1 f_2 + 2 f_3)$$

Proposition 4. $Z_G(1, \ldots , 1) = 1$.   For every term of the cycle index polynomial, the sum of the products of exponents and subscripts is the degree of the group.

Because our applications will be made to a variety of functions, not just boolean functions, the main theorem is derived in a quite general context.   The technique to be used in the present work is due originally to Pólya.[1]   The development of this theorem rests ultimately on the theorem of Froebenius, but the Pólya formulation is much more useful.

Let F be the class of all functions from a finite set D to a finite set R.   Suppose D has s elements and that G is a permutation group of degree s and order g acting on D.   Two functions $f_1, f_2 \, \epsilon \, F$ are called *equivalent* if and only if there exists a permutation $\alpha \, \epsilon \, G$ such that

$$f_1(d) = f_2(\alpha(d))$$

for all $d \, \epsilon \, D$.   Consider $R(|R| = q)$ to be represented as the union of r disjoint subsets, that is, $R = \bigcup_{i=1}^{r} R_i$ and $R_i \cap R_j = \emptyset$ if $i \neq j$.

Definition 5. Associate with every set R_i an indeterminate x_i and let ψ_i be the number of elements in R_i for $i = 1, \ldots , r$.   The *range-counting series* or *figure-counting series* is defined as

$$\psi(x_1, \ldots , x_r) = \sum_{i=1}^{r} \psi_i x_i$$

The convention of taking $x_1 = 1$ is often adopted.

Definition 6. The *function-counting series* $P(x_1, \ldots, x_r)$ is defined to be

$$P(x_1, \ldots, x_r) = \sum_{k_1} \cdots \sum_{k_r} p_{k_1, \ldots, k_r} x_1^{k_1} \cdots x_r^{k_r}$$

where $p_{k_1, \ldots, k_r}$ is the number of equivalence classes of functions with the property that, for k_i values of $d \in D$, $f(d) \in R_i$, where $i = 1, \ldots, r$; i.e., $|f^{-1}(R_i)| = k_i$.

EXAMPLE. Let F be the class of functions from $\{1,2,3\}$ into $\{T,F\}$. Let G be the group

$$G = \{1,(123),(132)\}$$

The eight functions are partitioned into four equivalence classes, and if we let $x_1 = 1$, $x_2 = x$, then

$$P(x) = 1 + x + x^2 + x^3$$

The reader should check this example by enumerating the eight functions and performing the calculation.

We now prove the famous theorem of Pólya which reduces the calculation of $P(x_1, \ldots, x_r)$ to the calculation of the cycle index and the range-counting series.

Theorem 7. (Pólya[2]) The function-counting series is obtained by substituting the figure-counting series into the cycle index polynomial of G:

$$P(x_1, \ldots, x_r) = Z_G(\psi(x_1, \ldots, x_r), \psi(x_1^2, \ldots, x_r^2), \ldots,$$
$$\psi(x_1^s, \ldots, x_r^s))$$

PROOF. Let $k_1, \ldots, k_r$ be a partition of s and let $\gamma \in G$. $I_{k_1, \ldots, k_r}(\gamma)$ denotes the number of functions invariant under γ such that for k_i values of $d \in D$, $f(d) \in R_i$ for $i = 1, \ldots, r$. Let $p_{k_1, \ldots, k_r}$ denote the number of equivalence classes with the latter property and note that $p_{k_1, \ldots, k_r}$ is the coefficient of $x_1^{k_1} \cdots x_r^{k_r}$ in $P(x_1, \ldots, x_r)$. Since equivalent functions have the same k_i's, Theorem 1 yields

$$p_{k_1, \ldots, k_r} = \frac{1}{g} \sum_{\gamma \in G} I_{k_1, \ldots, k_r}(\gamma)$$

The problem now is to find $\chi_\gamma(x_1, \ldots, x_r)$, which is defined as

$$\chi_\gamma(x_1, \ldots, x_r) = \sum_{k_1} \cdots \sum_{k_r} I_{k_1, \ldots, k_r}(\gamma) x_1^{k_1} \cdots x_r^{k_r}$$

Thus the main problem is to evaluate $I_{k_1, \ldots, k_r}(\gamma)$. The first step is to see what a single cycle of γ does to a function. Consider a function f such that a cycle $(d_1, \ldots, d_l)$ of length l, $d_i \in D$ for $i = 1, \ldots, l$, leaves f invariant. All the d_i $(i = 1, \ldots, l)$ must map into the same element of R_i, since $f(d_1, \ldots, d_l) = f$. The function-counting series for functions invariant under a cycle γ of length l is

$$\psi(x_1^l, \ldots, x_r^l) = \sum_{i=1}^r \psi_i x_i^l$$

because any choice of range element is permissible and all elements of the cycle must go into one and the same class.   Let γ have j_i cycles of length i for $i = 1, \ldots, s$. Because the cycles are disjoint,

$$\chi_\gamma(x_1, \ldots, x_r) = \psi^{j_1}(x_1, \ldots, x_r)\psi^{j_2}(x_1^2, \ldots, x_r^2) \cdots \psi^{j_s}(x_1^s, \ldots, x_r^s)$$

$$= \prod_{i=1}^{s} \psi^{j_i}(x_1^i, \ldots, x_r^i)$$

We now combine the results:

$$
\begin{aligned}
P(x_1, \ldots, x_r) &= \sum_{k_1} \cdots \sum_{k_r} p_{k_1, \ldots, k_r}\, x_1^{k_1} \cdots x_r^{k_r} \\
&= \sum_{k_1} \cdots \sum_{k_r} \frac{1}{g} \sum_{\gamma \in G} I_{k_1, \ldots, k_r}(\gamma) x_1^{k_1} \cdots x_r^{k_r} \\
&= \frac{1}{g} \sum_{\gamma \in G} \sum_{k_1} \cdots \sum_{k_r} I_{k_1, \ldots, k_r}(\gamma) x_1^{k_1} \cdots x_r^{k_r} \\
&= \frac{1}{g} \sum_{\gamma \in G} \chi_\gamma(x_1, \ldots, x_r) \\
&= \frac{1}{g} \sum_{\gamma \in G} \prod_{i=1}^{s} \psi^{j_i}(x_1^i, \ldots, x_r^i) \\
&= Z_G(\psi(x_1, \ldots, x_r), \psi(x_1^2, \ldots, x_r^2), \ldots, \psi(x_1^s, \ldots, x_r^s)) \quad \blacksquare
\end{aligned}
$$

EXAMPLE.   In the example following Definition 6

$$Z_G(f_1, f_2, f_3) = \tfrac{1}{3}(f_1^3 + 2f_3) \qquad \text{and} \qquad \psi(x) = 1 + x$$

Thus $P(x) = \tfrac{1}{3}((1 + x)^3 + 2(1 + x^3)) = 1 + x + x^2 + x^3$.

Corollary 8.   The total number of equivalence classes of functions from D to R under a group G is

$$Z_G(q, q, \ldots, q)$$

where q is the number of elements in R.

EXAMPLE.   For the example preceding Corollary 8 the number of classes is

$$Z_G(2, 2, 2) = \tfrac{1}{3}(2^3 + 2 \cdot 2) = 4$$

PROBLEMS

1.   Let $\varphi(n)$ be the number of integers not exceeding n and relatively prime to n. Show that φ is a multiplicative function; i.e. if $(r, s) = 1$, then $\varphi(rs) = \varphi(r)\varphi(s)$. $\varphi(n)$ is called the Euler φ function.

2.   Show that

$$\varphi(n) = n \prod_{p \mid n} \left(1 - \frac{1}{p}\right)$$

where the product is over all prime divisors of n.

3. The Möbius function is defined as

$$\mu(n) = \begin{cases} 1 & \text{if } n = 1 \\ 0 & \text{if } p^\alpha | n \text{ for any } \alpha > 1 \text{ and any prime } p \\ (-1)^k & \text{if } n = p_1 \cdots p_k, \text{ where the } p_i \text{ are } \textit{distinct} \text{ primes} \end{cases}$$

Show that

$$\sum_{d|n} \mu(d) = \begin{cases} 1 & \text{if } n = 1 \\ 0 & \text{if } n > 1 \end{cases}$$

4. Prove the following Möbius inversion theorem: If f is any function (from integers to integers) and if

$$F(n) = \sum_{d|n} f(d)$$

then

$$f(n) = \sum_{d|n} F(d)\mu\left(\frac{n}{d}\right) = \sum_{d|n} F\left(\frac{n}{d}\right)\mu(d)$$

5. Show that the group generated by the permutation $(1, \ldots, m)$, denoted by C_m, has cycle index

$$Z_{C_m}(f_1, \ldots, f_m) = \frac{1}{m} \sum_{d|m} \varphi(d) f_d^{m/d}$$

where $\varphi(d)$ is the Euler φ function. C_m is called the *cyclic group of degree and order m*.

6. Show that the cycle index of S_n on $\{1, \ldots, n\}$ is

$$Z_{S_n}(f_1, \ldots, f_n) = \frac{1}{n!} \sum_{(j)} \frac{n!}{\prod\limits_{i=1}^{n} j_i! i^{j_i}} f_1^{j_1} \cdots f_n^{j_n}$$

where the summation is over all partitions of n. [HINT: Show that the normalizer of an element with cycle structure $(j_1, \ldots, j_n)$ has cardinality $\prod\limits_{i=1}^{n} j_i! i^{j_i}$. This result is due originally to Froebenius.]

4 DE BRUIJN'S THEOREM

It is necessary to consider functions from a domain D to a range R with a group G defined on D and a group H defined on R. The idea of equivalence in this situation is a slight generalization of the concept of equivalence studied in the preceding section.

Definition 1. Let F be the class of functions from D to R with permutation groups G and H, of order g and h, respectively, defined on D and on R. Two functions f and g are called *equivalent under G and H* iff there exist permutations $\alpha \in G$, $\beta \in H$ such that $\beta g(d) = f(\alpha(d))$ for all $d \in D$.

Lemma 1. The number of equivalence classes of functions with G on the domain and H on the range is given by

$$\frac{1}{g}\frac{1}{h} \sum_{\alpha \epsilon G} \sum_{\beta \epsilon H} I(\alpha,\beta)$$

where $I(\alpha,\beta)$ is the number of functions with the property that

$$f(\alpha(d)) = \beta f(d)$$

PROOF.   This lemma is reduced to Froebenius' theorem by taking S to be the set of functions F and the group to be $\{(\beta,\alpha)|\beta \epsilon H, \alpha \epsilon G\}$ under the operation $(\beta_2,\alpha_2)(\beta_1,\alpha_1)$ $= (\beta_2\beta_1,\alpha_1\alpha_2)$. Thus (β,α) carries f into $\beta f\alpha$.   ▌

Now the appropriate theorem of De Bruijn may be stated.

Theorem 2.   The number of equivalence classes of functions with G on the domain and H on the range is given by

$$Z_G \left(\frac{\partial}{\partial z_1}, \cdots, \frac{\partial}{\partial z_s} \right) Z_H(h_1, \ldots, h_q)$$

where
$$h_t = \exp \left(\sum_{k=1}^{[s/t]} t z_{kt} \right) \qquad \text{for } t = 1, \ldots, q$$

evaluated at $z_1 = \cdots = z_s = 0$.

PROOF.   The problem is to evaluate $I(\alpha,\beta)$.   Assume α has b_i cycles of length i for $i = 1, \ldots, s$; suppose that β has c_i cycles of length i for $i = 1, \ldots, q$.   Attention will now be focused on one cycle for each permutation, say, a cycle α_1 of length m for α and a cycle β_1 of length n for β.   Consider a function f such that $f(\alpha_1(d)) = \beta_1 f(d)$.   For this f, $f(d)$ must be in one and the same block C of R for every $d \epsilon B$; where B is a G-class of D; otherwise f would not be invariant.   It will be shown that

$$n \,|\, m$$

To show this, assume that $m = nq + r$, where $0 \leq r < n$.   Since

$$f(\alpha_1(d)) = \beta_1 f(d)$$

it must be that

$$f(\alpha_1{}^m(d)) = \beta_1{}^m f(d)$$

This last fact is trivial to prove by induction on m.   Then

$$f(\alpha_1{}^m(d)) = f(d) = \beta_1{}^{nq+r} f(d) = \beta_1{}^r f(d)$$

which implies that $\beta_1{}^r = 1$.   This contradicts the definition of n as the order (or length) of β_1 unless $r = 0$.

Thus, as d runs through any block B of length m in D, $f(d)$ runs through a block C of R of length n exactly m/n times.   All the invariant functions are obtained as follows.   For every block B of D, associate all blocks C of R whose lengths divide the length of B.   There is still the possibility of assigning an arbitrary element of C to some fixed element of B.   Once this has been done, the images of all other elements of B are fixed by the requirement:

$$f(d) = r \Rightarrow f(\alpha d) = \beta r$$

Finally, $I(\alpha,\beta)$ is computed:

$$I(\alpha,\beta) = \prod_{l=1}^{s} \Big(\sum_{\substack{i|l \\ i \leq q}} ic_i \Big)^{b_l}$$

That is, for every block B of D, sum the number of elements in every block C of R whose length divides the length of B. Note that

$$\prod_{l=1}^{s} \Big(\sum_{\substack{i|l \\ i \leq q}} ic_i \Big)^{b_l} = \frac{\partial^{b_1}}{\partial z_1^{b_1}} \cdots \frac{\partial^{b_s}}{\partial z_s^{b_s}} \exp \Big(\sum_{l=1}^{s} z_l \sum_{\substack{i|l \\ i \leq q}} ic_i \Big)$$

evaluated at $z_1 = \cdots = z_s = 0$. This is easily proved by taking partial derivatives. Now the results can be combined:

$$\sum_{[f] \subseteq F} 1 = \frac{1}{g}\frac{1}{h} \sum_{\alpha \epsilon G} \sum_{\beta \epsilon H}' I(\alpha,\beta)$$

$$= \frac{1}{g} \sum_{\alpha \epsilon G} \frac{\partial^{b_1}}{\partial z_1^{b_1}} \cdots \frac{\partial^{b_s}}{\partial z_s^{b_s}} \frac{1}{h} \sum_{\beta \epsilon H} \exp \Big(\sum_{l=1}^{s} z_l \sum_{\substack{i|l \\ i \leq q}} ic_i \Big)$$

$$= Z_G \Big(\frac{\partial}{\partial z_1}, \cdots, \frac{\partial}{\partial z_s} \Big) \frac{1}{h} \sum_{\beta \epsilon H} \exp \Big(\sum_{l=1}^{s} z_l \sum_{\substack{i|l \\ i \leq q}} ic_i \Big)$$

Note that

$$\exp \Big(\sum_{l=1}^{s} z_l \sum_{\substack{i|l \\ i \leq q}} ic_i \Big) = \exp \Big(\sum_{i=1}^{q} ic_i \sum_{k=1}^{[s/i]} z_{ki} \Big)$$

$$= \prod_{i=1}^{q} \Big(\exp \Big(i \sum_{k=1}^{[s/i]} z_{ki} \Big) \Big)^{c_i}$$

$$\sum_{[f] \subseteq F} 1 = Z_G \Big(\frac{\partial}{\partial z_1}, \cdots, \frac{\partial}{\partial z_s} \Big) \frac{1}{h} \sum_{\beta \epsilon H} \exp \Big(\sum_{l=1}^{s} z_l \sum_{\substack{i|l \\ i \leq q}} ic_i \Big)$$

$$= Z_G \Big(\frac{\partial}{\partial z_1}, \cdots, \frac{\partial}{\partial z_s} \Big) \frac{1}{h} \sum_{\beta \epsilon H} \prod_{i=1}^{q} \Big(\exp \Big(i \sum_{k=1}^{[s/i]} z_{ki} \Big) \Big)^{c_i}$$

$$= Z_G \Big(\frac{\partial}{\partial z_1}, \cdots, \frac{\partial}{\partial z_s} \Big) Z_H(h_1, \ldots, h_q)$$

where

$$h_t = \exp \Big(t \sum_{k=1}^{[s/t]} z_{kt} \Big) \quad \text{for } t = 1, \ldots, q$$

and the function is evaluated at $z_1 = \cdots = z_s = 0$. $\blacksquare$

One is often interested in special classes of functions rather than an entire family. One class of functions of particular interest is the one-to-one onto functions, or *invertible functions*.

Theorem 3. The number of classes of invertible functions from D onto D with a group G on the domain and a group H on the range is given by

$$Z_G\left(\frac{\partial}{\partial z_1}, \cdots, \frac{\partial}{\partial z_s}\right) Z_H(z_1, \ldots, sz_s)$$

evaluated at $z_1 = \cdots = z_2 = 0$.

PROOF. Again, Froebenius's theorem may be used. It is necessary to evaluate $I'(\alpha,\beta)$ for $\alpha \in G$ and $\beta \in H$, remembering to count only those orbits which contain one-to-one functions.

Consider a cycle of α of length m and a cycle of β of length n. By the previous proof of De Bruijn's theorem,

$$n|m$$

Since we are considering one-to-one *onto* functions, we must have $m|n$ and so $m = n$. Thus $b_i = c_i$ for $i = 1, \ldots, s$; and the determination of $I'(\alpha,\beta)$ is now trivial, because this expression is now simply the number of permutations having b_i cycles of length i $(i = 1, \ldots, s)$. This number is well known to be

$$I'(\alpha,\beta) = \prod_{i=1}^{s} c_i! i^{b_i}$$

Note that this is also

$$\prod_{i=1}^{s} c_i! i^{b_i} = \frac{\partial^{b_1}}{\partial z_1^{b_1}} \cdots \frac{\partial^{b_s}}{\partial z_s^{b_s}} \prod_{j=1}^{s} (jz_j)^{c_i}$$

evaluated at $z_1 = \cdots = z_s = 0$. Now

$$\sum_{\substack{[f] \subseteq F \\ f1-1}} 1 = \frac{1}{g}\frac{1}{h} \sum_{\alpha \in G} \sum_{\beta \in H} I'(\alpha,\beta)$$

$$= \frac{1}{g}\frac{1}{h} \sum_{\alpha \in G} \sum_{\beta \in H} \prod_{i=1}^{s} c_i! i^{b_i}$$

$$= \frac{1}{g} \sum_{\alpha \in G} \frac{\partial^{b_1}}{\partial z_i^{b_1}} \cdots \frac{\partial^{b_s}}{\partial z_s^{b_s}} \frac{1}{h} \sum_{\beta \in H} \prod_{i=1}^{s} (iz_i)^{c_i}$$

$$= Z_G\left(\frac{\partial}{\partial z_1}, \cdots, \frac{\partial}{\partial z_s}\right) Z_H(z_1, \ldots, sz_s)$$

evaluated at $z_1 = \cdots = z_s = 0$. ∎

PROBLEMS

1. Imagine a square in the plane and let us color the sides of the square with three colors. Call two colorings equivalent if one can be obtained from the other by a rotation of the square and by permuting the colors. Show that there are six equivalence classes. (HINT: Use De Bruijn's theorem with G the rotation group of the square, that is, C_4. H is the symmetric group of degree 3.)

2. List the six types of colorings from the Prob. 1.

3. Show that the number of one-to-one functions from D *into* R with G on D and H on R is given by

$$Z_G\left(\frac{\partial}{\partial z_1}, \cdots, \frac{\partial}{\partial z_s}\right) Z_H(1 + z_1, \ldots, 1 + qz_q)$$

evaluated at $z_1 = \cdots = z_s = 0$.

5 STRUCTURE THEORY
FOR PERMUTATION GROUPS

A structure theory for permutation groups has been developed in some detail by Pólya,[1] Harary, and Harrison.[2] In this section a few results which will be used in our study of boolean functions are derived.

Definition 1. Permutation groups A and B on object sets X and Y are called *permutationally equivalent* if and only if A and B are isomorphic as abstract groups and there is a one-to-one correspondence $h\colon X \leftrightarrow Y$ such that if φ is the abstract isomorphism between A and B, then for every $x \in X$, $\alpha \in A$, we have $h(\alpha x) = (\varphi\alpha)h(x)$.

Thus, two groups may be isomorphic as abstract groups but not permutationally equivalent. Note that the degree is one invariant of permutationally equivalent groups. Groups which are not permutationally equivalent (not even isomorphic) and yet possess identical cycle indices are known.

EXAMPLE. Consider S_3 defined on $\{1,2,3\}$ and the group G given below as a permutation group on $\{1, \ldots, 4\}$.

$$G = \{1, (1)(4)(23), (2)(4)(13), (3)(4)(12), (4)(123), (4)(132)\}$$

G is isomorphic to S_3 but not permutationally equivalent, since the groups have different degrees.

Definition 2. Let A and B be permutation groups on sets X and Y, respectively. The degree of A is a and its order is m. Similarly, the degree of B is b and the order of B is n. The *direct product* of A and B, written $A \times B$, is defined to be $\{(\alpha,\beta) | \alpha \in A, \beta \in B\}$, where $A \times B$ operates on $X \times Y$ in the following way:

$$(\alpha,\beta)(x,y) = (\alpha(x),\beta(y))$$

Proposition 3. $A \times B$ is a permutation group on $X \times Y$ of order mn and degree ab.

We shall now establish the connection between the cycle indices of A and B and the cycle index of $A \times B$. Let

$$Z_A = \frac{1}{m} \sum_{(j)} c_{(j)} g_1^{j_1} \cdots g_a^{j_a}$$

and let

$$Z_B = \frac{1}{n} \sum_{(k)} d_{(k)} h_1^{k_1} \cdots h_b^{k_b}$$

Theorem 4. $Z_{A \times B} = Z_A \times Z_B$, where the cross operation for polynomials is defined as follows

$$Z_{A \times B} = \frac{1}{m} \frac{1}{n} \sum_{(j)} \sum_{(k)} c_{(j)} d_{(k)} \left(\prod_{p=1}^{a} g_p{}^{j_p} \right) \times \left(\prod_{q=1}^{b} h_q{}^{k_q} \right)$$

The cross operation on indeterminates is defined as

$$\left(\prod_{p=1}^{a} g_p{}^{j_p} \right) \times \left(\prod_{q=1}^{b} h_q{}^{k_q} \right) = \prod_{p=1}^{a} \prod_{q=1}^{b} g_p{}^{j_p} \times h_q{}^{k_q}$$

$$= \prod_{p=1}^{a} \prod_{q=1}^{b} f_{\langle p,q \rangle}{}^{j_p k_q (p,q)}$$

where $\langle p,q \rangle$ denotes the least common multiple of p and q and (p,q) means the greatest common divisor of p and q.

EXAMPLE. Let

$$Z_{S_2} = \tfrac{1}{2}(g_1{}^2 + g_2)$$

and

$$Z_{S_3} = \tfrac{1}{6}(h_1{}^3 + 3h_1 h_2 + 2h_3)$$

be the cycle indices for the symmetric group on two and three letters, respectively.

$$
\begin{aligned}
Z_{S_2 \times S_3} &= \tfrac{1}{12}((g_1{}^2 \times h_1{}^3) + 3(g_1{}^2 \times h_1 h_2) + 2(g_1{}^2 \times h_3) \\
&\quad + (g_2 \times h_1{}^3) + 3(g_2 \times h_1 h_2) + 2(g_2 \times h_3)) \\
&= \tfrac{1}{12}(f_1{}^6 + 3(g_1{}^2 \times h_1)(g_1{}^2 \times h_2) + 2f_3{}^2 + f_2{}^3 \\
&\quad + 3(g_2 \times h_1)(g_2 \times h_2) + 2f_6) \\
&= \tfrac{1}{12}(f_1{}^6 + 3f_1{}^2 f_2{}^2 + 2f_3{}^2 + 4f_2{}^3 + 2f_6)
\end{aligned}
$$

PROOF. It is easily verified that the cross operation on indeterminates is associative, commutative, and distributive over addition. It will be sufficient to examine the cycle structure of (α, β), where α is a cycle of length p, say, $(a_1, \ldots, a_p)$ and β is a cycle of length q, say, $(b_1, \ldots, b_q)$. The case $p = q$ is trivial, so we assume $p < q$. Upon examining an element $(a_1, b_1) \in X \times Y$ we see that (a_1, b_1) goes successively into (a_2, b_2), (a_3, b_3), $\ldots$, (a_p, b_p), (a_1, b_{p+1}), $\ldots$; we return to (a_1, b_1) after $\langle p,q \rangle$ steps, and the pq symbols are permuted in (p,q) steps of length $\langle p,q \rangle$. Recall that $pq = \langle p,q \rangle (p,q)$. The argument is completed by noting that the choice of a_1 and b_1 is arbitrary; any pair of elements one in α and one in β would have given the same result. **|**

We now indicate a new result which also has applications in switching theory. Although a generalized version of this theorem is known, a special case will be presented here.

Let B be a group of order g acting on object set X. The degree of B is assumed to be b. Let B^n denote $B \times \cdots \times B$. Thus B^n is a group of order g^n defined on X^n and hence has degree b^n.

Definition 5. The system $\{(\beta, \sigma) | \beta \in B^n, \sigma \in S_n\}$ is called the *semidirect product* of S_n by B^n.

The basic properties of this group are now derived.

Proposition 6.   The system $\{(\beta,\sigma)|\beta \epsilon B^n,\ \sigma \epsilon S_n\}$ is a group under the following operation:

$$(\beta_1,\sigma_1)(\beta_2,\sigma_2) = (\beta_1 \oplus \sigma_1(\beta_2),\ \sigma_1\sigma_2)$$

where $\sigma_1(\beta_2) = \sigma_1(\beta_{21},\ \ldots\ ,\beta_{2n}) = (\beta_{2\sigma_1^{-1}(1)},\ \ldots\ ,\beta_{2\sigma_1^{-1}(n)})$

and $\oplus$ denotes the group operation of B^n. For any $(x_1,\ \ldots\ ,x_n) \epsilon X^n$, $(\beta,\sigma)\ (x_1,\ \ldots\ ,x_n) = (\beta_1 x_{\sigma^{-1}(1)},\ \ldots\ ,\beta_n x_{\sigma^{-1}(n)}).$†

Corollary 7.   The order of this group is $n\ !\ g^n$, and the degree is b^n.

The system given in Definition 5 has been proved to be permutationally equivalent to the complete monomial representation of B. Using properties of the monomial representation, the following theorem was proved by Harrison.[2]

Theorem 8.   If B is a permutation group of order g and degree b acting on X, then the complete monomial representation of B is written $S_n \otimes B$ and has degree b^n and order $n!g^n$. If the cycle index of B is of the form

$$Z_B = \frac{1}{g} \sum_k b_k f_k^r$$

then the cycle index of $S_n \otimes B$ is

$$Z_{S_n \otimes B} = \frac{1}{n!g^n} \sum_{(j)} \frac{n!g^n}{\prod\limits_{i=1}^{n} j_i!(gi)^{j_i}} \bigtimes_{i=1}^{n} \left(\sum_k b_k \prod_{\substack{d|ik \\ d\dagger pi \\ p<k}} f_d^{e(d)} \right)^{\times j_i}$$

where the sum is over all partitions of n, and

$$e(jk) = \frac{1}{jk} \sum_{\substack{d|jk \\ d\dagger lj \\ l<k}} m^{d/k} \mu \left(\frac{jk}{d} \right) \qquad \text{for } j = 1, 2, \ldots$$

$\mu(a)$ is the Möbius function.

PROOF.   The proof is given in Appendix VI of Harrison.[2] |

EXAMPLE.   Let B be the cyclic group of degree and order 3.

$$Z_B = \tfrac{1}{3}(f_1{}^3 + 2f_3)$$
$$Z_{S_2 \otimes B} = \tfrac{1}{2}(\tfrac{1}{9}(f_1{}^3 + 2f_3)^{\times 2} + \tfrac{1}{3}(f_1{}^3 f_3{}^3 + 2f_3 f_6)$$
$$= \tfrac{1}{18}(f_1{}^9 + 8f_3{}^3 + 3f_1{}^3 f_3{}^3 + 6f_3 f_6)$$

† The notation $\sigma: (x_1,\ \ldots\ ,x_n) \rightarrow (x_{\sigma^{-1}(1)},\ \ldots\ ,x_{\sigma^{-1}(n)})$ means to permute the positions of the variables by σ, not their subscripts; e.g., $(12)(x_1,x_2,x_3) = (x_2,x_1,x_3)$ while $(23)(x_2,x_1,x_3) = (x_2,x_3,x_1)$.

PROBLEMS

1. Let A and B be permutation groups on X and Y, respectively, where $X \cap Y$ $= \emptyset$. Define the *direct union* of A and B, written as $A \cup B$, to be $\{(\alpha,\beta) | \alpha \in A, \beta \in B\}$

where
$$(\alpha,\beta)(z) = \begin{cases} \alpha(z) & z \in X \\ \beta(z) & z \in Y \end{cases}$$

What is the object set for $A \cup B$? What are the order and degree of $A \cup B$?

2. (Pólya[1]) Suppose that A is a group on X and B is a group on Y. Furthermore, assume that the cycle indices of A and B are known. What is a formula for the cycle index of $A \cup B$?

6 ENUMERATION OF BOOLEAN FUNCTIONS

We now specialize the general abstract results to the case of enumerating boolean functions. First, it is noticed that permutations of the atoms have a special effect on the algebra.

Theorem 1. Let A be a boolean algebra having k atoms and 2^k elements. The automorphism group of A is isomorphic to the symmetric group on k letters.

PROOF. Clearly, every automorphism preserves the partial order of A and hence maps minimal elements into minimal elements. Since the automorphism is one to one and onto, it is a permutation of the atoms. Let σ be a permutation of the atoms of A. Using the normal form expansion, we see that σ induces a mapping from A into A, that is,

$$\sigma : f = \sum_{i \in I} a_i \rightarrow \sigma f = \sum_{i \in I} a_{\sigma(i)}$$

To show the *onto* property, note that if we are given

$$f = \sum_{i \in I} a_i$$

then the function

$$\sigma^{-1}(f) = \sum_{i \in I} a_{\sigma^{-1}(i)}$$

maps onto f under σ.

Now we show that σ preserves the structure. Let $f = \sum_{i \in I} a_i$ and $g = \sum_{\in J} a_j$,

then

$$\sigma(f + g) = \sigma\left(\sum_{i \in I} a_i + \sum_{j \in J} a_j\right) = \sigma\left(\sum_{k \in I \cup J} a_k\right)$$
$$= \sum_{k \in I \cup J} a_{\sigma(k)} = \sum_{i \in I} a_{\sigma(i)} + \sum_{j \in J} A_{\sigma(j)}$$
$$= \sigma(f) + \sigma(g)$$

Similarly,
$$\sigma(fg) = \sigma(f)\sigma(g)$$

Next we compute

$$\sigma(\bar{f}) = \sigma\left(\sum_{i \notin I} a_i\right) = \sum_{i \notin I} a_{\sigma(i)} = (\overline{\sigma f})$$

Finally, we show that σ is one to one.   Suppose

$$\sigma f = \sigma g$$

This happens iff

$$f = g \quad \blacksquare$$

Corollary 2.   The automorphism group of the boolean algebra of functions is the symmetric group on the 2^n atoms, denoted by S_{2^n}.

In practice one defines a transformation group on the variables x_1, . . . , x_n.   A transformation σ of the variables induces a transformation h_σ of the domain.   Finally, h_σ induces an automorphism α_σ of the entire function algebra.   The situation is summarized in Fig. 1, where

$$X = \{x_1, \ . \ . \ . \ , x_n\}$$

$D = \{0,1\}^n$, and F_n is the free boolean algebra of functions of n variables.

Since the range of boolean functions is $\{0,1\} = R$, take $R_1 = \{0\}$ and $R_2 = \{1\}$.   With R_1, associate the indeterminate 1, and with R_2 associate the indeterminate x.   Thus, the range-enumerating series (cf. Sec. 3) for switching functions is

$$\psi(x) = 1 + x$$

The enumeration results for boolean functions can be obtained by constructing the cycle index of the group under consideration.   *It is important to note that this group must be of degree 2^n, that is, defined over the domain, not the set of variables.*

Before proceeding to the actual constructions, a trivial case is given as an example.

Let I_n be the identity group on the n variables. I_n is of order 1 and induces a group on the domain of degree 2^n.   The cycle index of the induced group is given by

$$Z_{I_n} = f_1^{2^n}$$

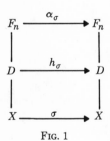

FIG. 1

Then by Pólya's theorem

$$P(x) = (1 + x)^{2^n} = \sum_{i=0}^{2^n} \binom{2^n}{i} x^i$$

which says that the number of switching functions of weight k is $\binom{2^n}{k}$.
Note by taking

$$P(1) = Z_{I_n}(2) = \sum_{i=0}^{2^n} \binom{2^n}{i} = 2^{2^n}$$

that we get the total number of functions.

PROBLEMS

1.   Characterize the class of endomorphisms of a boolean algebra.   (HINT: Examine mappings from atoms to atoms.)

2.   Conclude from Prob. 1 that F_n has 2^{n2^n} endomorphisms.   Show that the class of endomorphisms forms a semigroup.

3.   Find the automorphism group for the Post algebra of functions.

7   THE COMPLEMENTING GROUP C_2^n

In relay contact networks, the cost of a make contact is the same as the cost of a break contact.   Two functions will be considered as equivalent just in case one may be obtained from the other by complementing some of the variables.   For instance, let

$$f(x_1, x_2, x_3) = x_1(x_2\bar{x}_3 + \bar{x}_2 x_3)$$

and

$$g(x_1, x_2, x_3) = \bar{x}_1(\bar{x}_2\bar{x}_3 + x_2 x_3) = f(\bar{x}_1, \bar{x}_2, x_3).$$

In Fig. 1, we check that the networks have the same physical structure.   To make this intuitive concept more precise, we define a group of complementations on switching functions.

Definition 1.   The group $C_2 = \langle \{0,1\}, \oplus, 0 \rangle$ is defined with the operation of addition modulo 2.

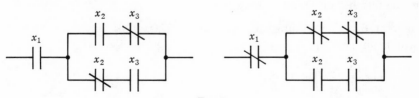

FIG. 1

Definition 2. The symbol C_2^n denotes $C_2 \times \cdots \times C_2$, that is, the abstract direct product of n copies of C_2. Thus, elements of C_2^n are n-tuples of 0's and 1's; the operation of the group is digit-wise modulo 2 addition. Of course, the identity element is $(0, \ldots ,0)$.

EXAMPLE. $C_2^2 = \begin{Bmatrix} (0,0),(1,0) \\ (0,1),(1,1) \end{Bmatrix}$ where, for instance, $(0,1) \oplus (1,1) = (1,0)$.

Now this group is defined on boolean functions.

Definition 3. Let $i \in C_2^n$ and let $f(x_1, \ldots ,x_n)$ be a boolean function of n variables. Define

$$if = (i_1, \ldots ,i_n)f(x_1, \ldots ,x_n) = f(x_1{}^{i_1}, \ldots ,x_n{}^{i_n})$$

where $x_j{}^{i_i} = \begin{cases} x_j & \text{if } i_j = 0 \\ \bar{x}_j & \text{if } i_j = 1 \end{cases}$ for $j = 1, \ldots , n$

Theorem 4. C_2^n is permutationally equivalent to $C_2 \times \cdots \times C_2$.

PROOF. Consider C_2 defined as a permutation group on the set consisting of 0 and 1. Using the definition of the product of permutation groups, it is evident that $C_2^n = C_2 \times \cdots \times C_2$. |

Theorem 5. $Z_{C_2^n} = \dfrac{1}{2^n}(f_1{}^{2^n} + (2^n - 1)f_2{}^{2^{n-1}})$

PROOF. By Theorems 4 and 5.4,

$$Z_{C_2^n} = \underset{i=1}{\overset{n}{\times}} \tfrac{1}{2}(f_1{}^2 + f_2)$$

It is claimed that

$$\underset{i=1}{\overset{n}{\times}} \frac{1}{2}(f_1{}^2 + f_2) = \frac{1}{2^n}(f_1{}^{2^n} + (2^n - 1)f_2{}^{2^{n-1}})$$

To show this by induction, we need only compute

$$\frac{1}{2^{n-1}}(f_1{}^{2^{n-1}} + (2^{n-1} - 1)f_2{}^{2^{n-2}}) \times \frac{1}{2}(f_1{}^2 + f_2)$$

$$= \frac{1}{2^n}(f_1{}^{2^n} + (2^{n-1} - 1)f_2{}^{2^{n-1}} + f_2{}^{2^{n-1}} + (2^{n-1} - 1)f_2{}^{2^{n-1}})$$

$$= \frac{1}{2^n}(f_1{}^{2^n} + (2^n - 1)f_2{}^{2^{n-1}}) \;\; |$$

Now that the cycle index has been computed, the problem of obtaining the number of classes is routine.

Theorem 6. The number of equivalence classes of functions having k atoms under C_2^n is

$$\frac{1}{2^n}\binom{2^n}{k} \qquad\qquad\qquad \text{if } k \equiv 1 \bmod 2$$

and $\dfrac{1}{2^n}\left(\binom{2^n}{k} + (2^n - 1)\binom{2^{n-1}}{k/2}\right) \qquad \text{if } k \equiv 0 \bmod 2$

PROOF. By Pólya's theorem,

$$Z_{C_2^n}(1 + x, 1 + x^2) = \frac{1}{2^n}((1 + x)^{2^n} + (2^n - 1)(1 + x^2)^{2^{n-1}})$$

$$= \frac{1}{2^n}\left(\sum_{k=0}^{2^n}\binom{2^n}{k}x^k + (2^n - 1)\sum_{j=0}^{2^{n-1}}\binom{2^{n-1}}{j}x^{2j}\right)$$

If $k \equiv 1 \bmod 2$, the coefficient of x^k is $\dfrac{1}{2^n}\dbinom{2^n}{k}$.

If $k \equiv 0 \bmod 2$, the coefficient of x^k is

$$\frac{1}{2^n}\left(\binom{2^n}{k} + (2^n - 1)\binom{2^{n-1}}{k/2}\right) \quad ❙$$

Theorem 7. The total number of equivalence classes of boolean functions under C_2^n is

$$\frac{1}{2^n}(2^{2^n} + (2^n - 1)2^{2^{n-1}})$$

PROOF. By Pólya's theorem, take $f_i = 1 + 1^i = 2$ in $Z_{C_2^n}$. ❙

Some typical calculations for this group have been made, and the results are tabulated in Table 1. We use T_n for the total number of

TABLE 1

The Number of Classes of Functions with k Atoms under C_2^n

k	N_n^k				
	n				
	1	2	3	4	5
0	1	1	1	1	1
1	1	1	1	1	1
2	1	3	7	15	31
3		1	7	35	155
4		1	14	140	1,240
5			7	273	6,293
6			7	553	28,861
7			1	715	105,183
8			1	870	330,460
9				715	876,525
10				553	2,020,239
11				273	4,032,015
12				140	7,063,784
13				35	10,855,425
14				15	14,743,445
15				1	17,678,835
16				1	18,796,230
T_n	3	7	46	4,336	134,281,216

equivalence classes and N_n^k for the number of classes of functions having k atoms.   Note that $N_n^k = N_n^{2^n-k}$.

As an example of the classification of functions induced on F_2 by C_2^2, the equivalence classes are listed below:

$$[0] \qquad\qquad\qquad [1]$$
$$[x,\bar{x}] \qquad\qquad\qquad [y,\bar{y}]$$
$$[\bar{x} + \bar{y},\ \bar{x} + y,\ x + \bar{y},\ x + y]$$
$$[\bar{x}\bar{y},\bar{x}y,x\bar{y},xy]$$
$$[x \oplus y,\ x \equiv y]$$

PROBLEMS

1. Give a direct derivation of the cycle index of C_2^n. (HINT: Show that no domain element is invariant under a nonidentity permutation of C_2^n. Since every element of C_2^n is self-inverse, the cycle structure of a nonidentity element is 2^{n-1} transpositions.)

2. (For mathematicians.)   Show that if H is the regular representation of a group of order p^k and type $(1, \ldots ,1)$, then $Z_H = \dfrac{1}{p^k} (f_1^{p^k} + (p^k - 1)f_p^{p^{k-1}})$ for any prime p and $k \geq 1$.

3. For Post functions, let the complementing group of $\neg$ be C_m, the cyclic group generated by $(0, 1, \ldots , m - 1)$. Define C_m^n as $C_m \times \cdots \times C_m$. Show that

$$Z_{C_m^n} = \frac{1}{m^n} \sum_{d|m} \sum_{t|d} t^n \mu\left(\frac{d}{t}\right) f_d^{m^n/d}$$

where $\mu(k)$ is the Möbius function.

4. Let D_m be the group of complementations by $\sim$ of a single variable in Post algebras. Show that

$$\begin{aligned} Z_{D_m} &= \tfrac{1}{2}(f_1{}^m + f_2^{m/2}) &&\text{if } m \equiv 0 \bmod 2 \\ Z_{D_m} &= \tfrac{1}{2}(f_1{}^m + f_1 f_2^{(m-1)/2}) &&\text{if } m \equiv 1 \bmod 2 \end{aligned}$$

and.

5. Show that the cycle index of the entire complementing group D_m^n is

$$Z_{D_m^n} = \frac{1}{2^n} (f_1^{m^n} + (2^n - 1)f_2^{m^n/2})$$

if $m \equiv 0 \bmod 2$.   (HINT: Induction on n.)

6. Show that the cycle index of D_m^n is

$$Z_{D_m^n} = \frac{1}{2^n} \sum_{k=0}^{n} \binom{n}{k} f_1^{m^{n-k}} f_2^{(m^{n-k}/2)(m^k - 1)}$$

if $m \equiv 1 \bmod 2$.   [HINT: Compute $\tfrac{1}{2}(f_1{}^m + f_1 f_2^{(m-1)/2})^{\times n}$.]

7. Conclude that the total number of equivalence classes of Post functions under D_m^n is

$$\frac{1}{2^n} (m^{m^n} + (2^n - 1)m^{m^n/2}) \qquad \text{if } m \equiv 0 \bmod 2$$

$$\frac{1}{2^n} \sum_{k=0}^{n} \binom{n}{k} m^{\frac{1}{2}(m^{n-k}+m^n)} \qquad \text{if } m \equiv 1 \bmod 2$$

8   THE SYMMETRIC GROUP S_n

The sort of equivalence induced on functions by C_2^n has practical significance because the intended applications were to branch-type networks where the cost of the elements corresponding to x_i and $\bar{x}_i$ was the same. In networks consisting of gate-type components, the cost of these two forms is different. It is certainly true that the cost of any network is independent of the labels on the inputs. For instance, the networks shown in Fig. 1 cost the same in any type of technology.

S_n is now defined as an operator group on boolean functions as suggested by the previous discussion.

Definition 1.   For any $\sigma \, \epsilon \, S_n$ and any $f \, \epsilon \, F_n$, define

$$\sigma f(x_1, \, . \, . \, . \, ,x_n) = f(x_{\sigma^{-1}(1)}, \, . \, . \, . \, ,x_{\sigma^{-1}(n)})$$

Thus, every $\sigma \, \epsilon \, S_n$ induces a permutation of the atoms of F_n as shown in the following example, where $\sigma = (12)(3)$ and we consider F_3

$$
\begin{aligned}
(0,0,0) &\rightarrow (0,0,0)\\
(0,0,1) &\rightarrow (0,0,1)\\
(0,1,0) &\rightarrow (1,0,0)\\
(0,1,1) &\rightarrow (1,0,1)\\
(1,0,0) &\rightarrow (0,1,0)\\
(1,0,1) &\rightarrow (0,1,1)\\
(1,1,0) &\rightarrow (1,1,0)\\
(1,1,1) &\rightarrow (1,1,1)
\end{aligned}
$$

By using the conventional decimal notation for atoms and writing the permutation of the atoms induced by σ in cyclic notation, it is seen

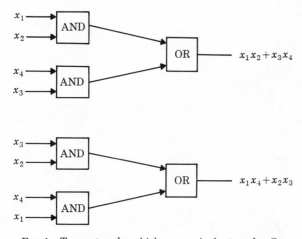

FIG. 1   Two networks which are equivalent under S_4.

that

$$\sigma \text{ induces } h_\sigma = (0)(1)(6)(7)(2,4)(3,5)$$

To derive the cycle index of S_n as a permutation group on $\{0,1\}^n$, we use Theorem 5.8.

Theorem 2. The cycle index for S_n as a permutation group on the domain of the boolean algebra of functions is

$$Z_{S_n} = \frac{1}{n!} \sum_{(j)} \frac{n!}{j_1! 1^{j_1} j_2! 2^{j_2} \cdots j_n! n^{j_n}} \underset{i=1}{\overset{n}{\times}} \left(\prod_{d|i} f_d^{e(d)} \right)^{\times j_i}$$

where the sum is over all partitions of n such that

$$\sum_{i=1}^{n} i j_i = n$$

and

$$\underset{i=1}{\overset{n}{\times}} y^{\times j_i} = y^{\times j_1} y^{\times j_2} \times \cdots \times y^{\times j_n}$$

where

$$y^{\times j_i} = \overset{j_i}{\overbrace{y \times y \times \cdots \times y}}$$

and

$$e(k) = \frac{1}{k} \sum_{d|k} 2^d \mu\left(\frac{k}{d}\right)$$

Here $\mu(l)$ is the Möbius function.

PROOF. Take B to be the identity group I whose cycle index is

$$Z_I = f_1^2$$

The result follows from Theorem 5-8. ∎

EXAMPLE. Let $n = 3$, so that the partitions of 3 are

(1) $j_1 = 3, j_2 = 0, j_3 = 0$
(2) $j_1 = 1, j_2 = 1, j_3 = 0$
(3) $j_1 = 0, j_2 = 0, j_3 = 1$

Thus
$$Z_{S_3} = \frac{1}{6}((f_1^2)^{\times 3} + 3(f_1^2) \times (f_1^2 f_2) + 2 f_1^2 f_3^2)$$
$$= \frac{1}{6}(f_1^8 + 3 f_1^4 f_2^2 + 2 f_1^2 f_3^2)$$

Now we apply Pólya's theorem to count the number of classes of functions with k atoms in their normal form expansion. N_n^k denotes this number. It is true that $N_n^0 = 1$ and $N_n^1 = n + 1$ for all $n \geq 1$. Cf. Table 2.

As a final example, we compute the cycle index of S_2 and show the tabulation.

EXAMPLE.

$$Z_{S_2} = \frac{1}{2}(f_1^4 + f_1^2 f_2)$$
$$P(x) = 1 + 3x + 4x^2 + 3x^3 + x^4$$

The 12 classes are shown below:

$[0]$ $[\bar{x}_1\bar{x}_2]$ $[x_1,x_2]$ $[\bar{x}_1 + \bar{x}_2]$ $[1]$

$[\bar{x}_1 x_2, x_1 \bar{x}_2]$ $[\bar{x}_1, \bar{x}_2]$ $[\bar{x}_1 + x_2, x_1 + \bar{x}_2]$

$[x_1 x_2]$ $[x_1 \oplus x_2]\,[x_1 \equiv x_2]$ $[x_1 + x_2]$

TABLE 1

The Total Number of Classes
under S_n

n	T_n
1	4
2	12
3	80
4	3,984
5	37,333,248
6	25,626,412,338,274,304

TABLE 2

The Number of Classes of Functions with k Atoms Under S_n

	N_n^k				
k	n				
	1	2	3	4	5
0	1	1	1	1	1
1	2	3	4	5	6
2	1	4	9	17	28
3		3	16	52	134
4		1	20	136	625
5			16	284	2,674
6			9	477	10,195
7			4	655	34,230
8			1	730	100,577
9				655	258,092
10				477	579,208
11				284	1,140,090
12				136	1,974,438
13				52	3,016,994
14				17	4,077,077
15				5	4,881,092
16				1	5,182,326
T_n	4	12	80	3,984	37,333,248

PROBLEMS

1. Give a direct construction of Z_{S_n}.

2. Derive the cycle index of S_n operating on the Post functions.

3. Count the number of nonisomorphic undirected graphs. [HINT: Derive the cycle index of S_n operating on the branches of the graph as induced by permuting the nodes. Thus if the graph has n points, the degree of S_n must be $n(n-1)/2$.]

9   THE GROUP OF COMPLEMENTATIONS AND PERMUTATIONS OF VARIABLES

The results of the preceding two sections are combined, and we now consider functions to be equivalent iff they differ by a complementation and/or permutation of the variables. It is interesting to observe that functions which differ by a complementation and/or permutation have isomorphic complexes on the n cube. As an example, Fig. 1 shows two functions f and g along with their geometric representations. It is clear that the functions are equivalent; the transformation which takes f into g is $(010)(12)$. By inspection, we see that the complexes are isomorphic.

Definition 1. Let $G_n = \{(i,\sigma)|i \epsilon C_2^n, \sigma \epsilon S_n\}$ be the group of complementations and permutations. G_n acts on boolean functions by

$$(i,\sigma)f(x_1, \ldots ,x_n) = f(x_{\sigma^{-1}(1)}^{i_1}, \ldots ,x_{\sigma^{-1}(n)}^{i_n})$$

According to the results of Sec. 5, G_n has the following group operation.

$$(i,\sigma)(j,\tau) = (i \oplus \sigma(j), \sigma\tau)$$

where $\sigma(j)$ denotes

$$\sigma(j) = \sigma(j_1, \ldots ,j_n) = (j_{\sigma^{-1}(1)}, \ldots ,j_{\sigma^{-1}(n)})$$

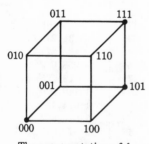

The representation of f

$$f(x_1,x_2,x_3) = \bar{x}_1\bar{x}_2\bar{x}_3 + x_1\bar{x}_2x_3 + x_1x_2x_3$$

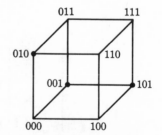

The representation of g

$$g(x_1,x_2,x_3) = \bar{x}_1\bar{x}_2x_3 + \bar{x}_1x_2\bar{x}_3 + x_1\bar{x}_2x_3$$

FIG. 1

EXAMPLE

$$((001), (123)) ((001), (132)) = ((001) \oplus (100), 1) = ((101), 1)$$
$$((001), (132)) ((001), (123)) = ((001) \oplus (010), 1) = ((011), 1)$$

The example indicates that the group operations do not commute. The following result shows some of the structure of G_n.

Proposition 2

$$(i,\sigma)^{-1} = (\sigma^{-1}(i),1)(0,\sigma^{-1})$$
$$(\sigma(i),\sigma) = (0,\sigma)(i,1)$$
$$(0,\sigma)(i,\sigma^{-1}) = (\sigma(i),1)$$

The construction of the cycle index of G_n is an immediate consequence of Theorem 5.8.

Theorem 3. The cycle index of G_n is given by

$$Z_{G_n} = \frac{1}{n!2^n} \sum_{(j)} \frac{n!2^n}{\prod\limits_{i=1}^{n} j_i!(2i)^{j_i}} \overset{n}{\underset{i=1}{\times}} \left(\prod_{d|i} f_d^{e(d)} + \prod_{\substack{d|2i \\ d \nmid i}} f_d^{g(d)} \right)^{\times j_i}$$

where the sum is over all solutions of $\sum\limits_{i=1}^{n} i j_i = n$

$$e(k) = \frac{1}{k} \sum_{d|k} 2^d \mu\left(\frac{k}{d}\right)$$

and

$$g(2k) = \frac{1}{2k} \sum_{\substack{d|2k \\ d \nmid k}} 2^{d/2} \mu\left(\frac{2k}{d}\right)$$

where $\mu(a)$ is the Möbius function.

EXAMPLE

$$Z_{G_2} = \tfrac{1}{8}((f_1^2 + f_2)^{\times 2} + 2(f_1^2 f_2 + f_4)) = \tfrac{1}{8}(f_1^4 + 3f_2^4 + 2f_1^2 f_2 + 2f_4)$$
$$P(x) = Z_{G_2}(1 + x, 1 + x^2, 1 + x^3, 1 + x^4) = 1 + x + 2x^2 + x^3 + x^4$$

TABLE 1

The Total Number of Classes
under G_n

n	T_n
1	3
2	6
3	22
4	402
5	1,228,158
6	400,507,806,843,728

TABLE 2

The Number of Classes of Functions with k Atoms
Under G_n

			N_n^k		
k			n		
	1	2	3	4	5
0	1	1	1	1	1
1	1	1	1	1	1
2	1	2	3	4	5
3		1	3	6	10
4		1	6	19	47
5			3	27	131
6			3	50	472
7			1	56	1,326
8			1	74	3,779
9				56	9,013
10				50	19,963
11				27	38,073
12				19	65,664
13				6	98,804
14				4	133,576
15				1	158,658
16				1	169,112
T_n	3	6	22	402	1,228,158

The classes are shown below:

[0] $[\bar{x}\bar{y},\bar{x}y,x\bar{y},xy]$ $[x,y,\bar{x},\bar{y}]$
  $[x \oplus y, x \equiv y]$ $[\bar{x} + \bar{y}, \bar{x} + y, x + \bar{y}, x + y]$ [1]

Table 1 indicates the number of classes for $1 \le n \le 6$, and Table 2 shows the numbers N_n^k.

PROBLEMS

1. Carry out a construction of G_n for Post functions similar to that of this section for boolean functions. (HINT: There are two choices for the complementing group, but only one of the groups satisfies the hypothesis of Theorem 5.8).

2. Show that the number of equivalence classes of boolean functions under G_n is the same as the number of distinct ways that one can paint the vertices of the n cube with two different colors. Two paintings of the n cube are *distinct* iff one cannot be transformed into the other under the symmetry group of the cube.

10 AN APPLICATION

In Table 1 the number of functions of n variables is shown with the number of classes of functions under G_n. It is clear from Table 1 that we can easily reduce the problems of synthesizing functions of three and four variables to enumeration. That is, a table of minimal networks for functions of four variables which can be used for design purposes can be constructed.

The classes under G_n are reproduced below for $n = 2$.

[0] $[\bar{x}_1\bar{x}_2, \bar{x}_1 x_2, x_1\bar{x}_2, x_1 x_2]$ $[x_1, x_2, \bar{x}_1, \bar{x}_2]$ $[x_1 \oplus x_2, x_1 \equiv x_2]$

[1] $[\bar{x}_1 + \bar{x}_2, \bar{x}_1 + x_2, x_1 + \bar{x}_2, x_1 + x_2]$

It is interesting to note that four of the classes have the property that the complements of the function are in different classes. If we also consider f equivalent to $\bar{f}$, the number of classes can be roughly cut in half and the number of entries in the tables cut in half. We consider this simplification first. It is convenient to obtain the negation of a boolean function by the action of a negation group to be denoted by N. N has order 2; one element is the identity mapping and the other element, denoted by η, has the property

$$\eta : f \rightarrow \bar{f}$$

for any boolean function f.

The situation is now as follows: We have a group G defined on the domain of the boolean functions and a group N on the range. The pertinent group on the functions is called the *exponentiation group* N^G. To count the number of such classes, we may apply the De Bruijn theorem once we have calculated Z_G and Z_N. The action of N on $\{0,1\}$ is to permute 0 and 1 so that N is actually the symmetric group of degree and order 2:

Thus

$$Z_N = \tfrac{1}{2}(f_1{}^2 + f_2)$$

The following lemma facilitates the calculations in using De Bruijn's theorem.

TABLE 1

n	2^{2^n}	T_n
1	4	3
2	16	6
3	256	22
4	65,536	402
5	4,294,967,296	1,228,158

Lemma 1.   A term $h_1{}^{j_1} \cdots h_r{}^{j_r}$ in Z_H gives rise to

$$Z_G \left(\sum_{t|1} tj_t, \; \ldots, \; \sum_{t|s} tj_t \right)$$

PROOF.   We compute $\dfrac{\partial}{\partial z_i} (h_1{}^{j_1} \cdots h_r{}^{j_r})$.

This yields

$$\frac{\partial}{\partial z_i} (h_1{}^{j_1} \cdots h_r{}^{j_r}) = \frac{\partial}{\partial z_i} \prod_{t=1}^{r} \exp \left(tj_t \sum_{k=1}^{\infty} z_{kt} \right)$$

$$= \frac{\partial}{\partial z_i} \exp \left(\sum_{t=1}^{r} \sum_{k=1}^{\infty} tj_t z_{kt} \right)$$

$$= \left(\exp \sum_{t=1}^{r} \sum_{k=1}^{\infty} tj_t z_{kt} \right) \sum_{t=1}^{r} \sum_{k=1}^{\infty} tj_t \delta_{i\,kt}$$

where $\delta_{i\,kt}$ is the Kronecker delta function, i.e.,

$$\delta_{i\,kt} = \begin{cases} 1 & \text{if } i = kt \\ 0 & \text{otherwise} \end{cases}$$

Taking every z_i equal to zero gives

$$\frac{\partial}{\partial z_i} (h_1{}^{j_1} \cdots h_r{}^{j_r}) = \sum_{t|i} tj_t \quad \blacksquare$$

Theorem 2.   Let G be any permutation group on the domain of boolean functions.   The number of classes of functions under N^G (transformations of G on the domain and complementation of the range) is given by

$$\tfrac{1}{2}(Z_G(2,2, \; \ldots ,2) + Z_G(0,2,0,2, \; \ldots ,0,2))$$

PROOF.   Use Lemma 1 and Theorem 4.2. $\blacksquare$

This theorem is applied to obtain the appropriate numbers for the three groups.

Theorem 3.   The number of classes of functions with C_2^n on the domain and N on the range is

$$\frac{1}{2^{n+1}} (2^{2^n} + (2^n - 1)2^{2^{n-1}+1})$$

PROOF.   The result follows from the closed form for $Z_{C_2^n}$. $\blacksquare$

Theorem 4.   The number of classes of functions with S_n on the domain and N on the range is exactly one-half the number of classes with just S_n on the domain.

PROOF.   Since the domain elements corresponding to (0) and to $(2^n - 1)$ are symmetric, every term of the cycle index contains a term f_1^k for $k \geq 2$. $\blacksquare$

The calculated numerical results are given in Table 1.

TABLE 1

Number of Classes under Groups Containing Negation

n	C_2^n	S_n	G_n
1	2	2	2
2	5	6	4
3	30	40	14
4	2,288	1,992	222
5	67,172,352	18,666,624	616,126
6	144,115,192,303,714,304	12,813,206,169,137,152	200,253,952,527,184

As an example of this classification, Appendix 3 lists one representative from each class of the functions of three variables under N^{G_3}.

A similar table of functions may be constructed for $n = 4$, and this construction will be accomplished directly. A synthesis procedure may be sketched briefly as follows.

Proposed Method. Given any function f, of four variables, find the function which is equivalent to f in the tables given in Appendix 3. If a function equivalent to f is not in the table, then complement f and use $\bar{f}$ instead.

The trouble with the method suggested is simply that we do not know a nonexhaustive way to tell if f and g are equivalent. In order to devise such a method, we must first construct a new way to represent switching functions which is much more natural for the present problem. The new coordinate representation will be the topic of the next section.

PROBLEMS

1. Show that the number of equivalence classes of boolean functions under G is greater than or equal to $2^{2^n}/g$, where g is the order of G.

2. Show that if the order of G is less than $2^{2^{n-2}-\varepsilon \log_2 n}$ for any $\varepsilon > 0$, then the number of equivalence classes of switching functions under G is asymptotic to $2^{2^n}/g$, where g is the order of G.

3. An equivalence class C is called *self-complementary* if $f \in C$ implies that $\bar{f} \in C$. Show that only classes of neutral functions may have this property. (Recall that the neutral functions are those whose weight is 2^{n-1}.)

4. Show that the number of self-complementary classes under a group G is $Z_G(0,2, \ldots, 0,2)$.

5. Conclude from Prob. 4 that the number of self-complementary classes under C_2^n is

$$(2^n - 1)2^{2^{n-1}-n}$$

whereas there are no such classes under S_n.

6. Show that if G is a group on the domain of the boolean functions whose order g does not exceed

$$\sqrt{\frac{2}{\pi}}\, 2^{2^{n-1}-n/2-\varepsilon\log_2 n}$$

for any positive ε, then the number of self-complementary classes of functions tends to zero with the number of classes of neutral functions. HINT: The number of self-complementary classes is greater than or equal to

$$\frac{1}{g}\binom{2^n}{2^{n-1}} \sim \frac{1}{g}\sqrt{\frac{2}{\pi}}\, 2^{2^n-n/2}$$

7. Conclude from Prob. 6 that almost all neutral classes are not self-complementary. Is this to be expected from the numerical results which have been previously reported?

8. Define an (n,k) network to be an n-input k-output network as shown in Fig. P8. Think of the network as realizing a function from $\{0,1\}^n$ into $\{0,1\}^k$. If G is a group on $\{0,1\}^n$ and H is a group on $\{0,1\}^k$, then the number of classes of functions can be calculated from De Bruijn's theorem. Show that if G is a group on the inputs and C_2^k acts on the outputs, then the number of classes of (n,k) networks is

$$\frac{1}{2^k}\left(Z_G(2^k,\ \ldots\ ,2^k) + (2^k-1)Z_G(0,2^k,\ \ldots\ ,0,2^k)\right)$$

Compare this result with Theorem 2.

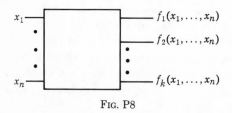

FIG. P8

9. Find a lower bound on the number of (n,k) networks with groups G and H on the inputs and outputs, respectively. Give inequalities on the order of G and/or H so that the lower bound is the asymptotic result.

10. (Lorens) Consider (n,n) networks which realize a function bilaterally, i.e., the network realizes a function f which has an inverse. Show that there are $2^n!$ such invertible functions. For groups G and H on the inputs and outputs, compute the number of classes of invertible functions. If $T(G,H)$ is the number of classes of invertible functions, notice that $T(G,H) = T(H,G)$.

11. (For those who know the theory of equations.) Explain the connection between invertible functions and simultaneous boolean equations.

12. (Lorens) Show that the number of invertible classes with C_2^n acting on both the range and the domain is given by

$$\frac{1}{2^{2n}}\left(2^n! + (2^n-1)^2(2^{n-1}!)2^{2^{n-1}}\right)$$

11 COORDINATE REPRESENTATION

The coordinate representation which will now be derived is in the same relation to the ordinary representation of a switching function as the Fourier transform is to ordinary functions of a real variable. This is not just an analogy, because it can be shown that the coordinate representation of a function f is exactly the (discrete version of the) Fourier transform of f. The details can be found in the work of Lechner.

First, switching functions will be represented by boolean matrices of order 2^n.

Definition 1. The *Kronecker delta function* is defined as

$$\delta_{ij} = \begin{cases} 1 & \text{if } i = j \\ 0 & \text{if } i \neq j \end{cases}$$

Definition 2. If a boolean function f is denoted by a sum of minterm functions

$$f(x_1, \ldots, x_n) = \sum_{i=0}^{2^n-1} \alpha_i m_i(x_1, \ldots, x_n)$$

where $\alpha_i \in \{0,1\}$ for $i = 0, \ldots, 2^n - 1$, then the *boolean matrix representation of f* is defined to be the $2^n \times 2^n$ matrix B_f, where

$$B_f = (\alpha_i \delta_{ij})$$

Thus, boolean functions are represented by $2^n \times 2^n$ diagonal matrices whose diagonal elements are 1 or 0.

EXAMPLE. $f(x_1, x_2) = m_0(x_1, x_2) + m_2(x_1, x_2) + m_3(x_1, x_2)$. B_f is given by

$$B_f = \begin{bmatrix} 1 & 0 & 0 & 0 \\ 0 & 0 & 0 & 0 \\ 0 & 0 & 1 & 0 \\ 0 & 0 & 0 & 1 \end{bmatrix}$$

Although diagonals are inefficient in representing functions, they do provide a representation in terms of matrices which will prove useful. The following proposition shows how to compute with the matrices.

Proposition 3

$$B_{f+g} = B_f + B_g$$
$$B_{fg} = B_f B_g$$
$$B_{f \oplus g} = B_f \oplus B_g$$
$$B_{\bar{f}} = \bar{B}_f \qquad \text{where only the main diagonal of } B_f \text{ is complemented}$$
$$B_0 = 0 \qquad 2^n \times 2^n \text{ zero matrix}$$
$$B_1 = I \qquad 2^n \times 2^n \text{ identity matrix}$$

The boolean representation is not particularly valuable, but it provides a method of constructing a real matrix representation.

Definition 4.   If f is any switching function of n variables with boolean representation B_f, then the *real representation matrix of f*, written R_f, is defined as

$$R_f = I - 2B_f$$

where I is the $2^n \times 2^n$ identity matrix.

EXAMPLE.   For f as in the preceding example,

$$R_f = \begin{bmatrix} -1 & 0 & 0 & 0 \\ 0 & 1 & 0 & 0 \\ 0 & 0 & -1 & 0 \\ 0 & 0 & 0 & -1 \end{bmatrix}$$

Thus, any function is represented as a $2^n \times 2^n$ diagonal matrix, where the diagonal matrices are $+1$ or -1.   The following proposition seems to imply that this representation is less natural.   It is not.

Proposition 5 $R_{f \oplus g} = R_f R_g = R_g R_f$
$R_{\bar{f}} = -R_f$
$R_0 = I \qquad 2^n \times 2^n$ identity matrix
$R_1 = -I$
$R_{f+g} = \frac{1}{2}(-I + R_f + R_g + R_f R_g)$
$R_{fg} = \frac{1}{2}(I + R_f + R_g - R_f R_g)$

EXAMPLE.   Let $g(x_1,x_2) = m_1(x_1,x_2) + m_2(x_1,x_2)$ and let f be as in the previous example.

$$R_g = \begin{bmatrix} 1 & 0 & 0 & 0 \\ 0 & -1 & 0 & 0 \\ 0 & 0 & -1 & 0 \\ 0 & 0 & 0 & 1 \end{bmatrix}$$

$$R_{fg} = \frac{1}{2}(I + R_f + R_g - R_f R_g)$$

$$= \frac{1}{2}\left(\begin{bmatrix} 1 & 0 & 0 & 0 \\ 0 & 1 & 0 & 0 \\ 0 & 0 & -1 & 0 \\ 0 & 0 & 0 & 1 \end{bmatrix} - \begin{bmatrix} -1 & 0 & 0 & 0 \\ 0 & -1 & 0 & 0 \\ 0 & 0 & 1 & 0 \\ 0 & 0 & 0 & -1 \end{bmatrix} \right) = \begin{bmatrix} 1 & 0 & 0 & 0 \\ 0 & 1 & 0 & 0 \\ 0 & 0 & -1 & 0 \\ 0 & 0 & 0 & 1 \end{bmatrix}$$

R_{fg} corresponds to $m_2(x_1,x_2)$, as it should.

To pass to a more convenient representation, the linear functions are now introduced.

Definition 6.   Every function of the form

$$f(x_1, \ldots ,x_n) = c_0 \oplus \bigoplus_{i=1}^{n} c_i x_i$$

where $c_i \epsilon \{0,1\}$ for $i = 1, \ldots, n$, is called a *linear* boolean function. If $c_0 = 0(1)$, the functions are called *odd* (*even*) linear functions.

Proposition 7. There are 2^n odd (even) linear functions. Every linear function except 0 and 1 has weight 2^{n-1}.

It is convenient to have a special notation for the odd linear functions.

Definition 8. Denote the odd linear functions by $l_0, l_1, \ldots, l_n, l_{12},$ $l_{13}, \ldots, l_{1n}, l_{123}, l_{124}, \ldots, l_{n-2,n-1,n}, \ldots, l_{1,2\ldots n}$ and define $l_{i,j,\ldots,p}$ $= x_i \oplus x_j \oplus \ldots \oplus x_p$

EXAMPLE. Choose $n = 3$:

$$
\begin{array}{ll}
l_0 = 0 & l_{12} = x_1 \oplus x_2 \\
l_1 = x_1 & l_{13} = x_1 \oplus x_3 \\
l_2 = x_2 & l_{23} = x_2 \oplus x_3 \\
l_3 = x_3 & l_{123} = x_1 \oplus x_2 \oplus x_3
\end{array}
$$

Note that a consequence of the notation is that

$$l_{ij\ldots k} = l_i \oplus l_j \oplus \cdots \oplus l_k$$

We now construct an important matrix which enables us to give the coordinate representation.

Definition 9. Let $R_{l_p} = (r_{ij}^p)$ be the real matrix representation of l_p. Define the transformation T by $T = (1/2^{n/2})(r_{jj}^p)$, where $(1/2^{n/2})r_{jj}^p$ is the (p,j) entry of T.

EXAMPLE. The notation of Definition 9 means that the pth row of T is the main diagonal of the real matrix representation of l_p. For example, if $n = 2$,

$$
R_{l_0} = \begin{bmatrix} 1 & 0 & 0 & 0 \\ 0 & 1 & 0 & 0 \\ 0 & 0 & 1 & 0 \\ 0 & 0 & 0 & 1 \end{bmatrix} \qquad
R_{l_2} = \begin{bmatrix} 1 & 0 & 0 & 0 \\ 0 & -1 & 0 & 0 \\ 0 & 0 & 1 & 0 \\ 0 & 0 & 0 & -1 \end{bmatrix}
$$

$$
R_{l_1} = \begin{bmatrix} 1 & 0 & 0 & 0 \\ 0 & 1 & 0 & 0 \\ 0 & 0 & -1 & 0 \\ 0 & 0 & 0 & -1 \end{bmatrix} \qquad
R_{l_{12}} = \begin{bmatrix} 1 & 0 & 0 & 0 \\ 0 & -1 & 0 & 0 \\ 0 & 0 & -1 & 0 \\ 0 & 0 & 0 & 1 \end{bmatrix}
$$

Then

$$
T = \frac{1}{2} \begin{bmatrix} 1 & 1 & 1 & 1 \\ 1 & 1 & -1 & -1 \\ 1 & -1 & 1 & -1 \\ 1 & -1 & -1 & 1 \end{bmatrix}
$$

Theorem 10.† $TT^T = I$.

† If $A = (a_{ij})$ is any matrix, then $A^T = (a_{ji})$ is called the *transpose* of A. If $AA^T = I$, then A is called *orthogonal*.

PROOF.   Evaluate $\dfrac{1}{2^n} \displaystyle\sum_{k=0}^{2^n-1} r_{kk}^i r_{kk}^j$. Note, however, that (cf. Prob. 4)

$$\text{tr }(R_{l_i}R_{l_j}) = \sum_{p=0}^{2^n-1}\sum_{k=0}^{2^n-1} r_{pk}^i r_{kp}^j = \sum_{k=0}^{2^n-1}\sum_{p=0}^{2^n-1} r_{pk}^i r_{kp}^j = \sum_{k=0}^{2^n-1} r_{kk}^i r_{kk}^j$$

Thus, the (i,j) entry of TT^T is

$$\frac{1}{2^n}\text{ tr }(R_{l_i}R_{l_j}) = \frac{1}{2^n}\text{ tr }(R_{l_i\oplus l_j}) = \frac{1}{2^n}(2^n - 2w(l_i\oplus l_j))$$

Since the weight of any nonzero odd linear function is 2^{n-1}, we have

$$w(l_i\oplus l_j) = 2^{n-1}(1 - \delta_{ij})$$
$$\frac{1}{2^n}(2^n - 2\cdot 2^{n-1}(1-\delta_{ij})) = \frac{1}{2^n}2^n\delta_{ij} = \delta_{ij}\quad\blacksquare$$

EXAMPLE. $n = 2$:

$$TT^T = \frac{1}{4}\begin{bmatrix} 4 & 0 & 0 & 0 \\ 0 & 4 & 0 & 0 \\ 0 & 0 & 4 & 0 \\ 0 & 0 & 0 & 4 \end{bmatrix}$$

Now the coordinate representation is derived by selecting a new basis for representing the switching functions.

We now change the representation of a given switching function by performing an orthogonal transformation of the space by T. More precisely, we let

$$\hat{F} = TR_fT^T$$

$\hat{F}$ will now provide the desired representation.

Theorem 11.   The i-j entry of $\hat{F}$ is $\dfrac{1}{2^{n-1}}(2^{n-1} - w(f\oplus l_{ij}))$.

PROOF.   Let $R_f = (r_i\delta_{ij})$ and let $T = \dfrac{1}{2^{n/2}}(t_{ij}) = \dfrac{1}{2^{n/2}}(r_{ji}^i)$. Then

$$\frac{1}{2^n}\sum_{p=0}^{2^n-1}\sum_{q=0}^{2^n-1} t_{ip}r_p\delta_{pq}t_{jq} = \frac{1}{2^n}\sum_{p=0}^{2^n-1} t_{ip}r_pt_{jp} = \frac{1}{2^n}\text{ tr }(R_f\oplus R_{l_{ij}})$$
$$= \frac{1}{2^n}(2^n - 2w(f\oplus l_i\oplus l_j)) = \frac{1}{2^{n-1}}(2^{n-1} - w(f\oplus l_i\oplus l_j))\quad\blacksquare$$

Note that the rows (columns) of $\hat{F}$ are merely permutations of one another, so that any one row (column) is sufficient for representing f. This prompts the following definition in which we choose 2^{n-1} times the first row of $\hat{F}$ to be the coordinates.

Definition 12. The *coordinate representation of f* is defined as

$$(f_0, f_{l_1}, \ldots, f_{l_n}, \ldots f_{l_1, \ldots, n})$$

where $$f_0 = 2^{n-1} - w(f)$$

and $$f_{l_{i_1} \ldots i_k} = 2^{n-1} - w(f \oplus l_{i_1} \oplus \cdots \oplus l_{i_k})$$

This representation is often called the *Fourier transform of f*.

EXAMPLES.   The functions of two variables are listed below with their coordinates.

Function	Coordinates
0	$(2,0,0,0)$
$\bar{x}_1 \bar{x}_2$	$(1,-1,-1,-1)$
$\bar{x}_1 x_2$	$(1,-1,1,1)$
$x_1 \bar{x}_2$	$(1,1,-1,1)$
$x_1 x_2$	$(1,1,1,-1)$
x_1	$(0,2,0,0)$
x_2	$(0,0,2,0)$
$\bar{x}_1$	$(0,-2,0,0)$
$\bar{x}_2$	$(0,0,-2,0)$
$x_1 \oplus x_2$	$(0,0,0,2)$
$x_1 \equiv x_2$	$(0,0,0,-2)$
$\bar{x}_1 + \bar{x}_2$	$(-1,-1,-1,1)$
$\bar{x}_1 + x_2$	$(-1,-1,1,-1)$
$x_1 + \bar{x}_2$	$(-1,1,-1,-1)$
$x_1 + x_2$	$(-1,1,1,1)$
1	$(-2,0,0,0)$

The coordinate representation may at first seem clumsy to work with, but it turns out to be very natural for the group invariance problem. Ninomiya[3] has worked out an entire theory of this coordinate representation.

We conclude this section by indicating a convenient method of computing the coordinates with a Karnaugh map for functions of three and four variables. The principle of computing the coordinates is to make up a set of stencils to cover the map of the function such that the number of 1's showing through the stencil is connected with the coordinates. The stencils for $n = 3$ are shown in Fig. 1 where the areas inside the heavy lines are assumed to be transparent. If $n = 4$, the construction is similar.

Proposition 13. The coordinate f_l of a function of three variables is $2N_l - w(f)$, where N_l is the number of 1's showing through the lth stencil covering the map of f.

PROOF. $w(f \oplus l)$ is the number of 0's in the squares in which $l = 1$ plus the number of 1's in the squares in which $l = 0$. Let N_l be the number of 1's showing through the lth stencil.

Thus
$$w(f \oplus l) = (2^{n-1} - N_l) + (w(f) - N_l)$$
$$f_l = 2^{n-1} - w(f \oplus l) = 2N_l - w(f) \quad \blacksquare$$

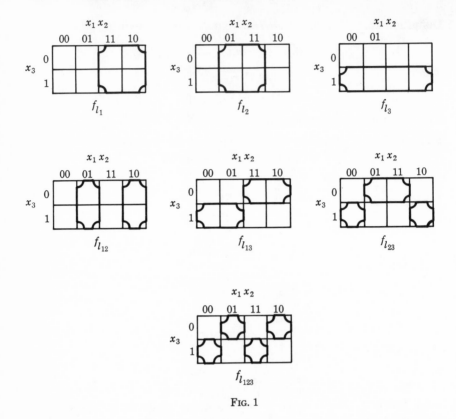

FIG. 1

To convert from the coordinate representation back to the expanded normal form, one uses the T matrix.

EXAMPLE. Given $f = (0,0,0,-2)$, write the matrix $\hat{F}$ by performing all cyclic permutations to f.

$$\hat{F} = \tfrac{1}{2}\begin{bmatrix} 0 & 0 & 0 & -2 \\ 0 & 0 & -2 & 0 \\ 0 & -2 & 0 & 0 \\ -2 & 0 & 0 & 0 \end{bmatrix}$$

$R_f = T^T\hat{F}T$, so that

$$R_f = \tfrac{1}{8}\begin{bmatrix} 1 & 1 & 1 & 1 \\ 1 & 1 & -1 & -1 \\ 1 & -1 & 1 & -1 \\ 1 & -1 & -1 & 1 \end{bmatrix}\begin{bmatrix} 0 & 0 & 0 & -2 \\ 0 & 0 & -2 & 0 \\ 0 & -2 & 0 & 0 \\ -2 & 0 & 0 & 0 \end{bmatrix}\begin{bmatrix} 1 & 1 & 1 & 1 \\ 1 & 1 & -1 & -1 \\ 1 & -1 & 1 & -1 \\ 1 & -1 & -1 & 1 \end{bmatrix}$$

$$= \tfrac{1}{8}\begin{bmatrix} -8 & 0 & 0 & 0 \\ 0 & 8 & 0 & 0 \\ 0 & 0 & 8 & 0 \\ 0 & 0 & 0 & -8 \end{bmatrix} = \begin{bmatrix} -1 & 0 & 0 & 0 \\ 0 & 1 & 0 & 0 \\ 0 & 0 & 1 & 0 \\ 0 & 0 & 0 & -1 \end{bmatrix}$$

Thus $f = \bar{x}_1\bar{x}_2 + x_1x_2 = (x_1 \equiv x_2)$

PROBLEMS

1. Prove that the mapping $B: f \to B_f$ is an isomorphism from F_n onto the boolean algebra of $2^n \times 2^n$ diagonal matrices.

2. What can be said about the mapping $R: f \to R_f$?

3. Show that, for any switching function f,

$$R_f R_f{}^T = I$$

(A^T, called the *transpose of* A, is obtained by replacing a_{ij} by a_{ji}.)

4. If $A = (a_{ij})$ is any $p \times p$ matrix, then the *trace of* A is defined to be tr $(A) = \sum_{i=1}^{p} a_{ii}$, that is, it is just the sum of the main diagonal elements. Show that, for any switching function f,

$$\text{tr } (R_f) = w(\bar{f}) - w(f) = 2^n - 2w(f)$$

5. Prove Propositions 5 and 7.

6. Let f be any switching function of n variables and associate f with a unique vertex on the 2^n-dimensional unit cube in real euclidean space. What does the map $f \to 1 - 2f$ do to the representation on the cube? Draw the case $n = 2$.

7. The order used in writing the odd linear functions has been chosen as $l_1, l_2, \ldots, l_{12}, \ldots, l_{1n}, \ldots, l_1 \ldots n$. For some purposes, it is more convenient to order in the following way. Write out a truth table for the n variables. Let the ith function be $h^i = l_{i_1 \ldots i_n} = x_{j_1} \oplus \cdots \oplus x_{j_n}$ where $i_1 \cdots i_n$ is the binary representation of i, that is, the ith row of the truth table. Thus,

$$x_{j_k} = \begin{cases} x_k & \text{if } i_k = 1 \\ 0 & \text{if } i_k = 0 \end{cases}$$

EXAMPLE. $n = 3$:

x_1	x_2	x_3	Linear function
0	0	0	$h^0 = l_0 = 0$
0	0	1	$h^1 = l_3 = x_3$
0	1	0	$h^2 = l_2 = x_2$
0	1	1	$h^3 = l_{23} = x_2 \oplus x_3$
1	0	0	$h^4 = l_1 = x_1$
1	0	1	$h^5 = l_{13} = x_1 \oplus x_3$
1	1	0	$h^6 = l_{12} = x_1 \oplus x_2$
1	1	1	$h^7 = l_{123} = x_1 \oplus x_2 \oplus x_3$

Show that, under this convention, the matrix T_n (n variables, so T_n is of order 2^n) can be written

$$T_n = \begin{bmatrix} T_{n-1} & T_{n-1} \\ T_{n-1} & -T_{n-1} \end{bmatrix}$$

where $T_0 = (1)$.

8. (Lechner) Show that $T_n = T_1{}^{[n]}$, where $T_1{}^{[n]}$ denotes $\overbrace{T_1 \times \cdots \times T_1}^{n}$, with the cross being the Kronecker product of matrices. If $A = (a_{ij})$ is a $m \times n$ matrix and $B = (b_{ij})$ is a $p \times q$ matrix, the *Kronecker product* $A \times B$ is defined to be the $mp \times nq$ matrix

$$A \times B = \begin{bmatrix} a_{11}B & \cdots & a_{1n}B \\ \cdots\cdots\cdots\cdots\cdots \\ a_{m1}B & \cdots & a_{mn}B \end{bmatrix}$$

9. Let $(f_0, f_{l_1}, \ldots, f_{l_1\ldots n})$ be the coordinate representation of f. Show that the sum of the squares of the coordinates is $2^{2(n-1)}$.

10. (Ninomiya) Show that

$$(f + g)_l = \tfrac{1}{2}(-2^{n-1}\delta_{l0} + f_l + g_l + (f \oplus g)_l)$$
$$(fg)_l = \tfrac{1}{2}(2^{n-1}\delta_{l0} + f_l + g_l - (f \oplus g)_l)$$
$$\bar{f}_l = -f_l \qquad 0_l = 2^{n-1}\delta_{l0} \qquad 1_l = -2^{n-1}\delta_{l1}$$

Find a formula for $(f \oplus g)_l$.

11. Devise a method for calculating the coordinates of f from a table of the coordinates of the atoms of f.

12 THE INVARIANTS OF N^{G_n}

We now give a complete set of invariants for switching functions under N^{G_n}. In general, invariants are numbers associated with switching functions such that when two functions have the same invariants, they are equivalent under the group.

In order to cut down on the number of functions in the tables to be constructed, we shall allow complementation on the range.

Definition 1. The *zero-order invariant* under the group N^{G_n} which consists of complementations and permutations of the variables and complementation of the function is defined as

$$\min\,(w(f),\ 2^n - w(f))$$

Theorem 2. The zero-order invariant is left fixed by every operation in N^{G_n}.

PROOF. $w(f)$ is invariant under every operation of G_n. Complementation of f produces

$$\min\,(w(\bar{f}),\ 2^n - w(\bar{f})) = \min\,(2^n - w(f),\ 2^n - 2^n + w(f))$$
$$= \min\,(w(f),\ 2^n - w(f)) \quad \blacksquare$$

Corollary 3. $\min\,(w(f),\ 2^n - w(f))$ is an invariant of G_n.

Theorem 4. The quantities $R_i{}^1 = \min\,(w(f \oplus x_i),\ 2^n - w(f \oplus x_i))$ for $i = 1, \ldots, n$, when rearranged as a sequence in ascending order, are invariants of N^{G_n}.

PROOF. Clearly, the $R_i{}^1$ are invariant under complementations of the variables and the function since

$$\min (w(\bar{f} \oplus x_i), 2^n - w(\bar{f} \oplus x_i)) = \min (w(1 \oplus f \oplus x_i), 2^n - w(1 \oplus f \oplus x_i))$$
$$= \min (w(f \oplus \bar{x}_i), 2^n - w(f \oplus \bar{x}_i)) = \min (w(f \oplus x_i), 2^n - w(f \oplus x_i))$$

When the $R_i{}^1$ are arranged in increasing order, they are unaffected by a permutation of the variables. |

Definition 5. Let $\{T_i{}^1\}$ be the set of $R_i{}^1$ when rearranged according to increasing order. $\{T_i{}^1\}$ is called the *set of first-order invariants of* N^{G_n}.

Corollary 6. The $T_i{}^1$ are also invariants under G_n.

The higher-order invariants are defined in an analogous fashion. The proof that these are invariants is omitted.

Definition 7. The sequence of *higher-order invariants* is obtained from the sequence of weights

$$w(f \oplus l_{i_1 \ldots i_k})$$

by reordering and complementing (i.e., the complement of w is $2^n - w$) to obtain the numerically smallest sequence *in a manner consistent with the reordering and complementing* of the first-order invariants.

The exact method of calculation is indicated by the following example and algorithm.

EXAMPLE. Let f be the function shown on the Karnaugh map of Fig. 1. Using stencils, we compute the weights to be

$$6; \ 10,10,6,6,; \ 10,6,6,6,6,10; \ 10,10,6,6,; \ 6$$

We wish to complement x_1 and x_2; so we perform a min operation on those coordinates.

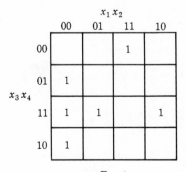

Fig. 1

This yields   6; 6,6,6,6,; 10,10,10,10,10,10; 10,10,10,10; 6

which corresponds to a symmetric function so that it is unnecessary to go further.

Algorithm 8.   Given a function f of n variables, the invariants are computed as follows:

(1) Compute the weights $(w(f),w(f \oplus x_1), \ldots ,w(f \oplus x_1 \oplus \cdots \oplus x_n))$.

(2) If $w(f) > 2^{n-1}$, replace each weight by its complement, i.e., w goes into $2^n - w$.

(3) If any first-order weight $w(f \oplus x_i)$ is greater than 2^{n-1}, complement that weight and all higher-order weights which involve x_i.

(4) Permute the first-order-weights so that they are in ascending order. Any permutation of the first-order weights must be consistently applied to the higher-order weights which involve the same variables.

(5) If some of the first-order weights are the same, try all permutations of these weights to obtain the smallest sequence of weights in lexicographic order. If some of the first-order invariants are 2^{n-1}, try all complementations of these variables to obtain the least sequence in lexicographic order.

(6) The final sequence obtained in this fashion is the set of invariants.

It will now be shown how the invariants characterize the class of functions.

Theorem 9.   Let f and g be boolean functions and assume that the invariants of f are identical with the invariants of g. Then f is equivalent to g under N^{G_n}.

PROOF.   Given two functions f and g expressed in coordinate representation, one passes to the invariants by the transformation

$$w(f \oplus l_{i_1} \ldots {}_{i_k}) = 2^{n-1} - f_{l_{i_1} \ldots {}_{i_k}}$$

When the min operations are performed and the weights reordered, then the invariants are available. But these latter operations on the coordinates correspond to the group operations on the variables. Thus f and g differ by just a group operation; i.e., they are equivalent. ▌

Definition 10.   A function f is said to be in *canonical form* iff the invariants of f are

$$(w(f),w(f \oplus x_1), \ldots ,w(f \oplus x_n), \ldots ,w(f \oplus x_1 \oplus \cdots \oplus x_n))$$

That is, no rearrangements or min operations are needed.

For use in synthesis, a table of representatives of functions along with their invariants are given in Appendixes 3 and 4 for functions of three or four variables. By use of techniques to be explained later, absolutely minimal networks have been constructed for these functions, and these networks are given in Appendix 5.   A summary of this synthesis procedure is included in the following result.

Algorithm 11.   (Synthesis by Table Look-up)   Given any function f of three or four variables, perform the following operations:

(1) Compute the invariants of f.
(2) Find the function with the same invariants in the appendix.
(3) Realize f by the suitably relabeled network given in the appendix.
(4) The method of relabeling is given by the computation of the invariants (cf. Appendix 4).

EXAMPLE.   Given the function f of three variables with index set $I' = \{0,1,3,5,7\}$, we note that f has $5 > 4$ minterms, so we work with $\bar{f}$ which has index set $I = \{2,4,6\}$. The weights of $\bar{f}$ are

$$3; 3,3,7; 3,3,3; 3$$

Since $7 > 4$, we complement x_3 and get

$$3; 3,3,1; 3,5,5; 5$$

Thus f is equivalent to either $f(x_1,x_2,\bar{x}_3)$ or $f(x_2,x_1,\bar{x}_3)$.   Now permute x_1 and x_3.   A quick check shows that f is symmetric in x_2 and x_3, and any choice leads to the same second-order invariants.   The invariants of f are

$$3; 133; 553; 5$$

Upon looking in Appendix 3, we find a function g with the same invariants, namely, the function numbered 6.   The transformation which takes $\bar{f}$ into g is

$$(0,(13))((001),1) = ((100),(13))$$

EXAMPLE.   Let f be the function of four variables with index $\{10,11,13\}$.   Computing the weights gives

$$3; 5,9,7,7; 7,9,9,5,9,7; 11,7,9,9; 7$$

Since $9 > 8$, we complement x_2; this yields

$$3; 5,7,7,7; 9,9,9,11,7,7; 5,9,9,7; 9$$

We should try all possible permutations of x_2, x_3, and x_4 to get the smallest lexicographic order.   Actually a little thought shows that the best choice is to interchange x_2 and x_4, because this minimizes the size of the second-order invariants. Thus the invariants are

$$3; 5,7,7,7,; 9,9,9,7,7,11; 9,9,5,7; 9$$

Thus f has the same invariants as the function numbered 8 in Appendix 4.   The group element α which takes f into the canonical form is

$$\alpha = ((0000), (24))((0100), (1)(2)(3)(4)) = ((0001), (24))$$

Note that we write down the operations performed on the function from right to left and then combine.

Thus far we have found the transformation which carries f into its canonical form.   Appendix 4 is a tabulation of "good" representatives, not canonical forms,† so that one must still find the transformation which takes f into the representative. To do so, simply multiply α on the left by the group element given in row 8 of the table in Appendix 4.   This yields

$$((0000),\ (24))((0001),\ (24)) = ((0100),\ (1)(2)(3)(4))$$

To check the answer, we write down the matrix representation of f

$$\begin{matrix} 1010 \\ 1011 \\ 1101 \end{matrix}$$

Complementing x_2 (that is the second column) yields

$$\begin{matrix} 1110 \\ 1111 \\ 1001 \end{matrix}$$

or index set $I' = \{9,14,15\}$, which is the standard sum of the function in row 8.

To find the minimal relay network, consult Appendix 5.   Number 8 says that the best possible network for this equivalence class is as shown in Fig. 2.   We must suitably relabel the network to realize f.   To do this, we compute the inverse:

$$((0100),\ (1)(2)(3)(4))^{-1} = ((0100),\ (1)(2)(3)(4))$$

Thus the desired network is as shown in Fig. 3.   An easy calculation shows that this network realizes f.   Appendix 5 guarantees its minimality.

† By our convention of considering any two functions which are equivalent under N^{G_n} to be interchangeable, it may not seem reasonable to use a representative different

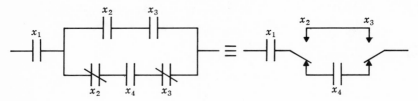

FIG. 2

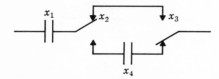

FIG. 3

PROBLEMS

1. Modify the method of computing coordinates to compute invariants.

2. Show that, if f and g are switching functions, the cubical complexes of f and g are isomorphic iff f is equivalent to g under G_n.

3. Find a complete set of invariants for C_2^n.

4. Find a complete set of invariants for S_n.

13 SUMMARY

In this long and involved chapter, techniques which enable us to replace individual functions by classes of equivalent functions have been developed. Furthermore, all the functions in an equivalence class possess the same structure, so that no information is lost in the identification.

The introduction of the invariants enables us to decide systematically when two functions are equivalent. By giving tables of representatives with minimal networks in the appendixes, synthesis of functions of three or four variables has been reduced to a table-look-up procedure.

The material on counting the number of equivalence classes is taken from the writer's doctoral dissertation.[2] The coordinate representation is adopted from the excellent paper by Ninomiya,[3] and invariants were first computed by Golomb.[1]

The coordinate representation is very important, and the presentation given here is deliberately brief. This representation is intimately connected with linear vector spaces (which we did not wish to present here), and the coordinates have application to some problems involving linearly separable switching functions.

from the canonical form. In an attempt to make the table useful for the synthesis of gate-type circuits, the best representatives have been chosen by different criteria.

CHAPTER 6 *functional properties and their utilization in synthesis*

1 INTRODUCTION

In this chapter several structural properties of switching functions will be given. In each case the structural property allows a special technique to be developed for synthesizing the function which is, in general, more economical than a completely general method. In the next chapter it will be shown that it is necessary to split combinational switching into these special cases.

2 DEGENERATE FUNCTIONS

Table 1 is a list of all 16 functions of two variables. A glance at the table shows that 6 functions are functions of no variables (0 and 1) or functions of 1 variable (p, $\bar{p}$, q, and $\bar{q}$).

Since functions of fewer than n variables are counted among the functions of n variables for all positive n, it is of interest to count the number of nondegenerate functions of n variables.

Definition 1. A function of n variables $f(x_1, \ldots ,x_i, \ldots ,x_n)$ is said to be *vacuous* in x_i iff $f(x_1, \ldots ,0, \ldots ,x_n) = f(x_1, \ldots ,1, \ldots ,x_n)$ for any $i = 1, \ldots , n$. A function f is said to be *nondegenerate* iff f is not vacuous in any variable.

The first problem to be decided is the determination of the number of nondegenerate functions of n variables. Let $\alpha(n)$ be this number.

TABLE 1

The Sixteen Switching Functions of Two Variables

p	q	0	$p \downarrow q$	$\bar{p}q$	$\bar{p}$	$p\bar{q}$	$\bar{q}$	$p \oplus q$	$p \mid q$	pq	$p \equiv q$	q	$\bar{p} + q$	p	$p + \bar{q}$	$p + q$	1
0	0	0	1	0	1	0	1	0	1	0	1	0	1	0	1	0	1
0	1	0	0	1	1	0	0	1	1	0	0	1	1	0	0	1	1
1	0	0	0	0	0	1	1	1	1	0	0	0	0	1	1	1	1
1	1	0	0	0	0	0	0	0	0	1	1	1	1	1	1	1	1

Lemma 2

$$2^{2^n} = \sum_{k=0}^{n} \binom{n}{k} \alpha(k)$$

PROOF. The 2^{2^n} functions consist of functions of no variables [there are $\alpha(0)$ such functions], functions of 1 variable [there are $\binom{n}{1}$ choices for the variable and $\alpha(1)$ choices for the functions], . . . , and finally, $\alpha(n)$ functions of n variables. Thus

$$2^{2^n} = \binom{n}{0} \alpha(0) + \binom{n}{1} \alpha(1) + \cdots + \binom{n}{n} \alpha(n) = \sum_{k=0}^{n} \binom{n}{k} \alpha(k) \quad \blacksquare$$

It is desirable to solve for $\alpha(n)$ directly. This can be done immediately.

Theorem 3. $\quad \alpha(n) = \sum_{k=0}^{n} \binom{n}{k} (-1)^{n-k} 2^{2^k}$

PROOF. The result is a special case of Prob. 1-3.9. $\quad \blacksquare$

In Table 2 a few values of $\alpha(n)$ are given. The values show that $\alpha(n)$ approaches 2^{2^n} rapidly. This means that as we increase the number of variables from n to $n + 1$, almost all of the functions obtained are new ones.

Now the experimental evidence of Table 2 is confirmed by showing that $\alpha(n)$ is asymptotic to 2^{2^n} (cf. Sec. 1-5).

Theorem 4. $\quad \alpha(n) \sim 2^{2^n}$

PROOF

$$\alpha(n) = 2^{2^n} + \sum_{k=0}^{n-1} \binom{n}{k} (-1)^{n-k} 2^{2^k}$$

$$\frac{\alpha(n)}{2^{2^n}} = 1 + \frac{\displaystyle\sum_{k=0}^{n-1} \binom{n}{k} (-1)^{n-k} 2^{2^k}}{2^{2^n}}$$

TABLE 2

n	2^{2^n}	$\alpha(n)$	Rel. % error $= \dfrac{2^{2^n} - \alpha(n)}{2^{2^n}} \times 100$
0	2	2	0
1	4	2	50
2	16	10	37.5
3	256	218	14.8
4	65,536	64,594	1.43
5	4,294,967,296	4,294,642,034	0.75

We wish to show that
$$\frac{\sum_{k=0}^{n-1} \binom{n}{k} (-1)^{n-k} 2^{2^k}}{2^{2^n}} = o(1)$$

However,

$$\sum_{k=0}^{n-1} \binom{n}{k} (-1)^{n-k} 2^{2^k} \leq \sum_{k=0}^{n-1} \binom{n}{k} 2^{2^k} \leq n \cdot n \cdot 2^{2^{n-1}}$$

To obtain the last bound, replace each of the n terms in the sum by the largest term of the sum, which is $\binom{n}{n-1} 2^{2^{n-1}}$.

$$\frac{n^2 2^{2^{n-1}}}{2^{2^n}} = \frac{2^{2 \log_2 n}}{2^{2^{n-1}}} = o(1)$$

Thus $\dfrac{\alpha(n)}{2^{2^n}} = 1 + o(1)$, that is,

$$\alpha(n) \sim 2^{2^n} \quad \blacksquare$$

Nondegeneracy of functions has a counterpart in the boolean forms (network realizations) which is now indicated.

Definition 5. A literal x of a function f is called *essential* iff x must appear in every normal form of f.

Theorem 6. Let x be a variable of a boolean function f and let the expansion of f with respect to x be

$$f = \bar{x} F_{x0} + x F_{x1}$$

then

(1) $F_{x0} = F_{x1}$ iff x and $\bar{x}$ are not essential.
(2) $F_{x0} > F_{x1}$ iff $\bar{x}$ is essential and x is not essential.
(3) $F_{x0} < F_{x1}$ iff x is essential and $\bar{x}$ is not essential.
(4) F_{x0} and F_{x1} are not comparable iff both x and $\bar{x}$ are essential.

PROOF.   The four cases are disjoint and exhaustive, so that only sufficiency must be shown.

(1) If x and $\bar{x}$ are not essential, then f is vacuous in x; so that if F is any form which denotes f, then $f = \bar{x}F + xF$ and, by the uniqueness of the expansion, $F_{x1} = F_{x0} = F$.

(2) If $\bar{x}$ is essential and x is not, there exists a form $f = \bar{x}G + H$, where G and H are vacuous in x.   Since $H = Hx + H\bar{x}$,

$$f = \bar{x}(G + H) + Hx$$

$F_{x0} = G + H$ and $F_{x1} = H$, so that $F_{x1} \leq F_{x0}$.   To show that the inequality is strict, suppose $F_{x0} \leq F_{x1}$; then $\bar{x}F_{x0} \leq F_{x1}$.   Then f can be represented as $f = H$, which contradicts that $\bar{x}$ is essential.

(3) Case 2 and symmetry.

(4) Suppose that both x and $\bar{x}$ are essential; then there is a form such that

$$f = \bar{x}G + xH + J$$

where G, H, and J are vacuous in x.   Since $J = \bar{x}J + xJ$, then write

$$f = \bar{x}(G + J) + x(H + J)$$

Take $F_{x0} = G + J$ and $F_{x1} = H + J$.   Assume $F_{x0} \leq F_{x1}$; then $G + J \leq H + J$ or $G + J = G + H + J$.   Thus f is written

$$f = x(G + H + J) + \bar{x}(G + J) = xH + G + J$$

which contradicts that x is essential.   The argument is symmetric for $F_{x1} \leq F_{x0}$. ∎

Theorem 6 may be used to tell if a given component is necessarily in a proposed realization of the function f.

Theorem 7.   Given a function f of n variables, let p be the number of variables in which the function is not vacuous and let q be the number of variables in which $x(\bar{x})$ is essential but $\bar{x}(x)$ is not.   Then at least $2p - q$ branch-type elements are needed to realize f.

PROOF.   Obvious. ∎

Theorem 7 provides a method for checking if a branch-type network is minimal, as is shown by the following example.

EXAMPLE.   Consider the network of Fig. 1, where

$$f(x,y,z) = xy + \bar{x}\bar{y}z$$

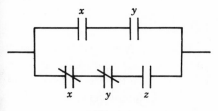

FIG. 1

Expanding with respect to the variables gives

$$f(x,y,z) = xF_{x1} + \bar{x}F_{x0} = xy + \bar{x}\bar{y}z$$

where $F_{x1} = y$ and $F_{x0} = \bar{y}z$. Since F_{x1} and F_{x0} are not comparable, both x and $\bar{x}$ elements will be needed in a minimal realization of f. With respect to y

$$f(x,y,z) = yF_{y1} + \bar{y}F_{y0} = yx + \bar{y}(\bar{x}z)$$

where $F_{y1} = x$ and $F_{y0} = \bar{x}z$. Note that F_{y1} and F_{y0} are incomparable. Expanding with respect to z gives

$$f(x,y,z) = zF_{z1} + \bar{z}F_{z0} = z(\bar{x}\bar{y} + xy) + \bar{z}(xy)$$

and $F_{z1} = \bar{x}\bar{y} + xy$ and $F_{z0} = xy$. Since $F_{z0} \leq F_{z1}$, only an element for z is needed.

Thus $p = 3$, $q = 1$, and at least $2 \cdot 3 - 1 = 5$ elements are required. A five-element network has been shown, so that it is clear that the network is minimal.

There are networks in which more than one contact is necessary for some variable. For such networks, the lower bound $2p - q$ cannot be obtained

PROBLEMS

1. Let $\varphi(k,n)$ be the number of nondegenerate functions of n variables with weight k. Show that

$$\varphi(k,n) = \sum_i \binom{n}{i} (-1)^i \binom{2^{n-i}}{k/2^i}$$

where the summation is over all integers i such that $2^i | k$. Of course, $\varphi(k,n) = \varphi(2^n - k, n)$.

2. Check the expression in Prob. 1 by showing that

$$\alpha(n) = \sum_{k=0}^{2^n} \varphi(k,n)$$

3. Find a five-contact realization for the following function and show that it is minimal:

$$f(x_1,x_2,x_3,x_4,x_5) = x_1x_3 + x_1x_2x_5 + x_2x_3x_4 + x_4x_5$$

4. Construct a function for which more than one contact is needed for some variable. Draw a network using $2p - q + 1$ contacts for this function and show that no relay network using $2p - q$ contacts is possible.

3   SYMMETRIC FUNCTIONS

The switching functions which are now to be studied possess a great deal of algebraic structure. If the mathematical structure is ignored and standard synthesis procedures are adopted, then the resulting realizations will be very expensive. For these reasons the mathematical structure will be carefully developed and exploited.

Definition 1.   A switching function $f(x_1, \ldots ,x_n)$ is called *symmetric* iff it is unchanged by any permutation of its variables, if that is, for every $\sigma \in S_n$, the symmetric group on n letters $\sigma f = f$.

EXAMPLE.   The following switching functions are symmetric:

(1) $f(x,y) = 0$
(2) $f(x,y) = x \oplus y$
(3) $f(x,y,z) = xy + yz + xz$

A very useful notation for symmetric functions is now developed.

Theorem 2.   A function of n variables is symmetric iff it may be specified by stating a set of natural numbers $A = \{a_1, \ldots ,a_k\}$, where $0 \leq a_j \leq n$ and $k = 0, \ldots ,n$, such that the function is 1 when and only when a_j of the variables are 1.

PROOF.   Suppose a function $f(x_1, \ldots ,x_n)$ is symmetric. If f sends a domain element of weight i (i ones and $n - i$ zeroes) into 1, then f must map *every* domain element of weight i into 1, since f is symmetric.   Thus f can be completely described by stating the weights of all domain elements mapped into 1; these are the a numbers. Conversely, if f is specified by a set of a numbers, then any permutation of the variables merely permutes all those elements of weight i among themselves for all i. Thus the function is unchanged by any permutation, and hence it is symmetric.   **|**

EXAMPLE.   For the functions in the first example, the sets A are:

(1) $A = \emptyset$
(2) $A = \{1\}$
(3) $A = \{2,3\}$

We write $S_A(x_1, \ldots ,x_n)$ for the symmetric function of n variables whose a numbers are elements of A.

EXAMPLE.   In our running example, the appropriate notation is

(1) $S_\emptyset(x,y)$
(2) $S_{\{1\}}(x,y)$
(3) $S_{\{2,3\}}(x,y,z)$

Theorem 2 gives an immediate method for telling how many symmetric functions of n variables exist.

Corollary 3.   There are 2^{n+1} symmetric functions of n variables.

PROOF.   For a function of n variables, the allowable a numbers are the $n + 1$ integers between 0 and n.   The number of functions is

$$\sum_{k=0}^{n+1} \binom{n+1}{k} = (1+1)^{n+1} = 2^{n+1} \quad \mathbf{|}$$

The S notation is useful in providing a calculus for symmetric functions.

Theorem 4. Given two symmetric functions of the same variables, $S_A(x_1, \ldots, x_n)$ and $S_B = (x_1, \ldots, x_n)$, the sum

$$S_A(x_1, \ldots, x_n) + S_B(x_1, \ldots, x_n)$$

is a symmetric function of the same variables whose set of a numbers is $C = A \cup B$.

PROOF.   The sum of symmetric functions is clearly symmetric while

$$S_C(x_1, \ldots, x_n) = S_A(x_1, \ldots, x_n) + S_B(x_1, \ldots, x_n) = 1$$

iff $S_A(x_1, \ldots, x_n) = 1$ or $S_B(x_1, \ldots, x_n) = 1$.

Thus the elements of C are those elements in A or in B, that is,

$$C = A \cup B \quad |$$

Theorem 5. Given two symmetric functions of the same variables $S_A(x_1, \ldots, x_n)$ and $S_B(x_1, \ldots, x_n)$, the product

$$S_A(x_1, \ldots, x_n) \cdot S_B(x_1, \ldots, x_n)$$

is a symmetric function of those variables whose set of a numbers is $C = A \cap B$.

Theorem 6 Given a symmetric function of n variables $S_A(x_1, \ldots, x_n)$, the complement $\bar{S}_A(x_1, \ldots, x_n)$ is a symmetric function of n variables whose a numbers are $Z_{n+1} - A$, where $Z_{n+1} = \{0, 1, \ldots, n\}$.

EXAMPLE.   We now form the complements of the functions we have been using in our examples.

    (1) $S_{\{0,1,2\}}(x, y)$
    (2) $S_{\{0,2\}}(x, y)$
    (3) $S_{\{0,1\}}(x, y, z)$

Combining the above results into one theorem yields:

Theorem 7. The set of symmetric switching functions of n variables forms a sub-boolean algebra of the boolean algebra of all switching functions.

Before developing a theory of symmetric functions, it is necessary to have a method for detecting symmetric functions. The following result is very useful.

Theorem 8. A boolean function $f(x_1, \ldots, x_n)$ is symmetric iff

$$f(x_1, x_2, \ldots, x_{n-1}, x_n) = f(x_2, x_3, \ldots, x_{n-1}, x_1, x_n)$$

and $f(x_1, \ldots, x_{n-2}, x_{n-1}, x_n) = f(x_1, \ldots, x_{n-2}, x_n, x_{n-1})$

PROOF. S_n is generated by $((1, \ldots, n-1))^{-1}$ and $(n-1, n)$ by Prob. 5-2.6.

function is invariant under every element of a group iff it is invariant under the generators of the group. |

EXAMPLE.   Let $f(x_1, \ldots, x_4) = \bar{x}_1x_2x_3x_4 + x_1\bar{x}_2x_3x_4 + x_1x_2\bar{x}_3x_4 + x_1x_2x_3\bar{x}_4$.
Writing f as a matrix gives

$$\begin{bmatrix} 0111 \\ 1011 \\ 1101 \\ 1110 \end{bmatrix}$$

Applying the permutation (123) to the columns gives

$$\begin{bmatrix} 1011 \\ 1011 \\ 0111 \\ 1110 \end{bmatrix}$$

which differs from f only in the order of the rows.   Now applying (34) to the matrix for f gives

$$\begin{bmatrix} 0111 \\ 1011 \\ 1110 \\ 1101 \end{bmatrix}$$

which is the same as f.   Since $(123)f = f = (34)f$, f is symmetric.   Note that the row weights are the a numbers.

Another advantage of this test is that one can perform it on any normal form corresponding to the function.   It is not necessary to use the expanded normal form.

Since the symmetric functions of n variables form a boolean algebra, it is natural to find the atoms of the algebra, since the atoms generate all the functions.   It is not surprising that the atoms are the functions whose A sets are singletons.

Definition 9.   The $n + 1$ *elementary symmetric functions* of n variables are defined as

$$S_{\{0\}} = \sigma_0(x_1, \ldots, x_n) = (\bar{x}_1\bar{x}_2 \cdots \bar{x}_n)$$
$$S_{\{1\}} = \sigma_1(x_1, \ldots, x_n) = (x_1\bar{x}_2 \cdots \bar{x}_n) + (\bar{x}_1x_2\bar{x}_3 \cdots \bar{x}_n)$$
$$+ \cdots + (\bar{x}_1 \cdots \bar{x}_{n-1}x_n)$$
$$\cdots \cdots \cdots \cdots \cdots \cdots \cdots \cdots \cdots \cdots \cdots$$
$$S_{\{n\}} = \sigma_n(x_1, \ldots, x_n) = (x_1 \cdots x_n)$$

Thus, $\sigma_i(x_1, \ldots, x_n)$ has weight $\binom{n}{i}$: each term is a minterm having i variables uncomplemented.

Theorem 10. $i \neq j$ implies $\sigma_i(x_1, \ldots, x_n)\sigma_j(x_1, \ldots, x_n) = 0$.

$$\sum_{i=0}^{n} \sigma_i(x_1, \ldots, x_n) = 1$$

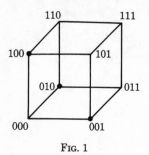

Fig. 1

The elementary symmetric functions are the atoms of the boolean algebra of symmetric functions.

Theorem 11.   Every symmetric function has a unique expansion as a sum of elementary symmetric functions.

PROOF.   Note that $S_{\{a_1,\ldots,a_r\}}(x_1, \ldots ,x_n) = \sum_{i=1}^{r} \sigma_{a_i}(x_1, \ldots ,x_n).$ ∎

The geometric interpretation of the elementary symmetric functions is interesting and useful.

Theorem 12.   The elementary symmetric functions $\sigma_i(x_1, \ldots ,x_n)$ $(i = 0, \ldots , n)$ form spheres (cf. Prob. 2-3.2) on the n cube. The centers are $(0, \ldots ,0)$ and $(1, \ldots ,1)$, and they have radii i and $n - i$ respectively. Conversely, any such sphere corresponds to an elementary symmetric function.

PROOF.   Note that $\sigma_i(x_1, \ldots ,x_n)$ has $\binom{n}{i}$ terms in its expanded normal form. Each term is of weight i; so its radius from the origin is i.   ∎

EXAMPLE. $\sigma_1(x_1,x_2,x_3)$ is shown on the three cube of Fig. 1. Note that the radius is 1 with respect to $(0,0,0)$ and 2 with respect to $(1,1,1)$.

A special branch-type network is useful in the synthesis of switching networks. The definition for this network, which is to realize all the elementary symmetric functions, is given by induction.

Definition 13.   The *symmetric function lattice* for functions of n variables is denoted by $N_S(n)$ and defined as the 1-input $(n + 1)$-output network of Fig. 5. $N_S(1)$ is defined by Fig. 2. If the network for realizing $N_S(n - 1)$ is denoted by Fig. 3, then $N_S(n)$ is defined as shown in Fig. 4. The full network is shown in Fig. 5.

Theorem 14. $N_S(n)$ uses $(n + 1)n$ elements.

PROOF.   The argument is an induction on n.

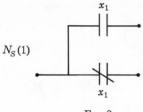

$N_S(1)$

FIG. 2

BASIS. $n = 1$.   Clearly, $N_S(1)$ uses two elements

INDUCTION STEP.   The network uses $n(n - 1)$ elements for $N_S(n - 1)$ by the induction hypothesis and then two elements at each of n output nodes.   The total number of elements is

$$n^2 - n + 2n = n^2 + n = n(n + 1) \quad |$$

Corollary 15.   Any symmetric function of n variables can be realized with $n(n + 1)$ branch-type elements.

EXAMPLE.   Realize $S_{\{2,3\}}$.   Clearly, the top two outputs of $N_S(3)$ when connected together realize $S_{\{2,3\}}$, Fig. 6.   Note that certain contacts in the network can be eliminated because they do not contribute to the realization of $S_{\{2,3\}}$.   When these

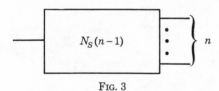

FIG. 3

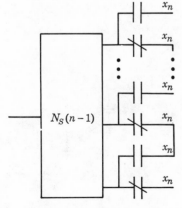

FIG. 4

elements are eliminated from the circuit of Fig. 6, the simpler network is as shown in Fig. 7.

We are now in a position to prove a result about element minimization using $N_S(n)$.

Theorem 16. In any branch-type realization of a symmetric function of n variables using $N_S(n)$ at least n elements are superfluous.

PROOF. The reader is asked to check each step of this proof against the network $N_S(n)$ to be certain of understanding the proof. For every $1 \leq k \leq n-1$ such that k is not in the a sequence there are two unnecessary contacts. If $a_i - a_j = 1$, then two contacts are superfluous. If more than two of the a_i are adjacent or if two or more of the adjacent numbers are missing, then at least one element per terminal is redundant. The worst possible case will be when all the a_i are even or all the a_i are odd.

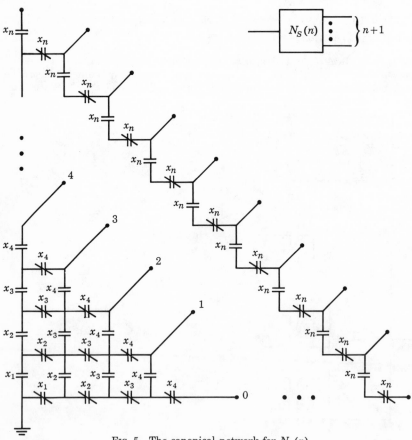

FIG. 5 The canonical network for $N_S(n)$.

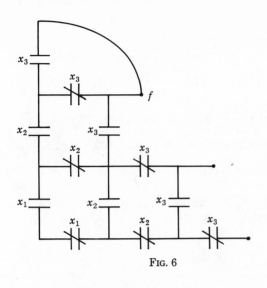

FIG. 6

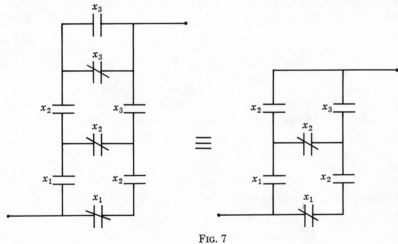

FIG. 7

CASE I.   Let n be even.

A. Assume all the odd terminals are selected, leaving all the even terminals. There are $n/2 + 1$ even terminals and we save

$$2\left(\frac{n}{2} + 1 - 2\right) + 1 + 1 = n \text{ contacts}$$

B. If the even terminals are selected, we leave $n + 1 - (n/2 + 1) = n/2$ odd terminals.   We save

$$2\frac{n}{2} = n \text{ contacts}$$

CASE II.   Let n be odd.

A. Assume the odd terminals are chosen, leaving $n + 1 - ([n/2] + 1) = n - [n/2]$ even terminals, since there are $[n/2] + 1$ odd terminals.   We save

$$2 \left(n - \left[\frac{n}{2} \right] - 1 \right) + 1 = 2n - 2 \left[\frac{n}{2} \right] - 1$$
$$= 2n - (n - 1) - 1 = n \text{ contacts}$$

B. Choosing the even terminals leaves $[n/2] + 1$ odd terminals.   We save

$$2 \left(\left[\frac{n}{2} \right] + 1 - 1 \right) + 1 = n - 1 + 1 = n \text{ contacts} \quad \blacksquare$$

Corollary 17.   Every symmetric function of n variables can be realized with at most n^2 elements.

The result will be more appreciated after Chap. 7, in which we shall see that most functions require many more than n^2 elements for their realization.

PROBLEMS

1.   A function f is called *symmetrizable* or *mixed symmetric* iff f is equivalent to a function g under C_2^n, where g is symmetric.

EXAMPLE. $x_1 \bar{x}_2 x_3 + x_1 x_2 \bar{x}_3 + \bar{x}_1 \bar{x}_2 \bar{x}_3 = f(x_1, x_2, x_3)$ is not symmetric, but under $(1,0,0) \, \epsilon \, C_2^3$, $g(x_1, x_2, x_3) = (1,0,0)f(x_1, x_2, x_3) = f(\bar{x}_1, x_2, x_3) = \sigma_1(x_1, x_3, x_3)$ is symmetric. Show that a sphere of radius r on the n cube with a near center C corresponds to a function equivalent under C_2^n to an elementary symmetric function, and conversely. The positions in which C has a 1 are the variables which are complemented.   The radius of the sphere is the subscript of the elementary symmetric function.

2.   (Arnold) Show that a function f is symmetrizable iff

$$f = (1, j)f$$

jth position
$$\downarrow$$

or $f = ((1, 0, \ldots, 0, 1, 0, \ldots, 0), (1, j))f$ for every $j = 2, \ldots, n$

How can one identify the variables to be complemented from this test?

3.   (*a*) Prove that

$$S_{\{a_1\}}(x_1, \ldots, x_n) = x_n S_{\{a_1 - 1\}}(x_1, \ldots, x_{n-1}) + \bar{x}_n S_{\{a_1\}}(x_1, \ldots, x_{n-1})$$

(*b*) Show that

$$S_{\{a_1, \ldots, a_k\}}(x_1, \ldots, x_n) = x_n S_{\{a_1 - 1, a_2 - 1, \ldots, a_k - 1\}}(x_1, \ldots, x_{n-1})$$
$$+ \bar{x}_n S_{\{a_1, \ldots, a_k\}}(x_1, \ldots, x_{n-1})$$

4.   The δ functions are defined as follows:

$$\delta_0 = 1$$
$$\delta_1 = \sum_{i=1}^{n} x_1$$
$$\delta_2 = \sum_{1 \le i < j \le n} x_i x_j$$
$$\cdots \cdots \cdots \cdots$$
$$\delta_n = x_1 x_2 \cdots x_n$$

Note that $\delta_k(x_1, \ldots, x_n) = 1$ iff at least k of the variables are 1. Show that

(a) $\delta_k(x_1, \ldots, x_n) = \displaystyle\sum_{0 \leq i_1 < i_2 \ldots < i_k \leq n} \cdots \sum x_{i_1} \cdots x_{i_k}$

$\qquad\qquad\qquad = S_{\{k, k+1, \ldots, n\}}(x_1, \ldots, x_n)$

$\qquad\qquad\qquad = \bar{S}_{\{0, 1, \ldots, k-1\}}(x_1, \ldots, x_n) \qquad$ for $k = 1, \ldots, n$

(b) $\delta_j \cdot \delta_k = \delta_{\max (j,k)}$

(c) $\delta_i + \delta_j = \delta_{\min (i,j)}$

(d) $\delta_k(x_1, \ldots, x_n) = S_{\{k, \ldots, n\}}(x_1, \ldots, x_n) = \bar{S}_{\{0, 1, \ldots, k-1\}}(x_1, \ldots, x_n)$

(e) $\delta_j \leq \delta_k$ iff $j \geq k$.

5. Show that every symmetric function has a unique expansion in terms of δ_i and $\bar{\delta}_i$.

6. Show that

$$\sigma_a(x_1, \ldots, x_n) = \sum_{\substack{i+j=a \\ 0 \leq i \leq k \\ 0 \leq j \leq n-k}} \sigma_i(x_1, \ldots, x_k)\sigma_j(x_{k+1}, \ldots, x_n)$$

Interpret the indices of the summation geometrically.

7. Show that any function of n variables is a symmetric function of $2^n - 1$ variables. (HINT: Replace each x_i by 2^{i-1} repetition of x_i. Then determine the a numbers.)

8. Show that $x_1 \oplus \cdots \oplus x_n = \displaystyle\sum_{k=0}^{[(n-1)/2]} \sigma_{2k+1}(x_1, \ldots, x_n)$

9. Let $x_j{}^{e_i} = \begin{cases} \bar{x}_j & \text{if } e_j = 1 \\ x_j & \text{if } e_j = 0 \end{cases}$. Show that

$$x_1{}^{e_1} \oplus x_2{}^{e_2} \oplus \cdots \oplus x_n{}^{e_n} = \begin{cases} x_1 \oplus \cdots \oplus x_n & \text{if } \displaystyle\sum_{i=1}^{n} e_i \equiv 0 \bmod 2 \\[2ex] \overline{(x_1 \oplus \cdots \oplus x_n)} & \text{if } \displaystyle\sum_{i=1}^{n} e_i \equiv 1 \bmod 2 \end{cases}$$

10. (Povarov[4]) Show that the number of equivalence classes under G_n which contain at least one symmetric function is

$$2^n + 2^{[n/2]} + 2[\tfrac{1}{2}(n + 1)] - n - 1$$

where $[x]$ is the largest integer not exceeding x.

11. (Povarov[4]) Show that the number of functions equivalent to some symmetric function under G_n is

$$2^{2n} - 2^{n+1} + 4$$

12. Give a test for telling if a function of n variables, expressed in coordinate notation, is symmetric.

13. How many self-dual symmetric functions of n variables are there? (n must be odd.)

14. Show that every symmetric function which is also a threshold function is one of the δ functions of Prob. 4.

4   PARTIALLY SYMMETRIC FUNCTIONS

In this section the concept of partially symmetric functions is defined and studied briefly.   The results which begin to emerge are so closely related to the corresponding results for symmetric functions that there must be a unifying theory.   This rather advanced theory is presented in the following section.

The basic idea of a partially symmetric function is that there is a subset of the variables in which the function is totally symmetric.

Definition 1.   A boolean function $f(x_1, \ldots, x_n)$ is said to be *partially symmetric* iff there exists at least one subset of at least two variables in which f is totally symmetric.

EXAMPLE. $f = x_1 x_2 + x_3$ is partially symmetric in the variables x_1 and x_2.

It is straightforward to test for partial symmetry.

Theorem 2.   A switching function f of n variables is partially symmetric iff there exists a transposition σ in the symmetric group on n letters such that $\sigma f = f$.

PROOF.   If $f(x_1, \ldots, x_n)$ is partially symmetric in $x_1, \ldots, x_i$ $(i > 1)$, then $(1,i)$ leaves f invariant.   Conversely, if the transposition (i,j) leaves f invariant, f is partially symmetric in a subset of the variables containing at least x_i and x_j.   ∎

A function of n variables requires in general $n(n-1)/2$ tests, since that is the number of transpositions.   If the function is partially symmetric, then the number of tests may be reduced.   Note that the set of all permutations which fix f is a subgroup.   Thus if (i,j) and (j,k) fix f, then so does $(i,k) = (i,j)(j,k)(i,j)$.

If one generates the transpositions in such a manner that $(1,2)$, $(1,3)$, $\ldots$, $(1,n)$ are tested first and if the function is invariant under all these transpositions, then f is totally symmetric because these $(n-1)$ transpositions also generate the symmetric group (cf. Prob. 5-2.4b).

The partially symmetric functions also form a boolean algebra.

Theorem 3.   The partially symmetric functions of n variables symmetric in the k variables $x_1, \ldots, x_k$ form a sub-boolean algebra of the boolean algebra of all switching functions.

PROOF.   It is clear that sums, products, and complements of these functions are again of this type.   ∎

As usual, a normal-form theorem results from identifying the atoms of the boolean algebra.

Theorem 4. Any function $f(x_1, \ldots ,x_n)$ symmetric in $x_1, \ldots ,$ x_k $(2 \leq k \leq n)$ may be written in the form

$$f(x_1, \ldots ,x_n) = \sum_{i=0}^{n} \sigma_i(x_1, \ldots ,x_k)f_i(x_{k+1}, \ldots ,x_n)$$

where

$$f_i(x_{k+1}, \ldots ,x_n) = f(\underbrace{1, \ldots ,1}_{i\text{ 1's}}, \underbrace{0, \ldots ,0}_{k-i\text{ 0's}}, x_{k+1}, \ldots ,x_n)$$

PROOF. Whether f is 1 or 0 depends only on the number of $x_1, \ldots , x_k$ which are 1 and the values of $x_{k+1}, \ldots , x_n$. If i of the variables $x_1, \ldots , x_k$ are 1, then $f = f_i$, since $\sigma_i(x_1, \ldots ,x_k) = 1$ and $\sigma_j(x_1, \ldots ,x_k) = 0$ if $j \neq i$. ▌

Corollary 5. There are $2^{(k+1)2^{n-k}}$ partially symmetric functions of n variables which are symmetric in k of the variables.

Theorem 4 can be used to develop synthesis procedures for partially symmetric functions, but this development will be postponed until the next chapter, when we study trees.

Rather than pursue the study of partially symmetric functions, we develop in the next section a theory which unifies these concepts.

EXAMPLE. Test $f(x_1,x_2,x_3) = \bar{x}_1\bar{x}_2\bar{x}_3 + \bar{x}_1\bar{x}_2 x_3 + \bar{x}_1 x_2\bar{x}_3 + x_1\bar{x}_2\bar{x}_3$ for partial symmetries. $(1,2)f = (1,3)f = f$, so f is totally symmetric.

EXAMPLE. Test $f(x_1,x_2,x_3,x_4) = x_1 x_2 + x_1 x_3 + x_2 x_3 x_4$ for partial symmetries. We test f by generating $(1,2)$, $(1,3)$, $(1,4)$, $(2,3)$, $(2,4)$, and $(3,4)$. Only $(2,3)$ leaves f invariant, so the function is partially symmetric in x_2 and x_3. Using Theorem 4, $f(x_1,0,0,x_4) = 0$, $f(x_1,1,0,x_4) = x_1$, and $f(x_1,1,1,x_4) = x_1 + x_4$. Thus

$$f(x_1,x_2,x_3,x_4) = x_1\sigma_1(x_2,x_3) + (x_1 + x_4)\sigma_2(x_2,x_3)$$

PROBLEMS

1. Note that every partially symmetric function has nontrivial group invariance. Construct an example to show that the converse is not true.

2. Let F_{n-k} be the free boolean algebra generated by $x_{k+1}, \ldots , x_n$ and let E_k denote the boolean algebra of symmetric functions in the variables $x_1, \ldots , x_k$. Show that the boolean algebra of partially symmetric functions described in Theorem 3 is exactly the tensor product of E_k and F_{n-k} (cf. Prob. 2-8.6).

3. Let f be a don't care function represented by $[f_0,f_1]$. Devise a test for deciding whether or not there exists an $f^* \in [f_0,f_1]$ such that f^* is completely specified and partially symmetric.

5 ρ-SYMMETRIC FUNCTIONS†

Let $X = \{x_1, \ldots ,x_n\}$ and let $\rho = \{\rho_1, \ldots ,\rho_k\}$ be any partition of X. Assume that the number of variables in ρ_i is r_i for $i = 1, \ldots , k$.

† The casual reader may wish to skip this section.

The system $\langle P_X, \vee, \wedge, 0, 1 \rangle$ is a lattice, where P_X is the family of all partitions of X, $\wedge$ is the intersection of the partitions and $\rho \vee \tau$ denotes the partition induced by the join of the two equivalence relations induced by ρ and τ. Let $0 = \{[x_1], \ldots, [x_n]\}$ and $1 = \{[x_1, \ldots, x_n]\}$.

EXAMPLE. Let $X = \{x_1, \ldots, x_6\}$ and $\rho = \{[x_1, x_2, x_3], [x_4, x_5][x_6]\}$ and $\tau = \{[x_1, x_3], [x_2, x_4, x_5, x_6]\}$. Then $\rho \cap \tau = \{[x_1, x_3][x_2], [x_4, x_5][x_6]\}$ and $\rho \vee \tau = \{[x_1, x_2, x_3, x_4, x_5, x_6]\} = 1$.

With this notation, the ρ-symmetric functions may be introduced.

Definition 1. A function $f(x_1, \ldots, x_n)$ is called ρ *symmetric* iff f is invariant under

$$S_\rho = S_{\rho_1} \times \cdots \times S_{\rho_k}$$

where S_ρ is the direct product of the groups S_{ρ_i} and S_{ρ_i} is the symmetric group on the variables in the block ρ_i for $i = 1, \ldots, k$.

Note that every boolean function is 0 symmetric, whereas the 1-symmetric functions are totally symmetric.

EXAMPLE. If $X = \{x_1, x_2, x_3\}$ and $\rho = \{[x_1, x_2], [x_3]\}$, the function $f = x_1 x_2 + x_3$ is ρ symmetric, since it is invariant under $S_{\{x_1, x_2\}} \times S_{\{x_3\}} = S_\rho$.

Proposition 2. If f is ρ' symmetric and $\rho \leq \rho'$, then f is ρ symmetric. If f is ρ symmetric and also ρ' symmetric, then f is $\rho \vee \rho'$ symmetric. For every function f there exists a maximal ρ such that f is ρ symmetric.

Now boolean algebras are associated with the partition ρ.

Definition 3. A is defined to be the one-to-one map which associates with every partition of X the following boolean algebra

$$A(\rho) = E_{\rho_1} \otimes \cdots \otimes E_{\rho_k}$$

where E_{ρ_i} is the boolean algebra of symmetric functions in the variables in the block ρ_i $(i = 1, \ldots, k)$.

EXAMPLE. Note that $A(0) = E_{\{x_1\}} \otimes \cdots \otimes E_{\{x_n\}}$ but $E_{\{x_i\}} = F_1$, so that $A(0) = F_1 \otimes \cdots \otimes F_1 = F_n$. At the other extreme

$$A(1) = E_{\{x_1, \ldots, x_n\}}$$

The following theorem on ρ-symmetric functions is fundamental.

Theorem 4. The following statements are equivalent:

(1) f is ρ symmetric.
(2) $f \in A(\rho)$
(3) f can be written uniquely in the form

$$f = \sum_{i_1 = 0}^{r_1} \cdots \sum_{i_k = 0}^{r_k} f_{i_1, \ldots, i_k} \sigma_{i_1}(\rho_1) \cdots \sigma_{i_k}(\rho_k)$$

where r_j is the cardinality of ρ_j and

$$f_{i_1,\ldots,i_k} = f(\overbrace{1,\ldots,1}^{i_1}, \overbrace{0,\ldots,0}^{r_1-i_1}; \overbrace{1,\ldots,1}^{i_2}, \overbrace{0,\ldots,0}^{r_2-i_2},\ldots,$$
$$\overbrace{1,\ldots,1}^{i_k}, \overbrace{0,\ldots,0}^{r_k-i_k})$$

PROOF. If f is invariant under $\sigma = (\sigma_1,\ldots,\sigma_k) \, \epsilon \, S_\rho$, then $\sigma_i f = f$ for $i = 1$, $\ldots, k$ and $f \, \epsilon \, E_{\rho_1} \otimes \cdots \otimes E_{\rho_k}$. (2) implies (3) by the salient property of tensor products (cf. Prob. 2-8.6.). Suppose f has this form and let $\alpha = (\alpha_1,\ldots,\alpha_k) \, \epsilon \, S_\rho$. Because α is an automorphism,

$$\alpha f = \alpha \left(\sum_{i_1} \cdots \sum_{i_k} f_{i_1,\ldots,i_k}\sigma_{i_1}(\rho_1) \cdots \sigma_{i_k}(\rho_k) \right)$$
$$= \sum_{i_1} \cdots \sum_{i_k} f_{i_1,\ldots,i_k}\alpha_1(\sigma_{i_1}(\rho_1))\alpha_2(\sigma_{i_2}(\rho_2)) \cdots \alpha_k(\sigma_{i_k}(\rho_k))$$
$$= f$$

and f is ρ symmetric. ∎

EXAMPLE. The reader should examine the special cases $\rho = 0$ and $\rho = 1$.

EXAMPLE. Let $X = \{x_1,x_2,x_3\}$ and $\rho = \{[x_1,x_2],[x_3]\}$. Then

$$A(\rho) = E_{\rho_1} \otimes E_{\rho_2}$$
where
$$E_{\rho_2} = \{0,1,x_3,\bar{x}_3\}$$

and $$E_{\rho_1} = \{0, 1, \bar{x}_1\bar{x}_2, x_1x_2, x_1 \oplus x_2, x_1 \equiv x_2, \bar{x}_1 + \bar{x}_2, x_1 + x_2\}$$

Thus $A(\rho)$ is the tensor product of E_{ρ_1} and E_{ρ_2}. To conclude the example, the following function f is written in the normal form:

$$f = x_1x_2x_3 + (x_1 \oplus x_2) + \bar{x}_3$$
Thus
$$f_{01} = 0; f_{00} = f_{10} = f_{11} = f_{20} = f_{21} = 1$$
$$f = \sigma_0(x_1,x_2)(\bar{x}_3) + \sigma_1(x_1,x_2)(\bar{x}_3 + x_3) + \sigma_2(x_1,x_2)(\bar{x}_3 + x_3)$$
$$= \sigma_0(x_1,x_2)(\bar{x}_3) + \sigma_1(x_1,x_2) + \sigma_2(x_1,x_2)$$

and f has been written in the form (3).

Corollary 5. $A(\rho)$ contains

$$\prod_{2^{i=1}}^{k} (r_i + 1)$$

functions.

EXAMPLE. For $\rho = 0$, $r_i = 1$ for $i = 1, \ldots, n$, so that $A(0)$ contains 2^{2^n} functions. For $\rho = 1$, $r_1 = n$; so that $A(1)$ contains 2^{n+1} functions.

$$\rho = \{[x_1,\ldots,x_k],[x_{k+1}],\ldots,[x_n]\}$$
then $A(\rho)$ contains

$$2^{\overbrace{(k+1)2\cdots 2}^{n-k}} = 2^{(k+1)2^{n-k}}$$

functions in agreement with Corollary 4.5.

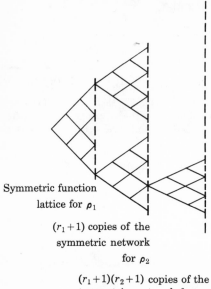

Symmetric function
lattice for ρ_1

(r_1+1) copies of the
symmetric network
for ρ_2

$(r_1+1)(r_2+1)$ copies of the
symmetric network for ρ_3

FIG. 1

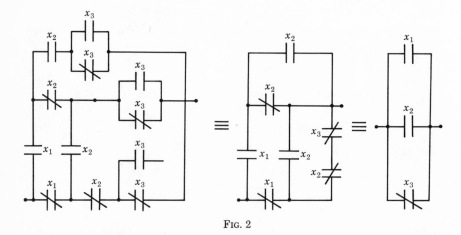

FIG. 2

The normal form for ρ-symmetric functions suggests the following synthesis procedure for branch-type networks.

Theorem 6.   Any ρ-symmetric function may be realized by a network of the following form (Fig. 1).   The number of components required is at most

$$\sum_{i=1}^{k} \prod_{j=1}^{i} (r_j + 1)r_i$$

PROOF.   It is immediately obvious that the network realizes the canonical form for a ρ-symmetric function.   Note that the required number of elements is

$$(r_1 + 1)r_1 + (r_1 + 1)(r_2 + 1)r_2 + \cdots = \sum_{i=1}^{k} \prod_{j=1}^{i} (r_j + 1)r_i \quad \blacksquare$$

EXAMPLE.   Let

$$f = x_1 x_2 x_3 + (x_1 \oplus x_2) + \bar{x}_3 = \sigma_0(x_1,x_2)\bar{x}_3 + \sigma_1(x_1,x_2) + \sigma_2(x_1,x_2)$$

Figure 2 uses

$$3 \leq 7 \leq (r_1 + 1)r_1 + (r_1 + 1)(r_2 + 1)r_2 = 3 \cdot 2 + 3 \cdot 2 = 12 \text{ contacts}$$

PROBLEMS

1.   Show that
   (a) $\rho \leq \rho' \Rightarrow A(\rho') \subseteq A(\rho)$
   (b) Relate $A(\rho \vee \rho')$ and $A(\rho \wedge \rho')$ to $A(\rho)$ and $A(\rho')$
2.   Show that the number of self-dual ρ-symmetric functions of n variables is

$$2^{\frac{1}{2} \prod_{i=1}^{k} (r_i+1)} \qquad \text{if } \prod_{i=1}^{k} (r_i + 1) \equiv 0 \bmod 2$$

$$0 \qquad \text{if } \prod_{i=1}^{k} (r_i + 1) \equiv 1 \bmod 2$$

Compare with Prob. 3.13.

6 MONOTONE FUNCTIONS

In calculus one studies monotone functions of a single real variable. It turns out that functions which are monotone in all their variables play an important role in switching theory.   These functions not only play a key role in theoretical investigations but have very simple realizations. The following notation is convenient.   Let

$$\mathbf{x} = (x_1, \ldots ,x_n) \qquad \mathbf{y} = (y_1, \ldots ,y_n) \qquad x_i, y_i \in \{0,1\}$$
$$\text{for } i = 1, \ldots , n$$
$$\mathbf{0} = (0, \ldots ,0) \qquad \mathbf{1} = (1, \ldots ,1)$$

Proposition 1.   The collection of n-tuples of zeroes and ones is a boolean algebra under the following operations:

$$\mathbf{x} + \mathbf{y} = (x_1 + y_1, \ldots ,x_n + y_n)$$
$$\mathbf{xy} = (x_1 y_1, \ldots ,x_n y_n)$$
$$\bar{\mathbf{x}} = (\bar{x}_1, \ldots ,\bar{x}_n)$$

EXAMPLE.   Take $n = 2$:
$$\mathbf{0} = (0,0) \qquad \mathbf{1} = (1,1)$$
$$\mathbf{x} = (1,0) \qquad \mathbf{y} = (0,1)$$
$$\mathbf{x} + \mathbf{y} = (1,0) + (0,1) = (1,1) = \mathbf{1}$$

Definition 2.   Let $\mathbf{x} = (x_1, \ldots, x_n)$ and let $\mathbf{y} = (y_1, \ldots, y_n)$.   Then define $\mathbf{x} \leq \mathbf{y}$ iff $x_i \leq y_i$ for every $i = 1, \ldots, n$.

EXAMPLE $\mathbf{x} = (0,1,0) \qquad \mathbf{y} = (0,1,1) \qquad \mathbf{z} = (1,0,1)$

Note that $\mathbf{x} \leq \mathbf{y} \qquad$ but $\qquad \mathbf{x} \nleq \mathbf{z}, \mathbf{z} \nleq \mathbf{y}$

and $\mathbf{y} \nleq \mathbf{z} \qquad$ and $\qquad \mathbf{z} \nleq \mathbf{y}$

Definition 3.   A boolean function of n variables is *monotone increasing* iff $\mathbf{x} \leq \mathbf{y}$ implies $f(\mathbf{x}) \leq f(\mathbf{y})$, where $\mathbf{x} = (x_1, \ldots, x_n)$ and

$$\mathbf{y} = (y_1, \ldots, y_n)$$

f is *monotone decreasing* iff $\mathbf{x} \leq \mathbf{y}$ implies $f(\mathbf{x}) \geq f(\mathbf{y})$.

EXAMPLE.   For $n = 2$, there are six monotone increasing (decreasing) functions.

Monotone increasing	*Monotone decreasing*
0	1
xy	$\bar{x}\bar{y}$
x	$\bar{x}$
y	$\bar{y}$
$x + y$	$\bar{x} + \bar{y}$
1	0

The algebraic structure of the monotone functions is immediately apparent.

Proposition 4.   Let $L^+(L^-)$ be the set of all monotone increasing (decreasing) functions of n variables.   The system $L^+(L^-)$ is a free distributive lattice on n generators $x_1, \ldots, x_n$ ($\bar{x}_1, \ldots, \bar{x}_n$).

Both L^+ and L^- contain the same number of functions by Prob. 1. Unfortunately, the number of elements of L^+ (L^-) is not known in general. This problem was originally suggested by Dedekind; and although some partial results are known, no general method of attack has been formulated.   The known results are collected in Table 1.

TABLE 1
Number of Monotone Increasing (Decreasing)

n	*Number of functions*	n	*Number of functions*
1	3	4	168
2	6	5	7,581
3	20	6	7,828,354

A glance at the monotone increasing functions suggests that they can be written without negation.   This observation is true in general.

Theorem 5.   A function $f(x_1, \ldots, x_n)$ is monotone increasing iff f can be denoted by a form which is a sum of products of the x_i, that is, no complements appear.

PROOF.   Since x_i is monotone increasing and the product of monotone functions is monotone, then f is monotone because the sum of monotone functions is monotone.
     Conversely, let $S = \{x | f(x) = 1\}$.   Unless f is the zero function, $S \neq \emptyset$.   Let x^i be a minimal element of S and let $S_i = \{y | y \geq x^i\}$.   Note that $S = \bigcup_i S_i$, where the union is over all minimal elements. f can be written as

$$f = \sum_{j \in S} m_j(x_1, \ldots, x_n) = \sum_i f_i$$

It will be shown that each f_i is a sum of elements in S_i.   Suppose, without loss of generality, that

$$x^i = (\overbrace{1, \ldots, 1}^{s}, \overbrace{0, \ldots, 0}^{n-s})$$

Then

$$f_i = \sum_{S_i} x_1 \cdots x_s x^{i_{s+1}}_{s+1} \cdots x_n^{i_n} \qquad \text{where } x_j^{i_j} = \begin{cases} \bar{x}_j & \text{if } i_j = 0 \\ x_j & \text{if } i_j = 1 \end{cases}$$

$$= x_1 \cdots x_s \sum_{S_i} x^{i_{s+1}}_{s+1} \cdots x_n^{i_n}$$

$$= x_1 \cdots x_s \prod_{j=s+1}^{n} (x_j + \bar{x}_j) = x_1 \cdots x_s$$

where the sum over S_i occurs by filling in the zeroes in all possible ways.   This has been denoted by the exponent notation. |

EXAMPLE.   Given the following monotone function, the form guaranteed by Theorem 5 is constructed.

x_1	x_2	x_3	f
0	0	0	0
0	0	1	1
0	1	0	0
0	1	1	1
1	0	0	0
1	0	1	1
1	1	0	1
1	1	1	1

Clearly, $S = \{(0,0,1),\ (0,1,1),\ (1,0,1),\ (1,1,0),\ (1,1,1)\}$. The minimal elements are $\mathbf{x}^1 = (0,0,1)$ and $\mathbf{x}^2 = (1,1,0)$. Thus

$$S_1 = \{(0,0,1),\ (1,0,1),\ (0,1,1),\ (1,1,1)\}$$
$$S_2 = \{(1,1,0),\ (1,1,1)\}$$

and $$f(x_1,x_2,x_3) = x_3 + x_1 x_2$$

Because monotone functions can be written in a normal form without negation, one might suspect that the minimal network for the function will not contain any negation elements. The following example, due to McNaughton,[3] shows that this suspicion is false.

EXAMPLE. $f = x_1 x_5 x_6 + x_2 x_3 x_4 + x_2 x_3 x_5 x_6$ has the minimal representation shown in Fig. 1. One can show that any network for this function f which does not have any break contacts requires more elements. This phenomenon has been discussed in detail by Calabi and Riley.[1]

It has been seen that monotone functions have a normal form in which negation does not appear. It will now be shown that a monotone function has a unique form of this type in which no product includes any other product.

Theorem 6. (Quine[2]) Every monotone function has a unique normal-form expression in which no variable appears complemented and no product includes another product.

PROOF. We can assume that

$$f = p_1 + \cdots + p_k = q_1 + \cdots + q_l$$

where $p_i(q_i)$ does not contain $p_j(q_j)$ for $j \neq i$. Let all the variables in p_i be set equal to 1 and all other variables be set equal to 0. Clearly, $p_i = 1$ and no other $p_j = 1$, because if it did, it would be contained in p_j. Since the forms are equivalent, some q_j equals 1. Thus the variables in q_j are a subset of those in p_i. If q_j did not contain all the variables in p_i, then one could find an assignment α (all variables in p_i

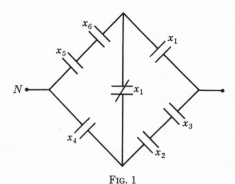

Fig. 1

and q_j equal to 1) which made $q_j = 1$ while $p_i = 0$. Thus $|p_1 + \cdots + p_k|_\alpha = 0$, since if another term were made 1 by this assignment, it would have been contained in p_i. Thus $p_i = q_j$. Thus the terms of the two forms are identical. ▮

One can enlarge the class of monotone functions by considering functions in which some variables are monotone increasing and the rest are monotone decreasing.

Definition 7. A function $f(x_1, \ldots, x_n)$ is said to be a *mixed monotone* (or a *unate*) function iff there is a nontrivial partition of the variables

$$\{x_1, \ldots, x_n\} = X = Y \cup Z$$

where $Y \cap Z = \emptyset$, such that f is monotone increasing on Y and monotone decreasing on Z.

Thus we can complement all the variables in Z to convert a mixed monotone function to an ordinary monotone function.

EXAMPLE. $f(x_1, x_2, x_3) = \bar{x}_1 x_3 + \bar{x}_1 x_2 + x_2 x_3$ is a mixed monotone function. $Y = \{x_2, x_3\}$, $Z = \{x_1\}$.

An example of a function which is not mixed monotone is given by $x_1 \oplus x_2$. We shall now give a procedure for detecting mixed monotone functions.

Algorithm 8. Given a function $f(x_1, \ldots, x_n)$, perform the following computations.

(1) Construct the space of prime subcubes.
(2) Construct the space E of essential prime subcubes. If E gives the unique minimal cover for f, continue. If not, f is not mixed monotone.
(3) Let $Y(Z)$ be the set of all variables in which every entry in the cover is either 1 (0) or x.
(4) If $X = \{x_1, \ldots, x_n\} = Y \cup Z$, then f is mixed monotone. If $Z = \emptyset$, $Y = X$, then f is monotone increasing.
(5) If $Y \cup Z$ is a proper subset of X, then f is not mixed monotone.

EXAMPLE. $f(x_1, x_2) = x_1 \oplus x_2$. The essential prime subcubes are $(0,1)$ and $(1,0)$. Thus $Y = \emptyset$, $Z = \emptyset$, and f is not monotone.

EXAMPLE. $f = \bar{x}_1 x_2 x_3 + x_1 x_2 x_3 + \bar{x}_1 x_2 \bar{x}_3 + \bar{x}_1 \bar{x}_2 x_3$. The set of prime cubes is $\{(0,x,1),(x,1,1),(0,1,x)\}$. Clearly, these are essential prime implicants. $Y = \{x_2, x_3\}$ and $Z = \{x_1\}$. Thus, f is mixed monotone.

We leave to the reader the routine work of showing that the algorithm works. More precisely, it must be shown that $f(x_1, \ldots, x_n)$ is mixed monotone iff f is covered by its essential prime subcubes and there exist disjoint sets Y and Z such that $X = Y \cup Z$ with f monotone increasing on X but monotone decreasing on Z.

PROBLEMS

1. Construct a one-to-one mapping from L^+ onto L^- which preserves structure.

2. Show that $f \in L^+ \cap L^-$ implies that $f = 0$ or $f = 1$.

3. (Gilbert[1]) Show that the number of monotone increasing functions is at least

$$2^{\binom{n}{[n/2]}}$$

where $[n/2]$ is the largest integer $\leq n/2$. (HINT: Construct this many functions.)

4. (Gilbert[1]) Given any function of n variables, show that f may be represented as

$$f(\mathbf{x}) = F(x_1, \ldots, x_k, \bar{g}_1, \ldots, \bar{g}_s)$$

where F is monotone increasing and g_j is a monotone function of

$$\{x_1, \ldots, x_k, \bar{g}_1, \ldots, \bar{g}_{j-1}\} \quad \text{and} \quad s = O(\log_2 n)$$

5. (McNaughton[3]) A switching function $f(x_1, \ldots, x_n)$ is called *linearly separable* or a *threshold function* iff there exist real numbers $a_1, \ldots, a_n, b$ such that

$$f(x_1, \ldots, x_n) = \begin{cases} 1 & \text{if } \sum_{i=1}^{n} a_i x_i \geq b \\ 0 & \text{if } \sum_{i=1}^{n} a_i x_i < b \end{cases}$$

Show that every linearly separable function is monotone increasing or decreasing. Is the converse true?

7 DECOMPOSABLE FUNCTIONS

All switching functions can be built up from functions of one and two variables by the connectives $(^-, +, \cdot)$. Sometimes functions can be decomposed into smaller functions. When such decompositions exist, economical realizations can be obtained.

For example, suppose that $\lambda(n)$ elements are required to realize most functions of n variables. Experience indicates that $\lambda(n)$ grows exponentially, that is, $\lambda(n) \approx 2^n$. If f is any function of $2n$ variables, then about $\lambda(2n) \approx 2^{2n}$ elements are needed. Suppose $f = g(f_1, f_2)$, where f_1 and f_2 are both functions of n variables. In this realization, the number of elements required is

$$2\lambda(n) + 4 \approx 2^{n+1} + 4 \ll 2^{2^n}$$

so that a considerable savings is obtained.

Definition 1. A switching function $f(x_1, \ldots, x_n)$ is called *decomposable* or *functionally separable* iff there exist functions g and h such that

$$f(x_1, \ldots, x_n) = g(h(x_{i_1}, \ldots, x_{i_s}), x_{i_{s+1}}, \ldots, x_{i_n})$$

for any $1 \leq s \leq n - 1$ and $\{x_{i_1}, \ldots, x_{i_s}\} \cap \{x_{i_{s+1}}, \ldots, x_{i_n}\} = \emptyset$.

EXAMPLE. Suppose $s = 1$ or $s = n - 1$. In these cases, trivial decompositions exist, so that only the range of values $s = 2, \ldots, n - 2$ are of interest. By convention, 0 and 1 are decomposable.

Functional decomposition is so important that a great deal of research work has been performed in this area. Curtis has written a massive book employing this approach to design. Because of the availability of his book, we content ourselves with a presentation of an algorithm for the detection of decomposable functions.

EXAMPLE.   The function f shown below is decomposable.

$$f \text{ has index set } I = \{0,7,9,14\}$$
$$f(x_1,x_2,x_3,x_4) = g(h(x_1,x_4),x_2,x_3)$$

where
$$h(x_1,x_4) = (x_1 \equiv x_4)$$

and
$$g(h(x_1,x_4),x_2,x_3) = \bar{x}_2\bar{x}_3h + x_2x_3\bar{h}$$

An algorithm for the detection of such functions is now derived. To make the test on a given function f, the first step is to partition the variables into two sets $x_{i_1}, \ldots, x_{i_s}$ and $x_{i_{s+1}}, \ldots, x_{i_n}$. Write a $s \times (n - s)$ matrix with the first set as column headings and the second set as row headings. The entries of the table are the function values.

EXAMPLE.   Let f have index set $\{0,7,9,14\}$. Three partition matrices for f are shown below.

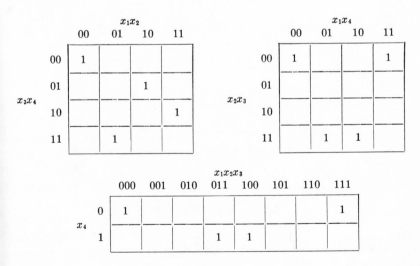

Definition 2.   Define the *row (column) multiplicity* of any array to be the number of distinct rows (columns).

Lemma 3.   Let p and q be the row and column multiplicities of a partition matrix. $p \leq 2^q$ and $q \leq 2^p$.

PROOF. Define a reduced matrix by deleting the nondistinct columns. The matrix will now have, say, 2^s rows and q columns. At most, 2^q rows can be distinct, since there are only 2^q q-place binary numbers. Thus $p \leq 2^q$. Transpose the array and repeat the argument for $q \leq 2^p$. ∎

Proposition 4. $q = 1$ iff $p \leq 2$ and only 0 and 1 appear as row vectors.

Proposition 5. $q = 2$ iff $p \leq 4$ and only one nontrivial row vector h may appear; the only other possibilities are 0, 1, or $\bar{h}$.

The pertinent result on decomposability is Theorem 6.

Theorem 6. (Ashenhurst[5]) $f(x_1, \ldots, x_n) = g(h(x_{i_1}, \ldots, x_{i_s}), x_{i_{s+1}}, \ldots, x_{i_n})$ iff the column multiplicity of the array having column headings $x_{i_1}, \ldots,$ x_{i_s} and row headings $x_{i_{s+1}}, \ldots, x_{i_n}$ is ≤ 2.

PROOF. If the multiplicity is ≤ 2, both cases are worked out. If $q = 1$, then, by Proposition 4, only 0 and 1 appear as rows and f may be written down as in the map method. The converse is also trivial. Suppose that $q = 2$. Now two functions g and h will be constructed. By Proposition 5, h is uniquely determined (up to complementation). g is constructed in the following way: Read off the ith row of the array. If it is 0, take $\alpha_{2i} = \alpha_{2i+1} = 0$; if it is 1, take $\alpha_{2i} = \alpha_{2i+1} = 1$. If the ith row denotes h, choose $\alpha_{2i} = 0$, $\alpha_{2i+1} = 1$; if it denotes $\bar{h}$, choose $\alpha_{2i} = 1$ and $\alpha_{2i+1} = 0$. Then

$$g(x_{i_1}, \ldots, x_{i_s}, h) = \sum \alpha_i m_i(x_{i_1}, \ldots, x_{i_s}, h)$$

The converse of the last case is also left to the reader. ∎

EXAMPLE. In the running example, the array is

	$x_1 x_4$			
$x_2 x_3$	**00**	**01**	**10**	**11**
00	1			1
01				
10				
11		1	1	

Thus $q = 2$ and f is decomposable with

$$h(x_1, x_4) = (x_1 \equiv x_4)$$

Note that the proof of the theorem says that $\alpha_1 = \alpha_6 = 1$ and all other $\alpha_i = 0$. Thus $g(x_2, x_3, h(x_1, x_4)) = \bar{x}_2 \bar{x}_3 h + x_2 x_3 \bar{h}$.

The procedure given in the proof of Theorem 6 is simple to apply, but it requires the generation of all nontrivial partitions of the n variables. This practical limitation can be somewhat overcome by devising decomposition charts as explained in the book of Curtis or by a computer program.

PROBLEMS

1. Find the boolean functions of n variables which are both symmetric and decomposable.

2. Show that almost all functions are not nontrivially decomposable in the sense of Definition 1.

3. (Povarov[1]) Show that a function $f(x_1, \ldots, x_n)$ is decomposable iff there exists a subset $x_{i_1} \cdots x_{i_r}$ of the variables $x_1, \ldots, x_n$, where $1 \leq i \leq n - 2$, and there is a function g of the remaining variables such that, in the decomposition of the function f with respect to $x_{i_1} \cdots x_{i_r}$, all the nonconstant coefficients are g or $\bar{g}$,

4. (Povarov,[1] Ashenhurst[5]) Show that the set of separable functions is closed under negation.

5. Show that the following functions are decomposable.
(a) $I = \{0,5,6,7,10,11,12,13\}$
(b) $I = \{6,7,8,12,14,15\}$

6. Devise charts which mechanize the algorithm embodied in Theorem 6.

7. Devise a synthesis method for decomposable functions.

8. (Ninomiya[3]) Show that a function which is symmetrizable and decomposable is just an atom or the complement of an atom or a linear function of all n variables.

9. Show that if f is decomposable and if g is equivalent to f under N^{G_n}, then g is also decomposable.

10. Let f be a switching function and define the *symmetry group of f* to be

$$U_f = \{\sigma \in G_n | \sigma f = f\}$$

If f can be written $f = g(h(x_{i_1}, \ldots, x_{i_s}), x_{i_{s+1}}, \ldots, x_{i_n})$, what relationships exist between U_h, U_g, and U_f?

11. Given a don't care function f represented by $[f_0, f_1]$, devise a method for determining if there exists an $f^* \in [f_0, f_1]$ such that f^* is completely specified and decomposable.

8 AN EXAMPLE

Consider the problem of designing a gate-type network to realize the given function of five variables. The index set is given by

$$I = \{2,3,5,7,9,11,14,15,17,19,22,23,26,27,29,31\}$$

First we try to decompose f,

		000	001	010	$x_1x_2x_3$ 011	100	101	110	111
	00								
	01		1	1		1			1
x_4x_5	10	1			1		1	1	
	11	1	1	1	1	1	1	1	1

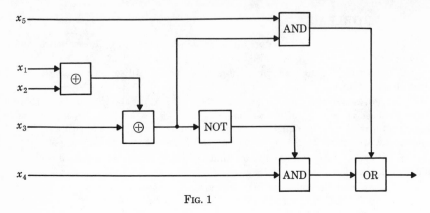

FIG. 1

Thus

$$g(x_4,x_5,h) = m_3 + m_4 + m_6 + m_7$$
$$= \bar{x}_4 x_5 h + x_4 \bar{x}_5 \bar{h} + x_4 x_5 \bar{h} + x_4 x_5 h$$
$$h(x_1,x_2,x_3) = x_1 \oplus x_2 \oplus x_3$$

Clearly h is a symmetric function and easy to realize. There is nothing that can be done to g. It is not partially symmetric or monotone. Just using a map gives

$$g(x_4,x_5,h) = (x_4\bar{h} + x_5 h)$$

The realization of f is given in Fig. 1.

The example suggests the following strategy for the realization of a given function. Attempt to test the given function for the special properties studied in this chapter. If the function possesses any of these properties, realize it by the appropriate special technique. If the function does not have any of these properties, attempt to decompose the function into smaller functions and repeat the tests on these functions. If this fails, the Quine algorithm should be used.

9 SUMMARY

In this chapter some structural properties of switching functions have been derived. Each of these special properties has been (or will be) exploited in developing synthesis procedures for switching functions.

In the next chapter, where perfectly general synthesis methods are presented, it will be seen that these functional properties provide an opportunity for significant savings in components.

The material in this chapter on symmetric functions is taken from the paper by Arnold and Harrison. The work on monotone functions is drawn from Gilbert,[1] McNaughton,[3] and Ninomiya.[3] The material on decomposable functions is due to Ashenhurst,[5] Povarov,[1] and Ninomiya.[3]

CHAPTER 7 *tree networks and general synthesis considerations*

1 INTRODUCTION

In this chapter the important class of tree networks is studied extensively. By using tree networks, general synthesis results are derived. A measure of the complexity of switching functions is discussed and is shown to be more or less independent of the primitive elements. It will be shown that almost all functions are as complex as they can be. The implications of this result are analyzed.

2 STANDARD TREE NETWORKS

One of the motivations for studying tree networks is that these networks realize all the minterm functions. Because there are networks which have this property and are not trees, some additional terminology is necessary.

Definition 1. A network with one input and 2^n outputs (expressed briefly as a $(1,2^n)$ network) is said to be a *complete fundamental network* iff every fundamental product (minterm) denotes the transmission function between the input terminal and one and only one output terminal. These networks are sometimes called *complete decoding networks* in the literature. The word *complete* is used to indicate that all 2^n outputs must be present. We shall not study *partial* trees.

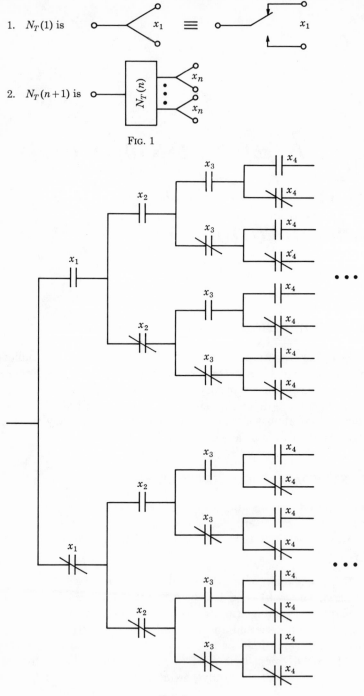

1. $N_T(1)$ is

2. $N_T(n+1)$ is

FIG. 1

FIG. 2

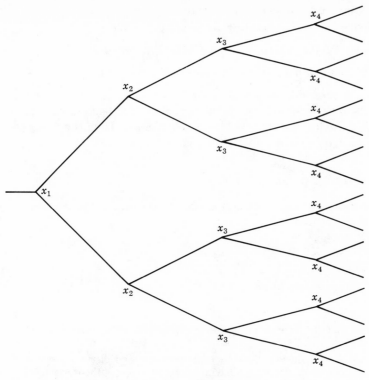

FIG. 3

Complete trees will now be defined. Since trees are most often constructed from relays, these components will be used in the examples, but electronic trees are also important. In particular, electronic trees are often used in the memory selection circuits of digital computers.

An example of the sort of tree to be defined is shown in Fig. 2. A simplified version of the same drawing is given in Fig. 3, in which transfer contacts are used at each vertex.

Definition 2. The *complete tree on n variables* is denoted by $N_T(n)$ and defined inductively as in Fig. 1.

We note that $N_T(n)$ is a complete decoding network; not every complete decoding network is a complete tree. Our next task is to count the number of elements in $N_T(n)$.

Proposition 3. The number of elements in $N_T(n)$ is

$$2^{n+1} - 2$$

PROOF. Basis $n = 1$, $N_T(1)$ uses two elements.

INDUCTION STEP. $N_T(n + 1)$ uses $2^{n+1} - 2 + 2^n \cdot 2 = 2^{n+2} - 2$, since two contacts are added to each of 2^n outputs. ∎

Recall that in a count of relay contacts, a transfer contact counts as two contacts, so that $N_T(n)$ uses $2^n - 1$ *transfer* contacts.

Proposition 4. $N_T(n)$ is a complete fundamental network.

PROOF.   The reader should prove this proposition by an induction on n. ∎

In Prob. 2, the reader will prove that $N_T(n)$ is a disjunctive network. It has been shown by E. F. Moore[2] that there is no disjunctive fundamental network with less than $2(2^n - 1)$ elements.   Thus the tree network is the best possible disjunctive fundamental network.

PROBLEMS

1.   (Marcus[2]) Show that the number of possible relabelings of the graph of the complete tree with n variables is

$$\prod_{i=0}^{n-2} (n - i)^{2^i}$$

[HINT: Let P_n be the desired number.   Show that

$$P_{n+1} = (n + 1)P_n^2$$

and then verify that the solution given satisfies the difference equation with initial condition $P_1 = 1$.]

2.   One obvious distinction between relay networks and electronic switching networks is that relay contacts form bilateral networks, whereas the electronic networks are unilateral.   One must exercise care in dealing with relay networks or a sneak path may be introduced.   Consider the network shown in Fig. P2a.   It might be thought that we could save a contact on the A relay by joining nodes 1 and 2 and removing one of the contacts labeled a.   The network with this simplification is shown in Fig. P2b.   The transmission function f_1 has been changed because ground was introduced through other paths than was intended.   These are the so-called *sneak paths.*†

In order to avoid sneak paths, a special class of networks is considered: the disjunctive networks.   Let N be a network with k outputs $1, \ldots , k$. N is called

† It is awkward to give a formal definition of sneak paths because the concept is subjective and depends on what the network designer thinks he wants.

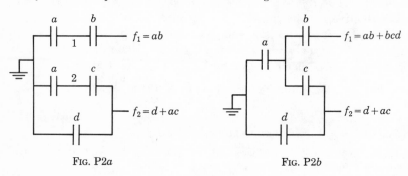

FIG. P2a   FIG. P2b

disjunctive iff $i \neq j$ implies $t_{ij} = 0$, i, $j = 1, \ldots, k$, where t_{ij} is the transmission function between nodes i and j. Show that the complete tree network is disjunctive. Is the symmetric function lattice disjunctive?

3. Give a formal graph-theoretic definition of the complete tree on n variables. Compare with Definition 2.

4. (Marcus[2]) A typical electronic tree is shown in Fig. P3. Show that the number of diodes required is $n \cdot 2^n$ in general. Show that if $n = 2^p$, another fundamental tree can be constructed with

$$2 \left(\sum_{i=1}^{p} 2^{p-i} 2^{2^i} \right)$$

components. This is quite a savings, i.e.; for $n = 8$, the first method requires 2,048 components and the latter method requires 608 components.

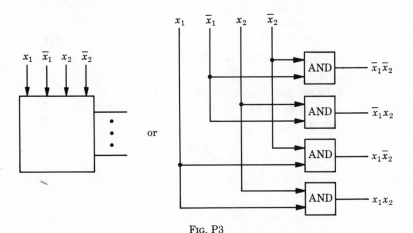

or

FIG. P3

5. Discuss the connection between trees and games like Twenty Questions.

6. Show that trees are equivalent to labeled bracketings. (HINT: Generalize on the example shown in Fig. P5.)

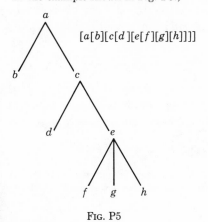

$[a[b][c[d][e[f][g][h]]]]$

FIG. P5

3 FOLDED TREES

Let us say that all the elements in the ith vertical group on a tree belong to the ith *bay* of the tree. Thus $N_T(n)$ has n bays.

Definition 1. A tree has *loading sequence* $a_1, \ldots, a_n$ iff the number of transfer contacts x_i is exactly a_i for $i = 1, \ldots, n$.

EXAMPLE. $N_T(n)$ has loading sequence $1, 2, 4, \ldots, 2^{n-1}$. For this reason $1, \ldots, 2^{n-1}$ is called a *standard loading sequence*.

The previous example shows that if $n = 7$, relay X_n must have 64 transfer contacts to realize N_T (7). It is clear that relays with this many elements are expensive and slow. It is desirable to find a way to equalize the contact loading in a tree network.† The desired network will contain the same number of relays and still be a complete fundamental network, but it will have a more uniform contact distribution.

EXAMPLE. Two complete fundamental networks with their loading sequences are shown in Fig. 1.

Definition 2 A *folded tree* is any relabeled complete tree, such that every path from the input to an output passes through one and only one vertex labeled x_i for all $i = 1, \ldots, n$.

EXAMPLE. The two networks in the example preceding Definition 2 are folded trees, and the network shown in Fig. 2 is not a folded tree.

Theorem 3. A labeled tree is a complete fundamental network iff the network is a folded tree.

PROOF. If the network is a folded tree, then every path from an input to an output corresponds to one and only one minterm. Since there are 2^n different minterms and 2^n different paths, the network is complete and fundamental. The proof of necessity is left as an exercise for the reader. |

We now consider the problem of obtaining more uniform contact distribution in a folded tree. The argument will be a type of existence proof; i.e., it will say that a certain distribution is obtainable, but the argument is not constructive.

Algorithm 4

  (1) Take the standard loading sequence $1, 2, 4, \ldots, 2^{n-1}$.
  (2) Form a new distribution by adding one or more units from a larger number to a smaller number. No numbers may be shifted to 1.
  (3) Repeat rule 2 as often as possible.

  † In electronic networks, the corresponding problem is the *fan-out problem;* i.e., the output of each element may be connected to the input of only a prescribed number of units.

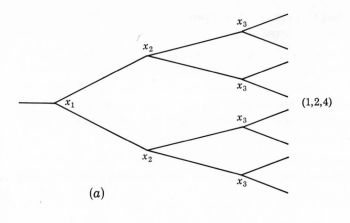

(1,2,4)

(a)

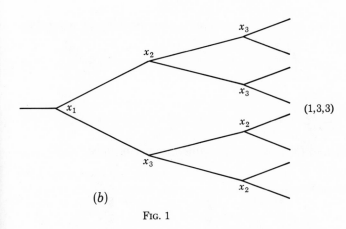

(1,3,3)

(b)

Fig. 1

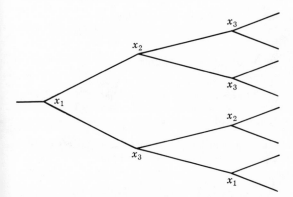

Fig. 2 A tree which is not a folded tree.

It will turn out that this algorithm will provide a procedure for achieving almost uniform contact distribution.

EXAMPLE.   1, 2, 4 goes into 1, 3, 3 under the algorithm.   Notice that 1, 2, 4 is the distribution of transfer contacts in Fig. 1a and 1, 3, 3 is the distribution for the network in Fig. 1b.

Definition 5. Given a set of numbers $a_1, \ldots, a_n$, let $b_1, b_2, \ldots, b_n = [a_1, \ldots, a_n]$, where this symbol denotes any numbers which may be obtained from $a_1, \ldots, a_n$ by

(1) Interchange of numbers
(2) A flow from a larger number to a smaller number with no flow allowed to the number 1

EXAMPLE. $4, 5, 1, 5 = [1,2,4,8]$
$$1, 10, 3, 10, 3 = [1,2,4,8,12]$$

Theorem 6. Let (a_i) and (b_i) be ordered as nondecreasing sequences. $b_1, \ldots, b_n = [a_1, \ldots, a_n]$ iff

(1) $\displaystyle\sum_{i=1}^{s} b_i \geq \sum_{i=1}^{s} a_i \qquad s = 1, \ldots, n$

(2) $\displaystyle\sum_{i=1}^{n} b_i = \sum_{i=1}^{n} a_i$

(3) Both (a_i) and (b_i) contain the same number of ones.

PROOF.   Assume $b_1, \ldots, b_n = [a_1, \ldots, a_n]$; then both sequences contain the same number of ones.   Also,

$$\sum_{i=1}^{n} b_i = \sum_{i=1}^{n} a_i$$

since the rules leave the sum invariant.   Since the sequences are ordered, flow must be to the left in the a_i and the sum $\displaystyle\sum_{i=1}^{s} b_i$ can only increase, i.e.,

$$\sum_{i=1}^{s} b_i \geq \sum_{i=1}^{s} a_i \qquad s = 1, \ldots, n$$

Conversely, assume (1) to (3).   Order the sequences such that

$$a_1 \leq a_2 \leq \cdots \leq a_n \qquad \text{and} \qquad b_1 \leq b_2 \leq \cdots \leq b_n$$

Assume there are $k(k \geq 0)$ ones in both sequences.   Replace the sequences by their k *reducts*, i.e., the last $n - k$ terms of the sequence.   We now have

$$a_{k+1}, \ldots, a_n \qquad \text{and} \qquad b_{k+1}, \ldots, b_n$$

still ordered as before.

If $a_{k+1} = b_{k+1}$, take a 1-reduct, proceed to $k + 2$, and continue. Bring a_{k+1} up to $b_{k+1}[b_{k+1} \geq a_{k+1}$ by (3)]. Proceed by allowing flow from the least a_j ($k + 1 \leq j \leq n$) which is larger than a_{k+1}. Continue this process until $a_{k+1} = b_{k+1}$ if this is possible. If $a_j - m = a_{k+1} + m \neq b_{k+1}$, take the next smallest integer a_q and allow flow from a_q until $a_{k+1} + p = b_{k+1}$. Repeat this part of the argument if necessary. When $a_{k+1} = b_{k+1}$, take a 1-reduct, reorder the sequences, and repeat. The process will terminate, since n is finite. ∎

EXAMPLE.   (of the proof) Given

$$1, 1, 9, 8, 9 \qquad \text{and} \qquad 1, 1, 6, 9, 11$$

Taking 2-reducts, we get

$$9, 8, 9 \qquad \text{and} \qquad 6, 9, 11$$

Reordering yields

$$8, 9, 9 \qquad \text{and} \qquad 6, 9, 11$$

Flow from 9 gives us

$$8, 9, 9 \qquad \text{and} \qquad 7, 8, 11$$

Flow from 11 gives us

$$8, 9, 9 \qquad \text{and} \qquad 8, 8, 10$$

Taking a 1-reduct gives us

$$9, 9 \qquad \text{and} \qquad 8, 10$$

Flow from 10 gives us 9, 9 and 9, 9. This completes the example.

Lemma 7. If $n \neq 3$, and $a_1, a_2, \ldots, a_n = [2,4,8, \ldots, 2^n]$, then the a_i are decomposable, i.e.,

$$a_i = b_i + c_i \qquad i = 1, \ldots, n$$

where

$$b_1, \ldots, b_n = [1, 2, \ldots, 2^{n-1}]$$

and

$$c_1, \ldots, c_n = [1, 2, \ldots, 2^{n-1}]$$

PROOF.   So order the a_i that

$$a_1 \leq a_2 \leq \cdots \leq a_n$$

We consider two cases: $a_1 = 2$ and $a_1 > 2$.

CASE I. $a_1 = 2$; take

B	as	$1, 2, \ldots, 2^{n-1}$
C	as	$1, 2, \ldots, 2^{n-1}$
A	as	$2, 4, \ldots, 2^n$

A flow has occurred in $4, 8, \ldots, 2^n$ to give $a_2, \ldots, a_n$; but such a flow corresponds to a flow in B or C, since

$$a_i > a_j$$

implies

$$b_i + c_i > b_j + c_j$$

which in turn implies a flow in the (b_i) or (c_i) to keep the sum invariant.

CASE II $\qquad\qquad a_1 > 2 \qquad$ or $\qquad a_1 \geq 3$

Since the (a_i) are ordered,

$$a_1 + (n - 1)a_2 \leq \sum_{i=1}^{n} 2^i = 2^{n+1} - 2$$

or
$$(n - 1)a_2 \leq (2^{n+1} - 2) - a_1$$
$$(n - 1)a_2 \leq 2^{n+1} - 2 - 3 = 2^{n+1} - 5 \qquad \text{since } a_1 \geq 3$$
$$a_2 \leq \frac{2^{n+1} - 5}{n - 1}$$
$$a_2 - 1 \leq \frac{2^{n+1} - 5}{n - 1} - 1$$

We claim that

$$\frac{2^{n+1} - 5}{n - 1} - 1 \leq 2^{n-1}$$

which is equivalent to

$$\frac{2^{n+1} - 5}{n - 1} \leq 2^{n-1} + 1$$
$$2^{n+1} - 5 \leq n\,2^{n-1} - 2^{n-1} + n - 1$$

or
$$2^{n+1} + 2^{n-1} = 5 \cdot 2^{n-1} \leq n\,2^{n-1} + n + 4$$

This is clearly true for $n \geq 5$. We check the other values by direct calculation.

$$n = 4 \qquad 40 \leq 4 \cdot 8 + 8 = 40$$
$$n = 3 \qquad 20 \not\leq 4 \cdot 3 + 3 + 4 = 19$$

Notice that $n \neq 3$ is specified in the hypothesis.

$$n = 2 \qquad 10 \leq 4 + 2 + 4 = 10$$
$$n = 1 \qquad 5 \leq 1 + 1 + 4 = 6$$

For $n \neq 3$,

$$2 \leq a_2 - 1 \leq 2^{n-1}$$

Since $a_1 \leq a_2$, also

$$2 \leq a_1 - 1 \leq 2^{n-1}$$

That is, these numbers lie between some powers of 2 in the set

$$2, \ldots, 2^{n-1}$$

Suppose
$$2^{q-1} < a_1 - 1 \leq 2^q$$
$$2^{p-1} < a_2 - 1 \leq 2^p \qquad \text{where } q \leq p \leq n - 1$$

Allow a flow from 2^q to 2^{q-1} until one of them reaches $a_1 - 1$ and the other reaches some number R. Then allow a flow from 2^p to 2^{p-1} until one of them reaches $a_2 - 1$ and the other reaches some number S. We now have

		L						
$a_1 - 1$	1	$2, 4, \ldots, 2^{q-2}, R, 2^{q+1},$	$\ldots, 2^{p-1},$	$2^p,$	$2^{p+1}, \ldots, 2^{n-1}$
1	$a_2 - 1$	$2, 4, \ldots, 2^{q-2}, 2^{q-1}, 2^q,$	$\ldots, 2^{p-2},$	$S,$	$2^{p+1}, \ldots, 2^{n-1}$
a_1	a_2	$4, 8, \ldots, 2^{q-1}, (R + 2^{q-1})$	$,$	$3 \cdot 2^{p-2}, (2^p + S), 2^{p+2}, \cdots, 2^n$
		L'						

Let (h_i) be the sequence

$$h_1, \ldots, h_{n-2}$$
$$= 4, 8, \ldots, 2^{q-1}, (R + 2^{q-1}), 3 \cdot 2^q, \ldots, 3 \cdot 2^{p-2}, (2^p + S), 2^{p+2}, \ldots, 2^n$$
$$\ 1\ 2 \qquad\quad q-2 \quad\ q-1 \qquad q \qquad\quad p-2\ \ p-1 \quad p \qquad\qquad n-2$$

The numbers appearing under the (h_i) index the terms in the sequence. Since there are no ones to the right of $L - L'$ and the terms are ordered, the proof will be complete if we can show

$$\sum_{j=1}^{i} h_j \leq \sum_{j=3}^{i+2} a_j \qquad i = 1, \ldots, n - 2$$

because then $a_3, a_4, \ldots, a_n = [\![h_1, \ldots, h_{n-2}]\!]$. Unfortunately, we must consider three cases:

CASE A. $i \leq q - 2$

$$\sum_{j=1}^{i} h_j = 4 + 8 + \cdots + 2^{i+1} = 4(1 + 2 + \cdots + 2^{i-1}) = 4(2^i - 1)$$

$$\sum_{j=3}^{i+2} a_j \geq i a_2 \geq i 2^{p-1} \geq i 2^{q-1} \qquad \text{since } p \geq q$$

Thus
$$\sum_{j=1}^{i} h_j \leq \sum_{j=3}^{i+2} a_j$$

iff
$$4(2^i - 1) \leq i 2^{q-1}$$

Take $i = q - 2$ for the worst case.   Then

$$4(2^{q-2} - 1) = 2^q - 4 \leq q 2^{q-1} - 2^q \qquad \text{or} \qquad 2^{q+1} \leq q 2^{q-1} + 4$$

This is clearly true for $q \geq 4$. We enumerate the cases when $q = 1, 2, 3$:

$$\begin{aligned}
q &= 1 & 4 &\leq 1 + 4 = 5 \\
q &= 2 & 8 &\leq 4 + 4 = 8 \\
q &= 3 & 16 &\leq 12 + 4 = 16
\end{aligned}$$

This completes Case A.

CASE B. $q - 1 \leq i \leq p - 2$.   Now,

$$\sum_{j=1}^{i} h_j = 4(2^{q-2} - 1) + (2^{q-1} + R) + 3 \cdot 2^q (2^{i-q+1} - 1)$$

$$= 3 \cdot 2^{i+1} - 4 - 3 \cdot 2^{q-1} + R$$

$$< 3 \cdot 2^{i+1} - 4 - 2^{q-1}$$

since $R < 2^q$.   Note that the first term of the a sequence is $4 = 2^2$ and that $q - 1 \geq 2$. Thus

$$\sum_{j=1}^{i} h_j < 3 \cdot 2^{i+1} - 4 - 4 = 3 \cdot 2^{i+1} - 8$$

Now compute

$$\sum_{j=3}^{i+2} a_j \geq i a_3 \geq i a_2 \geq i(2^{p-1} + 2)$$

because
$$a_2 - 1 > 2^{p-1} \qquad \text{or} \qquad a_2 \geq 2^{p-1} + 2$$

This case will be concluded if we can show that

$$3 \cdot 2^{i+1} - 8 \le i(2^{p-1} + 2)$$

Choosing $i = p - 2$,

$$3 \cdot 2^{p-1} - 8 \le (p - 2)(2^{p-1} + 2)$$

This is equivalent to

$$3 \cdot 2^{p-1} - 8 \le p \cdot 2^{p-1} - 2^p + 2p - 4$$

or
$$5 \cdot 2^{p-1} \le p \cdot 2^{p-1} + 2p + 4$$

This is clearly true for $p \ge 5$. As before, the other cases are enumerated.

$$
\begin{array}{rl}
p = 4 & 40 \le 32 + 12 = 44 \\
p = 3 & 20 \le 12 + 10 = 22 \\
p = 2 & 10 \le 4 + 8 = 12 \\
p = 1 & 5 \le 1 + 6 = 7
\end{array}
$$

This completes the proof of Case B.

CASE C. $p - 1 \le i \le n - 2$.

$$\sum_{j=1}^{i} h_j = 4(2^{q-2} - 1) + (2^{q-1} + R) + 3 \cdot 2^q(2^{p-q-1} - 1) + (2^p + S) + 2^{p+2}(2^{i-p+1} - 1)$$

$$= 2^q - 4 + 2^{q-1} + (3 \cdot 2^{q-1} - a_1 + 1) + 3 \cdot 2^{p-1} - 3 \cdot 2^q$$
$$+ 2^p + (3 \cdot 2^{p-1} - a_2 + 1) + 2^{p+2}(2^{i-p+1} - 1)$$

In the last equation we used the results

$$2^q + 2^{q-1} = a_1 - 1 + R \qquad 2^p + 2^{p-1} = a_2 - 1 + S$$

$$\sum_{j=1}^{i} h_j = 3 \cdot 2^q - 2 - a_1 - a_2 - 3 \cdot 2^q + 3 \cdot 2^p + 2^p + 2^{p+2}(2^{i-p+1} - 1)$$

$$= -2 - a_1 - a_2 + 2^{p+2} + 2^{i+1} - 2^{p+2}$$
$$= 2^{i+1} - a_1 - a_2 - 2$$

Now we compute

$$\sum_{j=3}^{i+2} a_j = \left(\sum_{j=1}^{i+2} a_j \right) - a_1 - a_2 \ge 2 + 4 + \cdots + 2^{i+2} - a_1 - a_2 \ge 2(2^{i+2} - 1)$$

$$- a_1 - a_2 = 2^{i+3} - a_1 - a_2 - 2$$

Clearly, $2^{i+3} - a_1 - a_2 - 2 \ge 2^{i+1} - a_1 - a_2 - 2$, so we are done with Case C. |

Finally, the main result is obtained.

Theorem 8.   There is a folded tree with contact distribution $a_1, a_2, \ldots,$ $a_n = [\![1,2, \ldots, 2^{n-1}]\!]$. In particular, an almost uniform distribution is possible.

PROOF.   The argument is an induction on n.

INDUCTION STEP.   Assume that we can get any distribution from $1, 2, \ldots,$ 2^{n-1} for the network $N_F(n)$. Let us construct $N_F(n + 1)$, and let the $n + 1$ variables be $x_1, \ldots, x_{n+1}$. Let x_1 be assigned to the first position in the network. The remaining contacts, which have an associated sequence $a_2, \ldots, a_{n+1} = [\![2, \ldots, 2^n]\!]$,

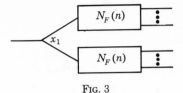

FIG. 3

can be decomposed into

$$a_i = b_i + c_i \qquad i = 2, \ldots, n+1$$

with
$$b_1, \ldots, b_n = [\![1, 2, \ldots, 2^{n-1}]\!]$$

and
$$c_1, \ldots, c_n = [\![1, 2, \ldots, 2^{n-1}]\!]$$

The induction hypothesis guarantees that (b_i) and (c_i) can have any desired distribution obtained from $2, \ldots, 2^{n-1}$.

Thus any desired distribution $a_1, \ldots, a_{n+1} = [\![1, 2, \ldots, 2^n]\!]$ may be obtained for $N_F(n+1)$, and the result follows by the induction principle. $N_F(n+1)$ looks like Fig. 3. ▌

We have shown that the contact loading can be adjusted until it is almost uniform. We can never do anything about the one in the (a_i) sequence. See Table 1 for a list of distributions for a few values of n.

TABLE 1

**Best Distributions of Contacts
in $N_F(n)$**

n	
1	1
2	1, 2
3	1, $(3)^2$
4	1, 4, $(5)^2$
5	1, $(7)^2$, $(8)^2$
6	1, $(12)^3$, $(13)^2$
7	1, $(21)^6$
8	1, $(36)^5$, $(37)^2$
9	1, $(63)^2$, $(64)^6$
10	1, $(113)^4$, $(114)^5$
11	1, $(204)^4$, $(206)^6$
12	1, $(372)^9$, $(373)^2$
13	1, $(682)^6$, $(683)^6$
14	1, $(1260)^{11}$, $(1261)^2$
15	1, $(2340)^8$, $(2341)^6$
16	1, (4368), $(4369)^{14}$
17	1, $(8191)^2$, $(8192)^{14}$
18	1, $(15420)^{15}$, $(15421)^2$
19	1, $(29127)^{18}$
20	1, $(55188)^{17}$, $(55189)^2$

The notation 1, 4, $(5)^2$ means 1, 4, 5, 5.

PROBLEMS

1. Strengthen Lemma 7 by working out the case $n = 3$.

2. Show that $2^n \equiv 2 \bmod (n - 1)$ is a necessary and sufficient condition for $n - 1$ relays to be evenly loaded in $N_F(n)$. [As usual we can not do anything about the one in (a_i) sequence.]

3. (a) Show that $2^n \equiv 2 \bmod 2$ implies $n \equiv 1 \bmod 2$.
   (b) Show that $2^n \equiv 2 \bmod 2$ implies $2||(n - 1)$, (that is, $2|n - 1$, but $2^2 \nmid n - 1$).
   (c) Show that $2^n \equiv 2 \bmod 2$ implies $n \equiv 3 \bmod 4$.
   (d) Show that there exist composite solutions of the congruence.

4. Investigate the following conjectures about the congruence of Prob. 3.
   (a) $n = 1 + 2 \cdot 3^i$ for $i > 1$ implies $2^n \equiv 2 \bmod (n - 1)$.
   (b) $2^n \equiv 2 \bmod (n - 1)$ implies $n \equiv 1 \bmod 6$.

5. Derive an algorithm for determining where the contacts are placed in an $N_F(n)$ network with a given allowable distribution.

6. (Fielder) Show that the best possible distribution in $N_F(n)$ is given by 1, p^{n-1-a}, $(p + 1)^a$, where $p(a)$ is the integer (fractional) part of $(2^n - 2)/(n - 1)$.

4 LUPANOV TREES

It is possible to construct complete fundamental networks which use fewer than the $2(2^n - 1)$ elements required in the folded-tree construction. The construction of these networks will now be discussed, and the trees which emerge from the discussion will be called Lupanov trees after O. B. Lupanov,[2] who is responsible for this construction.

Definition 1. A *solid sphere* on the n cube is defined to be the union of the set of points of an ordinary sphere with one of the centers of the sphere.

EXAMPLE. If $n = 3$, one sphere with radius 1 and center $(0,0,0)$ is

$$K_1{}^{(0,0,0)} = \{(0,0,1), (0,1,0), (1,0,0)\}$$

A solid sphere of radius 1 and center $(0,0,0)$ is

$$\{(0,0,0), (0,0,1), (1,0,0), (0,1,0)\}$$

Lemma 2. (Hamming) The n cube may be subdivided into at most $[2^n/(n + 1)]$ disjoint solid spheres of radius 1.

PROOF.   Any sphere of radius 1 has n points; so the corresponding solid sphere has $n + 1$ points. Since the n cube has 2^n vertices, there are at most $[2^n/(n + 1)]$ disjoint solid spheres.   **|**

Lemma 2 is reworked slightly in the following lemma, which is due to Lupanov.

Lemma 3. If $n = 2^k$ for some $k \geq 1$, then the n cube may be subdivided into $2^n/n$ nonintersecting spheres of radius 1.

PROOF. The argument will be an induction on n.

BASIS. $n = 2$. There are two disjoint spheres on the square; this disposes of the basis step of the proof.

INDUCTION STEP. Consider a cube of dimension $n - 1$. This cube contains $2^{n-1}/n$ disjoint solid spheres of radius 1 by Hamming's lemma. The centers c_i are given by

$$c_i = (c_{i1}, \ldots, c_{i\,n-1}) \qquad i = 1, \ldots, \frac{2^{n-1}}{n}$$

Consider the unit spheres on the n cube having centers

$$c_i = \{(c_{i1}, \ldots, c_{i\,n-1}, x)\} \qquad x \in \{0,1\} \text{ and } i = 1, \ldots, \frac{2^{n-1}}{n}$$

Constructing a unit sphere about each center gives us our $2^n/n$ spheres, but we must show that these spheres are disjoint. Let $K_1^{c_1}$ and $K_1^{c_2}$ be two intersecting spheres of radius 1 and centers c_1 and c_2, respectively. Assume $c_1 \neq c_2$. The last coordinate of c_1 and c_2 must be different. If it were the same, then there would be two nondisjoint solid spheres, contradicting Hamming's lemma and the choice of the c_i. Assume $c_{1n} = 0$ and $c_{2n} = 1$, and let $z \in K_1^{c_1} \cap K_1^{c_2}$. Thus $d(z,c_1) = d(z,c_2) = 1$. If the last coordinate of z is zero, then z and c_1 must disagree in some other coordinate because $d(z,c_1) = 1$, but this would imply $d(z,c_2) \geq 2$, which contradicts $d(z,c_2) = 1$. If the last coordinate of z is 1, a symmetric argument works. **|**

Before defining the Lupanov tree network, it is necessary to prove a lemma regarding the elementary symmetric functions realized by the spheres.

Lemma 4. If $\beta_1(x_1, \ldots, x_n)$ is the characteristic function of a sphere of radius 1 with center $c = (c_1, \ldots, c_n)$, then

$$x_i^{\bar{c}_i} \beta_1(x_1, \ldots, x_n) = x_1^{c_1} \cdots x_{i-1}^{c_{i-1}} x_i^{\bar{c}_i} x_{i+1}^{c_{i+1}} \cdots x_n^{c_n}$$

$$\text{for } i = 1, \ldots, n$$

where

$$\bar{c}_i = \begin{cases} 1 & \text{if } c_i = 0 \\ 0 & \text{if } c_i = 1 \end{cases} \quad \text{and} \quad x_j^{c_j} = \begin{cases} \bar{x}_j & \text{if } c_j = 0 \\ x_j & \text{if } c_j = 1 \end{cases}$$

PROOF. $\beta_1(x_1, \ldots, x_n)$ is 1 when and only when its arguments are n-tuples b of 0's and 1's such that $d(c,b) = 1$. This function is written in expanded normal form as a sum of n terms. If $c_i = 0$, then variable x_i appears uncomplemented in one and only one term. In this case, multiplication of β by x_i yields the term $x_1^{c_1} \cdots x_{i-1}^{c_{i-1}} x_i x_{i+1}^{c_{i+1}} \cdots x_n^{c_n}$. Since the distance from the center to this point must be 1, all other components must agree. If $c_i = 1$, then $\bar{x}_i \beta$ gives the only term in which x_i appears complemented. Again other components must agree to give the proper distance relation. **|**

Definition 5. A *Lupanov tree with n variables* is denoted by $N_L(n)$ and is defined as follows. Let r be a natural number such that $1 \leq r \leq n$.

(1) The input node of the network is connected to a standard tree on r variables $N_T(r)$.

(2) Connect together the outputs of $N_T(r)$ which form disjoint spheres. There will be $2^r/r$ such outputs by Lemma 3.

(3) To each of the outputs, connect a $N_T(n-r)$ network in the variables $x_{r+1}, \ldots, x_n$.

(4) To every output of the $N_T(n-r)$ trees which are connected to a terminal associated with a sphere having center $(c_1, \ldots, c_r)$, connect a bundle of contacts $x_1^{c_1}, x_2^{c_2}, \ldots, x_r^{c_r}$.

A typical Lupanov tree is shown in Fig. 1. Notice that any choice of r will result in such a tree. We shall shortly learn the best choice to make.

Theorem 6. $N_L(n)$ is a complete fundamental network.

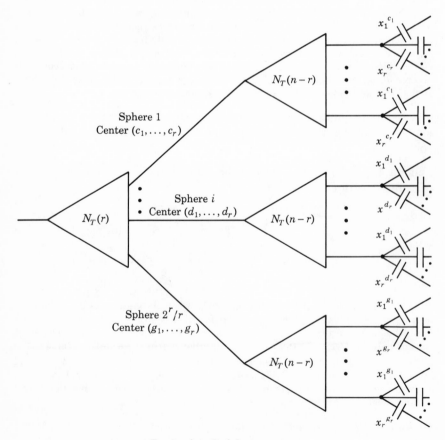

FIG. 1   A typical Lupanov tree.

PROOF. The network has

$$\frac{2^r}{r} \, 2^{n-r} r = 2^n$$

outputs.

A typical output of the first $N_T(r)$ network, associated with the sphere of center $(c_1, \ldots, c_r)$, will be called

$$\sigma(x_1, \ldots, x_r)$$

At the output of $N_T(n - r)$ which realizes $x_{r+1}^{i_{r+1}} \cdots x_n^{i_n}$ we have

$$\sigma(x_1, \ldots, x_r) \cdot x_{r+1}^{i_{r+1}} \cdots x_n^{i_n}$$

At the output of the entire network we get

$$\sigma(x_1, \ldots, x_r)(x_{r+1}^{i_{r+1}} \cdots x_n^{i_n}) x_j^{\bar{c}_i}$$

But $\sigma(x_1, \ldots, x_r) x_j^{\bar{c}_i} = x_1^{c_1} \cdots x_{j-1}^{c_{j-1}} x_j^{\bar{c}_i} \cdots x_r^{c_r}$
Thus a typical output is

$$x_1^{c_1} \cdots x_{j-1}^{c_{j-1}} x_j^{\bar{c}_i} \cdots x_r^{c_r} x_{r+1}^{i_{r+1}} \cdots x_n^{i_n}$$

The i's range over all 2^r possible values. As j goes from 1 through r, all combinations $x_j^{c_i} \sigma(x_1, \ldots, x_r)$ go through all combinations of minterms on the variables $x_1, \ldots, x_r$. $\blacksquare$

Definition 7. Let $\eta(n)$ denote the *least* number of contacts required to realize a complete fundamental network of n variables.

Proposition 8. $2^n \le \eta(n) \le 2^{n+1} - 2$

PROOF. The lower bound is obvious, and the upper bound comes from the complete tree. $\blacksquare$

It will be shown that, for large n, the Lupanov tree is more economical than the standard tree.

Theorem 9. $N_L(n)$ uses at most $\dfrac{2^{n+1}}{n} + \dfrac{2^{n+2}}{n - \log_2 n} + 2^n$ contacts.

PROOF. In step 1 of the construction we use a $N_T(r)$ network which requires $< 2^{r+1}$ contacts. In steps 2 and 3 we use $(2^r/r) N_T(n - r)$ networks. This requires

$$\frac{2^r}{r} (2^{n-r+1} - 2) < \frac{2^{n+1}}{r} \text{ contacts}$$

Step 4 requires $\dfrac{2^r}{r} \cdot 2^{n-r} \cdot r = 2^n$ contacts. The total number of contacts will be called $f_r(n)$ and is

$$f_r(n) < 2^{r+1} + \frac{2^{n+1}}{r} + 2^n$$

Select

$$r = 2^{[\log_2(n - \log_2 n)]} \le n - \log_2 n$$

or

$$2^{r+1} \le \frac{2^{n+1}}{n}$$

$$f_r(n) \le \frac{2^{n+1}}{n} + 2^n + \frac{2^{n+1}}{r}$$

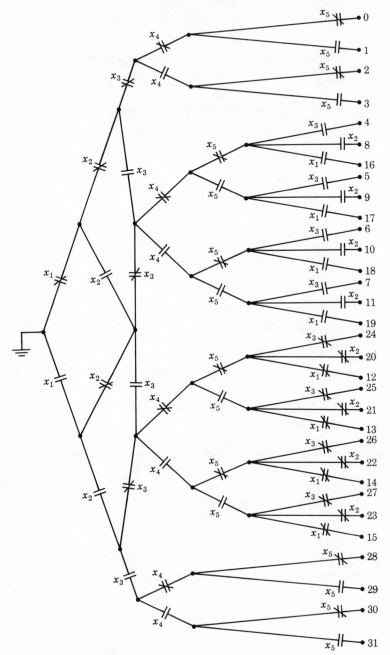

FIG. P3   A fundamental network of five variables using 60 elements. The decimal number at each output denotes the minterm realized.

To obtain a lower bound on r, take

$$r \geq \frac{n - \log_2 n}{2}$$

$$f(n) \leq \frac{2^{n+1}}{n} + 2^n + \frac{2^{n+2}}{n - \log_2 n} \quad \blacksquare$$

Corollary 10. $\eta(n) \sim 2^n$

PROOF. For all n, $\eta(n) \geq 2^n$ has already been established. From Theorem 9

$$\frac{2^{n+1}}{n} + 2^n + \frac{2^{n+2}}{n - \log_2 n} = 2^n \left(1 + \frac{2}{n} + \frac{4}{n - \log_2 n} \right)$$

$$= 2^n \left(1 + O\left(\frac{1}{n}\right) \right) = 2^n (1 + o(1))$$

Thus
$$\eta(n) \sim 2^n \quad \blacksquare$$

Corollary 10 shows what may be a surprising result: One can cut down the number of contacts in a complete fundamental network by a factor of 2 over the requirements of a complete tree. There is, of course, a price to be paid for the savings in contacts. In general, the Lupanov trees are not disjunctive networks, which means that they are unsuitable for certain constructions.

PROBLEMS

1. If you know coding theory, what is the connection between disjoint (solid) spheres and error-correcting codes?

2. Show that the n cube has at most $\left[2^n / \binom{n}{k} + 1 \right]$ disjoint solid spheres of radius k.

3. Construct $N_L(5)$. Taking $r = 2$, the network should use 66 elements by the construction. Can you eliminate six contacts to obtain the network shown in Fig. P3? Can you find a sneak path and thus show that the network in Fig. P3 is not disjunctive?

5 A UNIVERSAL NETWORK AND SHANNON'S SYNTHESIS METHOD

It is necessary to construct a universal network for the functions of two variables. This network can be used for synthesizing arbitrary functions of n variables.

Definition 1. Let $N_U(n)$ denote any 2^{2^n}-input single-output circuit which realizes every switching function of n variables as one of (and only one of) its transmission functions. Let $\tau(n)$ be the least number of elements required to realize $N_U(n)$.

Theorem 2. $2^{2^n} - 2 \leq \tau(n) \leq 2 \cdot 2^{2^n}$

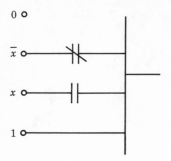

FIG. 1

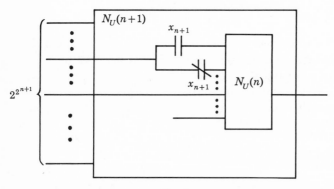

FIG. 2

PROOF. The argument will be an induction on n.

BASIS. $n = 1$. Four functions of one variable are realized by the network of Fig. 1, which uses $2 \leq 8$ contacts.

INDUCTION STEP. Assume $N_U(n)$ uses at most $2 \cdot 2^{2^n}$ contacts. The construction will be to use $N_U(n)$ to get all the functions of n variables which occur as functions of $n + 1$ variables and to construct the functions of precisely $n + 1$ variables from those n variables. $N_U(n + 1)$ will look like the network shown in Fig. 2. The functions of $n + 1$ variables are of two types: those which depend on at most n variables and those which depend on precisely $n + 1$ variables.

CASE I. If $f(x_1, \ldots, x_{n+1})$ depends on at most n variables, it is available in $N_U(n)$.

CASE II. If $f(x_1, \ldots, x_{n+1})$ depends on precisely $n + 1$ variables, we form

$$f(x_1, \ldots, x_{n+1}) = x_{n+1}f(x_1, \ldots, x_n, 1) + \bar{x}_{n+1}f(x_1, \ldots, x_n, 0)$$

where $f(x_1, \ldots, x_n, 1)$ and $f(x_1, \ldots, x_n, 0)$ are functions of n variables which are available from $N_U(n)$. Starting from $N_U(n)$, it costs two contacts for every function in this class, and there are $2^{2^{n+1}} - 2^{2^n}$ functions in this class. We therefore require for $N_U(n + 1)$ at most

$$2(2^{2^{n+1}} - 2^{2^n}) + 2 \cdot 2^{2^n} = 2 \cdot 2^{2^{n+1}} \text{ contacts}$$

The lower bound is obvious. ∎

It is important to have the best possible realization for $N_U(2)$. The network shown in Fig. 3 is a minimal network. Note that this particular $N_U(2)$ uses 18 elements.

We shall now show that Fig. 3 is the best possible network for $N_U(2)$. The method of proof consists of replacing the contact network by the labeled graph. It will be shown that there must be ≥ 18 branches (elements) in the graph.

Lemma 3.   (Shannon†) Any network which realizes

$$f_1 = (x \equiv y) \qquad f_2 = x \oplus y$$
$$f_3 = x + y \qquad f_4 = \bar{x} + \bar{y}$$

has nullity μ such that $\mu \geq 4$.

PROOF.   Let P_i be the nodes at which f_i is realized ($i = 1, \ldots, 4$).   All branches incident to P_1 are divided into two classes: those labeled x or y or those labeled $\bar{x}$ and $\bar{y}$.

† Unpublished memo which is reproduced in Seshu and Reed.

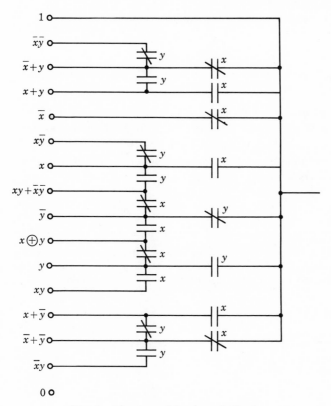

FIG. 3   A best possible network $N_U(2)$.

Clearly, both sets are nonempty, since $f_1(1,1) = 1$ and $f_1(0,0) = 1$. Thus the two distinct paths from output to P_1 constitute a circuit. If P_1 is split into two nodes, the nullity of the graph is reduced by 1, yet the realization of f_i ($i = 2, 3, 4$) is not changed. Clearly, no path from P_2 to the output went through P_1, since $f_1 f_2 = 0$ and f_2 is undisturbed. No path through P_3 or P_4 is involved, as a simple proof by contradiction shows.

A similar argument at the other terminals shows that the nullity of the graph can be reduced by 4. Since the nullity is a nonnegative integer,

$$\mu \geq 4 \quad \blacksquare$$

Theorem 4. (Shannon) The network shown in Fig. 3 is a minimal network for $N_U(2)$.

PROOF. Any universal network for $n = 2$ must contain the four functions denoted by $x \equiv y$, $x \oplus y$, $x + y$, $\bar{x} + \bar{y}$. Thus any network of this type has nullity μ where

$$\mu \geq 4$$

Since the number of edges e satisfies

$$e = \mu + v - p$$

where v is the number of vertices and p is the number of components,

$$e \geq v + 4 - 2 \geq 16 + 4 - 2 = 18 \quad \blacksquare$$

The network $N_U(n)$ can be used in synthesis, as indicated in the following theorem.

Theorem 5. Let M be a single-input n-output disjunctive network and let N be an n-input single-output network. Let M have have transmission functions u_{ak}, and let N have transmission functions v_{kb}, where $k = 1$, . . . , n. Then the single-input single-output network obtained by connecting M to N has transmission function

$$t_{ab} = \sum_{k=1}^{n} u_{ak} v_{kb}$$

PROOF. The picture is given by Fig. 4. We get t_{ab} by summing all possible paths from a to b. We classify each set of paths by the number of times a path crosses $L - L'$. Clearly, any path from a to b must cross $L - L'$ an odd number of times.

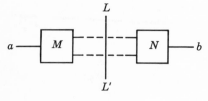

FIG. 4

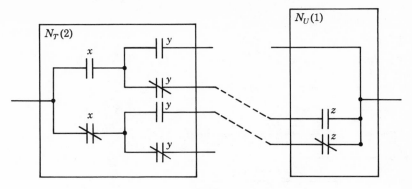

FIG. 5

The transmission function for the set of paths which cross $L - L'$ once is clearly $\sum_{k=1}^{n} u_{ak}v_{kb}$. The transmission function for any other set of paths is zero, since M is assumed to be disjunctive. $\blacksquare$

The importance of the previous theorem is that this technique gives a method for synthesizing any function of n variables.

Theorem 6. (Shannon) Any function of n variables may be realized by connecting together a $N_T(n - k)$ network and a $N_U(k)$ network. This holds for any k between zero and n.

PROOF. We expand any function f about $n - k$ variables to get

$$f(x_1, \ldots, x_n) = \sum_{i_1=0}^{1} \cdots \sum_{i_{n-k}=0}^{1} (x_1{}^{i_1} \cdots x_{n-k}{}^{i_{n-k}}) f(i_1, \ldots, i_{n-k}, x_{n-k+1}, \ldots, x_n)$$

(1)

where

$$x_j{}^{i_j} = \begin{cases} x_j & \text{if } i_j = 1 \\ \bar{x}_j & \text{if } i_j = 0 \end{cases}$$

The expressions $f(i_1, \ldots, i_{n-k}, x_{n-k+1}, \ldots, x_n)$ are functions of k variables and are available at the input of $N_U(k)$. The expressions $x_1{}^{i_1} \cdots x_{n-k}{}^{i_{n-k}}$ are all possible products of $n - k$ literals and are available at the output of $N_T(n - k)$. Since $N_T(n - k)$ is disjunctive, we apply the Theorem 5 to obtain the transmission function of f given in (1). $\blacksquare$

EXAMPLE. $n = 3, k = 1, f = x\bar{y}z + \bar{x}y\bar{z}$; see Fig. 5.

In general, this technique of synthesis leads to non-series-parallel networks and nonplanar networks.

PROBLEMS

1. Show that for any $\varepsilon > 0$ and n sufficiently large,

$$\tau(n) \leq (\tfrac{3}{2} - \varepsilon)2^{2^n}$$

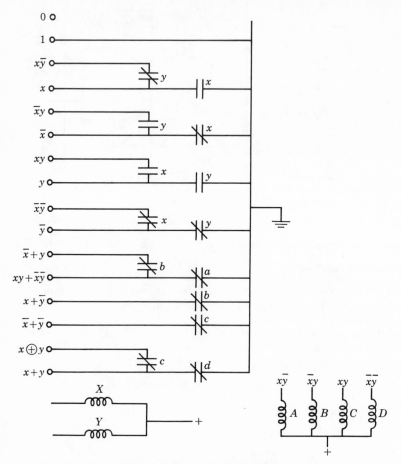

FIG. P2   The coils of A, B, C, and D are energized by the outputs $x\bar{y}$, $\bar{x}$, y, xy, and $\overline{xy}$, respectively.

2. (Kasay) Discuss the network in Fig. P2, which uses 14 contacts and is a $N_U(2)$ network. Can a better $N_U(2)$ network be constructed?

3. Use Theorem 6 to show that any function can be realized with $2^{n-1} + 16$ elements. (HINT: $k = 2$.)

4. Generalize Shannon's synthesis procedure, Theorem 6, to the following result. If M is a disjunctive (p,q) network with transmission functions u_{ij} between input i and output j and N is any (r,s) network with transmission functions v_{ij} between input i and output j, and if any output k of M is connected to one and only input $\tau(k)$, of N, then the transmission function of the resulting (p,s) network is

$$f_{ij} = \sum_{k=1}^{q} u_{ik} v_{\tau(k)j}$$

for $i = 1, \ldots, p$ and $j = 1, \ldots, s$.

5. (Yoeli[1]) Let N be a (p,q) network. Let $G_{11}(G_{12})$ be the square submatrix of the connection matrix of N corresponding to the input (output) terminals of N. Let G_{12} be the $p \times q$ matrix of transitions from inputs to outputs, and similarly for G_{21}. Let N_1 and N_2 be (p,q) and (q,r) networks, respectively, with matrices $G_{s,t}^{(i)}$. Show that connecting the outputs of N_1 to the inputs of N_2 gives a network N whose matrix G_{12} is given by

$$G_{12} = G_{12}^{(1)} \operatorname{adj} (G_{22}^{(1)} + G_{11}^{(2)})G_{12}^{(2)}$$

(HINT: Prob. 3-9.10)

6. Show by a counterexample that

$$G_{12} \neq G_{12}^{(1)}G_{12}^{(2)}$$

7. Discuss the case $p = r = 1$ with respect to Theorem 6.

8. In the special case $p = q = r = k$, does $G_{12} = G_{12}^{(1)}G_{12}^{(2)}$ hold?

6 A MORE GENERAL SYNTHESIS PROCEDURE

A new synthesis procedure is now given. This method has more theoretical importance than practical value. The theoretical implications will become clear presently.

A function of n variables is to be represented by a matrix (of the type used in Sec. 6.7) which has 2^k rows and 2^{n-k} columns for $0 \leq k \leq n$.

EXAMPLE. Consider $f(x_1,x_2,x_3,x_4) = x_1 \oplus x_2 \oplus x_3 \oplus x_4$. We choose $k = 2$. The matrix of the function f, denoted by $M(f)$, is given as

	x_3x_4			
	00	01	10	11
00	0	1	1	0
01	1	0	0	1
10	1	0	0	1
11	0	1	1	0

(rows labeled x_1x_2: 00, 01, 10, 11)

Let us arbitrarily partition the rows of $M(f)$ into p subsets $(1 \leq p \leq 2^k)$. Denote by $M(f_j)$ the $2^k \times 2^{n-k}$ matrix which is identical with the jth subset of $M(f)$ and zero elsewhere. Let us then partition the columns of the matrices $M(f_i)$ into groups of identical columns, letting $t(i)$ denote the number of such subsets. Clearly,

$$f_i(x_1, \ldots ,x_n) = \sum_{j=1}^{t(i)} f_{ij}(x_1, \ldots ,x_n) \qquad i = 1, \ldots , 2^k$$

where $f_{ij}(x_1, \ldots ,x_n)$ is the function which agrees with f_i in the jth group of columns and is equal to zero elsewhere.

Lemma 1. For any $0 \leq k \leq n$

$$f_{ij}(x_1, \ldots ,x_n) = f_{ij}^{(1)}(x_1, \ldots ,x_k)f_{ij}^{(2)}(x_{k+1}, \ldots ,x_n)$$

where
$$f_{ij}^{(1)}(x_1, \ldots ,x_k) = \Sigma x_1^{e_1} \cdots x_k^{e_k}$$

The summation is over the $(e_1, \ldots ,e_k)$'s corresponding to nonzero rows of $M(f_{ij})$ and

$$f_{ij}^{(2)}(x_{k+1}, \ldots ,x_n) = \Sigma x_{k+1}^{e_{k+1}} \cdots x_n^{e_n}$$

The summation is over the $(e_{k+1}, \ldots ,e_n)$'s corresponding to nonzero columns of $M(f_{ij})$.

PROOF. This is merely another form of the result about the existence of a normal form reworked to use the matrix specification of the function. **|**

EXAMPLE. For the parity function of four variables, we choose $p = 2$.

$$
\begin{array}{l}
\text{First subset} \\
\text{Second subset}
\end{array}
\left\{
\begin{array}{cccc}
0 & 1 & 1 & 0 \\
1 & 0 & 0 & 1 \\
1 & 0 & 0 & 1 \\
0 & 1 & 1 & 0
\end{array}
\right.
$$

Then
$$
M(f_1) =
\begin{bmatrix}
0 & 1 & 1 & 0 \\
1 & 0 & 0 & 1 \\
1 & 0 & 0 & 1 \\
0 & 0 & 0 & 0
\end{bmatrix}
\qquad
M(f_2) =
\begin{bmatrix}
0 & 0 & 0 & 0 \\
0 & 0 & 0 & 0 \\
0 & 0 & 0 & 0 \\
0 & 1 & 1 & 0
\end{bmatrix}
$$

$t_1 = 3$, $t_2 = 3$, so that partitioning yields

$$
M(f_1) =
\begin{bmatrix}
0 & 1 & 1 & 0 \\
1 & 0 & 0 & 1 \\
1 & 0 & 0 & 1 \\
0 & 0 & 0 & 0
\end{bmatrix}
\quad \text{and} \quad
M(f_2) =
\begin{bmatrix}
0 & 0 & 0 & 0 \\
0 & 0 & 0 & 0 \\
0 & 0 & 0 & 0 \\
0 & 1 & 1 & 0
\end{bmatrix}
$$

$$f_{11} = (\bar{x}_1 x_2 + x_1 \bar{x}_2)\bar{x}_3 \bar{x}_4$$
$$f_{12} = \bar{x}_1 \bar{x}_2 (\bar{x}_3 x_4 + x_3 \bar{x}_4)$$
$$f_{13} = (\bar{x}_1 x_2 + x_1 \bar{x}_2)x_3 x_4$$

Finally,

$$f_1 = f_{11} + f_{12} + f_{13} = \bar{x}_1 x_2 \bar{x}_3 \bar{x}_4 + x_1 \bar{x}_2 \bar{x}_3 \bar{x}_4 + \bar{x}_1 \bar{x}_2 \bar{x}_3 x_4 + \bar{x}_1 \bar{x}_2 x_3 \bar{x}_4$$
$$+ \bar{x}_1 x_2 x_3 x_4 + x_1 \bar{x}_2 x_3 x_4$$

that is, f has index set $I = \{1,2,4,7,8,11\}$

$$f_{21} = f_{23} = 0 \qquad \text{and} \qquad f_{22} = x_1 x_2 (\bar{x}_3 x_4 + x_3 \bar{x}_4) = f_2$$

The decomposition guaranteed by Lemma 1 is evident in the form of the f_{ij}.

Definition 2. A function $f(x_1, \ldots, x_n)$ is said to have a *proper represen-*
tation iff

$$f(x_1, \ldots, x_n) = \sum_{i=1}^{p} \sum_{j=1}^{t(i)} f_{ij}^{(1)}(x_1, \ldots, x_k)f_{ij}^{(2)}(x_{k+1}, \ldots, x_n)$$

where the partitions $A_1, \ldots, A_p$ have an identical number of rows s
with the exception of one subset which may have a smaller number of
rows. k and s are said to be the *parameters* of this proper representation.

Theorem 3. Every function has a proper representation.

PROOF. Use the lemma and take any pair of integers such that $2^k = ps + q$, where
$0 \leq q < p$. One can simply choose any s such that $1 \leq s \leq 2^k$; then p and q are
uniquely determined by Theorem 1-8.5. |

The general method of construction is as follows:

Algorithm 4 (Lupanov[1])

(1) Given a function f of n variables, choose a proper representation
   of p subsets where each subset except possibly one has s elements.
(2) Form p Lupanov trees, $N_L(n - k)$, in the variables $x_{k+1}, \ldots,$
   x_n.
(3) Partition the outputs of $N_L(n - k)$ into spheres. (The number
   of spheres depends on the parameter r, as in Sec. 4.)
(4) To each output connect $f_{ij}^{(1)}(x_1, \ldots, x_k)$.

Theorem 5. Every function of n variables can be realized by Algorithm 4.

PROOF. The algorithm is simply a mechanization of Theorem 3. |

A general network is shown in Fig. 1.

Theorem 6. The number of contacts required to realize a function of n
variables is at most $g(k,s,r)$, where

$$g(k,s,r) = \left(\frac{2^k}{s} + 1\right)\left(2^{n-k} + 2^{r+1} + \frac{2^{n-k+1}}{r} + \frac{sk2^{s+r}}{r}\right)$$

PROOF. There are $2^{r+1} + 2^{n-k} + 2^{n-k+1}/r$ contacts in each $N_L(n - k)$ network
(Theorem 4.9), and there are p such networks, where

$$p = \left[\frac{2^k}{s}\right] < \frac{2^k}{s} + 1$$

Thus $(2^k/s + 1)(2^{r+1} + 2^{n-k} + 2^{n-k+1}/r)$ elements are needed just for realizing the
trees.

Each tree has $(2^r/r)$ distinct outputs, and there are at most 2^s different functions
$f_{ij}^{(1)}(x_1, \ldots, x_k)$. Each of these functions will require at most $s \cdot k$ elements, since
one might begin from the expanded normal form, and each such function has weight s.

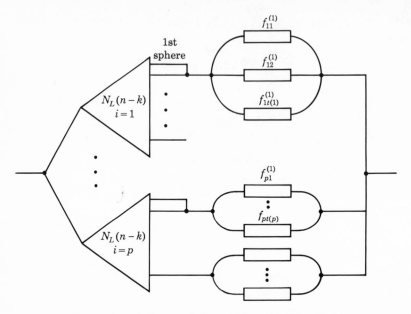

FIG. 1   A typical network for realizing Algorithm 4.

Thus there are

$$\frac{2^r}{r} \cdot 2^s sk = \frac{sk2^{r+s}}{r}$$

elements associated with every tree.

Adding these results gives the theorem. **∎**

EXAMPLE.   The synthesis procedure is illustrated by the function

$$f(x_1,x_2,x_3,x_4,x_5) = x_1x_2x_3x_4\bar{x}_5 + \bar{x}_1x_2\bar{x}_3x_4x_5 + \bar{x}_2\bar{x}_3\bar{x}_4x_5 + x_2x_3\bar{x}_4\bar{x}_5 + x_2x_3\bar{x}_4x_5$$
$$+ \bar{x}_1\bar{x}_2x_3x_4 + x_1\bar{x}_2\bar{x}_3x_4 + x_1\bar{x}_3\bar{x}_4x_5$$

$$M(f) = \begin{bmatrix} 0 & 1 \\ 0 & 0 \\ 1 & 0 \\ 1 & 1 \\ 0 & 0 \\ \hline 0 & 1 \\ 0 & 1 \\ 0 & 0 \\ 0 & 1 \\ 1 & 1 \\ \hline 1 & 0 \\ 0 & 0 \\ 0 & 1 \\ 0 & 0 \\ 0 & 1 \\ \hline 1 & 0 \end{bmatrix}$$

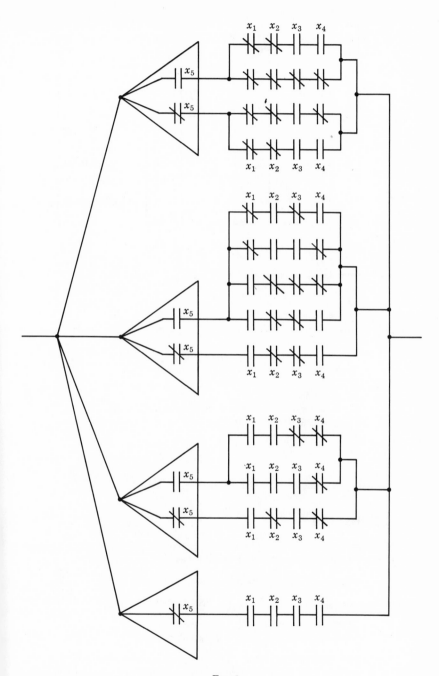

F<small>IG</small>. 2

$$M(f_1) = \begin{bmatrix} 0 & 1 \\ 0 & 0 \\ 1 & 0 \\ 1 & 1 \\ 0 & 0 \\ \hline 0 & 0 \\ 0 & 0 \\ 0 & 0 \\ 0 & 0 \\ 0 & 0 \\ \hline 0 & 0 \\ 0 & 0 \\ 0 & 0 \\ 0 & 0 \\ 0 & 0 \\ 0 & 0 \end{bmatrix} \quad M(f_2) = \begin{bmatrix} 0 & 0 \\ 0 & 0 \\ 0 & 0 \\ 0 & 0 \\ 0 & 0 \\ \hline 0 & 1 \\ 0 & 1 \\ 0 & 0 \\ 0 & 1 \\ 1 & 1 \\ \hline 0 & 0 \\ 0 & 0 \\ 0 & 0 \\ 0 & 0 \\ 0 & 0 \\ 0 & 0 \end{bmatrix} \quad M(f_3) = \begin{bmatrix} 0 & 0 \\ 0 & 0 \\ 0 & 0 \\ 0 & 0 \\ 0 & 0 \\ \hline 0 & 0 \\ 0 & 0 \\ 0 & 0 \\ 0 & 0 \\ 0 & 0 \\ \hline 1 & 0 \\ 0 & 0 \\ 0 & 1 \\ 0 & 0 \\ 0 & 1 \\ 0 & 0 \end{bmatrix} \quad M(f_4) = \begin{bmatrix} 0 & 0 \\ 0 & 0 \\ 0 & 0 \\ 0 & 0 \\ 0 & 0 \\ \hline 0 & 0 \\ 0 & 0 \\ 0 & 0 \\ 0 & 0 \\ 0 & 0 \\ \hline 0 & 0 \\ 0 & 0 \\ 0 & 0 \\ 0 & 0 \\ 0 & 0 \\ 1 & 0 \end{bmatrix}$$

and

$$f_{11}{}^{(1)} = \bar{x}_1\bar{x}_2x_3\bar{x}_4 + \bar{x}_1\bar{x}_2x_3x_4 \qquad\qquad f_{11}{}^{(2)} = \bar{x}_5$$
$$f_{21}{}^{(1)} = x_1\bar{x}_2\bar{x}_3x_4 \qquad\qquad f_{21}{}^{(2)} = \bar{x}_5$$
$$f_{31}{}^{(1)} = x_1\bar{x}_2x_3\bar{x}_4 \qquad\qquad f_{31}{}^{(2)} = \bar{x}_5$$
$$f_{41}{}^{(1)} = x_1x_2x_3x_4 \qquad\qquad f_{41}{}^{(2)} = \bar{x}_5$$
$$f_{12}{}^{(1)} = \bar{x}_1\bar{x}_2\bar{x}_3\bar{x}_4 + \bar{x}_1\bar{x}_2x_3x_4 \qquad\qquad f_{12}{}^{(2)} = x_5$$
$$f_{22}{}^{(1)} = \bar{x}_1x_2\bar{x}_3x_4 + \bar{x}_1x_2x_3\bar{x}_4 + x_1\bar{x}_2\bar{x}_3\bar{x}_4 + x_1\bar{x}_2\bar{x}_3x_4 \qquad\qquad f_{22}{}^{(2)} = x_5$$
$$f_{32}{}^{(1)} = x_1x_2\bar{x}_3\bar{x}_4 + x_1x_2x_3\bar{x}_4 \qquad\qquad f_{32}{}^{(2)} = x_5$$
$$f_{42}{}^{(1)} = f_{42}{}^{(2)} = 0$$

so that

$$f_{11} = (\bar{x}_1\bar{x}_2x_3\bar{x}_4 + \bar{x}_1\bar{x}_2x_3x_4)\bar{x}_5$$
$$f_{12} = (\bar{x}_1\bar{x}_2\bar{x}_3\bar{x}_4 + \bar{x}_1\bar{x}_2x_3x_4)x_5$$
$$f_{21} = x_1\bar{x}_2\bar{x}_3x_4\bar{x}_5$$
$$f_{22} = (\bar{x}_1x_2\bar{x}_3x_4 + \bar{x}_1x_2x_3\bar{x}_4 + x_1\bar{x}_2\bar{x}_3\bar{x}_4 + x_1\bar{x}_2\bar{x}_3x_4)x_5$$
$$f_{31} = x_1\bar{x}_2x_3\bar{x}_4\bar{x}_5$$
$$f_{32} = (x_1x_2\bar{x}_3\bar{x}_4 + x_1x_2x_3\bar{x}_4)x_5$$
$$f_{41} = x_1x_2x_3x_4\bar{x}_5$$
$$f_{42} = 0$$

The resulting network is sketched in Fig. 2.

PROBLEMS

1. (Ninomiya[3]) The following synthesis procedure is called the *sandwich method.* Expand a given function f of 4 variables as

$$f(x_1, x_2, \ldots, x_4) = \bar{x}_1\bar{x}_2v_0 + \bar{x}_1x_2v_1 + x_1\bar{x}_2v_2 + x_1x_2v_3$$

The method is to use the network of Fig. P1. Show that a sneak path exists unless

$$\bar{x}_1\bar{x}_2v_1v_2v_3 \leq f \qquad \bar{x}_1x_2v_0v_2v_3 \leq f$$
$$x_1\bar{x}_2v_0v_1v_3 \leq f \qquad x_1x_2v_0v_1v_2 \leq f$$

2. (Ninomiya[3]) Synthesize $f(x_1, x_2, x_3, x_4) = x_2\bar{x}_3\bar{x}_4 + x_1\bar{x}_3x_4 + x_1x_3\bar{x}_4 + x_3x_4(x_1 \equiv x_2)$ by using the sandwich method. (One can do it with nine contacts by utilizing a sneak path.)

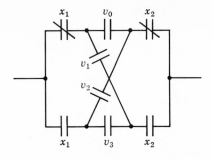

FIG. P1

3. Show that every ρ-symmetric function (Sec. 6-5) can be realized as follows: Use a symmetric function lattice for each block ρ_k to realize the elementary symmetric functions. These networks feed secondary coils which have make contacts arranged in a tree. See Fig. P3. Show that the number of contacts required is at most

$$\prod_{i=1}^{k} (r_i + 1) + \sum_{i=1}^{k} r_i(r_i + 1)$$

where $r_i = |\rho_i|$.

4. In the following sequence of problems, the techniques for synthesis by boolean matrices are derived. Show that if A and B are $k \times k$ connection matrices,

$$A \leq \chi(B) \qquad \text{iff} \qquad \chi(A) \leq \chi(B)$$

5. Show that if A and B are connection matrices, then $A \leq B$ implies $\chi(A) \leq \chi(B)$.

6. (Lunts[1]) Show that if $\chi(B) \leq \chi(C) \leq \chi(A)$, then $\chi(A) = \chi[(A*\bar{B}) + C]$.

7. Show that if $\chi(A) = \chi(B)$, where $A \leq C \leq B$, then
$$\chi(A) = \chi(C)$$
$$\chi(A) = \chi(A + B)$$
$$\chi(A) = \chi(AB)$$

EXAMPLE. (Elgot[2]) The general method proceeds as follows: Given $\chi(A)$, choose a matrix Y such that $Y \leq \chi(A)$. Then choose a matrix X such that $X \leq \chi(Y)$. (Usually one chooses $X = Y^2$ or $X = Y^3$.) Then $(A*\bar{X}) + Y$ is a solution, i.e., a matrix equivalent to A, where A is any solution [A could be $\chi(A)$]. If A is any solution, then every matrix B such that $A \leq B \leq \chi(A)$ is also a solution. Suppose

$$\chi(A) = \begin{bmatrix} 1 & x_1 \equiv x_2 & x_2\bar{x}_3 + \bar{x}_1\bar{x}_2x_3 & \bar{x}_1 \\ x_1 \equiv x_2 & 1 & x_1 \oplus x_3 & \bar{x}_2 \\ x_2\bar{x}_3 + \bar{x}_1\bar{x}_2x_3 & x_1 \oplus x_3 & 1 & x_1x_3 + \bar{x}_1x_2\bar{x}_3 + \bar{x}_1\bar{x}_2x_3 \\ \bar{x}_1 & \bar{x}_2 & x_1x_3 + \bar{x}_1x_2\bar{x}_3 + \bar{x}_1\bar{x}_2x_3 & 1 \end{bmatrix}$$

and Y is chosen as

$$Y = \begin{bmatrix} 1 & x_1x_2 & x_2\bar{x}_3 & \bar{x}_1 \\ x_1x_2 & 1 & \bar{x}_1x_3 & \bar{x}_2 \\ x_2\bar{x}_3 & \bar{x}_1x_3 & 1 & x_1\bar{x}_2x_3 \\ \bar{x}_1 & \bar{x}_2 & x_1\bar{x}_2x_3 & 1 \end{bmatrix}$$

so that $Y \leq \chi(A)$

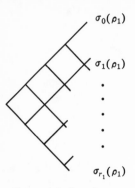

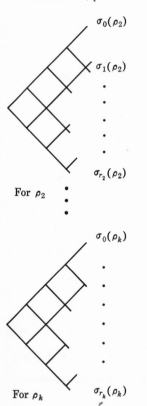

Symmetric function
network for ρ_1

For ρ_2

For ρ_k

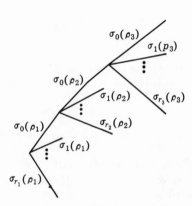

Fig. P3

We take $X = Y^2$

$$X = Y^2 = \begin{bmatrix} 1 & x_1 \equiv x_2 & x_2\bar{x}_3 & \bar{x}_1 \\ x_1 \equiv x_2 & 1 & (\bar{x}_1 + \bar{x}_2)x_3 + x_1x_2\bar{x}_3 & \bar{x}_2 \\ x_2\bar{x}_3 & (\bar{x}_1 + \bar{x}_2)x_3 + x_1x_2\bar{x}_3 & 1 & x_1\bar{x}_2x_3 + \bar{x}_1x_2\bar{x}_3 \\ & & & + \bar{x}_1\bar{x}_2x_3 \\ \bar{x}_1 & \bar{x}_2 & (\bar{x}_1\bar{x}_2x_3 + x_1\bar{x}_2x_3 & 1 \\ & & + \bar{x}_1x_2\bar{x}_3) & \end{bmatrix}$$

so that $\chi(X) = \chi(Y)$
Taking A as

$$A = \begin{bmatrix} 1 & x_1 \equiv x_2 & x_2\bar{x}_3 & \bar{x}_1 \\ x_1 \equiv x_2 & 1 & x_1 \oplus x_3 & \bar{x}_2 \\ x_2\bar{x}_3 & x_1 \oplus x_3 & 1 & x_1x_2x_3 \\ \bar{x}_1 & \bar{x}_2 & x_1x_2x_3 & 1 \end{bmatrix}$$

We compute

$$Z = (A * \bar{X}) + Y = \begin{bmatrix} 1 & x_1x_2 & x_2\bar{x}_3 & \bar{x}_1 \\ x_1x_2 & 1 & x_1\bar{x}_2\bar{x}_3 + \bar{x}_1x_3 & \bar{x}_2 \\ x_2\bar{x}_3 & x_1\bar{x}_2\bar{x}_3 + \bar{x}_1x_3 & 1 & x_1x_3 \\ \bar{x}_1 & \bar{x}_2 & x_1x_3 & 1 \end{bmatrix}$$

and $\chi(Z) = \chi(A)$
Now choose a new matrix U such that $\chi(U) = \chi(A)$ because $Z \leq U \leq \chi(A)$

$$U = \begin{bmatrix} 1 & x_1x_2 & x_2\bar{x}_3 & \bar{x}_1 \\ x_1x_2 & 1 & x_1 \oplus x_3 & \bar{x}_2 \\ x_2\bar{x}_3 & x_1 \oplus x_3 & 1 & x_1x_3 \\ \bar{x}_1 & \bar{x}_2 & x_1x_3 & 1 \end{bmatrix}$$

We stop with the circuit of Fig. P7.

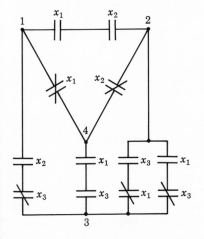

Fɪɢ. P7

8. Most of the synthesis methods developed in this book are for single-output networks. For multiple-output networks, devise an economical synthesis method using the technique of decomposition.

7 $\lambda(n)$: PRELIMINARIES AND A LOWER BOUND

An important function which yields a good deal of insight into the nature of the switching functions is studied in this section.

Definition 1. $\lambda(n)$ is defined to be the least integer such that any function of n variables may be realized with at most $\lambda(n)$ contacts.

A second definition may be given as follows: Let F_n be the set of all switching functions of n variables. If $f \in F_n$, then define $\nu(f)$ to be the number of contacts required in the most economical realization of f.

Definition 2. $\lambda(n) = \max_{f \in F_n} \nu(f)$

The reader should prove that Definitions 1 and 2 are equivalent. From the definition 1 we see two facts immediately.

Proposition 3. Any function of n variables may be realized with at most $\lambda(n)$ contacts. There exists at least one function which may be realized with $\lambda(n)$ contacts and no fewer will suffice.

It is quite important to get numerical results concerning the behavior of $\lambda(n)$, because such results will help evaluate the relative merits of special synthesis procedures.

Theorem 4. $\lambda(n) \leq 3 \cdot 2^{n-1} - 2$

PROOF. This result is established by using a series-parallel construction for an arbitrary function of n variables. The argument is an induction on n.

BASIS. By enumeration $\lambda(1) = 1, 3 - 2 = 1$; so the basis is completed.

INDUCTION STEP. Assume $\lambda(n - 1) \leq 3 \cdot 2^{n-2} - 2$. Since

$$f(x_1, \ldots, x_n) = x_1 f(1, x_2, \ldots, x_n) + \bar{x}_1 f(0, x_2, \ldots, x_n)$$

the number of contacts does not exceed

$$2 + 2(3 \cdot 2^{n-2} - 2) = 3 \cdot 2^{n-1} - 2 \quad \blacksquare$$

By using Shannon's synthesis method, one can do still better.

Theorem 5. $\lambda(n) \leq 2^{n-1} + 16$

PROOF. Cf. Prob. 5.3. ▮

Rather than try to improve the upper bounds, let us try instead to find a lower bound on $\lambda(n)$. The lower bound is derived by an ingenious argument due to Shannon.[2] A preliminary result about two-terminal networks is needed.

Lemma 6. The number of two-terminal networks with at most k branches does not exceed $(6k)^k$.

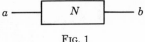

FIG. 1

PROOF.   Let N denote a generic two-terminal network as shown in Fig. 1.   We arrange the k branches, which will be denoted by

$a.$

1 ——————————————— 1'

2 ——————————————— 2'

· · · · · · · · · · · · · · · ·

$b.$

k ——————————————— k'

We connect together nodes $a, 1, 2, \ldots, k, b$.   The number of ways that this can be done does not exceed the number of ways one can insert dividers between the numbers of the sequence $a, 1, \ldots, k, b$.   Clearly, this number does not exceed 2^{k+1}. We still must account for nodes $1', \ldots, k'$. $1'$ may be connected to any of a, $1, \ldots, k, b$ or to some new point; i.e., there are $k + 3$ possibilities to which this node may be connected.   Similarly, $2'$ has at most $k + 4$ possibilities, $\ldots, k'$ has at most $k + 2 + k = 2k + 2$ possibilities.

There are at most $2^{k+1}(k + 3)(k + 4) \cdots (2k + 2)$ such networks.   Since if $k \geq 3$, $2^{k+1}(k + 3) \cdots (2k + 2) < (6k)^k$ (Prob. 1), we must enumerate the cases for $k = 1$ and $k = 2$ to complete the proof.   For $k = 1$, there is only one network. For $k = 2$, there are only six networks. $\blacksquare$

We shall now derive a lower bound for $\lambda(n)$ by using Lemma 6, which involves an interesting method of proof.   Suppose we are trying to show that $\lambda(n) > h(n)$.   We shall show that it is not possible for all functions of n variables to require less than $h(n)$ contacts.   That is, we shall show that there are not enough networks with less than $h(n)$ branches to represent all 2^{2^n} functions of n variables.   When we count the number of networks, we must take into account the different possible assignments of variables to the branches.

Theorem 7.   For all sufficiently large n and for any $\varepsilon > 0$, all functions of n variables require at least $(2^n/n)(1 - \varepsilon)$ contacts except an arbitrarily small fraction δ where $\delta > 0$.   For large n

$$\lambda(n) > \frac{2^n}{n}(1 - \varepsilon)$$

PROOF.   The number of functions of n variables which can be constructed from $(2^n/n)(1 - \varepsilon)$ contacts does not exceed the number of networks that can be built with this many branches, taking into account the number of assignments of variables to branches.   The number of networks which can be constructed from $(2^n/n)(1 - \varepsilon)$ branches is at most $(6 \cdot (2^n/n))(1 - \varepsilon)^{(2^n/n)(1-\varepsilon)}$.   There are $2n$ possible assignments of variables for each branch, so that the total number of possibilities is at most

$$(2n)^{(2n/n)(1-\varepsilon)} \left(6\frac{2^n}{n}(1 - \varepsilon) \right)^{(2n/n)(1-\varepsilon)} = v(n)$$

$$\log_2 v(n) = \frac{2^n}{n} (1 - \varepsilon)(1 + \log_2 6 + \log_2 (1 - \varepsilon) + n)$$

$$\log_2 v(n) = 2^n(1 - \varepsilon)(1 + o(1))$$

$$\log_2 v(n) < 2^n(1 - \varepsilon) \qquad n \text{ sufficiently large}$$

$$v(n) < 2^{2^n(1-\varepsilon)} \qquad n \text{ sufficiently large}$$

$$\frac{v(n)}{2^{2^n}} < \frac{2^{2^n(1-\varepsilon)}}{2^{2^n}} = 2^{-\varepsilon 2^n} = o(1)$$

Thus, for large n, $\qquad\qquad\qquad\qquad \lambda(n) > \frac{2^n}{n} (1 - \varepsilon)$ ❙

PROBLEMS

1. Show that if $k \geq 3$, then $2^{k+1}(k + 3)(k + 4) \cdots (2k + 2) < (6k)^k$.

2. Generalize the definition of $\lambda(n)$ to $(1,k)$ networks; call this new function $\lambda(k,n)$. Construct a synthesis procedure for realizing k functions of n variables. Use this to obtain an upper bound on $\lambda(k,n)$. [HINT: Use a procedure with $kN_T(n - m)$ networks and one $N_U(m)$ network. This will require at most $k(2^{n+1+m} - 2) + 2 \cdot 2^{2m}$ contacts.]

3. Show for the special case $k = 1$, $\lambda(n) < 6 \cdot 2^n/n$. (HINT: Use an $N_T(n - r)$ network connected to a $N_U(r)$ network. Choose $r = [\log_2 (n - \log_2 n)] - 1$.)

4. Riordan and Shannon have shown that the number of series-parallel networks with k branches is at most 4^k. Use this result to show that almost all switching functions require at least $(2^n/\log_2 n)(1 - \varepsilon)$ contacts (for any positive ε) in their realization in a series-parallel network.

5. Show that $\lambda(0) = 0$, $\lambda(1) = 1$, $\lambda(2) = 4$, and $\lambda(3) = 8$.

6. Show that $\lambda(4) \leq 14$. [It can be shown by more involved means that $\lambda(4) = 13$.]

8 AN UPPER BOUND FOR $\lambda(n)$ AND THE COMPLEXITY OF SWITCHING FUNCTIONS

So far, the best upper bound for $\lambda(n)$ that has been obtained is $6 \cdot 2^n/n$ (Prob. 7.3). Asymptotically, one can show that

$$\lambda(n) \leq 2 \cdot \frac{2^n}{n} (1 + \varepsilon) \qquad n \text{ sufficiently large and } \varepsilon > 0$$

by essentially the same argument. These results were originally due to Shannon, who could not resolve the discrepancy between the upper and lower bounds. Finally, Lupanov constructed a synthesis procedure which achieves a smaller bound on $\lambda(n)$. Lupanov's procedure has already been studied in Sec. 6.

Theorem 1. $\lambda(n) \leq \dfrac{2^n}{n}\left(1 + O\left(\dfrac{1}{\sqrt{n}}\right)\right)$

PROOF. By use of Lupanov's synthesis procedure and Theorem 6.6:

$$\lambda(n) \leq g(k,s,r) = \left(\frac{2^k}{s} + 1\right)\left(2^{n-k} + 2^{r+1} + \frac{2^{n-k+1}}{r} + \frac{sk2^{s+r}}{r}\right)$$

We must choose the parameters s, k, and r so that g is minimized.   The pertinent choices are

$$k = [2 \log_2 n] \qquad s = [n - 2\sqrt{n}] \qquad \text{and } r = 2^{[\frac{1}{2} \log_2 n]}$$

Thus
$$2 \log_2 n - 1 < k \le 2 \log_2 n$$
$$n - 1 - 2\sqrt{n} < s \le n - 2\sqrt{n}$$
$$\sqrt{n} - 1 < r \le \sqrt{n}$$

$$\lambda(n) \le g(k,s,r) \le \frac{2^{n+1}}{n^2} + 2^{\sqrt{n}+1} + \frac{2^{n+2}}{n^2(\sqrt{n}-1)} + \frac{2(\log_2 n)(n - 2\sqrt{n})}{\sqrt{n} - 1} 2^{n-\sqrt{n}}$$

$$+ \frac{2^n}{n - 1 - 2\sqrt{n}} + \frac{n^2 2^{\sqrt{n}+1}}{n - 1 - 2\sqrt{n}} + \frac{2^{n+1}}{(\sqrt{n} - 1)(n - 1 - 2\sqrt{n})}$$

$$+ \frac{2(\log_2 n)n^2 2^{n-\sqrt{n}}}{\sqrt{n} - 1}$$

$$\frac{\lambda(n)}{2^n/n} \le \frac{2}{n} + 2n2^{\sqrt{n}-n} + \frac{4}{n(\sqrt{n}-1)} + \frac{2(\log_2 n)(n - 2\sqrt{n})\sqrt{n}}{(1 - 1/\sqrt{n})2^{\sqrt{n}}}$$

$$+ \frac{1}{1 - 1/n - 2/\sqrt{n}} + \frac{n^3 2^{\sqrt{n}+1}}{(n - 1 - 2\sqrt{n})2^n} + \frac{2n}{(\sqrt{n} - 1)(n - 1 - 2\sqrt{n})}$$

$$+ \frac{2n^3 \log_2 n}{(\sqrt{n} - 1)2^{\sqrt{n}}}$$

$$\frac{\lambda(n)}{2^n/n} \le O\left(\frac{1}{n}\right) + o\left(\frac{1}{n}\right) + 1 + O\left(\frac{1}{\sqrt{n}}\right)$$

$$\frac{\lambda(n)}{2^n/n} \le 1 + O\left(\frac{1}{\sqrt{n}}\right) \ \blacksquare$$

Corollary 2. $\lambda(n) \sim \dfrac{2^n}{n}$

Corollary 2 confirms the engineer's rule of thumb that increasing the number of variables by 1 doubles the required hardware.

Our purpose in discussing $\lambda(n)$ rests in the following definition.

Definition 3.   Let $f \, \epsilon \, F_n$ and let $\nu(f)$ be the number of contacts in the best possible realization of f.   The *complexity* of f, written $\alpha(f)$, is defined as

$$\alpha(f) = \frac{\nu(f)}{\lambda(n)}$$

Theorem 4.   For almost all functions f, and any $\varepsilon > 0$,

$$\alpha(f) > 1 - \varepsilon$$

PROOF.   A lower bound on $\alpha(f)$ comes from a lower bound for $\nu(f)$ and an upper bound on $\lambda(n)$.

From Theorem 7.7, almost no functions can be realized with less than $(2^n/n)$ $(1 - \varepsilon_1)$ elements.   Thus for almost all f, $\nu(f) > (2^n/n)(1 - \varepsilon_2)$.   For almost all $f \, \epsilon \, F_n$,

$$\alpha(f) > \frac{(2^n/n)(1 - \varepsilon_1)}{(2^n/n)(1 - \varepsilon_2)} = (1 - \varepsilon_1)(1 - \varepsilon_2 + \varepsilon_2^2 - \cdots)$$

or $$\alpha(f) > 1 - \varepsilon$$

where $$\varepsilon = \varepsilon_1 + \varepsilon_2 \quad \blacksquare$$

PROBLEMS

1. Define $\mu(n)$ to be the least integer such that any function of n variables may be realized with not more than $\mu(n)$ contacts on the most heavily loaded relay. Show that

$$\mu(n) \sim \frac{2^n}{n^2}$$

2. Define $\tau(n)$ to be the least integer such that any fundamental network can be constructed with not more than $\tau(n)$ contacts on the most heavily loaded relay. Show that

$$\tau(n) \sim \frac{2^n}{n}$$

3. (Muller[2]) Assume that one has a functionally complete set of k primitive elements. Define a *cost* of each element to be the real number a_i, where $a_i > 0$. In any network composed of these elements define the cost of the network to be the sum of the costs of the components. Define the *complexity* φ of a network to be the smallest cost of any network equivalent to the original one. Show that changing the set of primitive elements causes the complexity of a network to change by merely a constant. Devise an analogy with language translation.

4. (Muller[2]) Define a new function $\eta(p,q)$ to be the maximum of the φ function over all p-input q-output networks. Show that

$$c_1 \frac{2^r}{r} \leq \eta(p,q) \leq c_2 \frac{2^r}{r}$$

where the c_i are constants, $r = p + \log_2 q$, and $1 \leq q \leq 2^{2^p}$.

5. Discuss the special case $p = n$, $q = 1$. Does this correspond to the relay case?

6. Can one conclude that almost all functions are as complex as possible with respect to any class of components?

9 IMPLICATIONS OF THE COMPLEXITY RESULTS

The results of the preceding section indicate that almost all single boolean functions are as complex as they can be.

This statement is somewhat independent of the hardware used to realize the functions, because it has been seen that different choices of primitive elements alter the complexity by a constant (Prob. 8.4).

Thus, research in combinational switching theory has become research into the nature of boolean functions. There is an analog in the present case with functions of a complex variable. One can show that almost all complex-valued functions are not continuous or not analytic and are otherwise nasty. The reason that this statement has so few implications for functions of a complex variable is that special classes of functions which are sufficient for most applications are available. We have already seen some functions which appear promising.

Definition 1. (Gavrilov) A function f is said to be *orderly* iff

$$\lim_{n \to \infty} \frac{n\varphi(f)}{2^n} = 0 \quad \text{or equivalently} \quad \varphi(f) = o\left(\frac{2^n}{n}\right)$$

where $\varphi(f)$ is the least number of components (or any weighted cost function) required to realize f.

EXAMPLE. Symmetric functions can be realized with at most n^2 contacts, so that

$$\lim_{n \to \infty} \frac{n^3}{2^n} = 0$$

and therefore every symmetric function is orderly.

It was exactly these considerations which led to the study of the special classes of functions in Chap. 6. The reader should construct proofs that these special classes of functions are orderly.

On the basis of the complexity results, one concludes that there is no synthesis procedure which will guarantee that every function of n variables can be constructed with $\leq c2^n/n$ elements.

PROBLEMS

1. (Shannon[2]) A function has nontrivial group invariance under G_n iff there exists a nonidentity element $\alpha \, \epsilon \, G_n$ such that $\alpha f = f$. Show that if a function has this property, a large savings in contacts can be made.

2. Show that almost all functions do not have nontrivial group invariance.

3. Show that every function with nontrivial group invariance is orderly.

4. Extend the ideas of Prob. 1 to synthesis with gate-type elements. (HINT: Use S_n.)

10 SUMMARY

In this chapter a variety of special networks were introduced and studied carefully. Some synthesis procedures were introduced. Both Shannon's procedure and the Lupanov method were used more for theoretical purposes than for practical results.

The material in this chapter on trees is due to Shannon,[2] Burks et al.,[2] and Lupanov.[1] Most of the material on $\lambda(n)$ and its implications is due to Shannon,[2] Lupanov,[1] and Muller.[2]

CHAPTER 8 *reliable design with unreliable components*

1 INTRODUCTION

Physical components are inherently unreliable, so that any realistic analysis or synthesis procedure should include the possibility of device failure. To take into account all the possibilities is a forbidding task, so that one is faced with a choice. Either restrictive assumptions can be made and a mathematically rigorously analysis carried out, or one can dispense with the theoretical approach and try to build a reliable circuit by employing cut-and-try techniques.

In this chapter, certain assumptions will be made and some results will be derived. The reader is cautioned against trying to use these methods in practical situations where the assumptions are not satisfied. Although the results to be presented here have only limited practical value, they form a theoretical basis on which to build further and more realistic theories.

The basic nature of the present subject requires a knowledge of the rudiments of probability theory. The reader who is unfamiliar with the theory can quickly learn enough for our purposes by reading the introductory chapters of the book by Feller.

The assumptions that will govern the present study of unreliable components are now given. We shall restrict attention to branch-type networks† only. It will be assumed that *the networks are designed and constructed perfectly. Failures occur only because elements fail to operate when they should.* It is also assumed that *the events "element x_i has*

† As usual, relays will be used as examples.

236

operated" are statistically independent.   All probabilities are independent of time.

PROBLEMS

1. Let $a = \Pr$ {contact is closed | coil is energized} and $c = \Pr$ {contact is closed | coil is unenergized}.   Show that a relay of this type corresponds to a noisy binary channel of the type studied in information theory.

2. In terms of a and c as defined in Prob. 1, how would one define a make contact?   How does one define a break contact?

2   THE BASIC PROPERTIES OF $h(p)$

The key idea in the entire study of constructing reliable networks from unreliable components is redundancy.   If each imperfect component is replaced by a suitably constructed network of the same components, such that the overall network will realize the same logical function as the original network, then one wishes to design the replacement networks to improve reliability.   To carry out this simple-sounding plan is not easy.

First, probabilities are associated with a relay contact.   A relay along with its associated probabilities is called a *crummy relay*.

Definition 1.   Given a relay contact x on relay X; then define

$$a = \Pr \{x \text{ closed} \mid X \text{ energized}\}$$
$$c = \Pr \{x \text{ closed} \mid X \text{ unenergized}\}$$

where $\Pr \{A|B\}$ is the probability of event A given that event B has occurred.

The idea of the probability of a two-terminal network having a closed path between its terminals will be essential in the study which follows.

Definition 2.   Given a two-terminal contact network A constructed from contacts which all have the probability p of being closed; then $h_A(p)$ denotes the probability of the two distinguished terminals being connected.

In any discussion of a single network, the subscript A will be dropped and $h(p)$ will be written for $h_A(p)$.

EXAMPLE.   Suppose that one has the network shown in the top of Fig. 1.   If one considers replacing this network by the bottom network of Fig. 1, some interesting facts can be observed.   Assume that the probability of any contact being closed is p; then the probability of the top network being closed is p and the probability of the bottom network being closed is

$$h(p) = 1 - (1 - p^2)^2 = 2p^2 - p^4$$

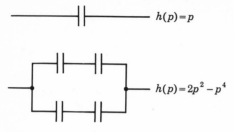

$h(p) = p$

$h(p) = 2p^2 - p^4$

Fig. 1

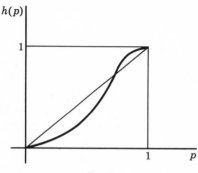

Fig. 2

In Fig. 2, $h(p)$ is plotted against p in the unit square $0 \leq p \leq 1$, $0 \leq h(p) \leq 1$. The curve intersects the graph of $h(p) = p$ when

$$p = 2p^2 - p^4 \qquad \text{or} \qquad p^3 - 2p + 1 = 0$$

Factoring out the root $p = 1$ leaves $p^2 + p - 1 = 0$, so

$$p = \frac{-1 \pm \sqrt{5}}{2}$$

Upon choosing the positive root, since $0 \leq p \leq 1$, one gets

$$p = 0.618$$

If a and c are so chosen that $a > 0.618 > c$, then the bottom circuit of Fig. 1 performs the same logical function as the original circuit; it uses four contacts instead of one, and it is more reliable. That is, if $c = 0.01$ and $a = 0.99$ and if the coils are then energized, the circuit probability is

$$1 - h(a) = 1 - 2(0.99)^2 + (0.99)^4 = 3.96 \times 10^{-4}$$
and
$$h(c) = 2(0.01)^2 - (0.01)^4 = 2 \times 10^{-4}$$

Thus a redundancy of four yields a spectacular improvement in reliability.

The example indicates that a general study of $h(p)$ and its properties is in order. First, a convenient way to compute $h(p)$ is indicated.

Definition 3.   Consider a two-terminal network A containing a relay contact y.   Define

$$f(p) = \Pr \{A \text{ closed} \mid y \text{ closed}\}$$
$$g(p) = \Pr \{A \text{ closed} \mid y \text{ open}\}$$

Theorem 4.   In any two-terminal network

$$h(p) = pf(p) + (1 - p)g(p)$$

PROOF.   This is just the usual expression for conditional probabilities, i.e.,

Pr $\{A$ closed$\}$ = Pr $\{A$ closed $\mid y$ closed$\}$ Pr $\{y$ closed$\}$
$$+ \Pr \{A \text{ closed} \mid y \text{ open}\} \Pr \{y \text{ open}\} \quad \blacksquare$$

Theorem 5.   If $0 \leq p \leq 1$, then $f(p) \geq g(p)$.

PROOF.   Every closed path through the network which connects the terminals when y is open still connects the terminals when y is closed. $\blacksquare$

The following theorem indicates how to calculate with the functions $h(p)$.

Theorem 6.   Let A_1 and A_2 be two-terminal networks with functions $h_1(p)$ and $h_2(p)$.   The series connection of A_1 and A_2 has associated with it the function $h_1(p) \cdot h_2(p)$.   The parallel combination of A_1 and A_2 has associated with it the function

$$1 - (1 - h_1(p))(1 - h_2(p)) = h_1(p) + h_2(p) - h_1(p)h_2(p)$$

PROOF.   The series result is clear.   The probability that the parallel network will be closed is 1 minus the probability that both A_1 and A_2 will open, but this latter quantity is $(1 - h_1(p))(1 - h_2(p))$. $\blacksquare$

One other technique for handling networks is needed.

Definition 7.   Let A_1 and A_2 be two-terminal networks having functions $h_1(p)$ and $h_2(p)$.   If every element of A_1 is replaced by an A_2 network, A_1 is said to be *composed* from A_2.   The special case when $A_1 = A_2$ is important.

Theorem 8.   If a network A has associated with it probability function $h(p)$, then the $(n - 1)$-th composition of A with itself is a network with probability function $h^{(n)}(p)$, where $h^{(1)}(p) = h(p)$ and $h^k(p) = h(h^{k-1}(p))$.

There is a graphical method, called the *staircase construction*, which is useful for computing $h^{(n)}(p)$.   The procedure is illustrated in Fig. 3.

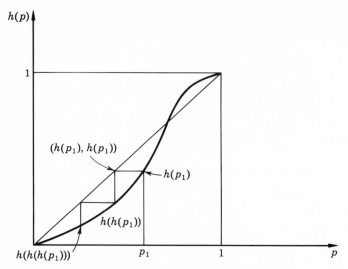

FIG. 3   The staircase construction.

PROBLEMS

1. Show that $h(p) = \sum_{k=0}^{m} A_k p^k (1 - p)^{m-k}$, where m is the total number of contacts in the network A and A_k is the number of ways one can choose a subset of k contacts in the network such that if these k contacts are closed and the remaining contacts open, then A is closed.

2. In the representation $h(p) = \sum_{k=0}^{m} A_k p^k (1 - p)^{m-k}$ the first nonzero term is,
say, $A_s p^s (1 - p)^{m-s}$. The integer s is called the *length* of the network A. Deduce
the relation of s to the length of paths in A.

3. Construct dual problems to Probs. 1 and 2 and solve them.

4. Suppose A is a planar network; then A has a dual. Show that

$$1 - h_A(1 - p) = h_{A^D}(p)$$

Note the special case when $A = A^D$. This yields $h(\frac{1}{2}) = \frac{1}{2}$.

3 SOME IMPORTANT INEQUALITIES ON $h'(p)$

The preceding section indicated that the graph of $h(p)$ versus p
is important in the study of reliable synthesis. The first step in the study
of the family of $h(p)$ curves is to obtain a lower bound on $h'(p)$.

Theorem 1. If $0 < p < 1$ and $h(p)$ is not identically zero, one, or p,
then

$$\frac{h'(p)}{(1 - h(p))h(p)} > \frac{1}{(1 - p)p}$$

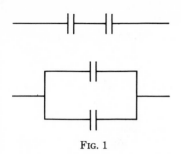

Fig. 1

PROOF.   The argument will be an induction on the number of contacts n in the network.

BASIS. $n = 1$ implies $h(p)$ is identically equal to p.   The theorem is then vacuously true.   For $n = 2$ there are only two nondegenerate networks shown in Fig. 1.   The analysis will be performed for the first network.   In this case

$$h(p) = p^2 \qquad h'(p) = 2p$$

and

$$\frac{h'(p)}{(1 - h(p))(h(p))} > \frac{1}{p(1 - p)}$$

holds iff

$$\frac{2p}{(1 - p^2)p^2} > \frac{1}{p(1 - p)}$$

which holds iff

$$\frac{2}{1 + p} > 1$$

or $2 > 1 + p$ or $p < 1$.   The hypothesis specifies this case, so the basis is satisfied. The proof for the parallel networks is similar.

INDUCTION STEP.   Assume the result for all networks containing less than n contacts.   Expand $h(p)$ around some contact on a path from the input to the output of the network.   Such a path exists because, if it did not, $h(p)$ would identically be zero.

$$h(p) = pf(p) + (1 - p)g(p)$$

Since the contact chosen lies on a path through the network, the general relation $f(p) \geq g(p)$ becomes, in this case, $f(p) > g(p)$.   Note that $1 - f(p) + g(p) = 0$ cannot hold for any fixed p (call it p') because, if this relation did hold and if $f(p') = 1$, then $g(p') = 0$ would imply that there was no path through the network of g (the network with the particular contact open).   In this situation there would be no cut set through the network of $f(p)$, which would imply that $f(p) = 1$ and $g(p) = 0$ for *every* p.   Thus $h(p)$ would be identically p, which would contradict the hypothesis. Thus if $0 < p < 1$, then

$$(1 - p)p(f - g)(1 - f + g) > 0$$

since every factor is greater than zero.   Multiplying this out yields

$$(p - p^2)(f - g - f^2 + 2fg - g^2) > 0$$

or $\quad pf - pg - pf^2 + 2pfg - pg^2 - p^2f + p^2g + p^2f^2 - 2p^2fg + p^2g^2 > 0$

or $\quad pf - pg - p^2f + 2pfg - pg^2 - pf^2 + p^2g + p^2f^2 - 2p^2fg + p^2g^2 > 0$

Add $pg^2 - g^2$ to both sides and rearrange the terms to get

$$-pf^2 + (pf - p^2f) - (g^2 - pg^2) - (pg - p^2g) > -(p^2f^2 + (g^2 - 2pg^2 + p^2g^2) + 2pfg - 2p^2fg)$$

or

$$-pf^2 + (1 - p)pf - (1 - p)g^2 - (1 - p)pg > -(p^2f^2 + (1 - p)^2g^2 + (1 - p)2pfg)$$

Add $pf + (1 - p)g$ to both sides. This gives

$$pf(1 - f) + (1 - p)fp + (1 - p)(1 - g)g - (1 - p)pg$$
$$> pf + (1 - p)g - (pf + (1 - p)g)^2$$
$$= h - h^2 = h(1 - h)$$

By the induction hypothesis, either $f'/(1 - f)f > 1/(1 - p)p$ or f is one of the three exceptional functions. In any event,

$$(1 - f)f \leq (1 - p)pf' \qquad \text{and} \qquad (1 - g)g \leq (1 - p)pg'$$

Using these results with the other inequality yields

$$p^2(1 - p)f' + (1 - p)pf + (1 - p)^2pg' - (1 - p)pg > (1 - h)h$$

or

$$pf' + f + (1 - p)g' - g > \frac{(1 - h)h}{(1 - p)p}$$

$$\frac{d(h(p))}{dp} = \frac{d}{dp}(pf + (1 - p)g) > \frac{(1 - h)h}{(1 - p)p}$$

Therefore

$$\frac{h'}{(1 - h)h} > \frac{1}{(1 - p)p} \quad\blacksquare$$

This important theorem will yield a great deal of information about $h(p)$. The following results are only a beginning.

Theorem 2. Any $h(p)$ curve may cross the diagonal at most once in the open interval $0 < p < 1$.

PROOF. Consider the equation

$$\frac{y'}{(1 - y)y} = \frac{1}{(1 - p)p}$$

$$\int \frac{dy}{(1 - y)y} = \int \frac{dp}{(1 - p)p}$$

$$\int \frac{dy}{y} + \int \frac{dy}{1 - y} = \int \frac{dp}{p} + \int \frac{dp}{1 - p}$$

$$\log y - \log (1 - y) = \log p - \log (1 - p) + \log C$$

$$\log \frac{y}{1 - y} = \log \frac{Cp}{1 - p}$$

$$\frac{y}{1 - y} = \frac{Cp}{1 - p}$$

where C is the constant of integration. This equation specifies a family of curves as shown in Fig. 2. Note that $C = 1$ implies that $y = p$ is a member of this family. Let $y_C(p)$ be a curve of this family with constant C. If $h(p) = y_C(p)$, then

$$p(1 - p)h' > h(1 - h) = y_C(1 - y_C) = p(1 - p)y_C'$$

so that

$$\frac{dh(p)}{dp} > \frac{dy_C(p)}{dp}$$

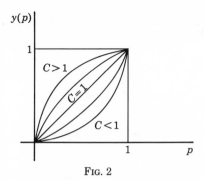

FIG. 2

Because any $h(p)$ function must cross curves of this family with a greater slope, an $h(p)$ function can cross the diagonal at most once, since $h(p)$, a polynomial, is continuous in p. |

Theorem 3. Any network A whose $h(p)$ function crosses the diagonal in the open interval $0 < p < 1$ may be composed with itself to obtain a new network which improves reliability.

$$\lim_{n \to \infty} h^{(n)}(p) = \begin{cases} 1 & p > p_0 \\ p_0 & p = p_0 \\ 0 & p < p_0 \end{cases}$$

where p_0 is the unique crossing point.

PROOF. Use the staircase construction. It should be noticed that the curve cannot have the form shown in Fig. 3, because

$$h(p_0) > \frac{(1 - h(p_0))h(p_0)}{(1 - p_0)p_0} = 1 \quad |$$

Corollary 4. If the $h(p)$ curve crosses the diagonal at some p_0 such that $0 < p_0 < 1$, then $h'(p_0) > 1$.

It is also necessary to obtain an upper bound on $h'(p)$. The proof to be given makes use of information theory in an unusual way. The

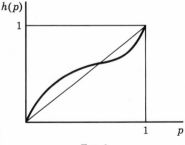

FIG. 3

reader who is not familiar with the concepts of channel capacity and entropy should consult the book by Shannon and Weaver.

Lemma 5. If $|a| > \varepsilon > 0$, then

$$(a + \varepsilon) \log (a + \epsilon) = a \log a + (1 + \log a)\varepsilon + \frac{\varepsilon^2}{2a} + O(\varepsilon^3)$$

PROOF. $(a + \varepsilon) \log (a + \varepsilon) = (a + \varepsilon) \log \left(a \left(1 + \frac{\varepsilon}{a} \right) \right) = (a + \varepsilon) \log a + (a + \varepsilon)$ $\log \left(1 + \frac{\varepsilon}{a} \right)$

By hypothesis, $|\varepsilon/a| < 1$, and therefore the power series for $\log (1 + \varepsilon/a)$ exists and converges.

$$(a + \varepsilon) \log (a + \varepsilon) = a \log a + \varepsilon \log a + (a + \varepsilon) \left(\frac{\varepsilon}{a} - \frac{1}{2} \left(\frac{\varepsilon}{a} \right)^2 + O(\varepsilon^3) \right)$$

$$= a \log a + \varepsilon \log a + \varepsilon - \frac{\varepsilon^2}{2a} + \frac{\varepsilon^2}{a} - \frac{\varepsilon^3}{2a} + O(\varepsilon^3)$$

$$= a \log a + (1 + \log a)\varepsilon + \frac{\varepsilon^2}{2a} + O(\varepsilon^3) \quad \blacksquare$$

The idea of the argument will be to use a binary channel as a model for a crummy relay. The basic setup is shown in Fig. 4.

Definition 6. Let $p = \Pr \{\text{contact closed} \mid \text{coil energized}\}$ and

$$q = 1 - p = \Pr \{\text{contact open} \mid \text{coil energized}\}$$

Let $P = \Pr \{\text{coil energized}\}$ and $Q = 1 - P = \Pr \{\text{coil unenergized}\}$. For $\varepsilon > 0$, let $p - \varepsilon = \Pr \{\text{contact closed} \mid \text{coil not energized}\}$ and $1 - p + \varepsilon = q + \varepsilon = \Pr \{\text{contact open} \mid \text{coil not energized}\}$. With these definitions we consider the binary channel shown in Fig. 4.

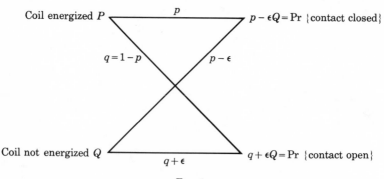

FIG. 4

Lemma 7. The rate of transmission of the channel of Fig. 4 is

$$R = \left(\frac{1}{4} - \left(Q - \frac{1}{2}\right)^2\right) \frac{\varepsilon^2}{2pq} + O(\varepsilon^3) \qquad \text{nits/sec†}$$

if $\min (p,q) > \varepsilon > 0$.

PROOF. For any channel whose output is called y and whose input is called z the rate is given by

$$R = H(y) - H_z(y)$$
$$= -(p - \varepsilon Q) \log (p - \varepsilon Q) - (q + \varepsilon Q) \log (q + \varepsilon Q)$$
$$\quad + (1 - Q)(p \log p + q \log q) + Q(p - \varepsilon) \log (p - \varepsilon) + Q(q + \varepsilon) \log (q + \varepsilon)$$
$$R = p \log p + q \log q - Qp \log p - Qq \log q$$
$$\qquad - \left(p \log p + (1 + \log p)(-\varepsilon Q) + \frac{\varepsilon^2 Q^2}{2p}\right)$$
$$\qquad - \left(q \log q + (1 + \log q)(\varepsilon Q) + \frac{\varepsilon^2 Q^2}{2q}\right)$$
$$\qquad + Q\left(p \log p + (1 + \log p)(-\varepsilon) + \frac{\varepsilon^2}{2p}\right)$$
$$\qquad\qquad + Q\left(q \log q + (1 + \log q)(\varepsilon) + \frac{\varepsilon^2}{2q}\right) + O(\varepsilon^3)$$
$$R = -\frac{\varepsilon^2 Q^2}{2p} - \frac{\varepsilon^2 Q^2}{2q} + \frac{\varepsilon^2 Q}{2p} + \frac{\varepsilon^2 Q}{2q} + O(\varepsilon^2)$$
$$R = \frac{\varepsilon^2 (Q - Q^2)}{2pq} + O(\varepsilon^3) = \frac{\varepsilon^2}{2pq}\left(\frac{1}{4} - \left(Q - \frac{1}{2}\right)^2\right) + O(\varepsilon^3)$$

This proof will be binding if we can justify the use of the lemma. This requires that the following four conditions be satisfied:

$$\left|\frac{\varepsilon}{p}\right| < 1 \qquad \left|\frac{\varepsilon}{q}\right| < 1$$
$$\left|\frac{\varepsilon Q}{p}\right| < 1 \qquad \left|\frac{\varepsilon Q}{q}\right| < 1$$

These conditions are guaranteed by the hypothesis $\min (p,q) > \varepsilon > 0$. ∎

Corollary 8. If $\varepsilon < \min (p,q)$ and if ε is so small that ε^3 is negligible, then the channel capacity C of our system is

$$C = \frac{\varepsilon^2}{8pq} \qquad \text{nits/sec}$$

PROOF. $C = \max_{0 \le Q \le 1} (R) = \frac{\varepsilon^2}{8pq}$ since $Q = \frac{1}{2}$ is the value which maximizes R. ∎

Theorem 9. If $\min (p,q) > \varepsilon > 0$ and if the network A under consideration has n contacts, then

$$\frac{dh}{dp} \le \left(\frac{n(1 - h)h}{(1 - p)p}\right)^{\frac{1}{2}}$$

† The units are information flow per unit time. See Prob. 2.

PROOF.   Consider the network A composed of n contacts with probabilities as given in the description of the channel.   The total capacity of the network A thought of as n separate channels is $n\varepsilon^2/8pq$.

We consider the whole network as a relay with probability of being closed equal to $h(p)$ and take our small positive number as $(h'(p))\varepsilon$ for some fixed p.   As a relay, the network has capacity

$$\frac{(h'(p)\varepsilon)^2}{8(1-h)h}$$

This capacity cannot exceed the capacity of the system when the n relays are used in the best possible way, i.e.,

$$\frac{(h'(p)\varepsilon)^2}{8(1-h)h} \leq \frac{n\varepsilon^2}{8(1-p)p} \qquad \text{or} \qquad \frac{dh}{dp} \leq \left(\frac{n(1-h)h}{(1-p)p}\right)^{\frac{1}{2}}$$

Thus if it is true for an arbitrary fixed p, it is true for any $0 < p < 1$.   ∎

PROBLEMS

1.   Show that $h(p)$ is a monotonically increasing function of p in the interval $0 < p < 1$ and that $h(0) = 0$ and $h(1) = 1$.

2.   Explain why the channel capacity given in Corollary 8 is expressed in nits per second rather than bits per second, which is more customary.

3.   The upper bound on h' depends on n, and the lower bound is independent of n. Discuss this fact.

4.   Using the upper bound for h', calculate the family of curves which $h(p)$ must cross with smaller slope.   Draw the curves for $0 \leq p \leq 1$ and a few values of the parameter.

4   QUORUM FUNCTIONS

The upper bounds on $h'(p)$ may be examined from the point of view of boolean functions.   One might ask what switching functions are best suited for improving reliability.   The crucial property of these functions would be that they have the largest slopes at p_0, the point of crossing. The following definition indicates the class of best possible functions.

Definition 1.   A function of n variables $f(x_1, \ldots, x_n)$ is said to be a *quorum function* if there exists s such that $0 \leq s \leq n$ and

$$f(x_1, \ldots, x_n) = \begin{cases} 0 & \text{if less than } s \text{ variables are 1} \\ 1 & \text{if more than } s \text{ variables are 1} \end{cases}$$

Now it is shown that these functions are the best possible functions for reliability.

Theorem 2.   If the h curve of any quorum function, denoted by $h_Q(p)$, crosses the h curve of some other function of n variables, say $h(p)$, then at the point of crossing p_0 one has

$$\frac{dh}{dp}\bigg|_{p=p_0} < \frac{dh_Q}{dp}\bigg|_{p=p_0}$$

PROOF.   The $h(p)$ polynomial of any function of n variables is a sum of terms of the form $p^i q^{n-i}$, there being one term of this form for each state when the function is 1. Hence for a quorum function, we have

$$h_Q(p) = \sum_{i=s+1}^{n} \binom{n}{i} p^i q^{n-i} + A p^s q^{n-s} \qquad 0 \le A \le \binom{n}{s}$$

$h(p)$ may be expressed as a polynomial, i.e.,

$$h(p) = \sum_{i=0}^{n} B_i p^i q^{n-i} \qquad 0 \le B_i \le \binom{n}{i}$$

To put both polynomials in a normal form, let

$$C(p) = \sum_{i=s+1}^{n} B_i p^i q^{n-i} + M p^s q^{n-s}$$

where $M = \min (A, B_s)$, and let

$$k = \begin{cases} s - 1 & \text{if } M = B_s \\ s & \text{if } M = A \end{cases}$$

Thus one may write

$$h_Q(p) = C(p) + \sum_{i=k+1}^{n} D_i p^i q^{n-i} \qquad 0 \le D_i \le \binom{n}{i}$$

and

$$h(p) = C(p) + \sum_{i=0}^{k} E_i p^i q^{n-i} \qquad 0 \le E_i \le \binom{n}{i}$$

Note that if $u(p) = p^i q^{n-i}$, then

$$u'(p) = i p^{i-1} q^{n-i} - (n - i) p^i q^{n-i-1} = \left(\frac{i}{p} - \frac{n-i}{q}\right) u(p)$$

$$u'(p) = \left(\frac{i - pn}{pq}\right) u(p)$$

or

$$\frac{u'(p)}{u(p)} = \frac{i - pn}{pq}$$

This is a monotonically increasing function of i.   Every term in the sum for $h_Q(p)$ corresponds to a larger value of i than the values of i in the sum for $h(p)$.   Let $u(p)$ be any term in the sum for $h(p)$ and let $u_Q(p)$ be a typical term in the sum for $h_Q(p)$. Then

$$\frac{u_Q'(p)}{u_Q(p)} > \frac{u'(p)}{u(p)}$$

Because the real numbers are dense, there exists a constant α such that

$$\frac{u'_Q}{u_Q} > \alpha > \frac{u'}{u}$$

Thus $\qquad\qquad u'_Q > \alpha u_Q \qquad$ and $\qquad \alpha u > u'$

Summing the series over the appropriate index sets yields

$$\sum_Q u'_Q > \alpha \sum_Q u_Q \qquad \text{and} \qquad \alpha \sum_h u > \sum_h u'$$

But when $p = p_0$, $\sum_Q u_Q = \sum_h u$; so that

$$\sum_Q u'_Q > \alpha \sum_Q u_q = \alpha \sum_h u > \sum_h u'$$

when $p = p_0$, or

$$\left.\frac{dh_Q(p)}{dp}\right|_{p=p_0} > \left.\frac{dh(p)}{dp}\right|_{p=p_0} \quad \blacksquare$$

Corollary 3. If $h(p_0) = h_Q(p_0)$, then

$$h(p) > h_Q(p) \qquad \text{for } 0 < p < p_0$$
and $\qquad\quad h(p) < h_Q(p) \qquad \text{for } p_0 < p < 1$

PROOF. Assume for the sake of contradiction that $h(p) \geq h_Q(p)$ for $p_0 < p < 1$. First compute $(h'_Q(p_0))^+$, the right-hand derivative of $h_Q(p)$ at p_0,

$$(h'_Q(p_0))^+ = \lim_{p \to p_0^+} \frac{h_Q(p) - h_Q(p_0)}{p - p_0}$$

Upon taking the limit from the right, so that $p_0 < p < 1$ and $h(p) \geq h_Q(p)$, and noting that $h(p_0) = h_Q(p_0)$, we get

$$(h'_Q(p_0))^+ = \lim_{p \to p_0^+} \frac{h_Q(p) - h_Q(p_0)}{p - p_0} \leq \lim_{p \to p_0^+} \frac{h(p) - h(p_0)}{p - p_0}$$
$$= (h'(p_0))^+$$

Since $h(p)$ and $h_Q(p)$ are polynomials, their derivatives exist and are continuous. The right-hand derivative is the same as the ordinary derivative, and what we have shown is

$$h'_Q(p_0) \leq h'(p_0)$$

which is a contradiction. A similar argument for left-hand derivatives establishes the result. $\quad \blacksquare$

PROBLEMS

1. Change the definition of a quorum function to a function which is 1 iff at least s variables are 1. Investigate this class of functions. What is the connection between this class and the symmetric functions?

2. Under what operations is the class of quorum functions closed?

5 NETWORKS OF GIVEN LENGTH AND WIDTH; HAMMOCK NETWORKS

In the problems of Sec. 2 the concept of length and width (the dual of length) were introduced.   Length and width are denoted by l and w, respectively.   These quantities are related to the order of flatness of $h(p)$ near $p = 0$ and $p = 1$.   In practical applications, interest will be focused in these regions.

The names *length* and *width* suggest that these concepts are properties of the two-terminal network (labeled graph).   In this section the concept of labeling a contact in a network is introduced.   The label will be a specialization of the distance function conventionally defined in graph theory.

Definition 1.   For any two-terminal network A with terminals 1, $1'$ the *label of contact x*, denoted by $\text{lb}(x)$, is defined inductively as follows:

(1) If a contact x is connected to terminal 1, then $\text{lb}(x) = 1$.
(2) $i = 1$
(3) If a contact y is connected to a contact x such that $\text{lb}(x) = i$ and $\text{lb}(y)$ is not defined, then take $\text{lb}(y) = i + 1$.
(4) If there are still contacts z in A for which $\text{lb}(z)$ is undefined, let $i = i + 1$ and go to step 3.   Otherwise, go to step 5.
(5) Halt.

The label function is intimately related to the length of paths in a network.   The exact correspondence is given in the following lemma.

Lemma 2.   If a contact x in A has $\text{lb}(x) = k \geq 1$, then there exists a path to terminal 1 of A through $k - 1$ other contacts and there is no path through a smaller number of contacts.

PROOF.   This is a direct consequence of the definition of the label function.   Notice how easy it is to do an induction on k.   ▌

The label function makes it easy to give a characterization of some important cut sets of a network.

Lemma 3.   If A is a network of length l, then for any $0 \leq k \leq l$, $C_k = \{x \in A \,|\, \text{lb}(x) = k\}$ is a cut set of A.

PROOF.   Every path through A starts at terminal 1 with a contact x such that $\text{lb}(x) = 1$ and ends at the right terminal with a contact z such that $\text{lb}(z) \geq l$.   This latter remark is true because, if it were not, the length of A would be less than l. The labels along a path change by 0 or ± 1 in passing from one contact to the next. Therefore, every path which goes from contacts x where $\text{lb}(x) = 1$ to those z with $\text{lb}(z) \geq l$ must pass through contacts w whose $\text{lb}(w)$ function assumes all intermediate values.   If all the contacts labeled k are removed from A, then all paths are broken.   Thus C_k is a cut set.   ▌

It is now possible to relate l and w to the number of branches in the graph under consideration.

Theorem 4. If a network A has length l and width w, it contains at least lw contacts.

PROOF. Since A has width w, every cut set contains at least w contacts. There are at least w contacts whose lb function is 1; at least w whose lb function is 2, . . . ; at least w whose lb function is l. Therefore, A contains at least lw contacts. **∎**

Corollary 5. If $h(p) = Ap^l$ near $p = 0$ and $1 - h(p) = B(1 - p)^w$ near $p = 1$ for some network A, then A has at least lw contacts.

Corollary 6. The lower bound of wl contacts can be achieved.

PROOF. Figure 1 exhibits two examples. **∎**

The set of all networks that have length l and width w and contain lw contacts will now be characterized. The general setup is shown in Fig. 2 for a network A with terminal nodes a and b.

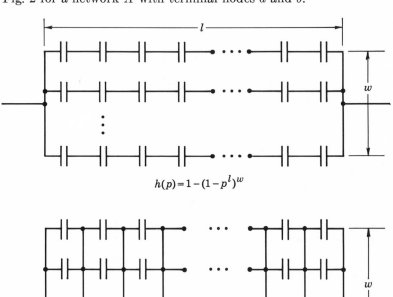

$$h(p) = 1 - (1 - p^l)^w$$

$$h(p) = [1 - (1 - p)^w]^l$$

FIG. 1

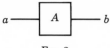

FIG. 2

Theorem 7. A network A of length l and width w that contains lw contacts with terminal nodes a and b is characterized as follows:

(1) Let $S_0 = \{a\}$ and $S_l = \{b\}$.
(2) There are $l - 1$ other subsets of nodes S_i with $i = 1, \ldots , l - 1$.
(3) There are exactly w elements connecting nodes in S_i to nodes in S_{i+1} $(i = 0, \ldots , l - 1)$.
(4) If a node in S_j has m elements connecting it to nodes in S_{j-1}, then it has m elements connected to elements in S_{j+1} $(j = 1, \ldots , l - 1)$.

Conversely, any network satisfying (1), (2), (3), and (4) has length l and width w and lw elements.

PROOF. From Lemma 3 the cut sets C_k have exactly w elements and these elements must run between elements of lower numbers and higher numbers. The nodes between elements whose labels are $j - 1$ and j will belong to S_j in the above characterization. Assume, for the sake of contradiction, that some node in S_j has m elements going to nodes in S_{j-1} and $m + p$ elements going to nodes in S_{j+1} and that $p > 0$. Of course, C_{j+1} is a cut set containing w elements. If $m + p$ elements of C_{j+1} leaving the node in question are replaced by the m elements going to nodes in S_{j-1}, then we still have a cut set, but it is now a cut set with fewer than w elements. This contradiction shows that any network of length l and width w with lw contacts is of this form.

Assume the network is of the required form. Any closed path from a to b must include nodes contained in $S_1, \ldots , S_{l-1}$. Hence, any path is of length at least l and A has length l. Let C be any cut set. We must show that C has at least w contacts. Consider the contact in C whose label is the least. Suppose one such contact is connected to node $e \in S_{j-1}$ and node $f \in S_j$. Either all elements from f to nodes in S_{j-1} are in C or the one in question is not essential to the cut set C and this redundant element may be eliminated to yield a smaller cut set. In the former case this group of elements can be replaced by an equal number, those going from f to S_{j+1} preserving the cut-set property. By continuing in this way, we reach the rightmost node without increasing the number of elements in the cut set. When the elements of this cut set are adjacent to $S_l = \{b\}$, the set has exactly w elements. Consequently, C had at least w elements, which is what we needed to prove. Note that A has w elements connecting S_i to S_{i+1} for $i = 0, \ldots , l - 1$. Therefore, A has exactly lw elements. $\blacksquare$

Among the networks of length l and width w we now know that there are networks which are minimal, i.e., which have exactly lw contacts. There is a special class of these minimal networks which deserve independent study and will be used extensively. These networks, called *hammock networks*, are obtained from the top network of Fig. 1 by a special construction.

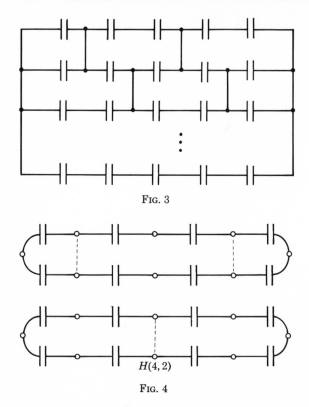

FIG. 3

$H(4,2)$

FIG. 4

Definition 8. A two-terminal network containing lw contacts and having length l and width w which is obtained from Fig. 1 by the use of alternate vertical connections (cf. Fig. 3) is called a *hammock network* of these dimensions and is denoted by $H(l,w)$.

As an example, $H(4,2)$ is constructed. In Fig. 4, two 2-by-4 networks are shown with the alternate connections inserted with dotted lines in two different ways. In Fig. 5, the same networks are redrawn with the alternate connections inserted and the vertical connections pulled together. Figure 6 shows some examples of $H(l,w)$. Hammock networks have some simple properties which are now derived.

Theorem 9. If $l \equiv w \equiv 0 \bmod 2$, there are two possible networks for $H(l,w)$.

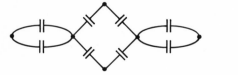
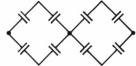

FIG. 5

$H(l, w)$

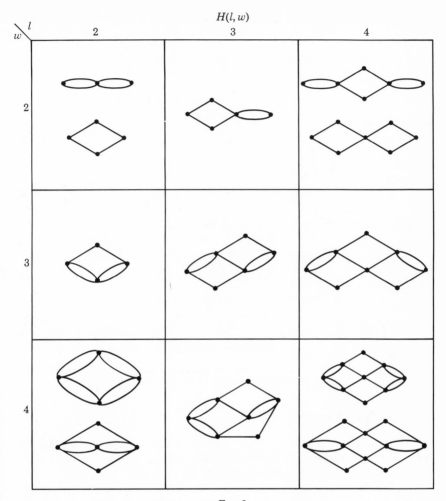

FIG. 6

PROOF. One constructs two different networks by the insertion of alternate connections. These networks are different (not isomorphic) because they do not have the same number of nodes (Prob. 5 of this section); hence, the ranks of the graphs are different. **|**

Theorem 10. If $l \equiv 1 \bmod 2$ or $w \equiv 1 \bmod 2$, then there is only one network $H(l,w)$.

PROOF. Problem 4 of this section and the preceding argument supply the proof. **|**

Theorem 11. $H^D(l,w) = H(w,l)$

PROOF. Since $H(l,w)$ is series-parallel and hence planar, it has a dual. It is clear that this dual is also a hammock network. We must show that $w^D = l$ and $l^D = w$.

The argument given below is for the case when l (or w) is odd. The reader should complete the remaining case. The rank of $H(l,w)$ is

$$\rho = \frac{l + 3 + w(l - 1)}{2} - 1$$

and the nullity of $H(l,w)$ is

$$\mu = lw - (l + 3 + w(l - 1))/2 + 1$$

Then the rank and nullity of H^D are

$$\rho^D = lw - \frac{l + 3 + w(l - 1)}{2} + 2$$

$$\mu^D = \frac{l + 3 + w(l - 1)}{2} - 2$$

since $\rho^D = \mu + 1$ and $\mu^D = \rho - 1$ for two-terminal graphs.

Rewriting the expressions for ρ^D and μ^D yields

$$\rho^D = \frac{w + 3 + l(w - 1)}{2} - 1$$

$$\mu^D = lw - \frac{w + 3 + l(w - 1)}{2} + 1$$

which shows that the dual of a $H(l,w)$ network is a $H(w,l)$ network. ∎

Theorem 12.   If $l = w \equiv 1 \bmod 2$, then

$$(H(l,w))^D = H(l,w)$$

PROOF.   Since l and w are odd, there exists only one network of these dimensions which gets mapped into itself by the duality transformation. ∎

PROBLEMS

1.   Show that $H(i,1)$, $i = 1, \ldots$, is a series connection of i elements and that $H(1,j)$ is a parallel connection of j elements for $j = 1, \ldots$.

2.   Find $h(p)$ for $H(4,3)$ as shown in Fig. P2.

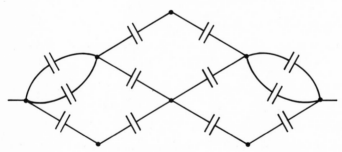

FIG. P2

3.   Find the $h(p)$ function for $H(3,3)$. Find the points of intersection of this curve with the line $y(p) = \frac{3}{2}p - \frac{1}{4}$. Show that $h(p) \le 8p^3$ for $0 \le p \le 1$.

4. Show that the number of vertices in $H(l,w)$ is

$$\frac{l + 3 + w(l - 1)}{2}$$

if $\qquad\qquad\qquad l \text{ or } w \equiv 1 \bmod 2$

5. If $l \equiv w \equiv 0 \bmod 2$, show that the numbers of nodes in the two networks $H(l,w)$ are

$$\frac{l + 2 + w(l - 1)}{2} \quad \text{and} \quad \frac{l + 4 + w(l - 1)}{2}$$

6 THE PLAN OF ATTACK AND OPENING BATTLE

It is our hope to be able to design arbitrarily reliable circuits starting from arbitrarily bad relays. For convenience, the solution to this problem will be divided into three sections: the opening, middle, and end games. We list below what we wish to accomplish at each stage.

1. Opening game. In the opening game, we take any a and c such that $a \neq c$ and design a network to move these points until they straddle the point $p = \frac{1}{2}$. The design of this network will ensure $h(a) < \frac{1}{2}$ and $h(c) > \frac{1}{2}$.

2. Middle game. The middle game will be to design a network in which a and c straddle $p = \frac{1}{2}$ and move a and c until a is near $p = \frac{1}{4}$ and c is near $p = \frac{3}{4}$.

3. End game. The end game will be to design a network which moves a from about $\frac{1}{4}$ to 0 and moves b from about $\frac{3}{4}$ to 1.

In this type of construction, the total number of contacts used will be the product of the number of contacts used in parts 1 to 3. It should be noted that in practical design problems one starts from near the extreme points zero and one; hence, only the end game is required.

We now proceed to develop the opening game. For the remainder of the chapter, the following abbreviations are used.

Definition 1. For a and c such that $0 < a < c < 1$, define

$$b = \frac{a + c}{2} \qquad d = \max (b, 1 - b) \qquad \varepsilon = \frac{c - a}{4}$$

Lemma 2. There exist two sequences of networks N_i and M_i ($i = 0, 1, \ldots$) such that for any i

(1) N_i uses no more than i contacts.
(2) M_i uses no more than i contacts.
(3) $h_{N_i}(b) < \frac{1}{2} \leq h_{M_i}(b)$
(4) $h_{M_i}(b) - h_{N_i}(b) \leq d^i$

Furthermore, either M_i can be obtained by shorting between two of the

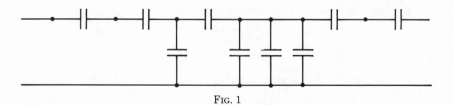

Fig. 1

nodes of N_i or network N_i can be obtained by opening a contact of M_i.

Before proceeding to the proof of the lemma, some remarks concerning the type of network to be used are in order. Both M_i and N_i will be derived from a ladder network. The number of horizontal and vertical elements may be different in general. The network might start with either a vertical or a horizontal group. The infinite ladder network may be thought of as one which crosses $h(p) = \frac{1}{2}$ at exactly $p = b$, while M_i and N_i are finite approximations which cross to the left and right of b. See Fig. 1 for a typical such network M_9 or N_9.

PROOF. The argument is an induction on i.

BASIS. $i = 0$. Take M_0 to be a short circuit and N_0 to be an open circuit. Clearly, all the conditions are satisfied, since $h_{M_0}(p) = 1$ and $h_{N_0}(p) = 0$.

INDUCTION STEP. Assume the result for $i - 1$. If M_{i-1} is obtained from N_{i-1} by shorting together two nodes, let M be the network obtained by adding a single contact between these nodes. Thus M has $\leq i$ contacts. On the other hand, if N_{i-1} is obtained by opening a contact of M_{i-1}, let M be the network obtained by putting another contact in series with this contact. In this case also, M has $\leq i$ contacts. Note that shorting the added contact causes M to become M_{i-1} and opening the added contact makes M into N_{i-1}. Thus

$$h_M(p) = p h_{M_{i-1}}(p) + (1 - p) h_{N_{i-1}}(p)$$

We take two cases now.

    1. If $h_M(b) < \frac{1}{2}$, let $N_i = M$ and $M_i = M_{i-1}$. Now, $h_{N_i}(b) < \frac{1}{2}$ and $h_{M_i}(b) \geq \frac{1}{2}$ by the inductive hypothesis. Also,

$$
\begin{aligned}
h_{M_i}(b) - h_{N_i}(b) &= h_{M_{i-1}}(b) - h_M(b) \\
&= h_{M_{i-1}}(b) - (b h_{M_{i-1}}(b) + (1 - b) h_{N_{i-1}}(b)) \\
&= (1 - b)(h_{M_{i-1}}(b) - h_{N_{i-1}}(b)) \\
&\leq (1 - b) d^{i-1} \leq d^i
\end{aligned}
$$

    2. Suppose $h_M(b) \geq \frac{1}{2}$. Take $M_i = M$ and $N_i = N_{i-1}$. $h_{N_i}(b) < \frac{1}{2}$ by inductive hypothesis, and $h_{M_i}(b) \geq \frac{1}{2}$ by assumption. We must compute

$$
\begin{aligned}
h_{M_i}(b) - h_{N_i}(b) &= h_M(b) - h_{N_i}(b) \\
&= b h_{M_{i-1}}(b) + (1 - b) h_{N_{i-1}}(b) - h_{N_{i-1}}(b) \\
&= b(h_{M_{i-1}}(b) - h_{N_{i-1}}(b)) \\
&\leq b d^{i-1} \\
&\leq d^i \quad \blacksquare
\end{aligned}
$$

Lemma 3. For every p such that $\frac{1}{2} - \varepsilon < h(p) < \frac{1}{2} + \varepsilon$, $dh/dp > \frac{3}{4}$.

PROOF. $\varepsilon = (c - a)/4 \le \frac{1}{4}$; thus, $\frac{1}{4} < h(p) < \frac{3}{4}$. Because $p(1 - p) \le \frac{1}{4}$ for all p, we have

$$\frac{dh}{dp} > \frac{(1 - h)h}{(1 - p)p} > \frac{\frac{3}{4} \cdot \frac{1}{4}}{\frac{1}{4}} = \frac{3}{4} \quad \blacksquare$$

Lemma 4. If $i = [(\log \varepsilon)/(\log d)]$, then either $|h_{N_i}(b) - \frac{1}{2}| \le \varepsilon/2$ or $|h_{M_i}(b) - \frac{1}{2}| \le \varepsilon/2$.

PROOF. Assume, for the sake of contradiction, that

$$|h_{M_i}(b) - \tfrac{1}{2}| > \frac{\varepsilon}{2} \quad \text{and} \quad |h_{N_i}(b) - \tfrac{1}{2}| > \frac{\varepsilon}{2}$$

If $i = [(\log \varepsilon)/(\log d)]$, then $i \le (\log \varepsilon)/(\log d)$ or $d^i \le \varepsilon$. Thus

$$h_{M_i}(b) - h_{N_i}(b) \le d^i \le \varepsilon$$

and we conclude

$$h_{M_i}(b) - h_{N_i}(b) \le \varepsilon$$

On the other hand,

$$h_{M_i}(b) - h_{N_i}(b) = (h_{M_i}(b) - \tfrac{1}{2}) - (h_{N_i}(b) - \tfrac{1}{2})$$

To obtain a lower bound, we take $h_{M_i}(b) - \frac{1}{2} > \varepsilon/2$ and $h_{N_i}(b) - \frac{1}{2} < -\varepsilon/2$; so that

$$h_{M_i}(b) - h_{N_i}(b) > \frac{\varepsilon}{2} - \left(\frac{-\varepsilon}{2}\right) = \varepsilon$$

which is a contradiction. $\blacksquare$

Finally, the main theorem can be proved. It states that, for any probabilities a and c, where $a \ne c$, one can design a network N which has the property that $h(a)$ and $h(c)$ are roughly $\frac{1}{2}$.

Theorem 5. Given $0 < a < c < 1$, let $b = (a + c)/2$,

$$d = \max(b, 1 - b) \quad \text{and} \quad \varepsilon = \frac{c - a}{4}$$

then there exists a network N such that N contains $\le [(\log \varepsilon)/(\log d)]$ contacts and

$$h_N(a) < \tfrac{1}{2} - \varepsilon \quad \text{and} \quad h_N(c) \ge \tfrac{1}{2} + \varepsilon$$

PROOF. Let $i = [(\log \varepsilon)/(\log d)]$. Now we take N to be whichever of N_i and M_i satisfies $|h_N(b) - \frac{1}{2}| \le \varepsilon/2$, since Lemma 4 guarantees that one of these networks will satisfy the inequality.

Since $h_N(b) - \frac{1}{2} \le \varepsilon/2$, $b \le a$ and we know that $h(p)$ is monotonically increasing,

$$h_N(a) - \frac{1}{2} \le \frac{\varepsilon}{2} \quad \text{or} \quad h_N(a) \le \frac{1}{2} + \frac{\varepsilon}{2} < \frac{1}{2} + \varepsilon$$

It remains only to show that

$$h_N(c) \ge \tfrac{1}{2} + \varepsilon$$

Suppose the contrary, namely, that $h_N(c) < \frac{1}{2} + \varepsilon$. Because $h(p)$ is a monotonically increasing function,

$$\frac{1}{2} - \varepsilon < \frac{1}{2} - \frac{\varepsilon}{2} \leq h_N(p) < \frac{1}{2} + \varepsilon \qquad \text{for } p \, \epsilon \, \{x | b \leq x \leq c\}$$

or
$$\frac{1}{2} - \varepsilon < h_N(p) < \frac{1}{2} + \varepsilon$$

This condition satisfies the hypothesis of Lemma 3; hence

$$\frac{dh_N}{dp} > \frac{3}{4} \qquad \text{for } p \, \epsilon \, \{x | b \leq x \leq c\}$$

Now we compute $h_N(c)$

$$h_N(c) = h_N(b) + (h_N(c) - h_N(b))$$
$$= h_N(b) + \int_b^c \frac{dh_N}{dp}\, dp$$
$$\geq \left(\frac{1}{2} - \frac{\varepsilon}{2}\right) + \frac{3}{4}(c - b)$$
$$\geq \frac{1}{2} - \frac{\varepsilon}{2} + \frac{3}{4}\left(c - \left(\frac{a + c}{2}\right)\right) = \frac{1}{2} - \frac{\varepsilon}{2} + \frac{3}{8}(c - a)$$
$$h_N(c) \geq \frac{1}{2} - \frac{\varepsilon}{2} + \frac{3\varepsilon}{2} = \frac{1}{2} + \varepsilon$$

However,
$$h_N(c) \geq \tfrac{1}{2} + \varepsilon$$
is a contradiction. ∎

7 THE MIDDLE GAME

In the middle game we wish to move a pair of points which straddle $p = \frac{1}{2}$ sufficiently far out that $h(\frac{1}{2} - \varepsilon) \leq \frac{1}{4}$ and $h(\frac{1}{2} + \varepsilon) \geq \frac{3}{4}$. The technique used will be to compose $H(3,3)$ with itself sufficiently many times to obtain the desired reliability. Because this network is self-dual, improvement of the upper and lower bounds is obtained simultaneously.

THEOREM 1. $H(3,3)$ has the following properties: $h(\frac{1}{2}) = \frac{1}{2}$, $h(p)$ lies above the curve $y = \frac{3}{2}p - \frac{1}{4}$ in the interval $\frac{1}{2} < p < 0.79667$, and $h(p)$ lies below the line $\frac{3}{2}p - \frac{1}{4}$, where $0.20333 < p < \frac{1}{2}$.

PROOF. If we compute $h(p)$ for $H(3,3)$, we deduce that

$$h(p) = 8p^3 - p^4(6(1 - p^3) + 6p(1 - p^2) + 7p^4 + 2p^4(1 - p))$$

The graph is drawn in Fig. 1. ∎

The reason for using the curve $y = \frac{3}{2}p - \frac{1}{4}$ will now become apparent.

Theorem 2. The number of compositions of $H(3,3)$ with itself necessary to reduce $h(\frac{1}{2} - \varepsilon) \leq \frac{1}{4}$ and $h(\frac{1}{2} + \varepsilon) \geq \frac{3}{4}$ is $-\left[-\dfrac{\log\,(1/4\varepsilon)}{\log\frac{3}{2}} \right]$.

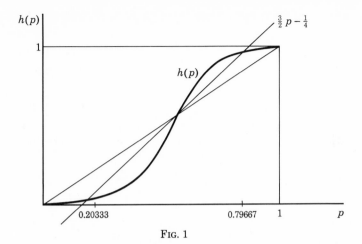

FIG. 1

PROOF. By Theorem 1, it is sufficient to consider the effect of composing $H(3,3)$ along the straight line $\frac{3}{2}p - \frac{1}{4}$, since an upper bound for the number of compositions along this line is also an upper bound for the number of composition along the $h(p)$ curve.

We now employ the staircase construction along $y(p) = \frac{3}{2}p - \frac{1}{4}$. We claim that the abscissa of the kth composition is $p_k = \frac{1}{2} - (\frac{3}{2})^k \varepsilon$ if we start at $p_0 = \frac{1}{2} - \varepsilon$. This claim is substantiated by a trivial induction on k. We choose s to be the least integer such that

$$p_s \leq \tfrac{1}{4}$$

Thus $p_{s-1} > \frac{1}{4}$ and we have

$$\tfrac{1}{2} - (\tfrac{3}{2})^s \varepsilon \leq \tfrac{1}{4} < \tfrac{1}{2} - (\tfrac{3}{2})^{s-1} \varepsilon$$

The upper bound gives

$$\left(\frac{3}{2}\right)^{s-1} < \frac{1}{4\varepsilon} \quad \text{or} \quad s < 1 + \frac{\log\,(1/4\varepsilon)}{\log \frac{3}{2}}$$

The same number s also works to show $h(\frac{1}{2} + \varepsilon) \geq \frac{3}{4}$, since $H(3,3)$ is self-dual. ∎

Corollary 3. The number of contacts used in this construction is less than $9(1/4\varepsilon)^{5.41}$.

PROOF. Since $H(3,3)$ uses 9 contacts, the total number of contacts is

$$9^s < 9 \cdot 9^{[\log\,(1/4\varepsilon)]/\log \frac{3}{2}} = 9\left(\frac{1}{4\varepsilon}\right)^{(\log 9)/(\log \frac{3}{2})} = 9\left(\frac{1}{4\varepsilon}\right)^{5.41} \quad ∎$$

Corollary 4. Given $0 < a < c < 1$, $b = (a + c)/2$, $d = \max\,(b, 1 - b)$, and $\epsilon = (c - a)/4$, one can construct a network whose reliability function has the property that $h(\frac{1}{2} - \varepsilon) \leq \frac{1}{4}$ and $h(\frac{1}{2} + \varepsilon) \geq \frac{3}{4}$. Furthermore, the number of contacts involved does not exceed

$$9\left[\frac{\log_2 \varepsilon}{\log_2 d}\right]\left(\frac{1}{c - a}\right)^{5.41}$$

PROBLEMS

1. Using $H(5,5)$ instead of $H(3,3)$ carry out an analysis of the type employed in this section.

8 THE END GAME

It is now possible to finish our problem by designing a network which will move the probabilities from $\frac{1}{4}$ and $\frac{3}{4}$ to 0 and 1.   The following lemma will be very useful in computational work.

Lemma 1. If $h(p) \le ap^r$, then

$$h^{(s)}(p) \le \frac{(a^{1/(r-1)})^{r^s} p^{r^s}}{a^{1/(r-1)}}$$

PROOF.   The argument will be an induction on s.

BASIS. $s = 1$

$$h^{(1)}(p) = h(p) \le \frac{a^{r/(r-1)} p^r}{a^{1/(r-1)}} = ap^r$$

INDUCTION STEP.   Assuming that

$$h^{(s-1)}(p) \le \frac{(a^{1/(r-1)})^{r^{s-1}} p^{r^{s-1}}}{a^{1/(r-1)}}$$

we compute [using the monotonicity of $h(p)$]

$$h^{(s)}(p) = h(h^{s-1}(p))$$
$$h^{(s)}(p) \le a \left(\frac{(a^{1/(r-1)})^{r^{s-1}} p^{r^{s-1}}}{a^{1/(r-1)}} \right)^r$$
$$h^{(s)}(p) \le \frac{a^{(r-1)/(r-1)} (a^{1/(r-1)})^{r^s} p^{r^s}}{a^{r/(r-1)}} = \frac{(a^{1/(r-1)})^{r^s} p^{r^s}}{(a^{1/(r-1)})} \quad \blacksquare$$

Lemma 2.   If a network contains k contacts and if $h(p) \le ap^r$, then

$$h^{(s)}(p) \le \frac{\left(a^{1/(r-1)}\right)^{n^{(\log r)/(\log k)}} p^{n^{(\log r)/(\log k)}}}{a^{1/(r-1)}}$$

where $k^s = n$.

PROOF.   Since the network uses k contacts, the composed network uses $k^s = n$ contacts.   Use the Lemma 1, where

$$r^s = 2^{s \log_2 r} = 2^{((\log_2 n) \log_2 r)/\log_2 k} = n^{(\log r)/(\log k)} \quad \blacksquare$$

Theorem 3.   For the network $H(3,3)$

$$h^{(s)}(p) \le \frac{1}{\sqrt{8}} (\sqrt{8} p)^{\sqrt{N}}$$

where the number of contacts N is given by

$$N \leq \left(\frac{\log \sqrt{8}\, h^{(s)}(p)}{\log \sqrt{8}\, p}\right)^2$$

PROOF. $h(p) \leq 8p^3$ for $H(3,3)$ (cf. Theorem 7.1), and thus, by Lemma 1,

$$h^{(s)}(p) \leq \frac{(\sqrt{8}\, p)^{3^s}}{\sqrt{8}}$$

Since each composition multiplies the number of contacts by 9, the total number is $N = 9^s$. $\sqrt{N} = 3^s$.

$$h^{(s)}(p) \leq \frac{1}{\sqrt{8}}\,(\sqrt{8}\, p)^{\sqrt{N}}$$

This gives (note the change of the direction of the inequality)

$$N \leq \left(\frac{\log \sqrt{8}\, h^{(s)}(p)}{\log \sqrt{8}\, p}\right)^2$$

As long as $p \leq 1/\sqrt{8}$, this result is valid.   Otherwise, the upper bound on h exceeds 1. $\blacksquare$

With these preliminaries disposed of, we return to the end game. Remember that our problem is to take a $p \leq \frac{1}{4}$ and improve this until $h(p) \leq \delta$.

Theorem 4.   Improving a circuit in which $p \leq \frac{1}{4}$ to a circuit in which $h(p) \leq \delta$ requires not more than

$$9\left(\frac{\log \sqrt{8}\, \delta}{\log \sqrt{8}\, \frac{1}{4}}\right)^2$$

contacts.

PROOF.   We again use $H(3,3)$ so that

$$N \leq 9\left(\frac{\log \sqrt{8}\, \delta}{\log \sqrt{8}\, \frac{1}{4}}\right)^2$$

The factor 9 comes from the fact that s must be an integer and hence N jumps by multiples of 9.   Surely this number of contacts suffices.   Since $H(3,3)$ is self-dual, symmetry shows that we move from $p \geq \frac{3}{4}$ to $h(p) \geq 1 - \delta$. $\blacksquare$

Now all three games may be combined to give the following theorem, which tells us that it is possible to design circuits that have arbitrary reliability even though the individual components are extremely bad.

Theorem   5.   (Moore-Shannon)   Given $\delta > 0$, $0 < a < c < 1$, $b = (a + c)/2$, $d = \max(b, 1 - b)$, and $\varepsilon = (c - a)/4$.   Then there

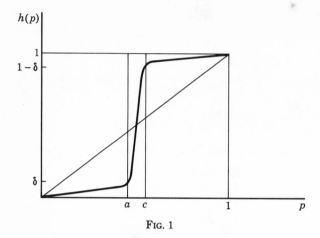

FIG. 1

exists a network such that

$$h(a) < \delta \qquad h(c) > 1 - \delta$$

using no more than

$$81 \left[\frac{\log \varepsilon}{\log d} \right] \left(\frac{1}{4\varepsilon} \right)^{5.41} \left(\frac{\log \sqrt{8}\, \delta}{\log \sqrt{8}\, \frac{1}{4}} \right)^2$$

contacts.

PROOF. Compose the opening, middle, and end games. |

Corollary 6. Given $\delta > 0$, and $0 < a < c < 1$, one can construct a network whose $h(p)$ curve passes between a and c in such a way that $h(a) < \delta$ and $h(c) > 1 - \delta$ as shown in Fig. 1.

PROBLEMS

1. Establish results similar to Lemma 1 when the inequality is reversed and when p is replaced by $1 - p$.

2. Show that

$$N \leq \left(\frac{\log \left(\sqrt{8}\, (1 - h^{(s)}(1 - p)) \right)}{\log \sqrt{8}\, (1 - p)} \right)^2$$

in the case discussed in Prob. 1.

9 THE MOST COMMON PRACTICAL PROBLEM

We briefly consider the problem of improving the reliability of circuits whose components are initially very good. We immediately obtain one answer by using the results of the preceding section.

Theorem 1. Given δ_1, $\delta_2 > 0$, $0 < a < \frac{1}{4}$, and $\frac{3}{4} < c < 1$, one may construct a circuit whose $h(p)$ function has the property that

$$h(a) \leq \delta_1 \qquad h(c) \leq 1 - \delta_2$$

This circuit uses N contacts, where

$$N \leq \max\left(9\left(\frac{\log \sqrt{8}\, \delta_1}{\log \sqrt{8}\, a}\right)^2, \, 9\left(\frac{\log \sqrt{8}\, \delta_2}{\log \sqrt{8}\,(1-c)}\right)^2\right)$$

PROOF. Obvious. ∎

It is interesting to reverse our thinking slightly and try to obtain a lower bound on the number of contacts necessary to achieve a certain reliability.

Theorem 2. Given δ_1, $\delta_2 > 0$, $0 < a < c < 1$, and a network A whose $h(p)$ function satisfies

$$h(a) \leq \delta_1 \qquad h(c) \geq 1 - \delta_2$$

Then the number of contacts N in A satisfies

$$N \geq \frac{\log \delta_1}{\log a} \frac{\log \delta_2}{\log (1 - c)}$$

PROOF. Assume A has length l and width w. There exists a path through l contacts from one terminal to the other. The probability that this path is closed when it should be open is a^l. If this happens, A is closed when it should be open, hence

$$\delta_1 \geq a^l \qquad \text{and} \qquad \log \delta_1 \geq l \log a \qquad \text{or} \qquad l \geq \frac{\log \delta_1}{\log a}$$

since dividing by a negative number reverses the inequality. A similar argument with cut sets yields

$$w \geq \frac{\log \delta_2}{\log (1 - c)}$$

But

$$N \geq lw \geq \frac{\log \delta_1}{\log a} \frac{\log \delta_2}{\log (1 - c)} \quad \blacksquare$$

EXAMPLE. Suppose $a = 0.1$ and $c = 0.9$. If we wanted a network which makes only one error in a million operations, we would need at least

$$\frac{\log 10^{-6}}{\log 0.1} \frac{\log 10^{-6}}{\log 0.1} = 36 \text{ contacts}$$

Theorem 1 tells us that we will not need more than 855 contacts.

10 UPPER BOUNDS ON ERROR PROBABILITIES WITH $H(l,w)$

In this section we shall attempt to estimate δ_1 and δ_2 as functions of a, c, l, and w. To proceed in this investigation, we consider the infinite network shown in Fig. 1.

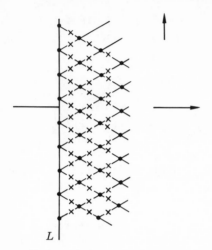

FIG. 1 Each symbol × denotes a crummy relay.

Definition 1. Let P_i be the probability of a node in the ith vertical column being connected to the common node L, $i = 1, 2, \ldots$. Naturally, $P_0 = 1$.

We wish to estimate P_n.

Lemma 2. $P_n < 2pP_{n-1} + 2pP_{n+1}$.

PROOF. Node *, Fig. 2, is connected to L if 1 (or 2) is connected to L and the contact between 1 (or 2) and * is closed. This has probability pP_{n-1} for node 1 and also pP_{n-1} for node 2. The analysis is similar for nodes 3 and 4. Note that we just add the probabilities as if they were disjoint. Since they are not disjoint, we get an upper bound for P_n. ∎

It is desirable to obtain a better upper bound for P_n. Noting from the preceding lemma that $P_{n+1} \leq P_n$, then

$$P_n < 2pP_{n-1} + 2pP_n$$
$$P_n < \frac{2p}{1 - 2p} P_{n-1} \tag{1}$$

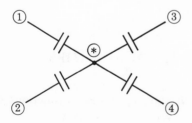

FIG. 2

Remembering that $P_0 = 1$,

$$P_n < \left(\frac{2p}{1 - 2p}\right)^n$$

If Eq. (1) is used in the lemma, we can compute a still better bound on P_n, namely, that

$$P_n < \frac{2p(1 - 2p)}{1 - 2p - 4p^2} P_{n-1}$$

This bound may be used in the lemma to obtain a still better bound, and the process may be continued indefinitely. We wish to know the outcome of this infinite iteration.

Theorem 3.   If $P_{n+1} < \alpha_j P_n$ and if $p < \frac{1}{4}$, then

$$P_n \leq \left(\frac{1 - \sqrt{1 - 16p^2}}{4p}\right) P_{n-1}$$

PROOF.   Substituting the hypothesis into the preceding lemma gives

$$P_n < 2pP_{n-1} + 2p\alpha_j P_n \qquad P_n < \frac{2p}{1 - 2p\alpha_j} P_{n-1}$$

Thus
$$\alpha_{j+1} = \frac{2p}{1 - 2p\alpha_j} = \frac{1}{1/2p - \alpha_j}$$

The hyperbola $y = \dfrac{1}{1/2p - x}$ is plotted in Fig. 3.   Consider the intersection of the curve with the diagonal $\alpha_{j+1} = \alpha_j$.   Let $\alpha_{j+1} = \alpha_j = \alpha$

$$\alpha = \frac{2p}{1 - 2p\alpha} \qquad \text{or} \qquad 2p\alpha^2 - \alpha + 2p = 0$$

which yields
$$\alpha = \frac{1 \pm \sqrt{1 - 16p^2}}{4p}$$

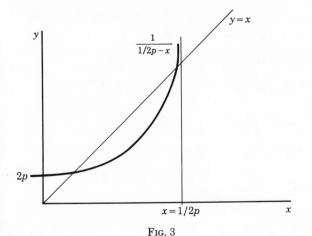

FIG. 3

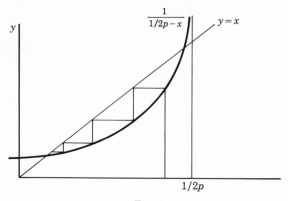

FIG. 4

We see from this expression that there are two roots for α when $p < \frac{1}{4}$, and this condition is specified by the hypothesis. We are faced with the problem of selecting which root we wish for α_0. Glancing at the staircase construction illustrated in Fig. 4, we see that the lower point of intersection corresponding to the negative root is a stable point of the iterative process. Thus the negative sign should be selected and

$$P_n \leq \left(\frac{1 - \sqrt{1 - p^2}}{4p}\right) P_{n-1} \quad \blacksquare$$

Corollary 4. $P_n \leq \left(\dfrac{1 - \sqrt{1 - p^2}}{4p}\right)^n$

Now the relation of the infinite network to ordinary $H(l,w)$ networks is established.

Lemma 5.   Any $H(l,w)$ may be decomposed as shown in Fig. 5.

Lemma 6.   Let $P^{(j)}$ be the probability that the left half of the network is connected to the jth node from the top of the right half of the network.

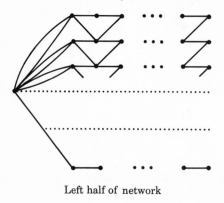

Left half of network   Right half of network

FIG. 5

Then

$$h(p) \leq P^{(1)}(2p - p^2) + P^{(2)}(2p - p^2) + \cdots$$

where the last term is

$$\begin{cases} P^{(k)}(2p - p^2) & \text{if } w \equiv 0 \text{ mod } 2 \\ P^{(k)}p & \text{if } w \equiv 1 \text{ mod } 2 \end{cases}$$

Where $k = \left[\dfrac{w + 1}{2}\right]$.

PROOF. The factors $2p - p^2$ are the probability of the network consisting of two contacts in parallel being closed. ∎

Theorem 7.

$$\delta_1 < \left(\frac{1 - \sqrt{1 - 16a^2}}{4a}\right)^{l-1} wa$$

$$\delta_2 < \left(\frac{1 - \sqrt{1 - 16(1 - c)^2}}{4(1 - c)}\right)^{w-1} l(1 - c)$$

PROOF. Clearly $P^{(i)} \leq P_{l-1}$, since adding contacts only increases the probability that the network is closed. Thus

$$\delta_1 < \left(\frac{1 - \sqrt{1 - 16a^2}}{4a}\right)^{l-1} wa$$

since if $w \equiv 0 \text{ mod } 2$, there are $w/2$ terms each multiplied by $2a$. If $w \equiv 1 \text{ mod } 2$, there are $(w - 1)/2$ terms multiplied by $2a$ and one term multiplied by a. By duality,

$$\delta_2 < \left(\frac{1 - \sqrt{1 - 16(1 - c)^2}}{4(1 - c)}\right)^{w-1} l(1 - c) \quad ∎$$

Corollary 8. If a and $1 - c$ are sufficiently small [so that a^4, or $(1 - c)^4$, is negligible], then

$$\delta_1 < \frac{w}{2}(2a)^l \qquad \delta_2 < \frac{l}{2}(2(1 - c))^w$$

PROOF. $\delta_1 < \dfrac{aw}{(4a)^{l-1}}(1 - \sqrt{1 - 16a^2})^{l-1}$. Since $a < \frac{1}{4}$,

$$\delta_1 < (1 - (1 - 8a^2 - O(a^4))^{l-1} \frac{aw}{(4a)^{l-1}}$$

$$\delta_1 < \frac{aw}{(4a)^{l-1}}(8a^2)^{l-1} = \frac{w}{2}(2a)^l$$

Similarly, $\delta_2 < \dfrac{l}{2}(2(1 - c))^w$ ∎

11 SOME CALCULATIONS

To get an idea of the number of components involved in obtaining a fixed reliability, we perform some computations. Suppose

$$a = 1 - c = 1/200$$

and we desire circuits with a reliability of 10^{-20}. By using only the end-game analysis, we get the results listed in the accompanying table. If one uses a $H(10,10)$ network, then the error probability is $\leq 10(10^{-2})^{10}$ $= 10^{-19}$ with a redundancy of 100 to 1. Note that our lower bound tells us that at least 68 contacts are required.

Number of stages	Redundancy	Reliability
1	0	10^{-6}
2	81	8×10^{-18}
3	729	4×10^{-51}

Those readers who know the results of Von Neumann[3] may be surprised at the modest redundancy required here. It is therefore interesting to discuss what makes relays essentially more desirable for reliability work than Sheffer stroke elements. One reason is our assumption about the perfect wiring. In effect, the logical functions AND and OR are obtained with perfect reliability, since we are dealing with relay contacts. This accounts, in some part, for the improvement over the results of Von Neumann.

Also, note that the construction for relays does not require an absolute minimal probability of successful operation like the majority organs in Von Neumann's scheme.

12   COHERENT SYSTEMS

A more general class of problems is now considered. Instead of restricting ourselves to networks of branch-type elements, we consider a large system of units connected together with the following properties:

1. There are a finite number n of subsystems.
2. Each subsystem either works or fails.
3. The probability of the ith system working is independent of the probabilities of the other subsystems working.

It is convenient to define n variables, $w_1, \ldots, w_n$, to record the performance of the subsystems. If subsystem i is working, $w_i = 1$; if subsystem i is not working, $w_i = 0$, where $i = 1, \ldots, n$. Let

$$\varphi(w_1, \ldots, w_n) = \varphi(\mathbf{w})$$

be 1 if the entire system works and 0 if the complete system fails. Thus φ is the *structure function* of the system. Note that φ is a map from $\{0,1\}^n$ into $\{0,1\}$; that is, it is a switching function. More formally, a coherent system is defined as follows.

Definition 1. A system is *coherent* iff

(1) $\varphi(\mathbf{1}) = 1$ where $\mathbf{1} = (1, \ldots, 1)$
(2) $\varphi(\mathbf{0}) = 0$ where $\mathbf{0} = (0, \ldots, 0)$
(3) If $\mathbf{v} \leq \mathbf{w}$, then $\varphi(\mathbf{v}) \leq \varphi(\mathbf{w})$.

These assumptions are very plausible; if every subsystem functions (fails), the system functions (fails). The third assumption says that increasing the number of subsystems which function correctly cannot hurt the performance of the whole system.

We note that the Moore-Shannon model of relay circuits fits the definition of a coherent system. We shall now derive a generalization of Theorem 3.1.

Definition 2. Let $p_i = \Pr\{i\text{th component functions}\} = \Pr\{w_i = 1\}$. Let $h(\mathbf{p}) = \Pr\{\text{system functions}\} = \Pr\{\varphi(\mathbf{w}) = 1\}$ where $(p_1, \ldots, p_n) = \mathbf{p}$.

Proposition 3. $h(0) = 0$ $h(1) = 1$
We shall speak of a structure function being *degenerate* in w_i iff

$$\varphi(w_1, \ldots, w_{i-1}, 0, w_{i+1}, \ldots, w_n) = \varphi(w_1, \ldots, w_{i-1}, 1, w_{i+1}, \ldots, w_n)$$

The following lemma, due to Esary and Proschan, is very useful.

Lemma 3. Given a coherent system with at least two nondegenerate components, and assuming that the subsystems are independent with probabilities $p_1, \ldots, p_n$ such that $0 < p_i < 1$ for $i = 1, \ldots, n$, then

$$\text{cov}\,(\varphi(\mathbf{w}), S(\mathbf{w})) > \text{var}\,(\varphi(\mathbf{w}))$$

where† $S(\mathbf{w}) = \sum_{i=1}^{n} w_i$.

We now obtain the main result.

Theorem 4. If a coherent system has probabilities p_i of the subsystems functioning, and if $0 < p_i < 1$, the subsystems are independent. If there are at least two nondegenerate subsystems, then

$$\sum_{i=1}^{n} p_i(1 - p_i)\,\frac{\partial h(\mathbf{p})}{\partial p_i} > h(\mathbf{p})(1 - h(\mathbf{p}))$$

PROOF. Expand the switching function $\varphi(\mathbf{w})$ around the variable w_i to get

$$\varphi(w_1, \ldots, w_n) = w_i\varphi_{i1} + (1 - w_i)\varphi_{i0}$$
$$h(\mathbf{p}) = \Pr\{\varphi(\mathbf{w}) = 1\} = \Pr\{w_i\varphi_{i1} + (1 - w_i)\varphi_{i0} = 1\}$$
$$= \Pr\{w_i = 1\}\,\Pr\{\varphi_{i1} = 1\} + \Pr\{w_i = 0\}\,\Pr\{\varphi_{i0} = 1\}$$
$$= p_i\,\Pr\{\varphi_{i1} = 1\} + (1 - p_i)\,\Pr\{\varphi_{i0} = 1\}$$

† cov denotes the *covariance* function and var the *variance* function. Cf. Feller.

Differentiating with respect to p_i gives

$$\frac{\partial h(\mathbf{p})}{\partial p_i} = \Pr \{\varphi_{i1} = 1\} - \Pr \{\varphi_{i0} = 1\} \tag{1}$$

Clearly, $w_i \varphi(\mathbf{w}) = w_i^2 \varphi_{i1} + w_i(1 - w_i)\varphi_{i0} = w_i \varphi_{i1}$

$$\Pr \{w_i \varphi_{i1}\} = \Pr \{w_i = 1\} \Pr \{\varphi_{i1} = 1\} = p_i \Pr \{\varphi_{i1} = 1\}$$

Thus

$$
\begin{aligned}
\text{cov } (\varphi(\mathbf{w}), w_i) &= \Pr \{w_i(\varphi(w)) = 1\} - \Pr \{w_i = 1\} \Pr \{\varphi(\mathbf{w}) = 1\} \\
&= p_i \Pr \{\varphi_{i1} = 1\} - p_i^2 \Pr \{\varphi_{i1} = 1\} - p_i(1 - p_i) \Pr \{\varphi_{i0} = 1\} \\
&= p_i(1 - p_i)(\Pr \{\varphi_{i1} = 1\} - \Pr \{\varphi_{i0} = 1\}) \\
\text{cov } (\varphi(\mathbf{w}), w_i) &= p_i(1 - p_i) \frac{\partial h}{\partial p_i}
\end{aligned}
$$

by Eq. (1).   By the linearity of the covariance function, ·

$$\text{cov } (\varphi(\mathbf{w}), S(\mathbf{w})) = \sum_{i=1}^{n} \text{cov } (\varphi(\mathbf{w}), w_i) = \sum_{i=1}^{n} p_i(1 - p_i) \frac{\partial h}{\partial p_i} \tag{2}$$

Note that

$$\text{var } (\varphi(\mathbf{w})) = \Pr \{\varphi(\mathbf{w}) = 1\} - (\Pr \{\varphi(\mathbf{w}) = 1\})^2 = h(\mathbf{p})(1 - h(\mathbf{p})) \tag{3}$$

Using the lemma with Eqs. (2) and (3) yields

$$\sum_{i=1}^{n} p_i(1 - p_i) \frac{\partial h(\mathbf{p})}{\partial p_i} > h(\mathbf{p})(1 - h(\mathbf{p})) \quad \blacksquare$$

PROBLEMS

1. Given a coherent system and a specification $\mathbf{w} = (w_1, \ldots, w_n)$ for the system, define

$$A(\mathbf{w}) = \{i | w_i = 1\} \qquad B(\mathbf{w}) = \{i | w_i = 0\}$$

If $\varphi(\mathbf{w}) = 1$, $A(\mathbf{w})$ is a *path;* if $\varphi(\mathbf{w}) = 0$, $B(\mathbf{w})$ is called a *cut*. A *minimal path (cut)* is a path (cut) such that no proper subset is also a path (cut). If the A_j are minimal paths $(j = 1, \ldots, r)$ and the B_k minimal cuts $(k = 1, \ldots, s)$, then show that

$$\prod_{k=1}^{s} \left(1 - \prod_{i \,\epsilon\, B_k} (1 - p_i)\right) \leq h(\mathbf{p}) \leq 1 - \prod_{j=1}^{r} \left(1 - \prod_{i \,\epsilon\, A_j} p_i\right)$$

2. Use Theorem 4 to characterize the set of possible $h(p)$ curves which can arise. Compare with the results of Sec. 3.

3. Prove Lemma 3.

13 SUMMARY

The principal result of this chapter is Theorem 8.5, which says that arbitrarily reliable circuits can be constructed from unreliable components.   Furthermore, inequalities which bound the number of contacts required for these constructions are given.

The technique used to achieve this reliability was to replace each contact in the network by a sufficiently large network of elements of the same type.   This construction is independent of the logical function realized by the network.   By taking the switching function into account, Kochen has shown that some savings can be obtained.

The first mathematical study of reliable circuitry was by Von Neumann.   Moore and Shannon carried out a similar program for relay networks and obtained results of a different form; this chapter is based on their work.   The generalizations of Sec. 12 are due to Esary and Proschan.

The reliability problem studied in this chapter is very important; much work is being done at both the practical and theoretical level.   For a summary of what was being done in 1962, see the book by Wilcox and Mann.   For generalizations involving the construction of reliable networks with gate-type components and with memory, see the monograph of Winograd and Cowan.

CHAPTER 9 *introduction to sequential machines*

1 INTRODUCTION

In contrast to the devices studied in the first eight chapters, a sequential machine, or automaton, is a device whose behavior at a particular instant of time depends not only on the present input to the machine, but generally on the entire past history of the machine, including the past inputs. For instance, the behavior of a dog who hears a bell ringing is influenced not only by the bell but by previous events in his life. An abstract system will be formulated in order to characterize automata. The first step is to provide inputs for our machines.

Definition 1. Let $\Sigma_k = \{\sigma_0, \ldots, \sigma_{k-1}\}$ denote the *input alphabet*. The $\sigma_i (i = 0, \ldots, k - 1)$ are called the *letters* of the input alphabet. The *input dictionary*, denoted by Σ_k^*, is defined to be the set of all words formed from Σ_k, where a *word* or *tape* means any finite sequence of letters.

Σ_k^* contains the word with no letters, the *null word*, which will be denoted by Λ.

Definition 2. The *length* of any word $x \in \Sigma_k^*$ is defined to be the number of letters in the word and is denoted by $\lg(x)$.

EXAMPLES
  (1) $\lg(\sigma_0\sigma_1\sigma_2) = 3$
  (2) $\lg(\sigma_0\sigma_1\sigma_2\sigma_2\sigma_0) = 5$
  (3) $\lg(\Lambda) = 0$

Definition 3. For $x, y \in \Sigma_k^*$, the *concatenation* of x and y is written xy and is defined by writing x followed by y.

EXAMPLE. Let $x = \sigma_0\sigma_1\sigma_2$ and $y = \sigma_2\sigma_1\sigma_0$; then

$$xy = \sigma_0\sigma_1\sigma_2\sigma_2\sigma_1\sigma_0 \qquad yx = \sigma_2\sigma_1\sigma_0\sigma_0\sigma_1\sigma_2$$

The abbreviation $x^n = \overbrace{xx \cdots x}^{n}$ is convenient, especially if we define $x^0 = \Lambda$. Then it can be observed that the length function has some of the formal properties of the logarithm.

$$\lg(xy) = \lg(x) + \lg(y)$$
$$\lg(x^n) = n\lg(x)$$

The effect of concatenation on the empty word is significant.

$$x\Lambda = \Lambda x = x \qquad \text{for any } x \in \Sigma_k^*$$

Since $(xy)z = x(yz)$ for any x, y, $z \in \Sigma_k^*$, concatenation is an associative operation and parentheses are generally not needed in grouping words.

The set of all words, Σ_k^*, will constitute the universe from which the inputs to the automata are drawn. The introductory theory will be developed for arbitrary k, but it will be shown eventually that binary inputs are sufficiently general.

Definition 4. A *sequential machine without output* over Σ_k is a triple $S = \langle S, M, a \rangle$, where S is a nonempty set called the *set of internal states*,† $a \in S$ is the *initial state*, and $M: S \times \Sigma_k \to S$ is called the *direct transition function*.

Normally, Σ_k should appear inside the parentheses and be part of the system, but since all of the machines to be studied will use the same alphabet, Σ_k is omitted. No confusion will arise in the use of the same symbol for the machine and for the set of internal states of the machine.

EXAMPLE. $S = \langle S, M, a_0 \rangle$, where $S = \{a_0, \ldots, a_5\}$ and M is defined by its graph as

$s \in S$	a_0	a_1	a_2	a_3	a_4	a_5
$M(s,\sigma_0)$	a_1	a_2	a_1	a_2	a_5	a_4
$M(s,\sigma_1)$	a_2	a_0	a_2	a_0	a_5	a_5

The action of the machine S may be described by a transition or Moore graph as shown in Fig. 1. The Moore graph is constructed by associating circles (or nodes) with each internal state and an arrow labeled σ connecting state a_i to state a_j iff $M(a_i,\sigma) = a_j$. One can think of the machine reading an input word, or tape, symbol by symbol and progressively passing from one state to the next.

† S is called *finite* iff the number of internal states is finite.

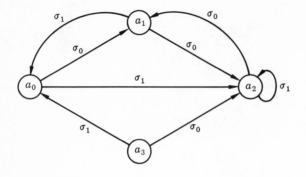

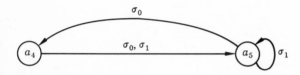

FIG. 1

PROBLEMS

1. Show that $\langle \Sigma_k^*, \cdot, \Lambda \rangle$ is the free monoid (semigroup with identity) on the k generators $\sigma_0, \ldots, \sigma_{k-1}$. The dot $\cdot$ denotes concatenation. Prove that this monoid with $k = 1$ is isomorphic to the monoid $\langle N, +, 0 \rangle$, where N denotes the natural numbers.

2. How many words are there in Σ_k^* whose lengths do not exceed n? Assume $k > 1$.

3. How many sequential machines $S = \langle S, M, a \rangle$ without output over Σ_k are there if the cardinality of S is n?

4. If one defines $\varphi_i = M(s, \sigma_i)$ for $i = 0, \ldots, k - 1$, show that the system $\langle S, \varphi_0, \ldots, \varphi_{k-1}, a \rangle$ is an equivalent model of a sequential machine. Thus every sequential machine is an abstract algebra.

2   RESPONSE FUNCTIONS

It is necessary to extend the domain of direct transition function M from $S \times \Sigma_k$ to $S \times \Sigma_k^*$. This can be done directly by requiring:

Condition 1

$$(\forall s)_S \quad M(s, \Lambda) = s$$
$$(\forall s)_S (\forall x)_{\Sigma_k*} (\forall \sigma)_{\Sigma_k} \quad M(s, x\sigma) = M(M(s, x), \sigma)$$

or

Condition 2

$$(\forall s)_S \quad M(s, \Lambda) = s$$
$$(\forall s)_S (\forall x)_{\Sigma_k*} (\forall \sigma)_{\Sigma_k} \quad M(s, \sigma x) = M(M(s, \sigma), x)$$

The reader should show that the two conditions are equivalent.

Proposition 3. Condition 1 is equivalent to Condition 2.

The extension of the function M to $S \times \Sigma_k^*$ now allows the determination of the state to which the machine will go if it is in state s and input word x occurs. Naturally, this state is $M(s,x)$.

EXAMPLE. Consider the machine given as an example in Sec. 1. We calculate $M(a_2,\sigma_0\sigma_1\sigma_1)$ by using both conditions:

$$\begin{aligned}
M(a_2,\sigma_0\sigma_1\sigma_1) &= M(M(a_2,\sigma_0\sigma_1),\sigma_1) \\
&= M(M(M(a_2,\sigma_0),\sigma_1),\sigma_1) \\
&= M(M(a_1,\sigma_1),\sigma_1) = M(a_0,\sigma_1) = a_2 \\
M(a_2,\sigma_0\sigma_1\sigma_1) &= M(M(a_2,\sigma_0),\sigma_1\sigma_1) \\
&= M(M(M(a_2,\sigma_0),\sigma_1),\sigma_1) \\
&= M(M(a_1,\sigma_1),\sigma_1) = M(a_0,\sigma_1) = a_2
\end{aligned}$$

There is a restriction of the M function which is useful enough to deserve a special name.

Definition 4. The *response function* of a machine $S = \langle S,M,a \rangle$ to any word $x \in \Sigma_k^*$ is defined by

$$rp_S(x) = M(a,x)$$

The function $rp_S(x)$ gives the state to which the machine goes when it starts from its initial state and receives input word x.

Theorem 5. $(\forall s)_S(\forall x,y)_{\Sigma_k^*} \quad M(s,xy) = M(M(s,x),y)$

PROOF. The argument is an induction on $\lg(x)$.

INDUCTION STEP. Assume the result for all tapes of length $\leq m$. Let $x \in \Sigma_k^*$ such that $\lg(x) = m$

$$M(s,\sigma xy) = M(M(s,\sigma),xy)$$

by Condition 2.

Since $\lg(x) = m$, the induction hypothesis holds and

$$M(s,\sigma xy) = M(M(M(s,\sigma),x),y)$$

Using Condition 2 again yields

$$M(s,\sigma xy) = M(M(s,\sigma x),y)$$

from which the result holds for all tapes. |

Corollary 6. $(\forall x,y)_{\Sigma_k^*} \quad rp_S(xy) = M(rp_S(x),y)$

Theorem 7. $(\forall s)_S(\forall x,y,z)_{\Sigma_k^*} \quad M(s,x) = M(s,y)$ implies $M(s,xz) = M(s,yz)$.

PROOF. $M(s,xz) = M(M(s,x),z) = M(M(s,y),z) = M(s,yz)$. |

Corollary 8. $(\forall x,y,z)_{\Sigma_k^*} \quad rp_S(x) = rp_S(y)$ implies $rp_S(xz) = rp_S(yz)$.

The meaning of Theorem 7 is the following: Given a machine S in state s and two different inputs x and y such that both x and y cause S to go into the same target state $t = M(s,x) = M(s,y)$, then the state which the machine goes into under xz is identical to the state it goes into under yz.

PROBLEMS

1. Let $S = \langle S, M, a_1 \rangle$, where $S = \{a_0, a_1, a_2, a_3, a_4, a_5\}$ and M is given by the following table:

s	a_0	a_1	a_2	a_3	a_4	a_5
$M(s, \sigma_0)$	a_1	a_2	a_1	a_2	a_5	a_4
$M(s, \sigma_1)$	a_2	a_0	a_2	a_0	a_5	a_5

Calculate $rp_S(\sigma_0\sigma_1\sigma_1)$, $rp_S(\sigma_1\sigma_1\sigma_0)$, and $M(a_2, \sigma_0\sigma_0\sigma_1)$.

2. Discuss how the concept of time enters into our discussion.

3. Define a function f from Σ_k^* to $S = \{a_0, a_1, a_2\}$ which is not the response function of any machine having the states S.

3 ACCESSIBLE STATES AND CONNECTED MACHINES

To illustrate some of the types of redundant states which may occur in sequential machines, let us examine the machine shown in Fig. 1.

$$T = \langle T, M, a_0 \rangle$$

where $T = \{a_0, a_1, a_2, a_3\}$

t	a_0	a_1	a_2	a_3
$M(t, \sigma_0)$	a_1	a_1	a_1	a_3
$M(t, \sigma_1)$	a_0	a_0	a_0	a_3

It is clear that a_3 is an unnecessary state, since it is not connected to the component of the machine containing the initial state. Although state a_2 is connected to the component of the graph containing the initial state, it is impossible for T to ever get to state a_2. From a practical point of view these states can be eliminated. These ideas motivate the following definitions.

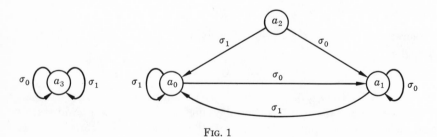

FIG. 1

Definition 1. A state s in a machine $S' = \langle S, M, a \rangle$ is called *accessible* iff there is some input $x \in \Sigma_k^*$ such that

$$s = rp_S(x)$$

Definition 2. Given a sequential machine $S = \langle S, M, a \rangle$, the *connected submachine of* S is defined as $S^c = \langle S', M', a \rangle$, where $S' = \{u \mid (\exists x)_{\Sigma_k^*} \ rp_S(x) = u\}$ and M' is the restriction of M from $S \times \Sigma_k \to S$ to $S' \times \Sigma_k \to S'$. A machine S is called *connected* iff $S = S^c$.

Proposition 3. For any machine S,

$$(S^c)^c = S^c \qquad \text{and} \qquad (\forall x)_{\Sigma_k^*} \ rp_{S^c}(x) = rp_S(x)$$

The preceding proposition indicates that it is only necessary to consider connected machines mathematically. An algorithm which computes S^c will be given; in later sections all machines will be assumed to be connected. The following theorem guarantees that an effective procedure exists for finding the set of accessible states.

Lemma 4. If $S = \langle S, M, a \rangle$ is a finite sequential machine with n states and if $u \in S$ is an accessible state such that $u = rp_S(y)$ for some $y \in \Sigma_k^*$ with $\lg(y) \geq n$, then there exists a word $z \in \Sigma_k^*$ such that $u = rp_S(z)$ and $\lg(z) < \lg(y)$.

PROOF. $u = rp_S(y)$, where $y = \sigma_{j_1} \cdots \sigma_{j_m}$ with $m \geq n$. Let $u_i \ (i = 0, \ldots, m)$ denote the states through which S passes.

$$
\begin{aligned}
u_0 &= a \\
u_1 &= rp_S(\sigma_{j_1}) = M(a, \sigma_{j_1}) \\
u_2 &= M(u_1, \sigma_{j_2}) \\
&\cdots \cdots \cdots \\
u_m &= M(u_{m-1}, \sigma_{j_m}) = u
\end{aligned}
$$

S has only n states; and since $m + 1 > n$, at least two of the u_i are equal. By Dirichlet's principle, $u_p = u_q$ for $0 \leq p < q \leq m$. Consider the tape $z = \sigma_{j_1} \cdots \sigma_{j_p} \sigma_{j_{q+1}} \cdots \sigma_{j_m}$. The resulting sequence of states is

$$
\begin{aligned}
u_0 &= a \\
u_1 &= M(u_0, \sigma_{j_1}) \\
&\cdots \cdots \cdots \\
u_p &= M(u_{p-1}, \sigma_{j_p}) \\
u_{q+1} &= M(u_p, \sigma_{j_{q+1}}) \\
&\cdots \cdots \cdots \\
u_m &= u
\end{aligned}
$$

z is a tape such that $u = rp_S(z)$; and since $\lg(z) = m - (q - p) < m = \lg(y)$, the theorem is proved. $\blacksquare$

Theorem 5. If $S = \langle S, M, a \rangle$ is a finite sequential machine with n states, then every accessible state is the response to some input word x such that $\lg(x) < n$.

PROOF. Let u be an accessible state so that there must exist a $y_1 \in \Sigma_k^*$ such that $u = rp_S(y)$. If $\lg(y_1) < n$, we are done. Otherwise, apply the lemma which says that there is a y_2 such that $u = rp_S(y_2)$ and $\lg(y_2) < \lg(y_1)$. If $\lg(y_2) \geq n$, apply the lemma to obtain y_3 etc. By the well ordering of the natural numbers, there will be a z such that $u = rp_S(z)$ and $\lg(z) < n$. ∎

There is a convenient geometric interpretation of sequential machines which is of practical value in constructing S^c and which is more natural than the Moore graph, since our machines have initial states.

Definition 6. The *right-tree* over Σ_k is a rooted vertex-labeled tree such that the root has out degree k and every other vertex has in degree 1 and out degree k.

Before prescribing the labeling of the tree, it is convenient to have a coordinate for every vertex of the tree.

Definition 7. The *height h* of a vertex of the right-tree over Σ_k is defined to be the least number of branches of the tree connecting the vertex to the root. The *coordinate* of a vertex in the tree is given by a pair (h, w), where h is the height of the vertex and w is the number of the vertex in the set of all vertices of height h, as numbered $0, 1, \ldots, k^h - 1$ starting from the leftmost vertex of the set of vertices of height h.

An example of a tree and some of its coordinates are shown in Fig. 2a.

Next we indicate a mapping which associates with every vertex of the tree a word of Σ_k^*.

Definition 8. The *right-label mapping* denoted by $\|(h, w)\|$ is defined by recursion to be the following transformation from the set of coordinates of vertices of the tree to Σ_k^*.

$$\|(0, 0)\| = \Lambda$$
$$\|(h, w)\| = \left\|\left(h - 1, \left[\frac{w}{k}\right]\right)\right\| \sigma_{|w|_k}$$

where $|w|_k$ denotes the residue of w modulo k, that is, the number $r \in \{0, \ldots, k - 1\}$ such $w \equiv r \bmod k$ and $[w/k]$ is the largest integer $\leq w/k$.

The reader should compute the labels of the right-tree shown in Fig. 2b from the tree given in Fig. 2a by means of Definition 8.

Proposition 9. The label mapping from the tree into Σ_k^* is one to one and onto.

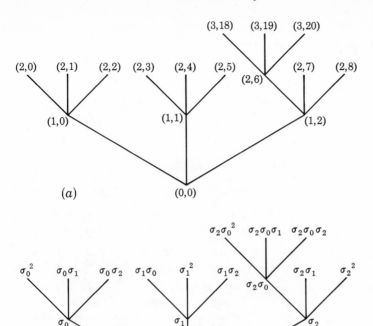

FIG. 2

The right-tree earns its name because concatenation is performed on the right. The left-tree could be defined in the obvious way. We note that the right-tree is infinite and that the right-tree over Σ_1 is very dull; it is just a straight line.

Definition 10. The *response tree* of a sequential machine S over Σ_k is defined to be the right-tree over Σ_k with the label $\|(h,w)\|$ replaced by $rp_S(\|(h,w)\|)$.

Again the response tree is infinite, but if S is finite, the states must be repeated as labels. This suggests *pruning* the tree by terminating any branch whose label is a state previously encountered in the tree. These ideas should be clarified by the example shown in Fig. 3.

$$U = \langle U, M, a_0 \rangle$$

u	a_0	a_1	a_2
$M(u,\sigma_0)$	a_0	a_2	a_2
$M(u,\sigma_1)$	a_1	a_0	a_0

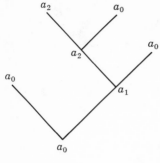

FIG. 3

The procedure for finding the response tree for a given machine S provides an efficient algorithm for computing S^c.

Theorem 11.   There is an effective procedure for computing the connected submachine of any given finite machine.

PROOF.   Given any finite machine S, the response tree is computed.   Any state in the response tree is accessible, and furthermore, every accessible state appears in the tree.   Theorem 5 guarantees that the construction of the response tree terminates and that the height of any accessible state is no more than $n - 1$. |

PROBLEMS

1.   Given the sequential machine $S = \langle S, M, a_0 \rangle$, construct the response tree and hence S^c.

	a_0	a_1	a_2	a_3	a_4	a_5
$M(s, \sigma_0)$	a_1	a_2	a_0	a_3	a_5	a_0
$M(s, \sigma_1)$	a_2	a_1	a_2	a_1	a_1	a_4
$M(s, \sigma_2)$	a_0	a_3	a_3	a_2	a_2	a_5

2.   The term "connected" is used to denote machines of a special kind as described in the preceding section.   Does a machine whose Moore graph is a connected graph have the property of being connected in our terminology?

3.   Write out the formal procedure for constructing the response tree of any finite machine.   (HINT: Theorem 5 will be necessary for proving the termination of the algorithm.)

4.   Given a finite sequential machine S, is the response tree of S unique?   If so, prove it.   If not, what modification to the tree must be made to obtain uniqueness?

4   THE FREE AUTOMATON: CONGRUENCE RELATIONS AND HOMOMORPHISMS

There is an infinite sequential machine which is, in some sense, a prototype for all sequential machines over the same input alphabet.

Definition 1. The free sequential machine over Σ_k is defined to be $F_k = \langle \Sigma_k^*, M, \Lambda \rangle$, where†

$$(\forall x)_{\Sigma_{k^*}} \quad M(x, \sigma_i) = x\sigma_i \qquad \text{for } i = 0, \ldots, k - 1$$

It will be shown in Prob. 1 that there is a structure-preserving mapping from the free machine F_k onto any connected sequential machine over Σ_k. The response tree of F_k is the entire right-tree.

Definition 2. Let $S = \langle S, M, a \rangle$ be any sequential machine over Σ_k. R is said to be a *right congruence relation on* S iff R is an equivalence relation on S which satisfies the *substitution property.*

$$(\forall u, v)_S \quad uRv \Rightarrow (M(u, \sigma_i)) R (M(v, \sigma_i)) \qquad \text{for } i = 0, \ldots, k - 1$$

Since Definition 2 holds for any sequential machine, the special case of a right congruence on Σ_k^* may be defined for the free machines as follows.

Definition 3. R is a *right congruence on* Σ_k^* iff R is an equivalence relation on Σ_k^* which satisfies the substitution property

$$(\forall x, y, z)_{\Sigma_{k^*}} \quad xRy \Rightarrow xzRyz$$

EXAMPLE. Consider the following relation R on Σ_k^*. For any x, $y \in \Sigma_k^*$, define xRy iff $\lg(x) = \lg(y)$. Clearly, R is an equivalence relation on Σ_k^*. R is also a right congruence on Σ_k^*, because if x and y have the same length, m, then xz and yz have the same length, $m + \lg(z)$.

Congruence relations will turn out to play an essential role in the theory of sequential machines. For this reason, it is important that the process used for testing a given equivalence relation for the substitution property be understood. Suppose that R is an equivalence relation on S and that S has cardinality n. Assume R is given as a collection of disjoint classes $R_1, \ldots, R_m$, where each R_i contains r_i elements. Note that $\sum_{i=1}^{m} r_i = n$. First select an element of set R_l, say, s_{l_1}, and test it against s_{l_2} to see if $M(s_{l_1}, \sigma_i) R M(s_{l_2}, \sigma_i)$ for $i = 0, \ldots,$ $k - 1$. This is easy to do by looking at either the tree or the M table. Note that it is unnecessary to test a state against itself and, similarly, that once s_{i_1} has been tested against s_{i_2}, testing s_{i_2} against s_{i_1} is unnecessary. Thus at most

$$\sum_{i=1}^{m} \frac{r_i(r_i - 1)}{2} = \frac{1}{2}\left(\left(\sum_{i=1}^{m} r_i^2\right) - n\right)$$

† F_k previously denoted the free boolean algebra on k generators. No confusion should result with the present usage.

tests are necessary, since once the condition fails to be satisfied the computation is halted.   Transitivity also allows a reduction in the number of tests.   In the following example the M table is given and the equivalence relation is $R = \{[a_0,a_1,a_2],[a_3,a_4],[a_5]\}$.

	a_0	a_1	a_2	a_3	a_4	a_5
$M(s,\sigma_0)$	a_3	a_4	a_3	a_1	a_1	a_0
$M(s,\sigma_1)$	a_2	a_1	a_0	a_4	a_3	a_1

Since $a_0 R a_1$, $M(a_0,\sigma_0) = a_3$ and $M(a_1,\sigma_0) = a_4$, so the substitution property is verified for σ_0 since $a_3 R a_4$.   Now $M(a_0,\sigma_1) = a_2$ and $M(a_1,\sigma_1) = a_1$. Since $a_1 R a_2$, the test for a_0 against a_1 is successfully concluded.   Note that the entire test requires $3 + 1 + 0 = 4$ tests.

It is desirable to obtain an idea of structual equality of sequential machines.   This suggests the idea of a structure-preserving mapping between sequential machines.

Definition 4.   If $S = \langle S,M,a \rangle$ and $T = \langle T,N,b \rangle$ are two sequential machines, then φ is said to be a *homomorphism* from S into (onto) T iff φ is a mapping from S into (onto) T such that

$$\varphi(a) = b$$
$$(\forall s)_S \quad \varphi(M(s,\sigma_i)) = N(\varphi(s),\sigma_i) \quad \text{for } i = 0, \ldots, k - 1$$

Definition 5.   A one-to-one homomorphism φ from S onto T is called an *isomorphism* between S and T.

EXAMPLE.   Machines S and T are shown in Fig. 1a.   The mapping φ is a homomorphism from S onto T where φ is given by the following table.

s	a_0	a_1	a_2
$\varphi(s)$	b_0	b_1	b_1

One pleasing implication of our definition is now clear.   Because our machines are defined to have initial states, if a homomorphism between two connected machines exists at all, it must be unique.   There do exist pairs of machines such that there are no homomorphisms between the machines.   See Fig. 1b for an example of a pair of machines for which no homomorphism exists.   That none exists can be seen as follows. Suppose a homomorphism φ existed, then $\varphi(a_0) = b_0$.   This implies that $\varphi(a_1) = b_0$, $\varphi(a_2) = b_1$.   The successor state to a_2 under σ_1 must map into b_1, but $\varphi(a_1) = b_1$ contradicts that φ is mapping, since $\varphi(a_1) = b_0$.

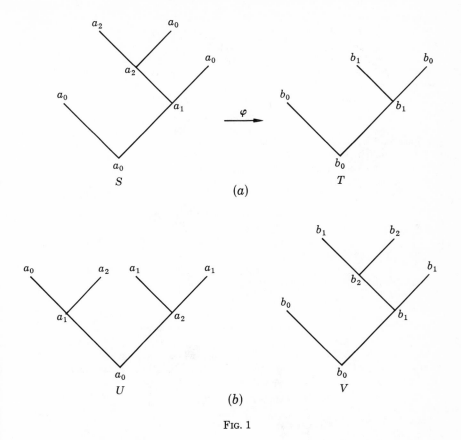

Fig. 1

PROBLEMS

1. Let $S = \langle S,M,a \rangle$ be any sequential machine over Σ_k. Show that the mapping $rp_S \colon \Sigma_k^* \to S$ is a homomorphism of the free machine F_k into (onto) $S(S^c)$.

2. Let S and T be two sequential machines. S is said to be *structurally stronger than* T iff there exists a homomorphism from S^c onto T^c. S and T are said to be *structurally equivalent* iff S^c and T^c are isomorphic. Show that structural equivalence is an equivalence relation. Show that S and T are structurally equivalent if S is structurally stronger than T and T is structurally stronger than S. The set of all machines isomorphic to S is often called the *structure type* of S.

3. A second definition of homomorphism is given below. Show that this definition is equivalent to Definition 4. The condition on a mapping φ from $S = \langle S,M,a \rangle$ into $T = \langle T,N,b \rangle$ is

$$\varphi(a) = b$$
$$(\forall u)_S (\forall x)_{\Sigma_k^*} \quad \varphi(M(u,x)) = N(\varphi(u),x)$$

4. Let $S = \langle S,M,a \rangle$ be any sequential machine and let T be any set with φ a mapping from S onto T. Prove that φ is a homomorphism from S onto some sequential machine having T as its set of states if and only if the relation R is a congruence relation on S. R is defined by uRv iff $\varphi(u) = \varphi(v)$ for any $u, v \in S$.

5. Show that if a homomorphism φ between two connected machines exists, then φ is unique. Construct an algorithm for determining the homomorphism if it exists and test for the existence of the map. What happens if the restriction of connectedness is dropped?

6. Considering machines $S = \langle S, M \rangle$ (no initial state specified), is the statement of Prob. 5 correct? A machine $S = \langle S, M \rangle$ is called *strongly connected* iff $(\forall u, v) s (\exists x)_{\Sigma_k^*} \; u = M(v, x)$. In other words, strongly connected machines are machines such that there is a transition from any state to any other state. Show that the homomorphic image of a (strongly) connected machine is (strongly) connected. For a homomorphism of machines without initial states, the structure-preserving property is simply $\varphi(M(u, \sigma_i) = M(\varphi(u), \sigma_i)$ for any $u \in S$ and $i = 0, \ldots, k - 1$.

7. (Fleck) Let $S = \langle S, M \rangle$ be a sequential machine without initial state. Prove that $G(S)$, the set of all isomorphisms from S onto S (automorphisms), is a group.

8. If φ is a homomorphism from $S = \langle S, M, a \rangle$ into $T = \langle T, N, b \rangle$, show that $\varphi(rp_S(x)) = rp_T(x)$ for any $x \in \Sigma_k^*$.

9. Let $S = \langle S, M, a \rangle$ be a sequential machine over the input monoid Σ_k^*. Define $x \equiv y(S) \Leftrightarrow (\forall s)_S M(s, x) = M(s, y)$. Show that $\equiv (S)$ is a congruence relation and that $\Sigma_k^* / \equiv (S)$ is a quotient semigroup.

10. Let $S = \langle S, M, a \rangle$ and define $\varphi_x = M(s, x)$. Show that the set $S^S = \{\varphi_x | x \in \Sigma_k^*\}$ is a semigroup of functions from S into S. Is S^S isomorphic to $\Sigma_k^* / \equiv (S)$? S^S is called the *semigroup of* S.

11. Let $S = \langle S, M, a \rangle$ be a connected machine whose semigroup is a group. Is S strongly connected? How can one decide if a given machine is a *group machine* (the semigroup is also a group) by glancing at the table M?

12. A machine $S = \langle S, M \rangle$ is called *reversible* iff

$$(\forall s, t)_S (\forall x)_{\Sigma_k^*} (\exists y)_{\Sigma_k^*} \quad M(s, x) = t \Rightarrow M(t, y) = s$$

Intuitively, this means that if state t is reachable from s, then s is reachable from t. How are the classes of connected, strongly connected, reversible, and group machines related?

5   QUOTIENT MACHINES

Now we begin to derive some nontrivial structural theorems for sequential machines. The reader will find that there is a one-to-one correspondence between congruence relations and quotient machines. First an important special congruence relation is defined.

Definition 1. The *equiresponse relation* of a sequential machine S is a relation $\perp (S)$ on Σ_k^* defined as $(\forall x, y)_{\Sigma_k^*} \; x \perp y(S)$ iff $rp_S(x) = rp_S(y)$.

Proposition 2. $\perp (S)$ is a right congruence on Σ_k^*.

PROOF. The proof that $\perp (S)$ is an equivalence relation on Σ_k^* may be safely left to the reader. It will be shown that the relation satisfies the substitution property.

Suppose that $x \perp y(S)$, that is, $rp_S(x) = rp_S(y)$; then from Corollary 2.8, we know that, for any word z, $rp_S(xz) = rp_S(yz)$ or that $xz \perp yz(S)$. |

Now a new way of constructing sequential machines can be given.

Definition 3. If R is a right congruence on Σ_k^*, then the *quotient sequential machine modulo R* is defined as $\top(R) = \langle T,N,b \rangle$, where

$$T = \{R[x] | x \in \Sigma_k^*\}$$
$$N(R[x],\sigma_i) = R[x\sigma_i] \qquad i = 0, \ldots, k - 1$$
$$b = R[\Lambda]$$

Whenever we define an algebraic structure whose domain is a set of equivalence classes, we must show that the operations defined on the equivalence classes are independent of the choice of representatives of the equivalence classes. To shorten the terminology, we shall say that the operations must be *well defined*. We now do this for Definition 3.

Proposition 4. N is well defined.

PROOF. It is necessary to show that if $x_1 R x_2$, then $N(R[x_1],\sigma_i) = N(R[x_2],\sigma_i)$. However $x_1 R x_2$ implies, because R is a right congruence, that $(x_1\sigma_i) R (x_2\sigma_i)$ for $i = 0$, $\ldots, k - 1$. That is, $R[x_1\sigma_i] = R[x_2\sigma_i]$. |

Figure 1 indicates a sequential machine $S = \langle S,M,a_0 \rangle$ along with the congruence classes of $\perp(S)$.

The four classes of $\perp(S)$ are

$$\{\Lambda,\sigma_0{}^2,\sigma_0{}^4,\sigma_1\sigma_0{}^3, \ldots\}$$
$$\{\sigma_0,\sigma_0{}^3,\sigma_1\sigma_0{}^2,\sigma_0\sigma_1\sigma_0{}^2,\sigma_1\sigma_0\sigma_1\sigma_0, \ldots\}$$
$$\{\sigma_1,\sigma_0\sigma_1,\sigma_1{}^2,\sigma_0{}^2\sigma_1,\sigma_0\sigma_1{}^2, \ldots\}$$
$$\{\sigma_1\sigma_0,\sigma_1\sigma_0\sigma_1,\sigma_1{}^2\sigma_0, \ldots\}$$

It is no accident that the number of classes is the same as the number of internal states in Fig. 1. The form of the correspondence is made clearer in the following theorem.

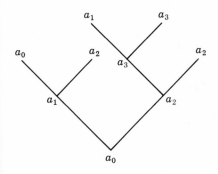

FIG. 1

Theorem 5.   If $S = \langle S,M,a \rangle$ is a sequential machine having equiresponse relation $\perp(S)$, then $\mathsf{T}(\perp(S))$ is isomorphic to S^c, the connected component of S.

PROOF.   First we pass from S to $S^c = \langle S',M',a \rangle$, and then we construct $\mathsf{T}(\perp(S)) = \langle T,N,b \rangle$. Now we examine the mapping

$$\varphi: u \to [x] = \{x | rp_S(x) = u\}$$

where $u \in S'$ and $[x]$ is an abbreviation for $\perp[x]$. Clearly, φ is *onto;* because if we are given any $[x]$, then $rp_S(x)$ tells us the preimage of the class. φ must be one to one because $[x] = [y]$ is equivalent to $x \perp y(S)$, which means that $rp_S(x) = rp_S(y)$. It remains only to show that φ is a structure-preserving map. Since $rp_S(\Lambda) = a$,

$$\varphi: a \to [\Lambda] = b$$

Suppose for any $u \in S'$, $\varphi: u \to [x]$; then

$$\varphi: M(u,\sigma_i) \to \{z | rp_S(z) = M(u,\sigma_i)\} = [x\sigma_i] \qquad \text{for } i = 0, \ldots, k-1$$

Since we can choose any element of the equivalence class for a representative, the obvious choice was $z = x\sigma_i$. This gives

$$\varphi: M(u,\sigma_i) \to [x\sigma_i] = N([x],\sigma_i) \qquad \text{for } i = 0, \ldots, k-1 \quad \blacksquare$$

Suppose that, instead of starting from a machine, we start from a congruence relation R on Σ_k^*. Then we pass to the machine $\mathsf{T}(R)$, which has an equiresponse relation $\perp(\mathsf{T}(R))$. The following theorem shows that the situation is not very complicated.

Theorem 6.   If R is a right-congruence relation on Σ_k^*, then R is the equiresponse relation of $\mathsf{T}(R)$. Symbolically

$$\perp(\mathsf{T}(R)) = R$$

PROOF.   Construct $\mathsf{T}(R)$ and note that $rp_{\mathsf{T}(R)}(x) = R[x]$. Thus $x \perp y(\mathsf{T}(R))$ iff $rp_{\mathsf{T}(R)}(x) = rp_{\mathsf{T}(R)}(y)$ iff $R[x] = R[y]$ iff xRy. $\quad \blacksquare$

Lemma 7.   Let R_1 and R_2 be right-congruence relations on Σ_k^*. There is a homomorphism from $\mathsf{T}(R_1)$ onto $\mathsf{T}(R_2)$ if and only if $R_1 \subseteq R_2$.

PROOF.   Construct $\mathsf{T}(R_1) = \langle T_1,M_1,a \rangle$ and $\mathsf{T}(R_2) = \langle T_2,M_2,b \rangle$. Suppose there is a homomorphism φ from $\mathsf{T}(R_1)$ onto $\mathsf{T}(R_2)$, and furthermore, assume xR_1y. We must show xR_2y. From Prob. 8 of the preceding section, φ maps $rp_{\mathsf{T}(R_1)}(x)$ into $rp_{\mathsf{T}(R_2)}(x)$. Thus xR_1y iff $x \perp y(\mathsf{T}(R_1))$ iff $rp_{\mathsf{T}(R_1)}(x) = rp_{\mathsf{T}(R_1)}(y)$. Using Prob. 8, the preceding sentence implies $rp_{\mathsf{T}(R_2)}(x) = rp_{\mathsf{T}(R_2)}(y)$ iff $x \perp y(\mathsf{T}(R_2))$ iff xR_2y. Thus we have shown $R_1 \subseteq R_2$.

Conversely, assume $R_1 \subseteq R_2$. For every class $R_1[x]$, there must exist a unique class in R_2 which contains $R_1[x]$ because $R_1 \subseteq R_2$ (cf. Prob. 1-4.7). This correspondence is called φ, and it is clear that φ is a mapping.

$$\varphi(R_1[\Lambda]) = R_2[\Lambda]$$

so that φ preserves initial states.

$$\varphi(M(R_1[x],\sigma_i)) = \varphi(R_1[x\sigma_i]) = R_2[x\sigma_i] = N(R_2[x],\sigma_i) \qquad \text{for } i = 0, \ldots, k-1$$

Clearly φ is onto. $\quad \blacksquare$

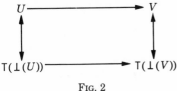

FIG. 2

Theorem 8. There is a homomorphism from a connected machine U onto a connected machine V iff $\perp(U) \subseteq \perp(V)$.

PROOF. The situation is shown in Fig. 2; the lemma and Theorem 5 provide the proof. ∎

Theorem 8 will turn out to be important in the future. In some sense the fact that V is a homomorphic image of U means that V can simulate U. This concept can be made more precise when we attach outputs to the machines. If we had a convenient method for computing $\perp(U)$ and $\perp(V)$, then we could check for a homomorphism between U and V by merely checking containment of relations. As it is, we have an algorithm for determining when a homomorphism exists between two machines, and the algorithm allows us to check when $\perp(U) \subseteq \perp(V)$ by Theorem 8.

Corollary 9. Two connected sequential machines U and V without output are isomorphic iff $\perp(U) = \perp(V)$.

PROOF. $\perp(U) = \perp(V)$ iff $\top(\perp(U))$ is isomorphic to $\top(\perp(V))$, but U is isomorphic to $\top(\perp(U))$ and V is isomorphic to $\top(\perp(V))$. ∎

Corollary 9 solves the problem of determining if two machines have identical equiresponse relations.

PROBLEMS

1. Consider the sequential machine $S = \langle S, M, a \rangle$, where M is given as

	a_0	a_1	a_2
$M(s, \sigma_0)$	a_0	a_0	a_1
$M(s, \sigma_1)$	a_1	a_2	a_1

(a) Does $\sigma_0 \sigma_1 \sigma_1 \perp \sigma_1 \sigma_1 \sigma_0 \sigma_1 (S)$ hold?

(b) Construct the classes of $\perp(S)$ for all words whose length does not exceed 3.

2. Construct a machine S over Σ_2 such that S has three states, is connected, and is such that

$$\sigma_0 \sigma_0 \perp \Lambda(S) \qquad \Lambda \perp \sigma_1(S) \qquad \sigma_0 \perp \sigma_0 \sigma_1 \sigma_0(S) \qquad \sigma_0 \sigma_1 \perp \sigma_0 \sigma_1 \sigma_1(S)$$

3. Show that if R is any right congruence on Σ_k^*, then $\top(R)$ is connected.

4. Find a right-congruence relation on Σ_k^* which is not the equality relation, but which has infinite rank.

5. Let R be a right-congruence relation on $S = \langle S,M,a \rangle$. The quotient machine S/R is defined as $S/R = \langle T,N,b \rangle$, where $T = \{R[s] | s \in S\}$, $b = R[a]$, and $N(R[s],\sigma_i) = R[M(s,\sigma_i)]$ for $i = 0, \ldots, k - 1$. Show that N is well defined.

6. Let $S = \langle S,M,a \rangle$ be a sequential machine and let R be a right congruence on S. Show that there is a homomorphism which maps S onto S/R.

7. Show that if there is a homomorphism taking S onto T, then there exists a right congruence R on S such that T is isomorphic to S/R.

8. Conclude that Probs. 5 to 7 are trivial, since sequential machines have the mathematical structure of abstract algebras (cf. Sec. 1-7).

6 THE LATTICE OF MACHINES

In the preceding section a one-to-one correspondence between right congruences over Σ_k^* and connected machines over Σ_k is indicated. This means that studying connected machines is equivalent to studying congruence relations, but it will turn out that operations on the congruence relations are generally more efficient than the corresponding operations on the machines from a computational point of view. The next step in our development is to sharpen the correspondence between machines and congruence relations.

Theorem 1. If L_k denotes the set of all right-congruence relations on Σ_k^* and if L_k' is the family of all structure types of sequential machines over Σ_k (cf. Prob. 4.2), then the partially ordered sets $\langle L_k, \subseteq \rangle$ and $\langle L_k', \rightarrow \rangle$ are isomorphic where $S_1 \rightarrow S_2$ means there is a homomorphism from S_1 onto S_2.

PROOF. The mapping $\top : R \rightarrow \top(R)$ is a mapping from right congruences to connected machines. $\top$ is onto, since, given any connected machine S, $\bot(S)$ maps onto S. The map is one to one because, if $\top(R_1)$ and $\top(R_2)$ are isomorphic, then $\bot(\top(R_1)) = \bot(\top(R_2))$, so $R_1 = R_2$. Furthermore, the partial order is preserved by Lemma 5.7. The inverse map of $\top$ is $\bot$. |

Theorem 1 establishes an isomorphism between two partially ordered sets. There is a natural extension of these sets to lattices. For L_k, the set of congruence relation on Σ_k^*, the greatest lower bound of two right congruences R_1 and R_2 is the intersection of R_1 and R_2, $R_1 \cap R_2$. Of course, the intersection of two right congruences is again a right congruence. The union of two equivalence relations is not necessarily an equivalence relation, so that the join operation must be selected with more care. The join is defined to be the least right congruence containing R_1 and R_2, denoted by $R_1 \sqcup R_2$. The operations which will extend L_k', the family of structure types of machines, to a lattice have not yet been chosen. The selection should be made in such a way that the lattices are isomorphic. This suggests the following choices. Let S_1, $S_2 \in L'_k$.

$$S_1 \wedge S_2 = \top(\bot(S_1) \cap \bot(S_2))$$
$$S_1 \vee S_2 = \top(\bot(S_1) \sqcup \bot(S_2))$$

Theorem 2. The lattice $\langle L_k, \subseteq, \cap, \sqcup \rangle$ is isomorphic to the lattice $\langle L'_k, \rightarrow, \wedge, \vee \rangle$ under the mapping $\top$.

Note that the minimal element of L'_k is the machine with one state; the maximal element of L_k is the universal binary relation. The maximal element of L'_k is the free algebra, and the minimal element of L_k is the equality relation.

The lattice L_1 is very well known and will be completely characterized in the problems at the end of this section. Unfortunately, L_2 is more complicated.

The meet of two machines is not defined in a satisfactory way because it is so hard to compute. Now we shall indicate a direct construction of the meet which has the advantage of showing us a way to construct new sequential machines from given machines, namely, the direct product operation.

Definition 3. If $S = \langle S,M,a \rangle$ and $T = \langle T,N,b \rangle$, then the *direct product* $S \times T$ is defined as $S \times T = \langle U,P,c \rangle$, where $U = S \times T$, $c = (a,b)$, and $P((s,t),\sigma_i) = (M(s,\sigma_i),N(t,\sigma_i))$ for $i = 0, \ldots, k - 1$.

Lemma 4. $rp_{S \times T}(x) = (rp_S(x),rp_T(x))$.

PROOF. The argument is an induction on the length of x.

BASIS. $\lg(x) = 0$, so that

$$rp_{S \times T}(\Lambda) = (a,b) = (rp_S(\Lambda),rp_T(\Lambda))$$

INDUCTION STEP. Assume the result for all tapes x such that $\lg(x) = n$, and let $y = x\sigma$

$$\begin{aligned} rp_{S \times T}(x\sigma) &= P(rp_{S \times T}(x),\sigma) = P((rp_S(x),rp_T(x)),\sigma) \\ &= (M(rp_S(x),\sigma),N(rp_T(x),\sigma)) \\ &= (rp_S(x\sigma),rp_T(x\sigma)) \quad | \end{aligned}$$

Theorem 5. $\bot(U \times V) = \bot(U) \cap \bot(V)$

PROOF $\qquad\qquad x \perp y \, (U \times V)$

iff $rp_{U \times V}(x) = rp_{U \times V}(y)$ iff $(rp_U(x),rp_V(x)) = (rp_U(y),rp_V(y))$ iff $rp_U(x) = rp_U(y)$

and $\qquad\qquad rp_V(x) = rp_V(y)$ iff $x \perp y \, (U)$ and $x \perp y \, (V) \quad |$

Corollary 6. $S \wedge T$ *is isomorphic to* $(S \times T)^c$

Corollary 6 indicates a method of constructing the meet of two machines without using congruence relations. An example of this con-

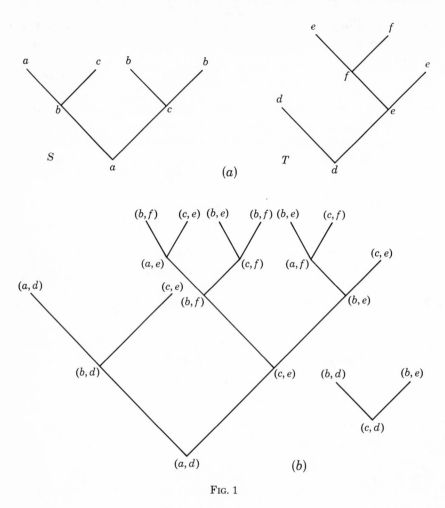

Fig. 1

struction is given in Fig. 1. The reader should note that the direct product of connected machines need not be connected.

Let S and T be as given in Fig. 1a. Then $S \times T$ is as given in Fig. 1b. Figure 1 should make the construction of the direct product clear.

PROBLEMS

On Σ_1^*, the set of natural numbers, we define the following relation for $m \geq 0$ and $q \geq 0$.

$$x \equiv y \ (q,m) \quad \text{iff} \quad [x < m \text{ and } x = y] \text{ or } [m \leq x \text{ and } m \leq y \text{ and } x \equiv y \text{ mod } q]$$

1. (Büchi) Describe the following relations and give their rank:

$$x \equiv y \ (1,0) \qquad x \equiv y \ (1,m) \qquad x \equiv y \ (0,m) \qquad x \equiv y \ (q,0)$$

2. What is the rank of $x \equiv y \ (q,m)$ for $q \geq 1$, $m \geq 0$?

3. Show that $x \equiv y \ (q,m)$ is a right congruence on Σ_1^*.

4. Are the congruence classes of $x \equiv y \ (q,m)$ closed under addition and multiplication? If so, prove it. If not, construct a counterexample.

5. Show that any right congruence on Σ_1^* is one of the relations $x \equiv y \ (q,m)$. (HINT: There are only two types of connected machines over Σ_1. One is the free machine (or equality relation). Draw the graphs and interpret the meanings of q and m.)

6. Let S and T be two machines with semigroups S^S and T^T, respectively. Show that the semigroup of $S \times T$ is $S^S \times T^T$.

7. (Hartmanis[3]) A machine $S = \langle S,M,a \rangle$ is said to contain a *clock* if there exists a homomorphic image of S which is essentially a machine over Σ_1. More formally, S is a *clock* iff for any $s \ \epsilon \ S$ and for all $i, j = 0, \ldots, k - 1$, $M(s,\sigma_i) = M(s,\sigma_j)$. Define the relation L on the set of states as follows: For any states u, $v \ \epsilon \ S$, uLv iff there is a state w and integers i and j such that $M(w,\sigma_i) = u$ and $M(w,\sigma_j) = v$. Denote by L' the reflexive and transitive closure of L, that is,

$$uL'v \Leftrightarrow (u = v) \lor u \mathbf{L} v$$

where $\mathbf{L}$ is the transitive closure of L. Show that L' is an equivalence relation on S, but not generally a congruence relation. If P is the least congruence relation containing L, show that S/P is a maximal clock, i.e., that any other clock of S is smaller than S/P.

8. Let S be a set of n elements and consider the class of equivalence relations on S. Any relation R can be represented by an $n \times n$ matrix of zeroes and ones; i.e., if $R = (r_{ij})$, then $r_{ij} = 1$ if iRj and $r_{ij} = 0$ otherwise. Thus, equivalence relations correspond to symmetric matrices with 1's on the main diagonal. Two relations R_1 and R_2 are *permutable* iff $R_1 R_2 = R_2 R_1$, where $R_1 R_2$ mean that $x R_1 R_2 y$ iff $(\exists z)_S \ x R_1 z$ and $z R_2 y$. Show that two relations are permutable iff their matrix products commute. How can $R_1 \cap R_2$ be computed? Derive a computation for $R_1 \sqcup R_2$ by using the matrix representation and the analysis theorem for connection matrices. (HINT: Prove $R_1 \sqcup R_2 = (R_1 R_2)^q$, where $q \leq [n/2]$.)

7   SUMMARY AND HISTORY

Having defined sequential machines without outputs over an input monoid, we have found that it is sufficient to consider only connected machines. Studying machines and homomorphisms between machines turned out to be equivalent to studying right congruences on input tapes. In particular, the mathematical structure of both systems is a lattice.

We found that corresponding to every homomorphism between machines there is a congruence relation on the states on the domain. Similarly, given any congruence relation on the states of a machine, one can construct a quotient machine which is a homomorphic image of the given machine.

The first rigorous study of sequential machines was by Moore[1]. His basic paper is very readable, and it is highly recommended to the reader. Some of the basic concepts were discovered by Huffman at roughly the same time. Our treatment uses much of the terminology of Rabin and Scott. The notation of Rabin and Scott has been widely, but not universally, accepted. Much of the material in Chap. 9 may be found in the books by Gill and by Ginsburg[1]. The fundamental connection between congruences and machines, although implicit in the Rabin and Scott paper, has been worked out by Büchi and Wright. This chapter is based primarily on their class notes.

CHAPTER 10 *sequential machines with output*

INTRODUCTION

The abstract model of machines studied in the preceding chapter is now extended by attaching outputs to the machines. One can imagine a gray box which operates on any tape from Σ_k^* by starting at the left-hand end of the tape and successively scanning the tape from left to right. We imagine the machine to be equipped with a separate output tape. We assume that the sequential machine prints a symbol on the output tape for every symbol read from the input tape. There is no reason for the output alphabet to be the same as Σ_k. The output sequence of a machine will depend on the input sequence and the internal workings of the machine in some, as yet unspecified, way. Roughly speaking, a sequential machine is called a *Mealy machine* if the output depends on both the present input and the internal state. A machine is called a *Moore machine* if the output depends on only the internal state.

It is shown in Gill's book that these two models are equivalent. For the most part, our discussion will center on Moore machines. We shall further restrict ourselves to the binary case in which only the two output symbols 0 and 1 are permitted. No loss of generality results from the second assumption.

Even with the assumptions made above, there are a variety of ways in which the output can be constructed mathematically. Associated with every state will be an output which is either zero or one. We shall call the set of states which cause a 1 output the *final states*. Now if we imagine a tape $x \in \Sigma_k^*$ fed into the machine, the device will pass through a succession of internal states giving a string of zeroes and ones

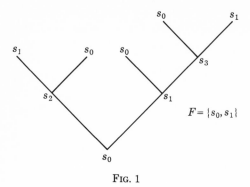

$$F = \{s_0, s_1\}$$

FIG. 1

as outputs.   If we ignore all the outputs except the last one, then a machine *accepts* or *recognizes* a tape if the last output is 1.   This model is often called a *recognition device*.   Now it is time to make these intuitive notions precise.

Definition 1.   An *automaton*, or *sequential machine over* Σ_k *with output*, is a quadruple $\langle S, M, a, F \rangle$, where S is a nonempty set of internal states, M is the transition function, $M : S \times \Sigma_k \to S$, $a \in S$ is the initial state, and $F \subseteq S$ is the set of states giving a one output.

Definition 2.   A word $x \in \Sigma_k^*$ is said to be *recognized* or *accepted* by a machine $S = \langle S, M, a, F \rangle$ iff $rp_S(x) \in F$.

   Figure 1 is an example of a sequential machine with output.   Note that the input word $\sigma_1 \sigma_0$ is recognized by S, but that the word $\sigma_0 \sigma_1 \sigma_0$ is not recognized.

   In Chap. 9 a variety of definitions were introduced in order to study machines without output.   It is necessary to modify these definitions for machines with outputs.

Definition 3.   Given a machine $S = \langle S, M, a, F \rangle$, the *connected submachine* is defined to be $S^c = \langle S', M', a, F' \rangle$, where $S' = \{s | (\exists x)_{\Sigma_k *} \ rp_S(x) = s\}$, M' is the restriction of M from $S \times \Sigma_k \to S$ to $S' \times \Sigma_k \to S'$, and $F' = F \cap S'$.

Definition 4.   Given two machines $S = \langle S, M, a, F \rangle$ and $T = \langle T, N, b, G \rangle$, φ is said to be a *homomorphism* from S into (onto) T iff φ is a mapping from S^c into (onto) T^c such that

$$\varphi(a) = b$$
$$(\forall s)_S \quad \varphi(M(s, \sigma_i)) = N(\varphi(s), \sigma_i) \quad \text{for } i = 0, \ldots, k - 1$$
$$(\forall u)_S \quad u \in F \Rightarrow \varphi(u) \in G$$

Definition 5. φ is said to be a *strong homomorphism* from $S = \langle S,M,a,F \rangle$ into (onto) $T = \langle T,N,b,G \rangle$ iff φ is a homomorphism in the sense of Definition 4 and, furthermore,

$$u \in F \Leftrightarrow \varphi(u) \in G$$

Definition 6. φ is said to be an *isomorphism* between S and T is φ is a strong homomorphism that is onto and one to one.

The reader is reminded about the convention imposed in the preceding chapter that all machines are henceforth assumed to be connected.

Definition 7. If $S = \langle S,M,a,F \rangle$ and $T = \langle T,N,b,G \rangle$ are two sequential machines, the *direct product* of two machines is defined as

$$S \times T = \langle U,P,c,H \rangle$$

where $U = S \times T$, $c = (a,b)$, $P((s,t),\sigma_i) = (M(s,\sigma_i),N(t,\sigma_i))$, for $i = 0$, . . . , $k - 1$, and $H = F \times G$.

There is still another operation which takes two machines and makes a new machine from them. This operation, called the *direct union*, is exactly the same as the direct product except for the final states. More precisely, we have the following definition.

Definition 8. If $S = \langle S,M,a,F \rangle$ and $T = \langle T,N,b,G \rangle$ are two sequential machines, the *direct union* is defined as

$$S \cup T = \langle U,P,c,H \rangle$$
where
$$U = S \times T$$
$$c = (a,b)$$
$$P((s,t),\sigma_i) = (M(s,\sigma_i),N(t,\sigma_i))$$
$$H = \{(s,t) | s \in F \text{ or } t \in G\}$$

PROBLEMS

1. Suppose two sets S and T are given such that $S \cap T \neq \emptyset$. The following device is used to make S and T act as if they were disjoint. S is replaced by $S' = \{(s,0)\} = S \times \{0\}$ and T is replaced by $T' = T \times \{1\}$. Show that $S' \cap T' = \emptyset$ even if $S \cap T \neq \emptyset$.

2. Let $S = \langle S,M,F \rangle$ and $T = \langle T,N,G \rangle$ be two sequential machines without initial states. The *direct sum* of S and T is defined to be $S \oplus T = \langle U,P,H \rangle$, where $U = \{(S \times \{0\}) \cup (T \times \{1\})\}$. $H = \{(F \times \{0\}) \cup (G \times \{1\})\}$. $P((s,0),\sigma_i) = (M(s,\sigma_i),0)$ for $s \in S$ and $P((t,1),\sigma_i) = (N(t,\sigma_i),1)$ if $t \in T$ and $i = 0$. . . . , $k - 1$. How does one compute the Moore graph of $S \cup T$ in terms of the graph for S and the graph for T?

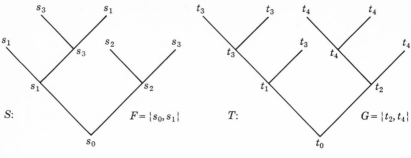

FIG. P3

3. Construct the response tree for $S \cup T$, where S and T are given in Fig. P3.

2   THE BEHAVIOR OF SEQUENTIAL MACHINES

The theory developed in the preceding chapter characterizes machines by their structure. Another common approach is the characterization of objects by their input-output relations or their behavior. If one is interested in the study of human beings, the difference between the two approaches is the same as the difference between anatomy and psychology. The possible reaction that a machine can have to an input $x \in \Sigma_k^*$ is to recognize x or to reject x. Intuitively, the behavior of a machine will be the set of tapes recognized by the machine.

Definition 1. The *behavior* of a machine $S = \langle S,M,a,F \rangle$ is defined to be

$$\beta_S = \{x \in \Sigma_k^* \mid rp_S(x) \in F\}$$

When no confusion will result, the subscript S will be dropped. The behavior of a machine S may be thought of as a partition of Σ_k^*, since every input word is in β_S or in $\Sigma_k^* - \beta_S$. This remark will help explain the following terminology.

Definition 2. Let R be an equivalence relation on Σ_k^* and let β be a subset of Σ_k^*. R is said to *refine* β iff xRy implies that $x \in \beta$ iff $y \in \beta$. Symbolically,

$$xRy \Rightarrow (x \in \beta \Leftrightarrow y \in \beta)$$

Thus if β were treated as an equivalence relation of rank 2, then Definition 2 would be simply the definition of the equivalence relation R refining the equivalence relation β.

Proposition 3. Given a machine $S = \langle S,M,a,F \rangle$ with behavior β_S, then $\perp (S)$ refines β_S.

PROOF. $x \perp y(S)$ iff $rp_S(x) = rp_S(y)$ implies $(rp_S(x) \, \epsilon \, F \Leftrightarrow rp_S(y) \, \epsilon \, F)$ iff $(x \, \epsilon \, \beta \Leftrightarrow y \, \epsilon \, \beta)$. $\blacksquare$

In the preceding chapter, it was possible to equate the study of machines without output to the study of congruence relations. The addition of outputs does not increase the complexity of the theory very much.

Definition 4.   Let R be a right-congruence relation on Σ_k^* and let $\beta \subseteq \Sigma_k^*$ such that R refines β. The *quotient sequential machine with output modulo R and β* is given by $\top(R,\beta) = \langle T,M,a,F \rangle$, where $T = \{R[x] | x \, \epsilon \, \Sigma_k^* \}$, $a = R[\Lambda]$, $M(R[x],\sigma_i) = R[x\sigma_i]$ for $i = 0, \ldots , k - 1$, and

$$F = \{R[x] | x \, \epsilon \, \beta\}$$

Note that R must refine β so that F is well defined.

Theorem 5.   If R is a right-congruence relation on Σ_k^* and if $\beta \subseteq \Sigma_k^*$ such that R refines β, then $\top(R,\beta)$ has β as its behavior.

PROOF.   First $\top(R,\beta)$ is constructed as in Definition 4. $\top(R,\beta) = \langle T,M,a,F \rangle$.

$$\beta_{\top(R,\beta)} = \{x | rp_{\top(R,\beta)}(x) \, \epsilon \, F\} = \{x | R[x] \, \epsilon \, F\} = \{x | x \, \epsilon \, \beta\} = \beta \quad \blacksquare$$

Our principal characterization theorem of the preceding chapter was to show that the lattice of right-congruence relations is isomorphic to the lattice of equivalence classes of isomorphic machines. Now this result can be extended to the case where the machines have outputs.

Lemma 6.   There is a homomorphism from S_1 onto S_2 iff $\perp(S_1) \subseteq \perp(S_2)$ and $\beta_{S_1} \subseteq \beta_{S_2}$.

PROOF.   Suppose there is a homomorphism from S_1 onto S_2. By Theorem 9-5.8, $\perp(S_1) \subseteq \perp(S_2)$. $x \, \epsilon \, \beta_{S_1}$ iff $rp_{S_1}(x) \, \epsilon \, F_1$, but under a homomorphism φ, we must have $\varphi(rp_{S_1}(x)) \, \epsilon \, F_2$. By Prob. 9-4.8, $rp_{S_2}(x) \, \epsilon \, F_2$ or $x \, \epsilon \, \beta_{S_2}$. Conversely, assume the existence of (R_1,β_1) and (R_2,β_2), where R_i is a right congruence on Σ_k^*, $\beta_i \subseteq \Sigma_k^*$, and R_i refines β_i for $i = 1, 2$. Then one forms $\top(R_1,\beta_1)$ and $\top(R_2,\beta_2)$. The mapping φ

$$\varphi : R_1[x] \to R_2[x]$$

is a homomorphism of the machines without output. It remains only to show that φ preserves the output, that is, $R_1[x] \, \epsilon \, F_1$ implies $R_2[x] \, \epsilon \, F_2$, but this is precisely the requirement $\beta_{S_1} \subseteq \beta_{S_2}$. $\blacksquare$

Proposition 7. S_1 and S_2 are isomorphic iff $\perp(S_1) = \perp(S_2)$ and $\beta_{S_1} = \beta_{S_2}$.

Proposition 7 can be interpreted as the statement that structural equivalence $(S_1 \leftrightarrow S_2)$ implies behavioral equivalence $(\beta_{S_1} = \beta_{S_2})$. Of course, behavioral equivalence alone does not imply structural equivalence.

Lemma 8. There is a one-to-one mapping of the structure types of machines onto the ordered pairs (R,β), where R is a right congruence on Σ_k^*, $\beta \subseteq \Sigma_k^*$ such that R refines β.

PROOF. $f: S \to (\perp(S), \beta_S)$ is the appropriate mapping. f is onto, since given a pair (R,β) with the property that R refines β, $\top(R,\beta)$ maps onto (R,β). Suppose $(R_1,\beta_1) = (R_2,\beta_2)$; then $\top(R_1,\beta_1)$ and $\top(R_2,\beta_2)$ are isomorphic sequential machines. It is also clear that if S_1 and S_2 are isomorphic, then $f(S_1) = f(S_2) = (\perp(S_1),\beta_{S_1}) = (\perp(S_2),\beta_{S_2})$ by Proposition 7. ∎

Theorem 9. Let $P_k = \{(R,\beta) | R$ is a right congruence on Σ_k^*, $\beta \subseteq \Sigma_k^*$, R refines $\beta\}$ and let P_k be the family of structure types of machines over Σ_k with output. The lattices $\langle P_k, \subseteq, \cap, \sqcup \rangle$ and $\langle P_k', \to, \wedge, \vee \rangle$ are isomorphic.

PROOF. The appropriate mapping is f as given in the proof of Lemma 8. The lemmas do the rest. ∎

To summarize the content of this section, we have shown that the sequential machines with output form a lattice which is isomorphic to a lattice of ordered pairs (R,β) of an appropriate kind.

PROBLEMS

1. Let β be any subset of Σ_k^*. Show that there is a sequential machine having β as its behavior. (HINT: The appropriate machine is not finite.)

2. Find a subset β of Σ_k^* which could not be the behavior of any finite machine.

3. Relate the behavior of $S \times T$ and $S \cup T$ to the behaviors of S and of T.

4. Find a finite machine over Σ_2 whose behavior is $\{\sigma_0\sigma_1^n | n \equiv 0 \bmod 3\}$.

5. Show that behavioral equivalence is a genuine equivalence relation.

6. Provide an example to show that behavioral equivalence does not imply structural equivalence.

7. Prove that $\Lambda \epsilon \beta_S$ iff $a \epsilon F$ for a machine $S = \langle S,M,a,F \rangle$.

8. Show that R refines β means that β is the union of some of the R equivalence classes.

9. A Mealy machine is defined as $S = \langle \Sigma,\Delta,S,M,a,f \rangle$, where Δ is the output alphabet and $f: S \times \Sigma \to \Delta$. Extend f to a length-preserving function from $S \times \Sigma^*$ into Δ^*. Prove that $f(s,xy) = f(s,x)f(M(s,x),y)$ for any $x, y \epsilon \Sigma^*$.

10. Given a Mealy machine $S = \langle \Sigma,\Delta,S,M,a,f \rangle$, define a function $h: \Sigma^* - \{\Lambda\} \to \Delta$ by the following rule: $h(x\sigma) = f(rp_S(x),\sigma)$. Intuitively, $h(y)$ gives the last letter of the output sequence initiated by y. Define

$$\bar{h}(\Lambda) = \Lambda$$
$$\bar{h}(\sigma_{i_1} \cdots \sigma_{i_m}) = h(\sigma_{i_1})h(\sigma_{i_1}\sigma_{i_2}) \cdots h(\sigma_{i_1} \cdots \sigma_{i_m}) \qquad m > 0$$

Show that $\bar{h}(x) = f(a,x)$. $\bar{h}$ is sometimes called the *natural extension* of h.

11. Given a Mealy machine $S = \langle \Sigma,\Delta,S,M,a,f \rangle$ one can construct a Moore machine which is equivalent to S by the following procedure:

1. Draw the graph of S.
2. For every state s_i in the graph, examine the arrows entering s_i. Split s_i into

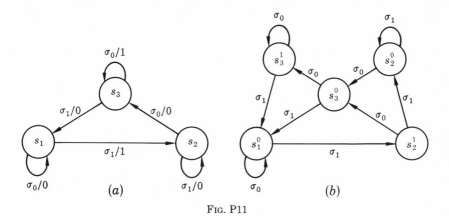

FIG. P11

as many different states as there are different outout symbols on these arrows.   Label
the states $s_i{}^0$, . . . , $s_i{}^m$.   The output of state $s_i{}^j$ is j.

3.   The transitions leaving these states go to the same s_i as before, but the proper
superscript is determined by the output associated with the transition.

Give a precise formulation of this construction and show that it works.   Check the
role of Λ.

EXAMPLE: Given the Mealy machine of Fig. P11a, the algorithm would produce
the equivalent Moore machine shown in Fig. P11b.

3   BEHAVIORAL EQUIVALENCE

The trouble with computing the behavior of a machine directly
from its definition is that the concept is not finitary in nature.   In
principle one cannot feed all possible tapes into the machine to decide
which input words cause the machine to go into a final state.   Some
finite experiments which do determine behavioral equivalence will be
discussed in this section.

The first question to be discussed is that of determining if the
behavior of a machine is empty.   That is, are there any tapes at all
which are accepted by the machine?

Theorem 1.   Let $S = \langle S, M, a, F \rangle$ be a connected machine with n states.
β_S is not empty iff S accepts a tape x such that $\lg(x) < n$.

PROOF.   Assume $x \, \epsilon \, \beta_S$ and $u = rp_S(x)$.   By Lemma 9-3.4, x can be replaced by a
tape z such as $u = rp_S(z)$ and $\lg(z) < n$.   Thus $z \, \epsilon \, \beta_S$. $\blacksquare$

Theorem 1 immediately gives an algorithm for determining if β_S
is empty, since there are only a finite number of tapes whose length is
less than n.

Suppose now that one is interested in determining if two machines
S and T have the same behavior.   This problem is of practical importance

because, if two machines have the same behavior, the cheaper machine is always the one constructed.

Theorem 2.   If S and T are connected machines, then β_S is not behaviorally equivalent to β_T iff there is a tape x which is accepted by one machine but not accepted by the other and $\lg(x) < mn$, where S has m states and T has n states.

PROOF.   If $S = \langle S,M,a,F \rangle$, define $\bar{S} = \langle S, M, a, S - F \rangle$. It is clear that $\beta_{\bar{S}} = \bar{\beta}_S = \Sigma_k^* - \beta_S$. The same notation is used for T. $\beta_S \neq \beta_T$ iff $\beta_{\bar{S} \times T} \neq \emptyset$ or $\beta_{S \times \bar{T}} \neq \emptyset$. The result follows from the construction of the direct product, Theorem 1, and the fact that $\beta_S \cap \beta_T = \beta_{S \times T}$. ∎

It is interesting to note that the bound supplied by Theorem 2 can be lowered to $\lg(x) \leq m + n - 2$ by a different approach.

There is another approach to the problem of determining behavioral equivalence which points out the reason for the definition of a strong homomorphism.   The following theorem yields a fairly rapid algorithm in case there happens to be a homomorphism between the machines under consideration.

Theorem 3.   Let S and T be connected machines and assume that there is a homomorphism φ from S onto T. S and T are behaviorally equivalent iff φ is a strong homomorphism.

PROOF. φ is the homomorphism from $S = \langle S,M,a,F \rangle$ onto $T = \langle T,N,b,G \rangle$, and assume $\beta_S = \beta_T$. For $u \in S$ there exists an $x \in \Sigma_k^*$ such that $rp_S(x) = u$. We must show that, for $\varphi(u) \in G$, $u \in F$. $\varphi(rp_S(x)) \in G$ implies $rp_T(x) \in G$, so that $x \in \beta_T$.   Therefore, $x \in \beta_S$, since $\beta_S = \beta_T$; so that $rp_S(x) \in F$, that is, $u \in F$.

Conversely, assume that φ is a strong homomorphism from S onto T.   By Lemma 2-6, $\beta_S \subseteq \beta_T$, and now assume that $x \in \beta_T$. This means that $rp_T(x) \in G$. But $rp_T(x) = \varphi(rp_S(x))$, so that we have $\varphi(rp_S(x)) \in G$. By the strength of the homomorphism, $rp_S(x) \in F$; so that $x \in \beta_S$. This shows that $\beta_S = \beta_T$. ∎

As an example of this theorem, two sequential machines are shown in Fig. 1.   We shall show that these machines are behaviorally equivalent. The unique homomorphism φ is given by the accompanying table.

s	a_0	a_1	a_2	a_3	a_4	a_5	a_6
$\varphi(s)$	b_0	b_1	b_2	b_3	b_4	b_3	b_4

In order to check if the homomorphism φ is strong, one searches along the $\varphi(s)$ row. Every entry in the $\varphi(s)$ row which is in G must come from a state $s \in F$ for the homomorphism to be strong.   Certainly, φ is strong in our example.   Theorem 3 does not provide a general solution to the behavioral equivalence problem, since the hypothesis of the theorem to the effect that there is a homomorphism from S onto T cannot be dropped.   In fact, it is possible for a machine S to be behavior-

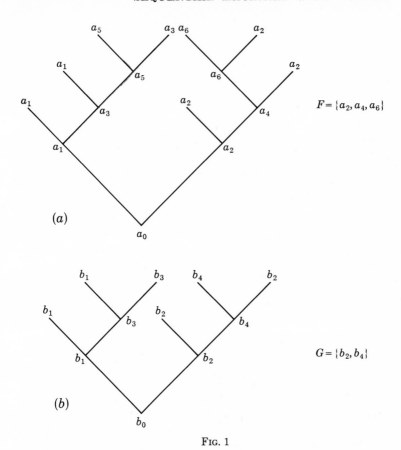

$F = \{a_2, a_4, a_6\}$

$G = \{b_2, b_4\}$

FIG. 1

ally equivalent to T and for no homomorphisms to exist between S and T or between T and S.

PROBLEMS

1. Prove that the bound in Theorem 2 can be lowered to $m + n - 2$. (HINT: Use the direct sum construction.)

2. Let S be a machine with n states. Show that if $x \in \beta_S$ and if $\lg(x) \geq n$, then there exist words $y, z, w \in \Sigma_k^*$ such that $x = yzw$, where $z \neq \Lambda$ and all tapes $yz^m w \in \beta_S$ for $m = 1, 2, \ldots$.

3. If S is a machine with n states, show that β_S is infinite iff there is a tape x such that $x \in \beta_S$ and $n \leq \lg(x) < 2n$.

4. Find a pair of machines S and T such that $\beta_S = \beta_T$ but there is no homomorphism from S onto T or from T onto S.

5. Show that there is an algorithm for deciding if the behavior of one machine is contained in the behavior of a second machine.

4 THE BEHAVIOR OF FINITE MACHINES

The preceding section provides effective procedures for determining if the behavior of two finite machines is the same. This still does not yield any characterization of the sets computed by finite machines. In other words, just what can we expect to obtain as the behavior of a finite sequential machine?

Theorem 1.   Let β be a subset of Σ_k^*. β is the behavior of a finite sequential machine over Σ_k iff there exists a right-congruence relation R of finite rank which refines β.

PROOF.   If S is a finite machine with behavior β_S, then $\perp(S)$ is a right congruence of finite rank on Σ_k^* which refines β_S. Conversely, given R of finite rank and $\beta \subseteq \Sigma_k^*$ which is refined by R, then $\top(R,\beta)$ has β as its behavior and is finite because R has finite rank. ▮

Theorem 1 does not yield an effective procedure for determining if a given set $\beta \subseteq \Sigma_k^*$ can be the behavior of a finite machine. There is, however, a natural congruence relation associated with β which turns out to play an important role in what follows.

Definition 2.   If β is any subset of Σ_k^*, then the *right congruence induced by β* is denoted by R_β and is defined as

$$x R_\beta y \Leftrightarrow (\forall z)_{\Sigma_k^*} \quad (xz \,\epsilon\, \beta \Leftrightarrow yz \,\epsilon\, \beta)$$

First it must be shown that the induced congruence relation deserves its name.

Proposition 3.   The right-congruence relation induced by β, R_β is a right-congruence relation.

PROOF.   Clearly, R_β is an equivalence relation. Now we show that R_β has the substitution property. Suppose $x R_\beta y$, then

$$
\begin{aligned}
x R_\beta y \Leftrightarrow &(\forall w)_{\Sigma_k^*} \quad (xw \,\epsilon\, \beta \Leftrightarrow yw \,\epsilon\, \beta) \\
&(\forall z,w)_{\Sigma_k^*} \quad (xzw \,\epsilon\, \beta \Leftrightarrow yzw \,\epsilon\, \beta) \\
&(\forall z,w)_{\Sigma_k^*} \quad ((xz)w \,\epsilon\, \beta \Leftrightarrow (yz)w \,\epsilon\, \beta) \\
&(\forall z)_{\Sigma_k^*} \quad xz R_\beta yz \quad ▮
\end{aligned}
$$

Another important aspect of R_β, namely, its maximality, is given in the following theorem.

Theorem 4. R_β refines β and is the maximal congruence on Σ_k^* which refines β.

PROOF. $x R_\beta y$ holds iff for all $z \,\epsilon\, \Sigma_k^*$, $xz \,\epsilon\, \beta \Leftrightarrow yz \,\epsilon\, \beta$. In particular, this relation holds for $z = \Lambda$. Thus, $x \,\epsilon\, \beta \Leftrightarrow y \,\epsilon\, \beta$ and we have shown that R_β refines β. Assume that S is a congruence relation on Σ_k^* which refines β. We shall show that $S \subseteq R_\beta$. $x S y$, so that for all $z \,\epsilon\, \Sigma_k^*$, $xz S yz$. Since S refines β, $xz \,\epsilon\, \beta \Leftrightarrow yz \,\epsilon\, \beta$, so that $x R_\beta y$. ▮

Theorem 5.   A subset β of Σ_k^* is the behavior of a finite sequential machine with output iff the induced congruence R_β has finite rank.

PROOF.   Cf. Theorem 1.   ▮

Theorem 5 is actually used to test if a set β is the behavior of a finite machine.   Consider the set $\beta = \{w^2 | w \in \Sigma_2^*\}$ and suppose that R_β has finite rank m.   The number of tapes of length n is 2^n, and for n sufficiently large, $2^n > m$.   Thus there are two *different* tapes x and y of length n in the same class of R_β.

$$x R_\beta y \Leftrightarrow (\forall z)_{\Sigma_k^*} \quad (xz \in \beta \Leftrightarrow yz \in \beta)$$

Choose $z = x$.   Thus $xz = x^2 \in \beta$, so that $yz = yx$ must be in β, that is, $y = w^2$, where $\lg(w) = \lg(x) = \lg(y) = n$.   Therefore, $x = w$ and $y = w$, that is, $x = y$, which is contradictory to the assumption that R_β has finite rank.   (Is $R_\beta = 0$, the equality relation?)

The characterization of Theorem 5 suggests the following definition.

Definition 6.   A set $\beta \subseteq \Sigma_k^*$ is called *regular* iff there exists a right congruence R which refines β and has finite rank.

Theorem 7.   A set $\beta \subseteq \Sigma_k^*$ is regular iff the induced congruence relation R_β has finite rank.

PROOF.   If β is regular, then there exists a relation R which refines β and has finite rank.   Therefore, $R \subseteq R_\beta$ so that $rk(R) \geq rk(R_\beta)$ and the rank of R_β must be finite. Suppose that R_β has finite rank.   From Theorem 4, R_β is a congruence which refines β; so β is regular.   ▮

Theorem 8.   A set $\beta \subseteq \Sigma_k^*$ is regular iff β is the behavior of a finite sequential machine with output over Σ_k.

PROOF.   Cf. Theorem 5 and Theorem 7.   ▮

The sequence of theorems developed up to now indicates that it is precisely the regular sets which are the behaviors of finite machines. It is natural to inquire into what operations on subsets of Σ_k^* preserve regularity.   We start with a simple operation, the transpose of a word.

Definition 9.   For $x \in \Sigma_k^*$, the *transpose of x, x^T*, is defined as

$$\Lambda^T = \Lambda$$
$$(x\sigma_i)^T = \sigma_i x^T \qquad x \in \Sigma_k^* \text{ and } i = 0, \ldots, k - 1$$

Thus, the transpose of a word is just the word written backwards.   The notion can be extended to subsets of Σ_k^* by performing the operation element-wise.

Definition 10.   For any subset $\beta \subseteq \Sigma_k^*$, *the transpose of β* is written β^T and defined by

$$\beta^T = \{x^T | x \in \beta\}$$

Theorem 11. $\beta \subseteq \Sigma_k^*$ is regular iff β^T is regular.

Proof. The method of proof is to give a congruence relation R which refines β and has finite rank. We shall construct an analogous relation R^T for β^T and then we shall prove

$$x^T R y^T \Leftrightarrow x R^T y$$

This will imply the $rk(R^T) = rk(R)$, which is finite. Define

$$x R y \Leftrightarrow (\forall w,z) \quad (wxz \in \beta \Leftrightarrow wyz \in \beta)$$

and

$$x R^T y \Leftrightarrow (\forall w,z) \quad (wxz \in \beta^T \Leftrightarrow wyz \in \beta^T)$$

Note R and R^T both refine β and β^T, respectively, and that both relations are right and left congruences on Σ_k^*. Suppose that $x R^T y$. Then for any w, z

$$wxz \in \beta^T \Leftrightarrow wyz \in \beta^T$$

or

$$z^T x^T w^T \in \beta \Leftrightarrow z^T y^T w^T \in \beta$$

As w and z run through Σ_k^*, so do w^T and z^T; so that the last equation is equivalent to $x^T R y^T$. We have shown that $x R^T y$ implies $x^T R y^T$. The reverse implication follows from noting that $(\beta^T)^T = \beta$ and symmetry. **|**

Although the sequential machines form a lattice, the regular subsets of Σ_k^* form a more powerful algebraic structure.

Theorem 12. Let R_k denote the family of regular subsets of Σ_k^*. The system $R_k = \langle R_k, \cap, \cup, \emptyset, \Sigma_k^* \rangle$ is a boolean algebra of sets.

PROOF. The reader can easily construct machines whose behavior is $\emptyset$ or is Σ_k^*. We have already constructed a machine to realize the complement of a regular set; i.e., if a finite machine $S = \langle S, M, a, F \rangle$ has β_S as its behavior, then $\bar{S} = \langle S, M, a, S - F \rangle$ has $\Sigma_k^* - \beta_S = \beta_{\bar{S}}$ as its behavior. Now suppose α, $\beta \in R_k$ and we shall show that $\alpha \cap \beta \in R_k$. If α is the behavior of a finite machine S and β is the behavior of a finite machine T, $\alpha \cap \beta$ is the behavior of $S \times T$, and $S \times T$ is finite if S and T are both finite. To show $\alpha \cup \beta \in R_k$, use the fact

$$\alpha \cup \beta = \overline{\bar{\alpha} \cap \bar{\beta}} \quad \textbf{|}$$

PROBLEMS

1. Show that

$$(x^T)^T = x \qquad x \in \Sigma_k^*$$
$$(xy)^T = y^T x^T \qquad x, y \in \Sigma_k^*$$
$$x^T = x \qquad x \in \Sigma_k$$

2. If the elements of a set $\beta \subseteq \Sigma_k^*$ are marked on the right tree, how does one find β^T? How does one determine if $\beta = \beta^T$?

3. If $x \in \Sigma_k^*$, show that $\{x\}$ is regular and is the behavior of a machine with $\lg(x) + 2$ internal states.

4. Show that any finite subset of Σ_k^* is in R_k.

5. Is the set $\{\sigma_0{}^p | p \text{ is any prime integer}\}$ regular?

6. Let α and β be regular sets. $\alpha\beta$ is defined as $\{xy | x \in \alpha, y \in \beta\}$ and is read α *concatenated with* β. Is $\alpha\beta$ regular? If so, prove it. If not, give a counterexample.

7. A set of nonnegative integers $\{x_i\}$ is said to be *ultimately periodic* iff there exists an integer m_0 and an integer q such for every integer $n \geq m_0$, $x_{n+q} = x_n$. Show that the regular sets over Σ_1^* are ultimately periodic sets of integers. Cf. Prob. 9-6.5.

8. Show that the following sets are not regular

$$\{\sigma_0^n \sigma_1^n | n \geq 1\} \qquad \{(\sigma_0 \sigma_1)^{n^2} | n \geq 1\}$$

9. Can you characterize the set of number theoretic functions $f(n)$ such that $\{(\sigma_0)^{f(n)} | n \geq 1\} = \beta_f$ is not regular?

10. (Krohn-Rhodes) Let f be any function from Σ_k^* into $\{0,1\}$. Define λ_t as a mapping from Σ_k^* into Σ_k^* given by $\lambda_t(x) = tx$. Thus $f\lambda_t$ is the function from Σ_k^* into $\{0,1\}$, $f\lambda_t(x) = f(tx)$. Given the behavior of a finite machine, define

$$f(x) = \begin{cases} 1 & x \epsilon \beta \\ 0 & x \notin \beta \end{cases}$$

Show that if β is regular, then the number of functions $f\lambda_t$ is finite. Conversely, given any $f: \Sigma_k^* \rightarrow \{0,1\}$, define $\beta_f = \{x | f(x) = 1\}$. Show that if the number of $f\lambda_t$ is finite, then β_f is regular.

11. Let β be regular and suppose that some finite subset of β is deleted. Show that the set which is left is regular.

SUMMARY AND HISTORY

After adding outputs to the sequential machines, we found the lattice of machines was isomorphic to a lattice of ordered pairs (R,β), where R is a right congruence which refines the subset β of Σ_k^*. This characterization of machines extends the results of the preceding chapter.

The important concept of behavior was defined and tests were developed for deciding if two machines are behaviorally equivalent. Next it was shown that any subset β of Σ_k^* could be the behavior of the free machine (Prob. 2.1). The behaviors of finite machines were characterized, and a test for determining if $\beta \subseteq \Sigma_k^*$ could be the behavior of any finite machine was suggested. The test amounts to computing the induced congruence relation R_β and checking to see if the rank of R_β is finite.

There are two important engineering problems which will be stated now, but the solution must be postponed until Chap. 12. First comes the *analysis problem*, which consists of finding the behavior of a given finite machine. The *synthesis problem* is to find a finite machine which has, as its behavior, a given regular set β. Once a solution to the synthesis problem is known, we can refine our demands and ask for economical machines satisfying the given specifications.

The material in this chapter on behavior and the behavioral point of view was first given by Burks and his collaborators; this presentation of the behavioral equivalence problem follows Rabin and Scott. The results on the mathematical structure of machines and the induced congruence relation are derived from the work of Büchi and Wright.

CHAPTER 11 *the minimization problem*

1 INTRODUCTION

As an illustration of the applications of the theory developed up to this point, the minimization problem for sequential machines will be solved. The problem is as follows: Given a finite machine S with behavior β_S, find a machine T with the least number of internal states such that the behavior of T is still β_S. The first question of interest is whether there exist any machines smaller than S which are behaviorally equivalent to S. Also, one might ask if a given machine S has more than one minimal machine associated with it; i.e., is the minimal machine having the same behavior as S unique? Finally, if minimal machines exist, how does one compute them?

Before beginning to solve these problems, the practical significance of state minimization should be stressed. A sequential machine can be realized in hardware using memory elements and combinational logic. The memory elements are usually more expensive than the combinational logic. Since the memory elements correspond to internal states, a first approach to economical realization of sequential machines would involve state minimization. There are some machines such that the cheapest realization is not the minimal state machine; but, in the large, state minimization is an economical method of design.

2 THE MINIMAL MACHINE HAVING A GIVEN BEHAVIOR

Suppose that one specifies a certain set $\beta \subseteq \Sigma_k^*$. It is known that there exists at least one sequential machine with behavior β. The first step in our plan of attack is to find the minimal such machine. The reader should notice that many of our remarks apply to infinite machines as well as finite ones, although our interest is mainly in finite machines.

Definition 1. If β is any subset of Σ_k^*, then the *sequential machine* $M(\beta)$ is defined to be $\top(R_\beta, \beta)$, where R_β is the congruence induced by β.

Intuitively, $M(\beta)$ is the minimal machine with behavior β, but this fact remains to be proved. $M(\beta)$ is well defined, since R_β is a congruence relation. It is also clear that $M(\beta)$ has behavior β by Theorems 10-4.4 and 10-2.5.

Theorem 2. If S is any sequential machine with behavior β, then there is a strong homomorphism from S onto $M(\beta)$.

PROOF. Since the behavior of both S and $M(\beta)$ is β and since $\perp(S)$ refines $R_\beta = \perp(\top(R_\beta, \beta)) = \perp(M(\beta))$, the hypotheses of Lemma 10-2.6 are satisfied; so there exists a homomorphism φ from S onto $M(\beta)$. φ is strong by Theorem 10-3.3. |

Corollary 3. If $\beta \subseteq \Sigma_k^*$ and if a machine T exists with the following two properties:

(1) T has behavior β

(2) T is a strong homomorphic image of any machine having behavior β

then T is isomorphic to $M(\beta)$.

Now we know that the minimal machine having a given behavior β is unique up to isomorphism. The specialization to the finite case is immediate.

Theorem 4. If a finite sequential machine S has behavior β, then either S has more states than $M(\beta)$ or S is isomorphic to $M(\beta)$.

PROOF. There is a homomorphism φ from S^c onto $M(\beta)$. φ must be a strong homomorphism by Theorem 10-3.3. If φ is not one to one, then S^c has more states than $M(\beta)$ and S must have more states than $M(\beta)$. If $S \neq S^c$, then S has more states than $M(\beta)$ even if φ is one to one. Suppose $S = S^c$ and φ is one to one, then φ is a strong homomorphism and one to one and φ is an isomorphism of S onto $M(\beta)$. |

While the theoretical results developed up to this point are interesting, no effective procedure for calculating $M(\beta)$ has been given. In order to compute $M(\beta)$, we need a procedure for computing R_β when β is given. When a machine S is given, it is desirable to find the minimal machine with the same behavior as S without computing the behavior of S first. These objectives will be realized shortly.

PROBLEMS

1. Let $S = \langle S, M, a, F \rangle$ be a sequential machine with output. If R is a congruence relation on S, then S/R, the quotient machine modulo R, has already been defined for machines without output. Extend the definition to machines with output. Does R have to be compatible with F in any way?

2. (Krohn-Rhodes) Let $\beta \subseteq \Sigma_k^*$ be regular. Define

$$f(x) = \begin{cases} 1 & \text{if } x \epsilon \beta \\ 0 & \text{if } x \notin \beta \end{cases}$$

The *minimal machine associated with output function* f is defined to be $\langle \{f\lambda_t | t \epsilon \Sigma_k^*\},$ $M, f, g\rangle$, where $M(f\lambda_t, \sigma) = f\lambda_{t\sigma}$ and $g(f\lambda_t) = f(t)$. Show that this minimal machine is isomorphic to $M(\beta)$ (cf. Prob. 10-4.10).

3   RELATIONS ON THE SET OF STATES

In an attempt to find an efficient algorithm for computing $M(\beta)$, a direct construction will now be given. A congruence relation will be constructed on the set of states of a machine S, and the resulting quotient machine will be seen to be isomorphic to $M(\beta_S)$. The method will be to relativize the theory of the preceding section from the free machine to a given machine.

Definition 1. If $S = \langle S, M, a, F\rangle$ is a sequential machine and R is an equivalence relation on S, R is said to *refine* F iff for any states $u, v \epsilon S$

$$uRv \Rightarrow (u \epsilon F \Leftrightarrow v \epsilon F)$$

Definition 2. If $S = \langle S, M, a, F\rangle$ is a sequential machine, the *congruence relation induced by* F is denoted by R_F and defined as

$$(\forall u, v)_S \quad uR_Fv \Leftrightarrow (\forall z)_{\Sigma_k^*} \quad (M(u,z) \epsilon F \Leftrightarrow M(v,z) \epsilon F)$$

Proposition 3. R_F refines F. R_F is a right congruence on S.

PROOF. R_F clearly refines F, and it is just as clear that R_F is an equivalence relation.   Suppose uR_Fv; then for any $z \epsilon \Sigma_k^*$, $(M(u,z) \epsilon F \Leftrightarrow M(v,z) \epsilon F)$. Taking $z = \sigma_i x$ gives $M(M(u,\sigma_i),x) \epsilon F \Leftrightarrow M(M(v,\sigma_i),x) \epsilon F$, which is exactly $M(u,\sigma_i)R_FM(v,\sigma_i)$.   **❙**

Lemma 4. If R is any right congruence on $S = \langle S, M, a, F\rangle$, then for any pair of states u and v,

$$uRv \Rightarrow (\forall z)_{\Sigma_k^*} \quad M(u,z)RM(v,z)$$

PROOF.   The result is an immediate induction on $\lg(z)$.   **❙**

Now it is verified that R_F is the largest congruence relation which refines F. This means that the quotient machine S/R_F will be minimal.

Theorem 5. Let R_F be the induced congruence relation on

$$S = \langle S, M, a, F\rangle$$

R_F is the largest congruence relation which refines F.

PROOF.   Let P be any congruence relation on S which refines F.   It will be shown that $P \subseteq R_F$.   If uPv, then for any $z \in \Sigma_k^*$, $(M(u,z))P(M(v,z))$ by Lemma 4.   Since P refines F, we have

$$(\forall z)_{\Sigma_k^*} \quad M(u,z) \in F \Leftrightarrow M(v,z) \in F$$

which is exactly uR_Fv.   ∎

It is natural to define S/R_F as a minimal machine, but this concept may be different from $M(\beta_S)$.   This possible discrepancy will have to be checked.

Definition 6.   Let $S = \langle S,M,a,F \rangle$ be a connected sequential machine and let R_F be the induced congruence relation of S.   *The minimal machine associated with* S, denoted by S^M, is defined to be

$$S/R_F = \langle \{ R_F[s] | s \in S \}, N, R_F[a], \{ R_F[s] | s \in F \} \rangle$$

and $N(R_F[s],\sigma_i) = R_F[M(s,\sigma_i)]$ for $i = 0, \ldots, k - 1$.

It is clear that S^M is well defined, since R_F is a right congruence on S; and the output set is unambiguously defined, since R_F refines F. S^M will turn out to have the properties that we desire, as can now be verified.

Theorem 7.   There is a strong homomorphism mapping S onto

$$S^M = S/R_F$$

PROOF.   By Prob. 9-5.6, there is a homomorphism φ mapping S onto S/R_F.   The explicit mapping is

$$\varphi: s \to R_F[s]$$

To show that φ is a strong homomorphism, suppose that $R_F[s]$ is a final state of S/R_F. Then $s \in F$ and φ is a strong homomorphism.   ∎

Corollary 8. $\beta_S = \beta_{S^M}$

PROOF.   Theorem 7 and Theorem 10-3.3 provide the proof.   ∎

So far, both $M(\beta_S)$ and S^M act like minimal machines for S.   The content of the next theorem is that both minimal machines associated with S are the same.

Theorem 9.   If $S = \langle S,M,a,F \rangle$ is a connected sequential machine with behavior β, then $M(\beta)$ is isomorphic to S^M.

PROOF.   Let $M(\beta) = \langle \{R_\beta[x] | x \in \Sigma_k^*\}, N, R_\beta[\Lambda], \{R_\beta[x] | x \in \beta\} \rangle$ and $S^M = \langle \{R_F[s] | s \in S\}, P, R_F[a], \{R_F[s] | s \in F\} \rangle$.   Consider the mapping α where

$$\alpha(R_\beta[x]) = R_F[rp_S(x)]$$

Clearly α is a mapping from $M(\beta)$ into S^M. α must be onto because S is connected. The function α preserves initial states because

$$\alpha(R_\beta[\Lambda]) = R_F[rp_S(\Lambda)] = R_F[a]$$

Suppose that

$$\alpha(R_\beta[x]) = R_F[rp_S(x)] = R_F[u]$$

where $u = rp_S(x)$. To show that α preserves the transition structure, we must compute

$$\begin{aligned}
\alpha(N(R_\beta[x],\sigma_i)) &= \alpha(R_\beta[x\sigma_i]) = R_F[rp_S(x\sigma_i)] = R_F[M(rp_S(x),\sigma_i)] \\
&= R_F[M(u,\sigma_i)] = P(R_F[u],\sigma_i) \\
&= P(\alpha(R_\beta[x]),\sigma_i) \qquad \text{for } i = 0, \ldots, k-1
\end{aligned}$$

Now it must be shown that α is a strong homomorphism; more precisely, we must show that $R_\beta[x]$ is a final state of $M(\beta)$ iff $R_F[rp_S(x)]$ is a final state of S^M. $R_\beta[x]$ is a final state of $M(\beta)$ iff $x \in \beta$, which is true iff $rp_S(x) \in F$, but this is precisely the condition for $R_F[rp_S(x)]$ to be a final state of S^M. The argument can be concluded once it is shown that α is one to one. Suppose that $R_F[rp_S(x)] = R_F[rp_S(y)]$; then $rp_S(x) R_F rp_S(y)$. By the definition of R_F

$$\begin{aligned}
(\forall z)_{\Sigma_k^*} \quad & M(rp_S(x),z) \in F \Leftrightarrow M(rp_S(y),z) \in F \\
(\forall z)_{\Sigma_k^*} \quad & (rp_S(xz) \in F \Leftrightarrow rp_S(yz) \in F) \\
(\forall z)_{\Sigma_k^*} \quad & xz \in \beta \Leftrightarrow yz \in \beta \\
& x R_\beta y
\end{aligned}$$

That is, $\qquad\qquad\qquad R_\beta[x] = R_\beta[y] \quad \blacksquare$

Now that both concepts of minimal machines have been proved to be the same, all the results that one could hope for are easily derived.

Corollary 10. If S and T are two behaviorally equivalent machines, then S^M is a strong homomorphic image of T.

Corollary 11. S^M is unique to within isomorphism.

Corollary 12. Two sequential machines S and T are behaviorally equivalent iff S^M is isomorphic to T^M.

The last corollary provides an excellent test for behavioral equivalence. Since an isomorphism is unique, if one exists at all, the behavioral equivalence problem can be considered to be completely solved once a convenient method for calculating S^M is given. In general, it is not difficult to use the definition of R_F to compute the induced congruence. Moore's method of merging states is essentially this process.

PROBLEMS

1. (Moore[1]) The relation R_F is sometimes called the *indistinguishability relation* on $S = \langle S,M,a,F \rangle$ because, if $u R_F v$, there are no tapes which cause S to give different outputs when the machine is started from u or v. An indistinguishability relation E_i is now defined as follows

$$u E_i v \Leftrightarrow (\forall x)_{\Sigma_k^*} \quad \lg(x) = i \Rightarrow (M(u,x) \in F \Leftrightarrow M(v,x) \in F)$$

In other words, $u E_i v$ iff u and v are indistinguishable by tapes of length i. Show that

$$u R_F v \Leftrightarrow u\Big(\bigcap_{i=0}^{n-2} E_i\Big)v$$

where S has n states. This means that if u and v are indistinguishable by all words of length not exceeding $n - 2$, then u and v are completely indistinguishable.   Show that $n - 2$ is the best possible upper bound.

2.   Does the bound in Prob. 1 change if one considers Mealy machines?

3.   Prove Corollaries 10 to 12.

4   A RECIPE FOR COMPUTING S^M

Now an explicit construction is given for computing the induced congruence relation R_F from a machine S.

The following algorithm will be worked out in sufficient detail that it could be immediately programmed for a digital computer.

Algorithm 1.   (State minimization of sequential machines)

(1) Let $h = 1$ and E_0 be the following equivalence relation:

$$uE_0v \Leftrightarrow (u \in F \Leftrightarrow v \in F)$$

(2) Construct for every pair of states u and v such that $uE_{h-1}v$

$uE_hv \Leftrightarrow M(u,\sigma_i)E_{h-1}M(v,\sigma_i)$ for every $i = 0, \ldots, k - 1$

(3) If $E_{h-1} = E_h$, go to rule 5.   Otherwise go to rule 4.

(4) Let h be replaced by $h + 1$ and return to step 2.

(5) Let $R_F = E_h$ and halt.

Having stated the algorithm, the first step is to show that the procedure will terminate when applied to a finite sequential machine.

Theorem 2.   The algorithm halts when applied to a finite machine. More exactly, there exists an integer h such that $E_{h-1} = E_h$.

PROOF.   Let S be a machine with output F and let S have n states.   Clearly, all the E_i are equivalence relations.   By step 2 of the procedure, $E_{i+1} \subseteq E_i$.   Thus we have

$$E_0 \supseteq E_1 \supseteq E_2 \supseteq \cdots \supseteq 0$$

where 0 denotes the equality relation on the set S of n states.   Taking ranks, we get

$$2 = rk(E_0) \leq rk(E_1) \leq \cdots \leq rk(0) = n$$

Thus there is an infinite sequence of integers between 2 and n which implies that there is an integer h such that

$$rk(E_{h-1}) = rk(E_h)$$

and since $E_{h-1} \supseteq E_h$, we must have $E_{h-1} = E_h$.   **∎**

The next property to be verified is that the algorithm actually computes the induced congruence relation on S.

Theorem 3. $uE_hv \Leftrightarrow (\forall z)_{\Sigma_k *}$ $\lg(z) = h \Rightarrow (M(u,z) \in F \Leftrightarrow M(v,z) \in F)$.

PROOF. The argument is an induction on h. The basis step where $h = 0$ is trivial.
Suppose that the theorem is true for $h - 1$ where $h \geq 1$

$$uE_h v \Leftrightarrow (\forall \sigma)_{\Sigma_k} \quad M(u,\sigma)E_{h-1}M(v,\sigma)$$

By the induction hypothesis,

$$uE_h v \Leftrightarrow (\forall \sigma)_{\Sigma_k}(\forall z)_{\Sigma_{k^*}} \quad \lg(z) = h - 1 \Rightarrow (M(M(u,\sigma),z) \, \epsilon \, F \Leftrightarrow M(M(v,\sigma),z) \, \epsilon \, F)$$
$$uE_h v \Leftrightarrow (\forall \sigma)_{\Sigma_k}(\forall z)_{\Sigma_{k^*}} \quad \lg(z) = h - 1 \Rightarrow (M(u,\sigma z) \, \epsilon \, F \Leftrightarrow M(v,\sigma z) \, \epsilon \, F)$$
$$uE_h v \Leftrightarrow (\forall z)_{\Sigma_{k^*}} \quad \lg(z) = h \Rightarrow (M(u,z) \, \epsilon \, F \Leftrightarrow M(v,z) \, \epsilon \, F) \quad |$$

Lemma 4. If there exists an h such that $E_{h-1} = E_h$, then $E_{h-1} = E_{h+m}$
for any natural number m.

PROOF. Since $E_{h-1} = E_h$ by hypothesis, we now proceed by induction on m.
Assume the result for $p \leq m$, then $E_m = E_{h-1}$. To complete the proof, we must show
that $E_{h-1} = E_{m+1}$.

$$uE_{m+1}v \Leftrightarrow M(u,\sigma_i)E_m M(v,\sigma_i)$$
$$\Leftrightarrow M(u,\sigma_i)E_{h-1}M(v,\sigma_i)$$
$$\Leftrightarrow uE_h v$$

This shows that $E_{m+1} = E_h = E_{h-1}$. $\quad |$

Theorem 5. If there exists an h such that $E_{h-1} = E_h$, then $E_{h-1} = R_F$.

PROOF. By Lemma 4, $E_{h-1} = E_{h+m}$ for all m. Thus

$$E_{h-1} = \bigcap_{i=0}^{\infty} E_i$$

Thus $uE_i v$ for every natural number i. By Lemma 3,

$$u(\bigcap_{i=0}^{\infty} E_i)v \Leftrightarrow (\forall i)_N (\forall z)_{\Sigma_{k^*}} \quad \lg(z) = i \Rightarrow (M(u,z) \, \epsilon \, F \Leftrightarrow M(v,z) \, \epsilon \, F)$$
$$\Leftrightarrow (\forall z)_{\Sigma^*} \quad (M(u,z) \, \epsilon \, F \Leftrightarrow M(v,z) \, \epsilon \, F)$$
$$\Leftrightarrow uR_F v \quad |$$

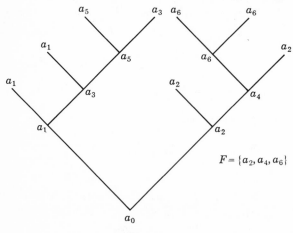

$$F = \{a_2, a_4, a_6\}$$

FIG. 1

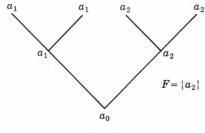

$$F = \{a_2\}$$

FIG. 2

EXAMPLE. $S = \langle S, M, a_0, F \rangle$, where $F = \{a_2, a_4, a_6\}$, Fig. 1. Proceeding through the calculation step by step yields:

(1) $h = 1$, $E_0 = \begin{cases} (a_0, a_1)(a_1, a_3)(a_2, a_4)(a_3, a_5)(a_4, a_6) \\ (a_0, a_3)(a_1, a_5)(a_2, a_6) \\ (a_0, a_5) \end{cases}$

(2) $E_1 = \begin{cases} (a_1, a_3)(a_2, a_4)(a_3, a_5)(a_4, a_6) \\ (a_1, a_5)(a_2, a_6) \end{cases}$

(3) $E_2 = E_1$

(4) $R_F = \{[a_1, a_3, a_5], [a_2, a_4, a_6], [a_0]\}$

(5) S^M is given by Fig. 2.

PROBLEMS

1.   The algorithm of this section can be abstracted slightly to provide an effective procedure for computing the largest congruence relation contained in a given equivalence relation.   Carry out the abstract argument.   Many problems considered in this book up to the present time can be characterized as problems of this type.   Name several such problems and explicitly give the equivalence relation and the congruence relation.

2.   Minimize the machine of Fig. P2.

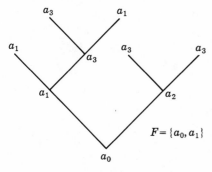

$$F = \{a_0, a_1\}$$

FIG. P2

3.   Minimize the machine in Prob. 2, but with the new output $F = \{a_0, a_2\}$.

4. Minimize the sequential machine given in Fig. P4, whose output $F = \{a_2, a_4\}$.

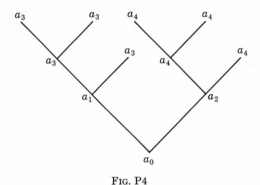

FIG. P4

5. Minimize the machine of Fig. P5, whose output is $\{a_2, a_4, a_6\}$.

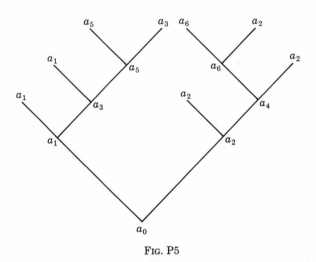

FIG. P5

6. Are any of the machines of Probs. 2 to 4 behaviorally equivalent?

7. Let S_1 and S_2 be two sequential machines with behaviors β_1 and β_2. Is $M(\beta_1 \cap \beta_2)$ isomorphic to $M(\beta_1) \wedge M(\beta_2)$? What about the dual case?

5 SUMMARY AND HISTORY

In this chapter the minimization problem for finite sequential machines has been completely solved. A number of interesting results occur in this study. For instance, the minimal machine is unique up to isomorphism. This means that any method of computing the minimal machine will lead to the same result.

Corollary 3.12 provides a very efficient test for behavioral equivalence of machines.   One minimizes the machine and checks to see if the resulting minimal machines are isomorphic.   Of course, the test for isomorphism is simple.

Historically, the minimization algorithm was presented by Huffman and Moore[1].   The induced congruence relation on Σ_k^* is due to Rabin and Scott, and Moore[1] first constructed R_F.   The material which unites both concepts is due to Büchi and Wright.

CHAPTER 12 *transition systems and regular expressions*

1 INTRODUCTION

In the summary to Chap. 10, the analysis and the synthesis problems of sequential machines were stated. In this chapter those problems will be solved. The first step will be to introduce *transition systems* which are related to sequential machines but appear to have more freedom in their internal structure.

Naturally, one would suspect that these finite machines can compute more than the regular subsets of Σ_k^*. It is an important and surprising result due to Myhill that this suspicion is false. An algorithm will be given to convert from any finite transition system to a finite sequential machine having the same behavior. Then a language of *regular expressions* will be introduced. A direct connection between transition systems and regular expressions will be presented, and both the analysis and synthesis problems will be solved.

2 TRANSITION SYSTEMS

We are about to study a system which is a generalization of a sequential machine. Before the formal definition is presented, an example is given in Fig. 1. We shall assume that the machine in Fig. 1 has two initial states s_0 and s_1. We note that the machine passes from s_2 to s_3 via the word of length zero; i.e., the machine has *spontaneous transitions* between internal states. Note that if the machine is in state s_0 and input σ_0 occurs, the machine passes to s_1 and to s_3. The machine simply has a

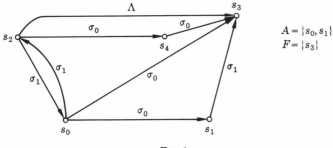

$A = \{s_0, s_1\}$
$F = \{s_3\}$

FIG. 1

great deal of freedom of choice in what it will do in response to a given input. These intuitive notions are now made precise.

Definition 1. A *transition system is* defined to be a quintuple

$$S = \langle S, M, A, F, P \rangle$$

where S is the nonempty set of *internal states*, $A \subseteq S$ is the set of *initial states*, $F \subseteq S$ is the set of *final states*, M is a *transition function* which maps $S \times \Sigma_k$ into 2^S, the set of all subsets of S, and P is a binary relation on S which holds between two states u and v in case there is a spontaneous transition from u to v. P is called the *spontaneous transition relation*.

EXAMPLE. The machine given in Fig. 1 is a transition system, where $S = \{s_0, \ldots, s_4\}$, $A = \{s_0, s_1\}$, $F = \{s_3\}$, $P = \{(s_2, s_3)\}$, and M is given by the following table.

	s_0	s_1	s_2	s_3	s_4
$M(s, \sigma_0)$	$\{s_1, s_3\}$	$\emptyset$	$\{s_4\}$	$\emptyset$	$\{s_3\}$
$M(s, \sigma_1)$	$\{s_2\}$	$\{s_3\}$	$\{s_0\}$	$\emptyset$	$\emptyset$

Thus, $M(s, \sigma_i)$ is the set of states that the machine gets to when it is in state s and input σ_i occurs.

Proposition 2. Every sequential machine is a transition system.

PROOF. Clearly, A must be a singleton, M must map $S \times \Sigma_k$ into singletons from 2^S, and P must be the empty relation $\emptyset$ on S.

Definition 3. The *transition relation* $|u, x, w|$ for a transition machine $S = \langle S, M, A, F, P \rangle$ is a subset of $S \times \Sigma_k^* \times S$ defined by

$$|u, \Lambda, v| \Leftrightarrow u \hat{P} v \qquad u, v \in S$$
$$|u, x\sigma, v| \Leftrightarrow (\exists w, q)_S \qquad |u, x, w| \wedge q \in M(w, \sigma) \wedge q \hat{P} v \qquad \text{for } \sigma \in \Sigma_k, x \in \Sigma_k^*$$

where $\hat{P}$ is the reflexive and transitive closure of P (cf. Sec. 1-4). The transition relation $|u, x, v|$ holds for states u and v and input word x when there is a transition from state u to state v via input x. The formal

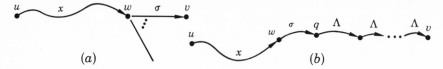

FIG. 2   The intuitive meaning of $|u, x\sigma, v|$.

definition of $|u,x\sigma,v|$ covers two cases. The first case is when $|u,x,w|$ holds and $v \in M(w,\sigma)$. The second case is when $|u,x,w|$ holds and σ takes the machine from w to q and there is a sequence of spontaneous transitions from q to v. Both situations are sketched in Fig. 2.

Definition 4.   The *response relation* is defined to be $\{(x,v)|(\exists a)_A|a,x,v|\}$. Now it is possible to define the behavior of a transition system.

Definition 5.   The *behavior* of a transition system $S = \langle S,M,A,F,P \rangle$ is defined to be

$$\beta_S = \{x|(\exists a)_A(\exists f)_F|a,x,f|\}$$

EXAMPLE.   For the machine in Fig. 1, certain of the relations are computed. The reader should check these results to be certain that the concepts involved are clearly understood.   First we compute $\hat{P}$

$$\hat{P} = \{(s_2,s_3),(s_0,s_0),(s_1,s_1),(s_2,s_2),(s_3,s_3),(s_4,s_4)\}$$

The relations $|s_0,\sigma_0\sigma_1,s_3|$ and $|s_0,\sigma_1,s_3|$ hold.   Note that $\sigma_1 \in \beta_S$, but that $\sigma_1{}^2 \notin \beta_S$.

The purpose of introducing the concept of the transition system is to facilitate the study of regular subsets of Σ_k^*. The transition system may be thought of as an abstract system or a graph which is devoid of interpretation.   It is the system $\langle S,M,a,F \rangle$ which is to be interpreted as being an abstraction of sequential machines.   Certain special types of transition systems are capable of a concrete physical interpretation.

PROBLEMS

1.   The relation R, defined below, is the analog of the induced congruence relation

$$uRv \Leftrightarrow (\forall x)_{\Sigma_k*}(\forall f)_F\ [|u,x,f| \Leftrightarrow |v,x,f|]$$

Is R a right congruence relation?

2.   Are programs for a digital computer transition systems?

3.   Let S and T be transition systems such that the initial states of T are the final states of S. What is the behavior of the combined machine in terms of β_S and β_T?

3   THE SUBSET CONSTRUCTION

A construction that converts a finite transition system into a finite sequential machine will now be indicated.   It will be shown that the behavior of the transition system and that of the sequential machine produced by the algorithm are the same. Despite the additional freedom of action which the transition system possesses, it can compute no more than an ordinary machine. The added flexibility of the transition system does cause an increase in the complexity of the corresponding sequential machine. If the original transition system had n states, the ordinary sequential machine might have as many as 2^n internal states.

Definition 1. Given the transition system $S = \langle S,M,A,F,P \rangle$ *the subset machine associated with S* is defined as

$$D(S) = \langle 2^S,N,B,G \rangle$$

where 2^S is the set of all subsets of S,

$$G = \{U \mid U \cap F \neq \emptyset\}$$
$$B = \{u \mid (\exists a)_A a \hat{P} u\}$$
$$N(U,\sigma_i) = \{v \mid (\exists u)_U (\exists w)_S \quad w \in M(u,\sigma_i) \wedge w \hat{P} v\}$$

for $U \in 2^S$ and $i = 0, \ldots, k - 1$. A transition system S is given in Fig. 1a, and the subset machine is given in Fig. 1b. The primary result of this section will be to show that the behavior of a transition system and its subset machine are identical. First a computational lemma is required.

Lemma 2. $rp_{D(S)}(x) = \{u \mid (\exists a)_A \quad |a,x,u|\}$ for $D(S) = \langle 2^S,N,B,G \rangle$ and $S = \langle S,M,A,F,P \rangle$.

PROOF. $rp_{D(S)}(\Lambda) = B = \{u : (\exists a)_A | a \hat{P} u\} = \{u : |(\exists a)_A| a,\Lambda,u|\}$
$rp_{D(S)}(x\sigma_j) = N(rp_{D(S)}(x),\sigma_j)$

By the induction hypothesis, $rp_{D(S)}(x) = \{u : (\exists a)_A | a,x,u|\}$. Let $U = rp_{D(S)}(x)$.

$$N(U,\sigma) = \{v \mid (\exists u)_U (\exists w)_S \quad w \in M(u,\sigma) \wedge w \hat{P} v\}$$

Since $u \in U$, $|a,x,u|$ holds, so that

$$rp_{D(S)}(x\sigma) = N(rp_{D(S)}(x),\sigma) = \{v \mid (\exists a)_A \quad |a,x\sigma,v|\} \quad \blacksquare$$

Theorem 3. (Myhill) If $S = \langle S,M,A,F,P \rangle$ is a transition system with behavior β, then $\beta_{D(S)} = \beta$, where $D(S) = \langle 2^S,N,B,G \rangle$.

PROOF. First assume that $x \in \beta_{D(S)}$. It will be shown that $x \in \beta$. If $x \in \beta_{D(S)}$, then $rp_{D(S)}(x) = U \in G$; however, $U \in G$ implies that there is an element $w \in U \cap F$ from the definition of G.

$$U = rp_{D(S)}(x) = \{u \mid (\exists a)_A | a,x,u|\}$$

Since $w \in U$ and $w \in F$, $|a,x,w|$ holds with $w \in F$. That is, $x \in \beta$. Conversely, suppose that $x \in \beta$. Then $|a,x,f|$ holds for $a \in A$, $f \in F$. Consider the set

$$U = \{u : (\exists a)_A | a,x,u|\}$$

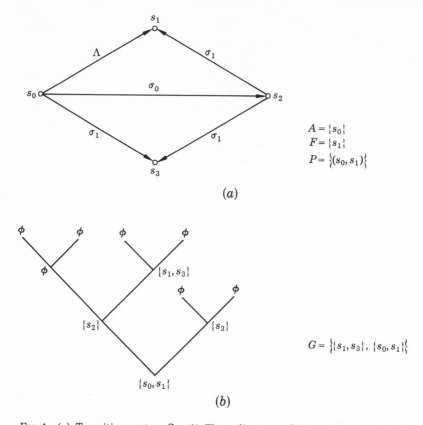

$A = \{s_0\}$
$F = \{s_1\}$
$P = \{(s_0, s_1)\}$

(a)

$G = \{\{s_1, s_3\}, \{s_0, s_1\}\}$

(b)

FIG. 1   (a) Transition system S.   (b) The ordinary machine corresponding to S.

It is clear that U is not empty, since $f \epsilon U$.   Because $f \epsilon F$, $U \cap F \neq \emptyset$, so that $U \epsilon G$.   But

$$U = rp_{D(S)}(x) \epsilon G$$

Therefore, $x \epsilon \beta_{D(S)}$. ∎

There are a number of interesting consequences of the subset construction.

Corollary 4.   There exists an effective procedure for converting a finite transition system into an ordinary finite sequential machine with the same behavior.

Corollary 5.   A sequential machine with several initial states is equivalent to a machine with just one initial state.

Corollary 6.   The behavior of any finite transition system is a regular subset of Σ_k^*.

The transition system will prove to be a powerful theoretical tool in investigating regular sets.

PROBLEMS

1. Carry out the subset construction for the transition system given in Fig. P1. The system is a trivial extension of Definition 1 in that the labels are not just letters of Σ_k, but words of Σ_k^*.

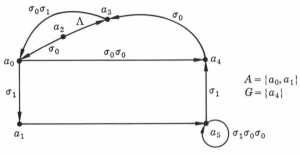

$$A = \{a_0, a_1\}$$
$$G = \{a_4\}$$

FIG. P1

2. (Bar-Hillel, Shamir) Let V be a nonempty set called the *vocabulary*. V^+ denotes the set of all nonnull finite strings of elements of V. A *language* is any subset of V^+. A *finite-state grammar* over V is defined as $F = \langle S, s_0, R \rangle$, where S is a nonempty set of *states*. $s_0 \in S$ is the *initial state*, and $R \subseteq S \times V \times S$. An element of R, that is, (s_i, v, s_j) is called a *rule* of the grammar associated with s_i. $x = v_{j_0} \cdots v_{j_{n-1}}$ is said to be *generated* by F iff there exist states $u_0, u_1, \ldots, u_n$ such that

$$s_0 = u_0 = u_n$$
$$(u_i, v_{j_i}, u_{i+1}) \in R \qquad i = 0, \ldots, n-1$$
$$u_i \neq s_0 \qquad i = 1, \ldots, n-1$$

Let ρ_F be the set of all words produced or generated by F. Show that for every finite transition system S with no spontaneous transitions, there exists a finite-state grammar F such that $\beta_S = \rho_F$.

3. (Bar-Hillel, Shamir) Show that for every finite-state grammar F there is a finite transition system S such that $\rho_F = \beta_S$.

4. In Probs. 2 and 3, V^+ does not contain the null word Λ. Analyze the implications of including the null string.

5. Let α be a regular subset of Σ^* and let φ be a homomorphism of Σ^*. Show that $\varphi(\alpha)$ is regular. This shows that the regular sets are closed under semigroup homomorphisms. Is the same result true for inverse homomorphisms?

4   THE LANGUAGE OF REGULAR EXPRESSIONS

There is a basic difficulty in finding methods for working with the behavior of sequential machines. Since the behavior is often an infinite subset of Σ_k^*, it is not meaningful to ask for algorithms for computing the behavior. To circumvent this difficulty, a language of regular expressions will now be defined for the express purpose of representing the behavior. First, we must endure the formal definitions.

Definition 1.   *The language of regular expressions, L,* is defined inductively as follows:

(1) Λ is a regular expression.

(2) $\emptyset$ is a regular expression.

(3) σ_i is a regular expression for $i = 0, \ldots, k - 1$.

(4) If α and β are regular expressions, then $\alpha \cup \beta$ is a regular expression.

(5) If α and β are regular expressions, then $\alpha\beta$ is a regular expression.

(6) If α is a regular expression, then α^* is a regular expression.

(7) There are no regular expressions other than those given by steps 1 to 6.

Definition 1 immediately affords a test to see if a collection of symbols is a regular expression. To provide an interpretation for the language L, a valuation mapping which associates a subset of Σ_k^* with every regular expression is constructed.

Definition 2.   *The valuation of a regular expression* or *the set denoted by a regular expression* is defined by the following procedure.   (The valuation of α is denoted by $|\alpha|$.)

(1) $|\emptyset| = \emptyset$, where $\emptyset$ is the empty set

(2) $|\Lambda| = \{\Lambda\}$

(3) $|\sigma_i| = \{\sigma_i\}$ for $i = 0, \ldots, k - 1$

(4) $|\alpha \cup \beta| = |\alpha| \cup |\beta|$

(5) $|\alpha\beta| = |\alpha| \; |\beta| = \{xy : x \in |\alpha|, \; y \in |\beta|\}$

(6) $|\alpha^*| = \{\Lambda\} \cup |\alpha| \cup |\alpha| \; |\alpha| \cup |\alpha| \; |\alpha| \; |\alpha| \cup \cdots$

The action of the valuation mapping on α^* may be written more compactly if one uses the abbreviation

$$|\alpha|^n = \overbrace{|\alpha| \; \cdots \; |\alpha|}^{n}$$

Thus $$|\alpha^*| = |\Lambda| \cup |\alpha| \cup |\alpha|^2 \cup \cdots$$

In order to clarify the concepts, some typical regular expressions, along with the sets denoted by the expressions, are tabulated.

Regular expression α	*Regular set $|\alpha|$*
1. $(\sigma_0 \cup \sigma_1 \cup \cdots \cup \sigma_{k-1})^*$	Σ_k^*
2. $(\sigma_0\sigma_1)^*$	The set of all sequences in Σ_2^* which start with σ_0, end with σ_1, and alternate between σ_0 and σ_1; also Λ
3. $(\sigma_0\sigma_1) \cup (\sigma_0\sigma_0\sigma_0)$	The set consisting of $\sigma_0\sigma_1$ and $\sigma_0\sigma_0\sigma_0$
4. $\sigma_1(\sigma_0 \cup \cdots \cup \sigma_{k-1})^*$	The set of all sequences of length at least 1 which begin with σ_1
5. $(\sigma_0^*\sigma_1\sigma_0^*)$	The set of all sequences containing exactly one σ_1 over Σ_2

Now the notion of equality is defined for regular expressions.

Definition 3. If α and β are regular expressions, we write

$$\alpha = \beta \text{ iff } |\alpha| = |\beta|$$

The analogy between regular expressions and boolean forms should be apparent. Two boolean forms were called equivalent if their valuation functions were equal. This provided an algorithm for checking on the equality of forms, since the valuation functions were finite objects. In the present case the situation is more complicated because $|\alpha|$ and $|\beta|$ are infinite objects in general, so that even testing for the equivalence of regular expressions will require more powerful methods.

Before proceeding to derive the connection between regular expressions and finite machines, we list some of the identities of the language of regular expression.

Theorem 4. For regular expressions α, β, and γ,

$$\alpha(\beta\gamma) = (\alpha\beta)\gamma$$
$$\alpha\beta \cup \alpha\gamma = \alpha(\beta \cup \gamma)$$
$$\beta\alpha \cup \gamma\alpha = (\beta \cup \gamma)\alpha$$
$$(\alpha \cup \beta)^* = (\alpha^* \cup \beta^*)^* = (\alpha^*\beta^*)^*$$
$$\alpha^* = (\Lambda \cup \alpha)^{r-1}(\alpha^r)^* \qquad \text{for } r = 1, \ldots$$
$$\Lambda\alpha = \alpha\Lambda = \alpha$$
$$\Lambda^* = \Lambda$$
$$\emptyset \cup \alpha = \alpha$$
$$\alpha\emptyset = \emptyset\alpha = \emptyset$$
$$\emptyset^* = \Lambda$$

PROOF. The arguments for all the statements are somewhat similar. As an example of the method, we prove that

$$(\alpha \cup \beta)^* = (\alpha^*\beta^*)^*$$
$$|(\alpha \cup \beta)^*| = \{\Lambda\} \cup |\alpha \cup \beta| \cup |\alpha \cup \beta|^2 \cup \cdots$$
$$= \{\Lambda\} \cup |\alpha| \cup |\beta| \cup |\alpha|^2 \cup |\alpha| \; |\beta| \cup |\beta| \; |\alpha| \cup |\beta|^2 \cup \cdots$$

On the other hand

$$|(\alpha^*\beta^*)^*| = \{\Lambda\} \cup |\alpha^*\beta^*| \cup |\alpha^*\beta^*|^2 \cup \cdots$$
$$= \{\Lambda\} \cup |\alpha^*| \; |\beta^*| \cup |\alpha^*| \; |\beta^*| \; |\alpha^*| \; |\beta^*| \cup \cdots$$
$$= \{\Lambda\} \cup |\alpha| \cup |\beta| \cup |\alpha|^2 \cup |\alpha| \; |\beta| \cup |\beta| \; |\alpha| \cup |\beta|^2 \cup \cdots \quad \blacksquare$$

PROBLEMS

1. Show that for regular expressions α and β, and γ,

$$\alpha \cup \beta = \beta \cup \alpha$$
$$\alpha \cup \alpha = \alpha$$
$$\alpha \cup (\beta \cup \gamma) = (\alpha \cup \beta) \cup \gamma$$

2. Suppose that one deals with the subset of *commutative* regular expressions, that is, $\alpha\beta = \beta\alpha$. Prove that

$$(\alpha \cup \beta)^* = \alpha^*\beta^* \quad \text{and} \quad (\alpha^*\beta)^* = \Lambda \cup \alpha^*\beta^*\beta$$

3. (Eggan) Let h be a mapping from regular expressions into the natural numbers defined below. [$h(\alpha)$ will be read *the star height of* α.]
  (a) $h(\Lambda) = h(\emptyset) = h(\sigma_i) = 0 \quad i = 0, \ldots, k-1$
  (b) If α and β are regular expressions, $h(\alpha\beta) = h(\alpha \cup \beta) = \max(h(\alpha), h(\beta))$.
  (c) If α is a regular expression, $h(\alpha^*) = h(\alpha) + 1$.   Find the star height of the following two regular expressions:

$$\sigma_0^*(\sigma_1 \cup \sigma_2^*)^* \qquad \sigma_0^* \cup ((\sigma_1^*\sigma_2) \cup \sigma_3)^*$$

Show that for every nonnegative integer n, there is a regular expression having star height n.

4. (McNaughton-Yamada) Write a regular expression which describes the set of words in which there were never three consecutive σ_0's or there have been three consecutive σ_1's since the last three consecutive σ_0's.

5. Construct a finite set of rules for defining the transpose of a regular expression so that $|\alpha^T| = |\alpha|^T$. Try to do the same problem for complementation; i.e., define $\bar{\alpha}$ so that $|\bar{\alpha}| = \overline{|\alpha|}$. (It is known that this is impossible for complementation. Where does the difficulty lie?)

6. Find a counterexample for the following equality

$$(\alpha \cup \beta)^* \stackrel{?}{=} \alpha^* \cup \beta^*$$

5   THE ANALYSIS AND SYNTHESIS THEOREMS

The theorems of this section will connect the concepts of regular expressions and regular subsets. Sometimes, the regular subsets are also called *regular events* in the literature. The following two important theorems are due to Kleene.[2]

Theorem 1.   There is an algorithm which applies to any regular expression α and yields a finite sequential machine whose behavior is $|\alpha|$.

PROOF.   The argument is an induction on the shape of a regular expression α. We shall construct finite transition systems whose behaviors are $|\alpha|$. From these one obtains the appropriate finite sequential machine by the subset construction.

  (1) If $\alpha = \emptyset, \Lambda, \sigma_0, \ldots, \sigma_{k-1}$, then the problem is trivial.

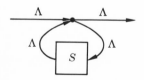

FIG. 1   Transition system for $|\alpha^*|$.

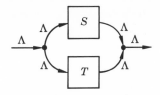

FIG. 2   Transition system for $|\alpha| \cup |\beta|$.

FIG. 3   Transition system for $|\alpha| \| |\beta|$.

(2) If there is a transition system S having behavior† $|\alpha|$, then the transition graph shown in Fig. 1 has behavior $|\alpha^*|$.

(3) If transition systems S and T have behaviors $|\alpha|$ and $|\beta|$,.respectively, then the transition system having behavior $|\alpha \cup \beta|$ is as shown in Fig. 2.

(4) If S and T are transition systems having behaviors $|\alpha|$ and $|\beta|$, respectively, then the reader may show that the machine of Fig. 3 has behavior $|\alpha|\,|\beta|$.

Since all finite transition systems may be replaced with finite sequential machines by the subset construction, the theorem is established. ∎

The proof for the synthesis theorem was facilitated by the use of transition systems. Likewise, the analysis theorem can be given in terms of transition systems, but the constructive argument of the proof is more useful if given in terms of an ordinary sequential machine.

For the purposes of the discussion, let $S = \langle S, M, a_1, F \rangle$, where $S = \{a_1, \ldots, a_n\}$ and $F = \{a_{l_1}, a_{l_2}, \ldots, a_{l_r}\}$, where $r \geq 0$. We shall also assume that the input alphabet is Σ_2. This leads to no loss of generality, but it does simplify the calculations which follow.

Definition 2.   The function α_{ij}^k is defined from the machine S over Σ_2 relative to the ordering of the states into regular expressions as follows. For $n \geq i \geq 1$, $n \geq j \geq 1$, and $n \geq k \geq 0$, define

$$\alpha_{ij}^0 = \sigma_0 \cup \sigma_1 \cup \Lambda_{ij} \qquad \text{if there is a transition from } a_i \text{ to } a_j \text{ via } \sigma_0 \text{ and via } \sigma_1$$

$$= \sigma_0 \cup \Lambda_{ij} \qquad \text{if there is a transition from } a_i \text{ to } a_j \text{ via } \sigma_0 \text{ but not via } \sigma_1$$

$$= \sigma_1 \cup \Lambda_{ij} \qquad \text{if there is a transition from } a_i \text{ to } a_j \text{ via } \sigma_1 \text{ but not via } \sigma_0$$

$$= \Lambda_{ij} \qquad \text{if there is no transition which takes } a_i \text{ to } a_j$$

where $\Lambda_{ij} = \begin{cases} \Lambda & i = j \\ \emptyset & i \neq j \end{cases}$

$$\alpha_{ij}^k = \alpha_{ij}^{k-1} \cup \alpha_{ik}^{k-1}(\alpha_{kk}^{k-1})^*\alpha_{kj}^{k-1} \qquad \text{for } k \geq 1$$

† In Figs. 1 to 3 the single transition into (out of) a transition system symbolizes one line to (from) each initial (final) state.

Theorem 3. α_{ij}^k is the set of input words which cause S to leave state a_i and go into state a_j without passing through a_l for $l > k$.

PROOF.   The argument is an induction on k.

BASIS.   For $k = 0$, the result is trivial.

INDUCTION STEP.   It is possible for a transition from a_i to a_j to pass through a_k any number of times.   If the machine does not pass through a_k, the resulting set is $|\alpha_{ij}^{k-1}|$ and, by the induction hypothesis, we are through.

If S passes through a_k exactly once, the sequence of inputs which causes a_i to go into a_j will be called x.   Then it must be the case that $x = yz$, where y causes S to go from a_i to a_k and z causes S to go from a_k to a_j.   Thus by the inductive hypothesis, y is denoted by α_{bk}^{k-1} and z is denoted by α_{kj}^{k-1}.   Clearly,

$$|\alpha_{ik}^{k-1}\alpha_{kj}^{k-1}| \subseteq |\alpha_{ij}^k| = |\alpha_{ij}^{k-1} \cup \alpha_{ik}^{k-1}(\alpha_{kk}^{k-1})^*\alpha_{kj}^{k-1}|$$

Finally, if S goes through a_k more than one time, the sequence is denoted by $\alpha_{ij}^{k-1} \cup \alpha_{ik}^{k-1}(\alpha_{kk}^{k-1})^*\alpha_{kj}^{k-1}$.   ∎

Theorem 4.   Given $S = \langle S, M, a_1, F \rangle$, where $F = \{a_{l_1}, \ldots, a_{l_r}\}$ for $r \geq 0$ with n states, the behavior of S is denoted by the regular expression

$$\begin{cases} \alpha_{1l_1}^n \cup \cdots \cup \alpha_{1l_r}^n & \text{if } r > 0 \\ \emptyset & \text{if } r = 0 \end{cases}$$

PROOF.   Theorem 3 gives the required result.   Note that $r = 0$ implies that the regular expression for S is $\emptyset$.   ∎

Corollary 5. $\alpha_{ij}^i = (\alpha_{ij}^{i-1})^*\alpha_{ij}^{i-1}$ and $a_{ij}^j = \alpha_{ij}^{j-1}(\alpha_{jj}^{j-1})^*$

Corollary 6.   There is an effective procedure which applies to a finite sequential machine S and yields a regular expression α such that $|\alpha|$ is the behavior of S.

Theorems 1 and 4 present solutions to the synthesis problem and to the analysis problem, respectively.   Now we know that the language of regular expressions denotes only regular subsets of Σ_k^*; and, conversely, for every regular subset β of Σ_k^* there is a regular expression which denotes β.

Theorem 7.   The sets denoted by the regular expressions form a boolean algebra of sets.

PROOF.   Cf. Theorem 10-4.12.   ∎

By combining the analysis and synthesis theorems, we get a decision procedure for equality of regular expression.

Theorem 8.   Two regular expressions α and β are equal iff the sequential machines associated with α and β are behaviorally equivalent.

PROOF.   Given α and β, the appropriate transition systems are constructed and the subset machines are computed.   Corollary 11-3.12 gives an algorithm for checking if the two machines have the same behavior.   ∎

The two Kleene theorems have been stated in the form which is most useful for our engineering applications.   For theoretical purposes, the following restatement is often used.

Theorem 9 (Kleene).   The class of regular sets is the least family which contains the finite sets and is closed under the operations of finite union, concatenation, and *.

PROBLEMS

1.   (McNaughton-Yamada) The *size* of a regular expression is defined to be the number of letters in the expression.   Show that the size of α_{ij}^k is at most $2 \cdot 4^k$.

2.   (McNaughton-Yamada) Show that the size of the regular expression describing the behavior of an n-state minimal sequential machine is at most $(n - 1)2 \cdot 4^n$.

3.   It is convenient to use the connectives $\cap$ and $^-$ in the language of regular expressions.   Naturally,

$$|\alpha \cap \beta| = |\alpha| \cap |\beta| \qquad |\bar{\alpha}| = \Sigma_k^* - |\alpha|$$

Rework Prob. 4.4 by using the additional connectives.

4.   Provide counterexamples for the following two cases.

$$\alpha\beta \cap \alpha\gamma \stackrel{?}{=} \alpha(\beta \cap \gamma) \qquad (\alpha \cap \beta)^* \stackrel{?}{=} \alpha^* \cap \beta^*$$

5.   (Elgot[1]) We write $x \leq y$ iff there is a word $u \, \epsilon \, \Sigma_k^*$ such that $y = xu$.   For any subset α of Σ_k^*, we define

$$\text{Int}(\alpha) = \{u \, \epsilon \, \alpha | (\forall x) \quad x \leq u \Rightarrow x \, \epsilon \, \alpha\}$$

$\text{Int}(\alpha)$ is read "the *interior* of α."   The *interior of* α is the set of words u in α such that every initial segment of u is in α.   A set α is called *open* iff $\alpha = \text{Int}(\alpha)$.   Show that arbitrary unions and intersections of open sets are open sets.   Show that if α is open, then $(\alpha \neq \emptyset$ iff $\Lambda \, \epsilon \, \alpha)$.   Conclude that we have a topology for Σ_k^*.

6.   (Medvedev) Show that if α is regular, then $\text{Int}(\alpha)$ is regular.

7.   (Elgot[1]) Show that the intersection of all the open sets containing a given regular set is open and is regular.

8.   Devise an extension of the analysis theorem for boolean matrices for the purpose of systematically obtaining the regular expression associated with a sequential machine.   [HINT: Write as a primitive connection matrix $A = (\alpha_{ij}^0)$.]

9.   Write out an algorithm for associating a transition system with any given regular expression α such that the behavior of the transition system is $|\alpha|$.

10.   In the proof of the synthesis theorem, the transition system whose behavior is $|\alpha^*|$ appears to have redundant Λ's in the system.   These Λ's are present for the purpose of isolation.   Explain in detail and relate to Prob. 9.   [HINT: Consider the expression $(\sigma_0^* \gamma)^*$, where $\Lambda \notin |\gamma|$.]

11.   Give a mathematical model for an asynchronous sequential machine.   Show that our two characterizations of regular sets are equivalent for these machines. (HINT: Put k relations on Σ_k^*.)

6 APPLICATIONS OF THE ANALYSIS AND SYNTHESIS THEOREMS

In practical design problems, one is handed the specifications that a given machine must fulfill and then asked to construct the machine. The specifications are usually what we have precisely called the behavior. One desires an algorithm which synthesizes a finite machine from its behavior.   Certain limitations must naturally be imposed.   If one tried to construct a finite machine to realize a nonregular set as its behavior, we know the attempt would be doomed to failure.   Such difficulties can be overcome if the language in which the behavior is given is fixed. Our choice will naturally be the language of regular expressions.   The following theorem is what we were hoping for.

Theorem 1.   There exists an algorithm which applies to any regular expression α and yields a minimal finite sequential machine with the behavior $|\alpha|$.   The algorithm is

(1) Draw the transition system.
(2) Use the subset construction to form the corresponding sequential machine.
(3) Minimize the machine.
(4) Build it.

EXAMPLE.   Construct a machine which gives a 1 output when the input sequence has a number of σ_1's which is congruent to 0 mod 2.   The regular expression is

$$\sigma_0^*(\sigma_1\sigma_0^*\sigma_1\sigma_0^*)^*$$

First a transition system S is associated with the regular expression, Fig. 1.   Note that the extra Λ's are not inserted where they are not needed for the purposes of isolation.   The output set of this transition system is $\{a_4\}$, and the spontaneous transition relation is

$$P = \begin{Bmatrix} (a_1,a_2) & (a_5,a_6) \\ (a_2,a_3) & (a_7,a_3) \\ (a_3,a_4) & \end{Bmatrix}$$

The reflexive and transitive closure of P is written

$$\hat{P} = P \cup \begin{Bmatrix} (a_1,a_3) & (a_2,a_4) \\ (a_1,a_4) & (a_7,a_4) \end{Bmatrix} \cup 0$$

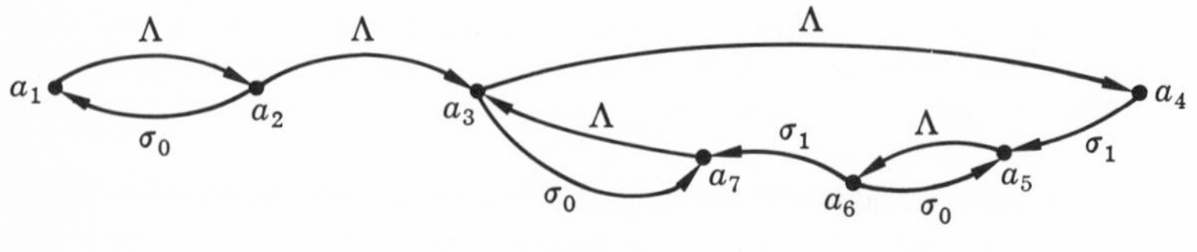

Fig. 1

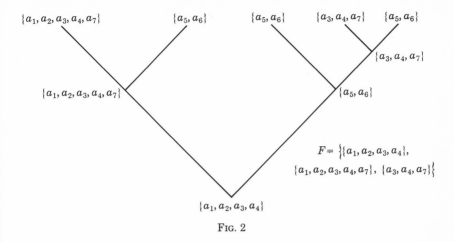

$$F = \left\{ \{a_1, a_2, a_3, a_4\}, \{a_1, a_2, a_3, a_4, a_7\}, \{a_3, a_4, a_7\} \right\}$$

FIG. 2

By employing the subset construction, $D(S)$ is produced, Fig. 2. Minimization yields the system shown in Fig. 3. For simplicity, the labels on $D(S)$ are changed as shown in Fig. 4. It is clear that $D(S)$ is indeed a mod 2 counter, but to provide an example of the analysis theorem, we shall compute the regular expression describing $D(S)$. The behavior of $D(S)$ is denoted by the regular expression α_{11}^2

where
$$\alpha_{11}^2 = \alpha_{11}^1 \cup \alpha_{12}^1 (\alpha_{22}^1)^* \alpha_{21}^1$$
$$\alpha_{11}^1 = (\alpha_{11}^0)^*$$
$$\alpha_{12}^1 = (\alpha_{11}^0)^* \alpha_{12}^0$$
$$\alpha_{22}^1 = \alpha_{22}^0 \cup \alpha_{21}^0 (\alpha_{11}^0)^* \alpha_{12}^0$$
$$\alpha_{21}^1 = \alpha_{21}^0 (\alpha_{11}^0)^*$$

The primitive regular expressions are read from the response tree. They are

$$\alpha_{11}^0 = \sigma_0 \cup \Lambda$$
$$\alpha_{12}^0 = \sigma_1$$
$$\alpha_{22}^0 = \sigma_0 \cup \Lambda$$
$$\alpha_{21}^0 = \sigma_1$$

$$\{a_5, a_6\} \qquad \{a_1, a_2, a_3, a_4\}$$

$$\{a_1, a_2, a_3, a_4\}$$

$$\{a_5, a_6\}$$

$$F = \left\{ \{a_1, a_2, a_3, a_4\} \right\}$$

$$\{a_1, a_2, a_3, a_4\}$$

FIG. 3

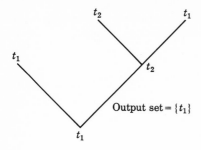

Output set $= \{t_1\}$

FIG. 4

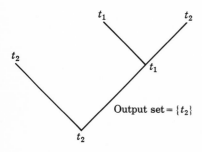

Output set $= \{t_2\}$

FIG. 5

Now, we retrace all steps and compute

$$\alpha_{11}^1 = \sigma_0^*$$
$$\alpha_{12}^1 = \sigma_0^* \sigma_1$$
$$\alpha_{22}^1 = \sigma_0 \cup \sigma_1 \sigma_0^* \sigma_1 \cup \Lambda$$
$$\alpha_{21}^1 = \sigma_1 \sigma_0^*$$

Finally, the behavior of $D(S)$ is given by

$$\sigma_0^* \cup \sigma_0^* \sigma_1 (\sigma_0 \cup \sigma_1 \sigma_0^* \sigma_1)^* \sigma_1 \sigma_0^*$$

The resulting regular expression does not resemble the expression that we started with, but the two expressions are actually equivalent, as the reader should show. Suppose that the labels on $D(S)$ were reversed, as shown in Fig. 5. Carrying out a similar analysis yields the following regular expression for the behavior:

$$\alpha_{22}^2 = (\sigma_0^* (\sigma_1 \sigma_0^* \sigma_1)^*)^*$$

The reader should check to see that this expression is equivalent to the preceding two expressions.

PROBLEMS

1. Show that $\alpha \cup \Lambda = \alpha$ iff $\Lambda \in |\alpha|$.

2. (Eggan) Show that if α and β are regular expressions, then

$$(\alpha \cup \beta)^* \cap (\overline{\alpha \alpha^*}) = (\alpha^* \beta \alpha^*)^*$$

iff

$$(\alpha^* \beta \alpha^*)^* \cap \alpha \alpha^* = \emptyset$$

3. (Eggan) The definition of star height is extended to regular subsets.   If γ is a regular subset of Σ_k^*, then *the star height of the subset* is written $h(\gamma)$.

$$h(\gamma) = \min \{h(\alpha) : |\alpha| = \gamma\}$$

What is the star height of the subset computed by the mod 2 counter in this section? Can you generalize?

4. (Raney, Elgot, Brzozowski) We now define a new operator on regular sets, the derivative of α with respect to σ, where $\sigma \in \Sigma_k$.

(a) $\dfrac{\partial \Lambda}{\partial \sigma} = \dfrac{\partial \emptyset}{\partial \sigma} = \emptyset$

(b) $\dfrac{\partial \sigma_i}{\partial \sigma} = \begin{cases} \Lambda & \text{if } \sigma_i = \sigma \\ \emptyset & \text{otherwise} \end{cases}$

(c) $\dfrac{\partial}{\partial \sigma} (\alpha \cup \beta) = \dfrac{\partial \alpha}{\partial \sigma} \cup \dfrac{\partial \beta}{\partial \sigma}$

(d) $\dfrac{\partial (\alpha^*)}{\partial \sigma} = \left(\dfrac{\partial \alpha}{\partial \sigma} \right) \alpha^*$

(e) $\dfrac{\partial (\alpha \beta)}{\partial \sigma} = \left(\dfrac{\partial \alpha}{\partial \sigma} \right) \beta \cup \delta_\alpha \dfrac{\partial \beta}{\partial \sigma}$

where $\delta_\alpha = \begin{cases} \Lambda & \text{if } \Lambda \in |\alpha| \\ \emptyset & \text{otherwise} \end{cases}$

We extend the definition to taking derivatives with respect to sequences by

$$\frac{\partial \alpha}{\partial \Lambda} = \alpha$$

$$\frac{\partial \alpha}{\partial (\sigma x)} = \frac{\partial}{\partial x} \left(\frac{\partial \alpha}{\partial \sigma} \right)$$

Prove that

$$\left| \frac{\partial \alpha}{\partial x} \right| = \{w | xw \in \alpha\}$$

5. (Ginsburg-Spanier) It is often more convenient to work with regular sets than with the expressions.   Let α, β be subsets of Σ^* and define the *right quotient* of α by β, written α/β as

$$\alpha/\beta = \{w | (\exists y)_\beta \quad wy \in \alpha\} = \{w | w\beta \cap \alpha \neq \emptyset\}$$

The *left quotient* of α by β is written $\beta \backslash \alpha$ and is defined as

$$\beta \backslash \alpha = \{w | (\exists y)_\beta \quad yw \in \alpha\} = \{w | \beta w \cap \alpha \neq \emptyset\}$$

What is the relation between quotients and derivatives?

6. (Ginsburg-Spanier) Prove that if α is a regular subset of Σ^* and β is an *arbitrary* subset of Σ^*, then α/β is regular.   Conclude that $\beta \backslash \alpha$ is regular by writing β/α in terms of α/β and transposition.

7. Show that if α is regular, then the set of initial (terminal) segments of words in α is regular.   (HINT: Express in terms of quotients.)

8. (Ginsburg-Spanier) Show that

$$\alpha/(\beta \cup \gamma) = \alpha/\beta \cup \alpha/\gamma$$
$$(\alpha \cup \beta)/\gamma = \alpha/\gamma \cup \beta/\gamma$$
$$\alpha/\beta\gamma = (\alpha/\gamma)/\beta$$
$$(\alpha\gamma)/\beta = \alpha(\gamma/\beta) \cup \alpha/(\beta/\gamma)$$

9. Show that

$$(\beta\backslash\alpha)/\gamma = \beta\backslash(\alpha/\gamma) = \{w|(\exists y)_\beta(\exists z)_\gamma \quad ywz \, \epsilon \, \alpha\}$$

This shows that if α is regular then the set of all solid subtapes of α is regular.

10. (Brzozowski) Derivatives can be used to provide a synthesis procedure for regular expressions. The derivative approach can be made to yield a minimal sequential machine. The method is as follows:

(a) Given a regular expression α, compute $\left\{\dfrac{\partial\alpha}{\partial x}\middle| x \, \epsilon \, \Sigma^*\right\}$, where the successive derivatives are computed by the lexicographic order of the $x \, \epsilon \, \Sigma^*$.

(b) The process will terminate with a finite number of distinct derivatives.

(c) The initial state is denoted by α. The other states are the distinct $\partial\alpha/\partial x$.

(d) If $\partial\alpha/\partial x\sigma = \partial\alpha/\partial y$, then there is a transition from $\partial\alpha/\partial x$ to state $\partial\alpha/\partial y$ by input σ.

(e) The set of final states is $\left\{\dfrac{\partial\alpha}{\partial x}:\Lambda \, \epsilon \, \left|\dfrac{\partial\alpha}{\partial x}\right|\right\}$

EXAMPLE.   Let $\alpha = \sigma_0^*(\sigma_1\sigma_0^*\sigma_1\sigma_0^*)^*$

$$\frac{\partial\alpha}{\partial\sigma_0} = \alpha$$

$$\frac{\partial\alpha}{\partial\sigma_1} = (\sigma_0^*\sigma_1\sigma_0^*)(\sigma_1\sigma_0^*\sigma_1\sigma_0^*)^*$$

$$\frac{\partial\alpha}{\partial\sigma_1\sigma_0} = \frac{\partial\alpha}{\partial\sigma_1}$$

$$\frac{\partial\alpha}{\partial\sigma_1\sigma_1} = \alpha$$

The tree is given in Fig. P5. Prove that the construction works; that is,

(a) Prove that for any regular expression α, the set $\left\{\dfrac{\partial\alpha}{\partial x}\middle| x \, \epsilon \, \Sigma^*\right\}$ is finite (cf. Prob. 10-4.10)

(b) Step 2 of the algorithm requires that a test for distinct derivatives be made. Is it sufficient to check if $\partial\alpha/\partial x$ may be transformed into $\partial\alpha/\partial y$ by repeated application of

$$\alpha \cup \alpha = \alpha$$
$$\alpha \cup (\beta \cup \gamma) = (\alpha \cup \beta) \cup \gamma$$
$$\alpha \cup \beta = \beta \cup \alpha$$

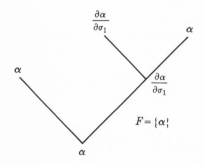

FIG. P5

(c) Give an algorithm for checking if $\Lambda \epsilon \beta$, where β is any regular expression.

(d) Prove that the constructed machine is minimal and has behavior α (cf. Prob. 11-2.2).

(e) Is this method an algorithm?

7 SUMMARY

The concept of a transition system was introduced in this chapter. Although transition systems are independently interesting, the concept was used only as a device in the proof of the synthesis theorem.   The inherent difficulty in specifying the behavior was overcome by introducing the language of regular expressions.   The language of regular expressions is a rather good medium in which to specify the behavior of a finite sequential machine.

Historically, the language of regular expressions was introduced by Kleene.[2] Most of the treatment in this chapter follows the work of Büchi, Copi, Elgot, and Wright. The presentation of the analysis theorem is an adaptation of the method of McNaughton and Yamada. The proof of the synthesis theorem given here was first published by Ott and Feinstein.

CHAPTER 13 _definite events and probabilistic machines_

1 INTRODUCTION

In this chapter an important family of regular subsets, the definite events, will be studied. Crudely stated, a sequential machine is p definite if the action of the machine at any given time depends exclusively on the past p inputs. Thus the definite events form a generalization of the finite subsets of Σ_k^*. Another important feature of definite machines is that they have "feedback-free" realizations.

Probabilistic sequential machines will be introduced; they form a parallel to the probabilistic combinational circuits of Chap. 8. These machines require more mathematical background for their study. For that reason our introduction will be superficial, although it will be shown that these machines (under suitable assumptions) recognize definite events.

2 INTRODUCTION TO DEFINITE SUBSETS

Before the definite subsets can be introduced, some terminology is required.

Definition 1. For any x, $y \in \Sigma_k^*$, y is said to be a _solid subtape_ of x iff there exist tapes w, $z \in \Sigma_k^*$ such that $x = wyz$. y is said to be a _prefix_ of x iff there is a word $z \in \Sigma_k^*$ such that $x = yz$. y is said to be a _suffix_ of x iff there is a word $w \in \Sigma_k^*$ such that $x = wy$.

Note that w and z in the preceding definition may be empty. It will be necessary to consider the lengths of certain prefixes and suffixes.

Definition 2. x is a p *prefix* (*suffix*) of y iff x is a prefix (suffix) of y and $\lg(x) = p$. For any word $x \in \Sigma_k^*$ such that $\lg(x) \geq p$, the p suffix of x is denoted by $x^{(p)}$.

It is convenient to approach the concept of definite subsets in an indirect way.

Definition 3. Let $p \geq 0$ and if α is any subset of Σ_k^*, α is said to be *weakly p definite* iff for all $x \in \Sigma_k^*$ such that $\lg(x) \geq p$, $x \in \alpha$ iff $x^{(p)} \in \alpha$. Symbolically,

$$(\forall x)_{\Sigma_k^*} \quad \lg(x) \geq p \Rightarrow (x \in \alpha \Leftrightarrow x^{(p)} \in \alpha)$$

There is a second definition of weakly p definite which is useful in many situations.

Definition 4. α is *weakly p definite* iff for any x, $y \in \Sigma_k^*$ such that $\lg(x) \geq p$, $\lg(y) \geq p$ and $x^{(p)} = y^{(p)}$ implies $x \in \alpha$ iff $y \in \alpha$. In symbols,

$$(\forall x,y)_{\Sigma_k^*} \quad \lg(x) \geq p \wedge \lg(y) \geq p \wedge x^{(p)} = y^{(p)} \Rightarrow (x \in \alpha \Leftrightarrow y \in \alpha)$$

Proposition 5. Definition 3 is equivalent to Definition 4.

PROOF. Assume Definition 3 and suppose that for arbitrary y, $z \in \Sigma_k^*$, $\lg(y) \geq p$ and $\lg(z) \geq p$ with $y^{(p)} = z^{(p)}$. We must show $y \in \alpha$ iff $z \in \alpha$. Since $\lg(y) \geq p$ and $\lg(z) \geq p$, both y and z satisfy the hypothesis of Definition 3. Therefore

$$y \in \alpha \Leftrightarrow y^{(p)} \in \alpha \qquad z \in \alpha \Leftrightarrow z^{(p)} \in \alpha$$

Since $y^{(p)} = z^{(p)}$, $y \in \alpha \Leftrightarrow z \in \alpha$.

Conversely, assume Definition 4 holds for a set α. Assume $z \in \Sigma_k^*$ such that $\lg(z) \geq p$. We must show that $z \in \alpha$ iff $z^{(p)} \in \alpha$. Since Definition 4 holds for all x and y in Σ_k^* with $\lg(x) \geq p$ and $\lg(y) \geq p$, we choose $x = z$ so $\lg(z) \geq p$, and we choose $y = z^{(p)}$. Because $(z^{(p)})^{(p)} = z^{(p)}$, Definition 4 tells us that

$$z \in \alpha \Leftrightarrow z^{(p)} \in \alpha \quad \blacksquare$$

Proposition 6. If α is weakly p definite and $q \geq p$, then α is weakly q definite.

Finally the concept of a *definite subset or definite event* is introduced.

Definition 7. For $p \geq 1$, a subset α is said to be *p definite* iff α is weakly p definite but not weakly $p - 1$ definite. α is called 0 *definite* iff α is weakly 0 definite.

It should be clear that the definite events are a generalization of finite subsets of Σ_k^*. For instance, the set $\alpha = \{x\sigma_0\sigma_0 | x \in \Sigma_k^*\}$ is 2 definite and is an infinite set. There are regular subsets of Σ_k^* which are not definite; for instance, the regular expression $\sigma_0^*\sigma_1\sigma_0^*$ denotes a set which is not definite. The set denoted by this regular expression is the class of all words of Σ_k^* containing exactly one σ_1.

Now we shall relate the concept of a weakly p-definite event to the concept of a p-definite event.

Theorem 8.   For $p \geq 1$, if α is weakly p definite, then α is p definite iff there exists a word $x \, \epsilon \, \alpha$ and a word $y \, \epsilon \, (\Sigma_k^* - \alpha)$ such that $\lg(x) \geq p - 1$, $\lg(y) \geq p - 1$, and $x^{(p-1)} = y^{(p-1)}$.

PROOF.   If α is p definite, α is not weakly $p - 1$ definite by Definition 7.   The result now follows by negating Definition 4 for $p - 1$ and using the fact that α is also weakly p definite.   The argument is reversible. |

Theorem 9.   Every weakly p-definite subset α is q definite for some q such that $0 \leq q \leq p$.

PROOF.   Let S be the set of natural numbers m for which α is weakly m definite. S is not empty, since $p \, \epsilon \, S$.   Let q be the *least* integer in S.   If $q = 0$, α is 0 definite and we are done.   If $q \geq 1$, then α is not weakly $q - 1$ definite by the minimality of q.   Hence α is q definite. |

Proposition 10.   A subset α is p definite for at most one p.

PROOF.   Suppose α is p definite and q definite with $p < q$. α is not weakly $q - 1$ definite.   Since α is weakly p definite and $q - 1 \geq p$, α is weakly $q - 1$ definite by Proposition 6.   This contradicts the fact that α is not weakly $q - 1$ definite. |

Proposition 10 guarantees that the following definition is unambiguous.

Definition 11.   If α is p definite, p is called the *degree* of α and written $\deg(\alpha) = p$.

Definition 12.   A subset α is called *definite* iff there is a natural number p such that α is p definite.

The definitions and propositions of this chapter have introduced us to definite events.   The crucial idea of the p-definite events is that they are completely characterized by their p suffixes.

PROBLEMS

1.   Show that $\emptyset$ and Σ_k^* are 0-definite subsets.   Show that there are no other 0-definite subsets.

2.   Show that if α is a finite subset of Σ_k^*, then α is p definite, where $p = 1 + \max\{\lg(x) | x \, \epsilon \, \alpha\}$.

3.   Show that if α and β are definite events, then $\alpha \cup \beta$, $\alpha \cap \beta$, and $\bar{\alpha}$ are definite subsets.   Show that $\deg(\alpha \cup \beta) \leq \max(\deg(\alpha), \deg(\beta))$, $\deg(\alpha \cap \beta) \leq \max(\deg(\alpha), \deg(\beta))$, and that $\deg(\bar{\alpha}) = \deg(\alpha)$.   Conclude that the definite subsets form a boolean algebra of sets.

4.   For the purposes of this problem, let

$$\Sigma^i = \{x \, \epsilon \, \Sigma_k^* | \lg(x) = i\}$$

If α is a weakly p-definite subset, show that α may be written

$$\alpha = (\alpha \cap \bigcup_{i<p} \Sigma^i) \cup \Sigma_k^* (\alpha \cap \Sigma^p)$$

Conversely, if $\alpha_0 \subseteq \bigcup\limits_{i<p} \Sigma^i$ and $\alpha_1 \subseteq \Sigma^p$, show that the subset

$$\alpha = \alpha_0 \cup \Sigma_k^* \alpha_1$$

is weakly p definite. Show that this problem provides a *unique* form for weakly p-definite subsets. What can one say about the regular expressions denoting weakly p-definite subsets?

5. Using Prob. 4, show that every weakly p-definite subset of Σ_k^* is a regular subset of Σ_k^*.

3   DEFINITE MACHINES AND DEFINITE TRANSITION FUNCTIONS

Since every definite subset is regular, it is reasonable to expect a close connection between the concepts we have defined for subsets of Σ_k^* and related ideas for automata.

Definition 1.   A sequential machine S is called *definite (p definite, weakly p definite)* iff the behavior of S is definite (p definite, weakly p definite).

We wish to extend these concepts to take into account the transition function of a machine S.

Definition 2.   If $S = \langle S, M, a, F \rangle$ is a sequential machine, then M is a *weakly p-definite transition function* iff, for any s, $t \in S$ and for any $x \in \Sigma_k^*$, $\lg(x) \geq p$ implies $M(s,x) = M(t,x)$, that is,

$$(\forall s,t)_S (\forall x)_{\Sigma_k^*} \quad \lg(x) \geq p \Rightarrow M(s,x) = M(t,x)$$

For $p \geq 1$, M is *p definite* iff M is weakly p definite, but not weakly $p - 1$ definite. M is *0 definite* iff M is weakly 0 definite. M is *definite* if M is p definite for some p.

Now we begin to establish some relations between definite transition functions and definite machines.

Theorem 3.   If $S = \langle S, M, a, F \rangle$ is a p-definite, connected, minimal sequential machine, then M is a p-definite transition function.

PROOF.   Let s and t be states in S. Since S is connected, there exist words w_1, $w_2 \in \Sigma_k^*$ such that $s = rp_S(w_1)$ and $t = rp_S(w_2)$. Let $x \in \Sigma_k^*$ with $\lg(x) \geq p$ and define $u = M(s,x), v = M(t,x)$. For any $z \in \Sigma_k^*$, $M(u,z) = M(M(s,x),z) = M(M(rp_S(w_1)x),z) = rp_S(w_1xz)$. Similarly, $M(v,z) = rp_S(w_2xz)$. Since $\lg(xz) \geq p$ and since S is weakly p definite, $w_1xz \in \beta_S$ iff $w_2xz \in \beta_S$, and therefore $M(u,z) \in F$ iff $M(v,z) \in F$. We have shown uR_Fv, where R_F is the induced congruence on S. Since S is minimal, uR_Fv implies $u = v$, but this is precisely $M(s,x) = M(t,x)$. It has therefore been established that M is weakly p definite.

To show that M is not weakly $p - 1$ definite, note that S is not weakly $p - 1$ definite. Using Theorem 2.8, there exist words x, y, and $z \in \Sigma_k^*$ such that $\lg(x) \geq p - 1$ with $yx \in \beta_S$ and $zx \notin \beta_S$. This means that $rp_S(yz) \in F$ and $rp_S(xz) \in S - F$. Let $s = rp_S(y)$ and $t = rp_S(z)$. $M(s,x) \in F$ and $M(t,x) \in S - F$. Therefore, $M(s,x) \neq M(t,x)$ and M is not weakly $p - 1$ definite.   ∎

The converse of Theorem 3 is also true and will be required in the sequel.

Theorem 4.   If $S = \langle S, M, a, F \rangle$ is a connected minimal machine possessing a p-definite transition function, then S is p definite.

PROOF.   Assume that M is p definite and that x, $y \in \Sigma_k^*$ with $\lg(x) \geq p$, $\lg(y) \geq p$, and $x^{(p)} = y^{(p)}$.   It must be shown that $x \in \beta$ iff $y \in \beta$.   We write

$$x = w_1 x^{(p)} \qquad y = w_2 y^{(p)}$$

Let $s = rp_S(w_1)$ and $t = rp_S(w_2)$. $M(s, x^{(p)}) = M(t, x^{(p)})$, since M is weakly p definite.   Thus $rp_S(x) = M(s, x^{(p)}) = M(t, y^{(p)}) = rp_S(y)$.   Thus $x \in \beta_S$ iff $y \in \beta_S$.   Thus S is weakly p definite.

Suppose there exists an input x such that $\lg(x) \geq p - 1$ and there exist states s and t such that $M(s, x) \neq M(t, x)$, since M is not weakly $p - 1$ definite.   Because S is a connected machine, there exist y, $z \in \Sigma_k^*$

$$s = rp_S(y) \qquad \text{and} \qquad t = rp_S(z)$$

Hence,
$$rp_S(yx) \neq rp_S(zx)$$

Also let $u = rp(yx)$ and $v = rp(zx)$.   There must exist a tape $w \in \Sigma_k^*$ such that

$$(M(u, w) \in F \text{ and } M(v, w) \in S - F) \qquad \text{or} \qquad (M(u, w) \in S - F \text{ and } M(v, w) \in F)$$

because S is minimal.   Since $\lg(xw) \geq p - 1$, and because

$$rp(yxw) \in F \qquad \text{and} \qquad rp(zxw) \in S - F$$

we have $yxw \in \beta_S$ and $zxw \notin \beta_S$ (or vice versa).   Thus, we have exhibited two words, yxw and zxw, with the same $p - 1$ suffix such that one is in β_S and one is not.   By Theorem 2.8, S is p definite. $\blacksquare$

We are eventually going to find a lower bound on the number of states of a p-definite machine.   In the course of this investigation, some independently interesting results will occur.   For one of these results, an inductive proof will be required.   The following two definitions are designed to construct a function on which the induction will depend.

Definition 5.   Let M be a transition function, that is, $M: S \times \Sigma_k \to S$, and let s, $t \in S$. s and t are said to be *one-equivalent* iff

$$M(s, \sigma_i) = M(t, \sigma_i)$$

for *every* $i = 0, \ldots, k - 1$.

Definition 6.   If s and t are *distinct*, one-equivalent states and M is a transition function, then the *contracted transition function* $M_{s,t}$ is defined as a function from $(S - \{s\}) \times \Sigma_k \to S - \{s\}$ by

$$M_{s,t}(u, \sigma_i) = \begin{cases} M(u, \sigma_i) & \text{if } M(u, \sigma_i) \neq s \\ t & \text{if } M(u, \sigma_i) = s \end{cases}$$

for $u \in S - \{s\}$ and $i = 0, \ldots, k - 1$.

It is essential to note that the contracted transition function is defined only for states s and t that are distinct and one-equivalent.

Proposition 7. If M is a transition function and if s and t are distinct one-equivalent states, then for any $x \in \Sigma_k^*$

$$M_{s,t}(u,x) = \begin{cases} M(u,x) & \text{if } M(u,x) \neq s \\ t & \text{if } M(u,x) = s \end{cases}$$

for $u \in (s - \{s\})$.

PROOF. The argument is an immediate induction on $\lg(x)$. $\blacksquare$

The first property to be investigated is the connection between the original table and the contracted table with respect to definiteness.

Theorem 8. Let M be a transition function and let $M_{s,t}$ be the contracted transition function with respect to two distinct one-equivalent states s and t. If M is weakly p definite, then $M_{s,t}$ is weakly p definite. If $M_{s,t}$ is weakly p definite, then M is weakly $p + 1$ definite.

PROOF. Suppose that M is weakly p definite and consider an $x \in \Sigma_k^*$ such that $\lg(x) \geq p$. We must show that

$$M_{s,t}(u,x) = M_{s,t}(v,x)$$

for any $u, v \in S$. The first step is to compute both quantities.

$$M_{s,t}(u,x) = \begin{cases} M(u,x) & \text{if } M(u,x) \neq s \\ t & \text{if } M(u,x) = s \end{cases}$$
$$M_{s,t}(v,x) = \begin{cases} M(v,x) & \text{if } M(v,x) \neq s \\ t & \text{if } M(v,x) = s \end{cases}$$

Suppose $M(u,x) \neq s$ and $M(v,x) \neq s$; then $M_{s,t}$ is weakly p definite because M is. If $M(u,x) = s$ and $M(v,x) = s$, then, since $t = t$, we have that $M_{s,t}(u,x) = M_{s,t}(v,x)$ and therefore $M_{s,t}$ is weakly p definite. It cannot be that $M(u,x) = s$ and $M(v,x) \neq s$, since this situation contradicts that M is weakly p definite.

To prove the second assertion, assume that $M_{s,t}$ is weakly p definite, and let u, $v \in (S - \{s\})$. If $y \in \Sigma_k^*$ such that $\lg(y) \geq p + 1$, then it must be shown that

$$M(u,y) = M(v,y)$$

Let $y = x\sigma$ with $\sigma \in \Sigma_k$ and $\lg(x) \geq p$. Since $M_{s,t}$ is weakly p definite,

$$M_{s,t}(u,x) = M_{s,t}(v,x)$$

By the Proposition 7, there are three cases.

(1) $M(u,x) = M(v,x)$
(2) $M(u,x) = s \qquad M(v,x) = t$
(3) $M(u,x) = t \qquad M(v,x) = s$

In all three cases, $M(u,x\sigma) = M(v,x\sigma)$. In case 1 the result is obvious. In cases 2 and 3 the result holds because states s and t are one-equivalent. $\blacksquare$

Corollary 9. A contracted table is definite iff the original table is definite.

PROOF.   Theorems 8 and 2.9. |

It is now possible to assemble our results about definite tables and get a bound on the number of states of a p definite automaton.   First it is necessary to show the existence of one-equivalent states.

Theorem 10.   If M is a definite table and the number of states in S is at least two, then there exist two distinct one-equivalent states.

PROOF.   Suppose that M is p definite.   If M is 0 definite, then, since the number of states is at least two, there are distinct states s and t such $M(s,x) = M(t,x)$ for all $x \in \Sigma_k^*$ such that $\lg(x) \geq 0$.   In particular, $s = M(s,\Lambda) = M(t,\Lambda) = t$ contradicts that M is 0 definite, since s and t are distinct.   Thus $p \geq 1$ and there must exist a tape x such that $\lg(x) \geq p - 1$ and there exist two states u and v such that $s = M(u,x) \neq M(v,x) = t$ because M is not weakly $p - 1$ definite.   For any $\sigma \in \Sigma_k^*$, $\lg(x\sigma) = p$ and

$$M(s,\sigma) = M(u,x\sigma) = M(v,x\sigma) = M(t,\sigma)$$

because M is weakly p definite.   Thus we have exhibited two distinct states s and t which are one-equivalent. |

Theorem 11.   If M is a definite transition function and if S has n states, then M is weakly $n - 1$ definite.

PROOF.   The argument is an induction on the number of states and will indicate one reason for the study of contracted tables.

BASIS.   If $n = 1$, then M is weakly 0 definite.

INDUCTION STEP.   Suppose M is definite and there are n elements in S, where $n \geq 2$.   By Theorem 10 there exist distinct states s and t which are one-equivalent. $M_{s,t}$ is definite by Corollary 9, and furthermore, $M_{s,t}$ is weakly $n - 2$ definite by the induction hypothesis; hence, M is weakly $n - 1$ definite by Theorem 8. |

Finally, the results can be combined to give a proof of an important theorem.

Theorem 12.   If $S = \langle S,M,a,F \rangle$ is p definite, then S has at least $p + 1$ states.

PROOF.   Let $S^M = \langle T,N,a,G \rangle$ be the connected minimal machine of S. N is p definite by Theorem 3.   If T has n states, then N is weakly $n - 1$ definite by Theorem 11.   Thus, S^M is weakly $n - 1$ definite by Theorem 4.   Since S^M is p definite, p is the least integer for which S^M is weakly p definite.   Since S^M is weakly $n - 1$ definite,

$$p \leq n - 1$$

or $n \geq p + 1$.   Since the number of states of S is not smaller than n, the result follows. |

PROBLEMS

1.   Show that Theorem 12 is false for transition systems.   (HINT: Σ_1 is sufficient. Construct a machine whose behavior is $\beta_n = \{\sigma_0^{ni+i} \mid i = 1, 2, \ldots ; 0 \leq j \leq i - 1\}$ and which has n states.)

2. Show that Theorem 12 is a "best possible" result in that the lower bound cannot be raised.

3. If M is a transition function, the *strongly contracted transition function* $\bar{M}$ is defined by identifying all one-equivalent states. Show that if the number of states is at least two, then M is p definite iff $\bar{M}$ is $p-1$ definite.

The problems that follow require a slight knowledge of vector spaces.

4. Let $S = \langle S, M, a_1, F \rangle$ with $S = \{a_1, \ldots, a_n\}$. The *transition matrix* $A(x)$ for $x \in \Sigma_k^*$ is an $n \times n$ matrix whose i-j element $a_{ij}(x)$ is given by

$$a_{ij}(x) = \begin{cases} 1 & \text{if } M(a_i, x) = a_j \\ 0 & \text{otherwise} \end{cases}$$

where $i, j = 1, \ldots, n$. Show that

    (a) Each row of $A(x)$ contains a single 1.
    (b) $A(\Lambda) = I$, the $n \times n$ identity matrix.
    (c) $A(xy) = A(x)A(y)$
    (d) If $x = \sigma_{i_1} \cdots \sigma_{i_m}$, then $A(x) = A(\sigma_{i_1}) \cdots A(\sigma_{i_m})$

5. Show that

$$V = \{(x_1, \ldots, x_n) | x_i \in Q, \sum_{j=1}^{n} x_j = 0\}$$

is a vector space of dimension $n-1$ over Q, the field of rational numbers.

6. Show that if v is a vector in V and if A is any $n \times n$ transition matrix, then vA is a vector in V.

7. A *constant transition matrix* is a $n \times n$ matrix with one column all ones and all other columns zero. Show that a transition matrix A is constant iff $VA = \{0\}$. VA is defined by

$$VA = \left\{ \sum_{i=1}^{r} v_i A \mid v_i \in V, r = 0, 1, \ldots \right\}$$

The symbol $\{0\}$ is the set whose only element is the zero vector.

8. Show that the following statement is equivalent to Theorem 11. If $A_1 \cdots A_m$ (A_i are transition matrices) is a constant matrix, then every product $A_1 \cdots A_{n-1}$ is a constant matrix. ($A_i = A_j$ possibly for $i \neq j$.)

9. (Yuval) Prove the theorem stated in Problem 8 directly.

4 A TEST FOR DEFINITENESS

The preceding results give insight into the nature of definite events, but no way to recognize a definite automaton has been presented. It is desirable to find an algorithm for this purpose which will, at the same time, yield the degree of a definite event.

Algorithm 1. Given a finite connected machine $S = \langle S, M, a, F \rangle$ with n internal states, assume that the set of final states is an equivalence relation of rank 2 on S.

(1) Let $h = 1$ and set $E_0 = F$, the output equivalence relation.
(2) Construct
$$uE_hv \Leftrightarrow M(u,\sigma_i)E_{h-1}M(v,\sigma_i) \qquad \text{for every } i = 0, \ldots , k - 1$$
(3) If $E_h = S \times S$ (that is, if $E_h = 1$, the universal relation) go to rule 5. Otherwise, go to rule 4.
(4) If $h = n - 1$, go to rule 6. If $h \neq n - 1$, then replace h by $h + 1$ and go to rule 2.
(5) S is h definite.
(6) S is not definite.

It is certainly clear from the algorithm that the process will terminate when applied to a finite machine. It is still necessary to show that the algorithm works.

Theorem 2. If $E_h = 1$, then S is h definite.

PROOF.
Clearly
$$uE_hv \Leftrightarrow (\mathbf{\forall}x)_{\Sigma_k*} \quad \lg(x) = h \Rightarrow (M(u,x) \; \epsilon \, F \Leftrightarrow M(v,x) \; \epsilon \, F)$$

For any $y,z \; \epsilon \; \Sigma_k^*$, let $u = rp_S(y)$ and $v = rp_S(z)$. Since $E_h = 1$, uE_hv. Therefore

$$(\mathbf{\forall}x,y,z)_{\Sigma_k*} \quad \lg(x) = h \Rightarrow (rp_S(yx) \; \epsilon \, F \Leftrightarrow rp_S(zx) \; \epsilon \, F)$$

Thus S is weakly h definite by Definition 2.4, since yx and zx are arbitrary words of Σ_k^* whose lengths exceed h and have the same h suffix. h is the least integer such that S is weakly h definite; therefore, S is h definite. $\blacksquare$

Theorem 3. If $E_h \neq 1$ for any h such that $1 \leq h \leq n - 1$, then S is not definite.

PROOF. Suppose S is p definite for some p, then $p \leq n - 1$ by Theorem 3.12. $\blacksquare$

The construction is illustrated by the following example, Fig. 1. Let $S = \langle S,M,a_0,F \rangle$, where $F = \{a_2\}$. Since the E_i are equivalence rela-

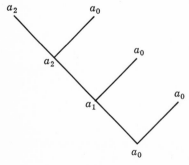

FIG. 1

tions, the usual computational shortcuts are used

$$E_0 = F = \{(a_0,a_1)\} \qquad E_1 = \{(a_1,a_2)\} \qquad E_2 = \begin{Bmatrix} (a_0,a_1) \\ (a_0,a_2) \\ (a_1,a_2) \end{Bmatrix} = 1$$

Thus S is 2 definite, and, in fact,

$$\beta_S = \{x\sigma_0{}^2 | x \in \Sigma_k^*\}$$

PROBLEMS

1. Design a sequential machine to realize the following regular expression over Σ_2. Test to see if the machine is definite and, if it is, find the degree.

$$\alpha = \sigma_0\sigma_1\sigma_0 \cup \sigma_1\sigma_1\sigma_0\sigma_1\sigma_0 \cup (\sigma_0 \cup \sigma_1)^*(\sigma_1\sigma_0 \cup \sigma_1\sigma_1\sigma_1 \cup \sigma_0\sigma_0\sigma_1)$$

2. The algorithm of this section detects p-definite machines for $p \geq 1$. What about $p = 0$? Is an algorithm necessary or is 0 definiteness trivial to verify?

3. (Simon, Gill) A Mealy machine $S = \langle \Sigma,\Delta,S,f,g \rangle$ is said to have *memory order* p iff

$$(\forall s,t)_S(\forall x,z)_{\Sigma^*} \quad \lg(x) \geq p \wedge g(s,x) = g(t,x) \Rightarrow f(s,x) = f(t,x)$$

Intuitively, every sequence whose length is at least p is a *homing experiment* for S; a *homing experiment* is simply a tape which distinguishes the various final states of S. For $p \geq 1$, S is said to have *maximal memory* p if S has order p but not order $p - 1$. What is the relation between definite machines and machines which have memory of a finite order? Give examples of machines in one class but not the other if it is possible.

4. Give a synthesis method for definite events. (HINT: First assume $\alpha = \Sigma_k^*\{z\}$ and characterize the induced congruence relation. Generalize to $\alpha = \Sigma_k^*\alpha_1$, etc.)

5. Give an upper bound for the number of states in a machine recognizing a p definite event.

5   PROBABILISTIC MACHINES

A mathematical formulation of probabilistic sequential machines is now introduced. Although the literature on reliable circuitry is quite large, almost no work has been done on probabilistic sequential machines. The following material is due almost entirely to M. O. Rabin.[1]

Consider a probabilistic sequential machine S in internal state s_i when input σ occurs. The machine will be assumed to pass to state s_j with probability $p_j(s_i,\sigma)$. These transition probabilities are assumed to be fixed and are independent of time and previous inputs. A more formal definition is now presented.

Definition 1. A *probabilistic sequential machine* over Σ_2 is defined as $S = \langle S,P,s_0,F \rangle$, where $S = \{s_0, \ldots ,s_n\}$ is a nonvoid set of *internal states*, $s_0 \in S$ is the *initial state*, and $F \subseteq S$ is the set of *final states*. P is a function from $S \times \Sigma_2$ into $[0,1]^{n+1}$, called the *table of transition* *probabilities*, i.e.,

$$P(s,\sigma) = (p_0(s,\sigma), p_1(s,\sigma), \ldots, p_n(s,\sigma))$$

where $1 \geq p_i(s,\sigma) \geq 0$ for $i = 0, \ldots, n$ and $\sum_{j=0}^{n} p_j(s,\sigma) = 1$.

It is convenient to use a matrix calculus for deriving the probability associated with input words of Σ_2^*. (Note that we take $k = 2$ for simplicity.)

Definition 2.   The $(n+1, n+1)$, matrix $A(\sigma)$ is defined as

$$A(\sigma) = (p_j(s_i,\sigma))$$

where $i, j = 0, \ldots, n$.

Proposition 3.   For $x = \sigma_{i_1} \cdots \sigma_{i_m} \epsilon \Sigma_2^*$,

$$A(x) = A(\sigma_{i_1}) \cdots A(\sigma_{i_m}) = (p_j(s_i, x))$$

PROOF.   The argument is a trivial induction on m. ∎

Note the matrices $A(x)$ are *stochastic* matrices, i.e., the sum of the entries of each row is unity.

Finally, it is desirable to associate with each $x \epsilon \Sigma_2^*$ the probability of its being in the behavior of a probabilistic machine.

Definition 4.   Let $S = \langle S, P, s_0, F \rangle$, where $F = \{s_{i_0}, \ldots, s_{i_r}\}$ and take $I = \{i_0, \ldots, i_r\}$.   Define, for any $x \epsilon \Sigma_2^*$, the *probability of x being accepted* as

$$p(x) = \sum_{i \epsilon I} p_i(s_0, x)$$

EXAMPLE.   Consider $S = \langle S, P, s_0, \{s_1\} \rangle$, where $S = \{s_0, s_1\}$.   we take

$$A(\sigma_0) = \begin{bmatrix} 1 & 0 \\ \frac{1}{2} & \frac{1}{2} \end{bmatrix} \qquad A(\sigma_1) = \begin{bmatrix} \frac{1}{2} & \frac{1}{2} \\ 0 & 1 \end{bmatrix}$$

The machine can be illustrated by the tree of Fig. 1, where the branches are labeled

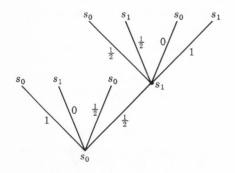

FIG. 1

with the transition probabilities. Suppose that one is interested in the response of the machine to input word $x = \sigma_0\sigma_1\sigma_1$. An easy calculation shows that

$$A(\sigma_0\sigma_1\sigma_1) = \begin{bmatrix} \frac{1}{4} & \frac{3}{4} \\ \frac{1}{8} & \frac{7}{8} \end{bmatrix}$$

For machines S, $p(\sigma_0\sigma_1\sigma_1)$ is the upper right entry of $A(\sigma_0\sigma_1\sigma_1)$, i.e.,

$$p(\sigma_0\sigma_1{}^2) = \tfrac{3}{4}$$

PROBLEMS

1. Let

$$P_0 = \begin{bmatrix} 1 & 0 \\ \frac{1}{2} & \frac{1}{2} \end{bmatrix} \qquad P_1 = \begin{bmatrix} \frac{1}{2} & \frac{1}{2} \\ 0 & 1 \end{bmatrix}$$

Show that if

$$P_{\delta_1} \cdots P_{\delta_n} = \begin{bmatrix} m & p \\ q & r \end{bmatrix}$$

where $\delta_i \epsilon \{0,1\}$, then $p = .\ \delta_n\delta_{n-1} \cdots \delta_1$, where p is written in the binary scale. Show that

$$r = p + \frac{1}{2^n} \qquad q = 1 - \frac{1}{2^n} - p \qquad m = 1 - p$$

2. Show that every ordinary machine is a probabilistic sequential machine (cf. Prob. 3.4).

6 THE BEHAVIOR OF PROBABILISTIC MACHINES

The concept of *behavior* becomes slightly more complicated for a probabilistic machine than for an ordinary machine. The tapes accepted by a probabilistic machine now depend on a parameter. The idea is that if a particular $x \epsilon \Sigma_2^*$ is fed into the machine, it is possible that the machine might accept x and yet reject x the next time the experiment is run. Thus we shall specify a criterion for acceptance.

Definition 1. Let S be a probabilistic sequential machine and λ be a real number such that $0 \leq \lambda < 1$; then the *behavior* of S is defined to be

$$\beta_S(\lambda) = \{x | x \epsilon \Sigma_2^*, p(x) > \lambda\}$$

λ is called the *cut point* of the behavior.

Proposition 2. S is an ordinary sequential machine iff $\beta_S = \beta_S(\lambda)$ for any λ such that $0 \leq \lambda < 1$.

PROOF. If S is an ordinary machine, $M(s,\sigma) = (p_0, \ldots, p_n)$ has one entry equal to 1 and all others equal to 0. Thus $x \epsilon \beta_S$ implies that there exists an i such that $p_i(s_0, x) = 1$. Therefore, $p(x) = 1 > \lambda$, so that $x \epsilon \beta_S(\lambda)$. The argument is reversible. ∎

Proposition 2 shows that the behaviors of probabilistic machines include the regular subsets. An example to show that probabilistic machines compute more than the regular subsets will be given.

Proposition 3. If $0 \leq \lambda < \lambda_1 \leq 1$, then $\beta_S(\lambda_1) \subseteq \beta_S(\lambda)$.

Theorem 4. Let $S = \langle S, P, s_0, F \rangle$ be a probabilistic machine over Σ_2 with $S = \{s_0, s_1\}$, $F = \{s_1\}$, and

$$A(\sigma_0) = \begin{bmatrix} 1 & 0 \\ \frac{1}{2} & \frac{1}{2} \end{bmatrix} \qquad A(\sigma_1) = \begin{bmatrix} \frac{1}{2} & \frac{1}{2} \\ 0 & 1 \end{bmatrix}$$

There exists a real number λ such that $0 \leq \lambda < 1$ and $\beta_S(\lambda)$ is not regular.

PROOF. Let $x = \delta_1 \cdots \delta_n \epsilon \Sigma_2^*$; then by Prob. 5.1, $p(x) = . \delta_n \delta_{n-1} \cdots \delta_1$. The values $p(x)$ are dense in the interval $[0,1]$. By Proposition 3 and the denseness of the $p(x)$, the sets $\beta_S(\lambda)$ are different for different λ, and hence there are uncountably many such sets. There are only a countable number of regular sets, so there must exist a number λ such that $\beta_S(\lambda)$ is not regular. █

PROBLEMS

1. Let $w_1, w_2, \ldots$ be any enumeration of Σ_2^* and let $\lambda = . w_1 w_2 \cdots$. Then for S as in Theorem 4, show that $\beta_S(\lambda)$ is not regular. Note that $\lambda = . w_1 \cdots$ is not a rational number. This problem provides a constructive proof of Theorem 4.

2. Show that λ is rational and $0 \leq \lambda < 1$ iff $\beta_S(\lambda)$ is regular.

3. Show that Theorem 4 generalizes to sets over Σ_k.

7 ACTUAL AUTOMATA

It is natural to introduce the following definition of an *isolated cut point*. The argument which leads to this definition is developed in Prob. 1.

Definition 1. A cut point λ is *isolated*† with respect to S iff there exists a positive number δ such that, for all $x \epsilon \Sigma_2^*$,

$$|p(x) - \lambda| \geq \delta$$

In realistic design situations, one often finds that all the transition probabilities are positive.

Definition 2. A probabilistic sequential machine is called *actual* iff

$$(\forall s)_S (\forall \sigma)_{\Sigma_2} \quad p_i(s,\sigma) > 0 \qquad \text{for } i = 0, \ldots, n$$

The first question to be answered is the nature of events computed

† More simply, λ is *isolated* iff λ is not an accumulation point of $\{p(x) | x \epsilon \Sigma_2^*\}$.

by actual machines.   Before answering this question, we must establish some facts about stochastic matrices with all positive entries.

Definition 3.   If a is a column vector, $a = \begin{bmatrix} a_1 \\ \cdots \\ a_n \end{bmatrix}$, define

$$\|a\| = \max_i a_i - \min_i a_i$$

If A is a matrix with columns $a_1, \ldots, a_n$, define $\|A\| = \max_i \|a_i\|$.

Lemma 4.   If $P = (p_{ij})$ is an $n \times n$ stochastic matrix, and if $\Delta = \min_{i,j} p_{ij}$, and if a is a column vector $a = \begin{bmatrix} a_1 \\ \cdots \\ a_n \end{bmatrix}$, then $\|Pa\| \leq (1 - 2\Delta)\|a\|$.

PROOF.   Let $Pa = \begin{bmatrix} b_1 \\ \cdots \\ b_n \end{bmatrix}$.   There is no loss of generality in assuming that

$$b_1 = \max_i b_i \qquad b_2 = \min_i b_i$$
$$a_1 = \max_i a_i \qquad a_2 = \min_i a_i$$

Clearly,

$$b_1 = p_{11}a_1 + p_{12}a_2 + \cdots + p_{1n}a_n \leq p_{11}a_1 + p_{12}a_2 + p_{13}a_1 + \cdots + p_{1n}a_1$$

because we replace a_i $(i = 3, \ldots, n)$ by a_1, which is the largest a_i.   Thus, $b_1 \leq a_1 - p_{12}(a_1 - a_2)$.   Using a dual argument, $b_2 \geq a_2 + p_{21}(a_1 - a_2)$.   Thus $\|Pa\| = b_1 - b_2 \leq (a_1 - a_2)(1 - p_{12} - p_{21})$. $p_{12} \geq \Delta$ and $p_{21} \geq \Delta$ implies

$$\|Pa\| \leq \|a\|(1 - 2\Delta) \quad \blacksquare$$

Corollary 5.   If $P_1, \ldots, P_k$ are all $n \times n$ stochastic matrices with every element larger than $\Delta > 0$, then for any $1 \leq i_1, \ldots, i_n \leq k$, $\|P_{i_1}P_{i_2} \cdots P_{i_n}\| \leq (1 - 2\Delta)^{m-1}$.

PROOF.   Induction on m since for any column vector a_i, $\|a_i\| \leq 1$. $\blacksquare$

Definition 6.   Let $A = (a_{ij})$ be any matrix and define the *norm of A*, written $|A|$, as

$$|A| = \max_{i,j} |a_{ij}|$$

Lemma 7.   If P is a stochastic $n \times n$ matrix, and $a = \begin{bmatrix} a_1 \\ \cdots \\ a_n \end{bmatrix}$, then $|Pa - a| \leq \|a\|$.

PROOF.   Let $\qquad\qquad Pa = \begin{bmatrix} b_1 \\ \cdots \\ b_n \end{bmatrix}$

Then $|b_i - a_i| = |p_{i1}a_1 + p_{i2}a_2 + \cdots + p_{in}a_n - a_i|$
Since we have that

$$\sum_{j=1}^{n} p_{ij} = 1$$

$|b_i - a_i| \leq p_{i1}|a_1 - a_i| + \cdots + p_{i,i-1}|a_{i-1} - a_i| + p_{i,i+1}|a_{i+1} - a_i| + \cdots$
$$+ p_{in}|a_n - a_i| \leq \|a\|$$

The resulting bound is independent of i, so that $|Pa - a| \leq \|a\|$. ∎

Corollary 8.   If P is a stochastic $n \times n$ matrix and A is any $n \times n$ matrix, then $|PA - A| \leq \|A\|$.

The preceding lemmas are now used to characterize the behavior of actual machines with isolated cut points. The behaviors of these machines are just the definite events.

Conversely, every definite event is computed by an actual machine with isolated cut point. This latter remark is left as a problem.

Theorem 9.   If S is an actual machine with isolated cut point λ, then $\beta_S(\lambda)$ is definite.

PROOF.   Let $|p(x) - \lambda| \geq \delta > 0$ for any $x \in \Sigma_2^*$ because λ is isolated. Assume, since S is actual, that every element of the stochastic matrices $A(\sigma)$ for $\sigma \in \Sigma_2$ is greater than Δ, where $\Delta > 0$. Assume that S has just one final state s_n, that is, $F = \{s_n\}$. The general proof is exactly the same as this special case.

Finally, let q be the *least* integer such that

$$(1 - 2\Delta)^{q-1} < 2\delta$$

If $z = \sigma_{i_1} \cdots \sigma_{i_q} \in \Sigma_2^*$, then $A(z) = A(\sigma_{i_1}) \cdots A(\sigma_{i_q})$. By Corollary 5,

$$\|A(z)\| \leq (1 - 2\Delta)^{q-1} < 2\delta$$

For any $x \in \Sigma_2^*$, $p(x)$ is the last element of the first row of $A(x)$. By use of Corollary 8,

$$|p(yz) - p(z)| \leq |A(yz) - A(z)| = |A(y)A(z) - A(z)| \leq \|A(z)\| \leq (1 - 2\Delta)^{q-1} < 2\delta$$

Thus, for any z such that $\lg(z) = q$,

$$|p(yz) - p(z)| < 2\delta \tag{1}$$

We shall show that (1) implies $(p(yz) > \lambda \Leftrightarrow p(z) > \lambda)$. Assume that $p(yz) > \lambda$ and $p(z) \leq \lambda$. Since λ is isolated, we have $p(yz) - \lambda \geq \delta$ and $p(z) - \lambda \leq -\delta$ because $p(z) - \lambda$ is a nonpositive quantity. Thus

$$|p(yz) - p(z)| = |(p(yz) - \lambda) - (p(z) - \lambda)| \geq 2\delta$$

which is a contradiction. The assumption $p(yz) \leq \lambda$ and $p(z) > \lambda$ leads to a similar contradiction. We have shown that

$$(\forall z)_{\Sigma_2^*} \lg(z) = q \Rightarrow (yz \in \beta_S(\lambda) \Leftrightarrow z \in \beta_S(\lambda)) \tag{2}$$

Thus $\beta_S(\lambda)$ is weakly q definite by (2) and hence q definite by the minimality of q. ∎

Theorem 10. If α is a definite event, there exists an actual probabilistic machine with isolated cut point λ such that $\alpha = \beta_S(\lambda)$.

PROOF. Cf. Prob. 2. ▮

PROBLEMS

1. Suppose one wishes to test if $x \, \epsilon \, \beta_S(\lambda)$. One could run x through S a large number of times and count the number of times the machine accepted x. We call this experiment $E(x)$. By the law of large numbers, there exists for any $x \, \epsilon \, \Sigma_2^*$ with $p(x) \neq \lambda$ and every $\varepsilon > 0$, a number $N(x,\varepsilon)$ such that

$$\Pr \left\{ E(x) \mid \lambda < \frac{m(E(x))}{N(x,\varepsilon)} \Leftrightarrow x \, \epsilon \, \beta_S(\lambda) \right\} \geq 1 - \varepsilon$$

where $m(x)$ is the number of times that x is accepted. This means that the probability of getting the correct answer by the experiment is greater than $1 - \varepsilon$. What logical difficulty does this experimental approach encounter? Explain how the concept of isolated cutpoints avoids the difficulty.

2. Prove Theorem 10 by actually constructing a machine.

3. Let S be a probabilistic machine with isolated cut point λ. Show that $\beta_S(\lambda)$ is regular.

8 SUMMARY

We have studied a particular subclass of regular sets, the definite events. It is interesting to note that nontrivial techniques are needed to study even this simple family.

Probabilistic machines are very interesting and important, and much attention is being given to their theory. It is to be hoped that such a theory may indicate techniques for increasing the realiability of sequential circuits and, ultimately, digital computers. (Cf. Winograd and Cowan).

The material on definite events is taken from Perles, Rabin, and Shamir. The material on probabilistic automata is due to Rabin.[1] Recently, A. Paz has obtained further important results on probabilistic automata.

realization and the
state-assignment problem

1 INTRODUCTION

In this chapter the techniques used to realize sequential circuits are developed. Such realizations require the encoding of the states into m-tuples of zeroes and ones in an efficient way. This problem, called the state-assignment problem, is under active investigation and involves an understanding of both combinational and sequential switching theory.

We shall provide some methods for the partial solution of this problem.

2 COMPONENTS FOR SEQUENTIAL SWITCHING

The components studied in Chap. 3 do not include devices capable of storing information. A sequential machine has this storage capability, and hence additional components must be introduced for the physical realization.

The circuit of Fig. 1 is called a *flip-flop*. It is the central building block of electronic sequential machines. The external action of the circuit is as follows: If we initially assume the circuit to be in the reset state, the 0 output is high. When a 1 occurs at S, the device switches states and the 1 (0) output is high (low). This situation will remain until a 1 occurs on the R line, which will restore the circuit to its original state. This flip-flop circuit thus has two states, and r flip-flops are capable of representing 2^r states

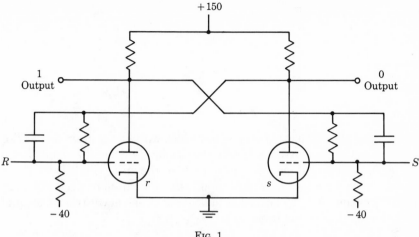

FIG. 1

The internal operation is as follows: Suppose that the circuit is as shown in the figure. A 1 on the R line does nothing, since tube r is already conducting. A 1 on the S line starts tube s conducting. As tube a conducts, its plate voltage falls. This falling potential is coupled to the grid of tube r, which causes this tube to start to cut off. As cutoff occurs, the plate voltage of tube r causes the grid of tube s to rise, which continues the process until s is fully conducting and r is fully cut off. By the symmetry of the circuit, this is the only case we need consider.

A transistor version of a flip-flop is shown in Fig. 2. The action of the circuit is analogous to that of the circuit shown in Fig. 1.

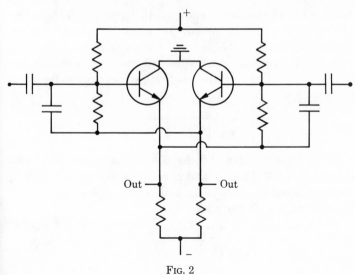

FIG. 2

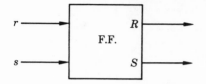

Having shown that actual circuits which exhibit the desired behavior exist, we shall henceforth work with the idealized device (flip-flop) shown in Fig. 3, with its tabular description where the state is labeled 1 if the flip-flop is set (reset). It is understood that the flip-flop is set (reset) iff the $S(R)$ output is 1. The dashes indicate that one never tries to set and reset the flip-flop at the same time.

s	r	Present state	Next state
0	0	0	0
0	0	1	1
0	1	0	0
0	1	1	0
1	0	0	1
1	0	1	1
1	1	0	—
1	1	1	—

While it is possible to construct more exotic memory circuits, this simple flip-flop device is sufficient for our purposes. The reader interested in hardware should consult the book of Braun.

To illustrate the realization of a sequential machine, consider the example shown in Fig. 4. The machine has three states, so two flip-flops

State	a	b	c
Output	0	0	1

are required. These flip-flops A and B have four states, namely, both reset (denoted by $\bar{A}\bar{B}$ or 00), A reset and B set (denoted by $\bar{A}B$ or 01), A set and B reset (denoted by $A\bar{B}$ or 10), and both set (denoted by AB or 11). Let us arbitrarily code the states by

$$\varphi: \begin{matrix} a \to 00 \\ b \to 01 \\ c \to 11 \end{matrix} \qquad (1)$$

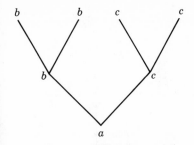

FIG. 4

The logical design of the circuit will be completed when we derive forms for the set, reset, and output signals. We do this easily by rewriting the description of the machine given in Fig. 4 and Eq. (1) into the following tabular form. Note the convention of writing i for σ_i ($i = 0, 1$).

x	A	B	A	B	Output
0	0	0	0	1	0
0	0	1	0	1	0
0	1	0	1	0	0
0	1	1	1	1	1
1	0	0	1	1	0
1	0	1	0	1	0
1	1	0	1	0	0
1	1	1	1	1	1

To determine the set signal for flip-flop A, we search down the second A column for a 1 entry. If a 1 is present and there is no 1 in the first A column, this means that the flip-flop must be set under this condition and this term must be included in the set function. If a 1 is present in both A columns, then the device passes from the set condition to the set condition, so that no additional input is needed. For the reset case, simply search for 0's which are preceded by 1's.

In this problem

$$S_A = x\,\bar{A}\bar{B}$$
$$S_B = \bar{x}\,\bar{A}\bar{B} + x\,\bar{A}\bar{B} = \bar{A}\bar{B}$$

$$R_A = 0$$
$$R_B = 0$$
$$\text{Output} = AB$$

The final circuit is shown in Fig. 5.

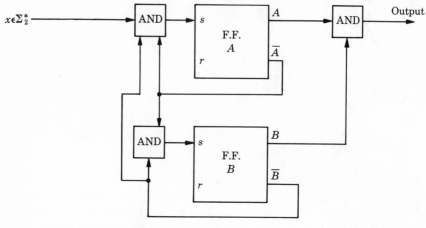

PROBLEMS

1. Discuss how one would physically realize sequential machines with relays. Is the process basically different? (See Caldwell[1] or Marcus.[1])

2. Sometimes one uses delay units instead of flip-flops as the fundamental memory elements of sequential machines. Assume the existence of a device, shown below, which receives an input i at time t and gives the output i at time $t + 1$. ─────▶▭────▶ Show that every sequential machine may be realized by the configuration of Fig. P2. Show that if n delay elements, p binary inputs, and q binary outputs are used, then the number of possible combinational networks is $2^{(n+q)2^{n+p}}$.

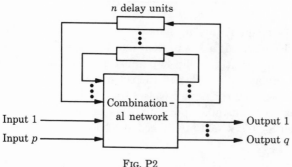

FIG. P2

3. (Huffman[2]) A machine $S = \langle \Sigma, \Delta, S, f, g \rangle$ is called *information lossless* iff $(\forall x,y)_{\Sigma^*}(\forall s)_S \quad g(s,x) = g(s,y) \wedge f(s,x) = f(s,y) \Rightarrow x = y$. Intuitively, one can recover the input from knowledge of the output, initial state, and final state. Characterize these machines by using the model of Prob. 2 and the information in Chap. 5.

4. Let α be a finite subset of Σ_k^*. α is a *code* iff the monoid generated by α, that is α^*, is free. In the engineering literature, this condition is called *unique decipherability*. Give an algorithm for testing a finite set α for unique decipherability.

5. Show that if S is definite, then S has a feedback-free realization.

3 THE PRECISE FORMULATION

The example of Sec. 2 indicates that a state assignment is a special type of mapping from the set of states into p-tuples of zeroes and ones. More formally, we have Definition 1.

Definition 1.   Let $S = \langle S, M, a, F \rangle$ be a sequential machine with r internal states.   A *state assignment* φ is defined as a one-to-one function

$$\varphi: S \rightarrow \{0,1\}^p$$

where
$$p \geq - [- \log_2 r]$$

The inequality on p is equivalent to

$$r \leq 2^p$$

which simply says that $- [- \log_2 r]$ is the least number of flip-flops capable of representing r internal states.   The economical reader may have wondered why we did not require that $p = - [- \log_2 r]$.   The answer is that examples are known where the insertion of extra flip-flops causes such a reduction in the combinational logic that the total cost of the circuit is lowered.

We now wish to count the total number of state assignments.   If S contains r states, then there are $\binom{2^p}{r} r!$ possible assignments, since there are $\binom{2^p}{r}$ ways to select r distinct state encodings and $r!$ ways to permute them.

EXAMPLE.   Let S have three states and let φ_1 and φ_2 denote state assignments for S:

	φ_1	φ_2
s_0	000	010
s_1	011	111
s_2	001	011

Note that φ_2 may be converted to φ_1 by interchanging coordinates 1 and 2 and then complementing coordinate 1.   This suggests that a new definition of the equivalence of state assignments is required.

Definition 2.   Two state assignments φ_1 and φ_2 are *equivalent* iff there exists an $\alpha \, \epsilon \, G_n$ (cf. Sec. 5-9) such that

$$\varphi_1(s) = \alpha(\varphi_2(s)) \qquad \text{for all } s \, \epsilon \, S$$

EXAMPLE.   In the previous example, $\alpha = ((100),(12)(3))$.   The number of classes can now be easily computed, since the cycle index of G_n is known.

Theorem 3.   Let S be a sequential machine with r internal states.   The number of state assignments involving p $(p \geq -[-\log_2 r])$ bistable memory elements (1-1 mappings from S into $\{0,1\}^p$) is given by

$$\frac{d^r}{dz^r} Z_{G_p}(1 + z, 1, \ldots, 1)$$

evaluated at $z = 0$.

PROOF.   This is a special case of Prob. 5-4.3 where $Z_G = f_1{}^r$.   Note that this result may be written

$$\frac{r!}{p!2^p} \sum_{\alpha \, \epsilon \, G_p} \binom{j_1(\alpha)}{r}$$

where $j_1(\alpha)$ is the number of cycles of length 1 in the permutation α. ∎

Corollary 4.   Let S be a sequential machine with r states.   The number of state assignments involving p bistable memory elements, where $p = -[-\log_2 r]$, is

$$\frac{(2^p - 1)!}{(2^p - r)!p!}$$

PROOF.   In this case only the identity term in G_p can contribute to the sum, so that the result is

$$\frac{r!}{p!2^p} \binom{2^p}{r} = \frac{r!}{p!2^p} \frac{2^p!}{r!(2^p - r)!}$$
$$= \frac{(2^p - 1)!}{(2^p - r)!p!} \quad ∎$$

EXAMPLE.   Suppose $r = 3$, $p = 2$, $Z_{G_2} = \frac{1}{8}(f_1{}^4 + 3f_2{}^2 + 2f_1{}^2f_2 + 2f_4)$.   Thus the desired result is, by Corollary 4,

$$\frac{(2^2 - 1)!}{2} = \frac{6}{2} = 3$$

If we take $r = 2$, $p = 2$, then the number is

$$\frac{1}{8} \left(\frac{d^2}{dz^2}\right) ((1 + z)^4 + 3 + 2(1 + z)^2 + 2) = \frac{2}{8}\left(\binom{4}{2} + 2\binom{2}{2}\right) = \frac{2}{8}(6 + 2) = 2$$

Table 1 shows the number of classes of state assignments for a few small values of p and r.

TABLE 1

r	p			
	1	2	3	4
1	1	1	0	0
2	1	2	3	3
3	1	3	10	38
4	1	4	22	169
5	1	5	40	516

PROBLEMS

1. Let $T(p,r)$ be the number of equivalence classes of state assignments involving r states and p memory units. Show that

$$T(p,r) \sim \frac{(2^p - 1)!}{(2^p - r)!p!}$$

2. (Gilbert[3]) A state assignment is called *degenerate* iff there is a column that is constant over all states or if two columns are identical over all states. If $T(p,r)$ denotes the number of classes of state assignments and if $S(p,r)$ denotes the number of classes of nondegenerate state assignments, then show that

$$S(p,r) = \sum_{i=1}^{p} T(i,r)(-1)^{p-i} \binom{p}{i}$$

$$\left[\text{HINT: Show } T(p,r) = \sum_{i=1}^{r} S(i,r) \binom{p}{i}. \right]$$

3. (Gilbert[3]) Show that

$$T(p,r) = \frac{r!}{p!} \sum_{i=1}^{p} \mathcal{S}(p+1, i+1)2^{-i} \binom{2^i}{r}$$

where $\mathcal{S}(j,k)$ denotes the Stirling numbers of the first kind. (HINT: This problem requires an identity involving Stirling numbers.)

4. Under what circumstances could the requirement that φ is one to one be dropped?

4 DECOMPOSITION OF MACHINES

Our experience with switching functions indicates that decomposable functions are quite cheap to realize. If it is possible to decompose sequential machines into constituent parts, then the state assignments will decompose. Thus decomposition is a reduction technique; it does not help select the best encodings.

Fortunately, mathematicians have studied the decomposition of abstract algebras. Our first step is simply to apply this theory.

We shall find it convenient to decompose machines without any regard to the outputs. After the machine is decomposed, the outputs can be chosen to preserve the behavior of the original machine.

The first type of decomposition is one in which a given machine is decomposed as the direct product of two machines. Note that since outputs are suppressed, the same result holds for direct sums.

Lemma 1. If S is a sequential machine and R_1, R_2 are right-congruence relations such that $R_1R_2 = R_2R_1$, then

$$R_1R_2 = R_1 \sqcup R_2$$

PROOF.   Cf. Prob. 1-4.15 ∎

Theorem 2.   Let S be a sequential machine.   If there exist two right-congruence relations on S such that

$$R_1 \sqcup R_2 = 1 \qquad R_1 \cap R_2 = 0$$

and
$$R_1 R_2 = R_2 R_1$$

then S is isomorphic to the direct product of S/R_1 and S/R_2.

PROOF.   Form $S/R_1 = \langle \{R_1[s] | s \in S\}, P, b \rangle$ and $S/R_2 = \langle \{R_2[s] | s \in S\}, Q, c \rangle$.   Consider the mapping φ: $s \to (R_1[s], R_2[s])$. φ is a homomorphism of $S = \langle S, M, a \rangle$ into $S/R_1 \times S/R_2$, since

$$\varphi(a) = (R_1[a], R_2[a]) = (b, c)$$
$$\varphi(M(s, \sigma)) = (R_1[M(s, \sigma)], R_2[M(s, \sigma)])$$
$$= (P(R_1[s], \sigma), Q(R_2[s], \sigma))$$

Suppose $(R_1[s], R_2[s]) = (R_1[t], R_2[t])$; then

$$s R_1 t \wedge s R_2 t \qquad \text{so } (s, t) \in R_1 \cap R_2$$

Since $R_1 \cap R_2 = 0$, $s = t$, which proves that φ is one to one.   To show that φ is onto, suppose we have $(R_1[s], R_2[t])$.   Since $R_1 R_2 = R_2 R_1 = R_1 \sqcup R_2 = 1$, we have

$$(s, t) \in 1 \Leftrightarrow (s, t) \in R_1 R_2$$

i.e., there exists a w such that

$$s R_1 w \qquad \text{and} \qquad w R_2 t$$

Therefore, $w \in R_1[s]$ and $w \in R_2[t]$, so that w maps, under φ, onto $(R_1[s], R_2[t])$. ∎

EXAMPLE.   A machine S is shown in Fig. 1.   Let

$$R_1 = \{[s_0, s_5, s_7], [s_1, s_3, s_4], [s_2, s_6]\}$$

and
$$R_2 = \{[s_0, s_1], [s_2, s_4, s_5], [s_3, s_6, s_7]\}$$

Then $R_1 \cap R_2 = 0$, $R_1 \sqcup R_2 = 1$, and $R_1 R_2 = R_2 R_1$, so that S must be isomorphic to $S/R_1 \times S/R_2$.   The quotient machines are shown in Fig. 2.   The reader can form the direct product of S/R_1 and S/R_2 and show that it is isomorphic to S.

A decomposition theorem which will settle the issue of machine decomposition versus minimization can now be proved.

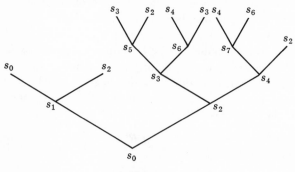

FIG. 1

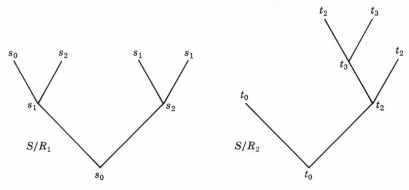

FIG. 2

Definition 3. Let R_1 and R_2 be equivalence relations on a set S. If $R_1 \supseteq R_2$, then R_1/R_2 is defined as

$$R_1/R_2 = \{(R_2[s], R_2[t]) | sR_1t; s, t \in S\}$$

and R_1/R_2 is the *quotient decomposition of R_1 with respect to R_2.*

EXAMPLE. Let $S = \{1,2,3,4,5\}$, $R_1 = \{[1,2,3], [4,5]\}$, and $R_2 = \{[1,2],[3],[4,5]\}$. Clearly, $R_1 \supseteq R_2$. Thus R_1/R_2 is defined and is

$$R_1/R_2 = \{[[1,2],[3]], [[4,5]]\}$$

as a partition. Writing R_1/R_2 as a relation,

$$R_1/R_2 = \{([1,2], [3]), ([3], [1,2]), ([1, 2], [1,2]), ([3], [3]) ([4, 5], [4,5])\}$$

Proposition 4. If R_1 and R_2 are equivalence relations (partitions) on a set S and $R_1 \supseteq R_2$, then R_1/R_2 is an equivalence relation (partition) on the set of equivalence classes of S under R_2.

The following theorem is usually called the second isomorphism theorem in algebra. Its direct application to sequential machines is due to Cherniavskii and Kozmidiadi.

Theorem 5. Let $S = \langle S,M,a \rangle$ be a sequential machine and let R_1, R_2 be right-congruence relations on S such that $R_1 \supseteq R_2$. R_1/R_2 is a congruence on S/R_2, and S/R_1 is isomorphic to $(S/R_2)/(R_1/R_2)$.

PROOF. Let $S/R_2 = \langle T,N,b \rangle$, where $T = \{R_2[s] | s \in S\}, N(R_2[s],\sigma) = R_2[M(s,\sigma)]$ and $b = R_2[a]$. Suppose that

$$R_2[s](R_1/R_2)R_2[t]$$

then sR_1t and $M(s,\sigma)R_1M(t,\sigma)$, because R_1 is a right congruence on S. Then

$$R_2[M(s,\sigma)](R_1/R_2)R_2[M(t,\sigma)] \Leftrightarrow N(R_2[s],\sigma)(R_1/R_2)N(R_2[t],\sigma)$$

which shows that R_1/R_2 is a right congruence on S/R_2.

Let $S/R_1 = \langle U,P,c \rangle$, where $U = \{R_1[s] | s \in S\}, P(R_1[s],\sigma) = R_1[M(s,\sigma)]$, and $c = R_1[a]$.

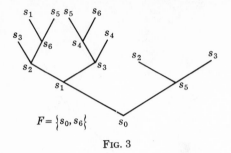

$F = \{s_0, s_6\}$

FIG. 3

Finally, let $(S/R_2)/(R_1/R_2) = \langle V, Q, d \rangle$, where $V = \{R_1/R_2[R_2[s]] | s \; \epsilon \; S\}$, $Q(R_1/R_2[R_2[s]], \sigma) = R_1/R_2[N(R_2[s], \sigma)] = R_1/R_2[R_2[M(s, \sigma)]]$, and $d = R_1/R_2[R_2[a]]$.

Let φ map $R_1[s] \to R_1/R_2[R_2[s]]$. Clearly, φ is onto. φ is a homomorphism because

$$\varphi(R_1[a]) = R_1/R_2[R_2[a]] = d$$
$$\varphi(N(R_1[s], \sigma)) = \varphi(R_1[M(s, \sigma)]) = R_1/R_2[R_2[M(s, \sigma)]]$$
$$= Q(R_1/R_2[R_2[s]], \sigma) = Q(\varphi(R_2[s]), \sigma)$$

To show that φ is one to one, assume

$$R_1/R_2[R_2[s]] = R_1/R_2[R_2[t]]$$

then

$$R_2[s](R_1/R_2)R_2[t]$$

iff sR_1t, so $R_1[s] = R_1[t]$ and φ is one to one. ▌

Theorem 5 and Prob. 8 say that it may be better to try to decompose a given sequential machine before minimizing the number of states. The reason is that the minimal machine is a quotient machine modulo a right congruence, say, R. The only congruence relations preserved in S/R are those which included R. Thus good opportunities for decompositions are often lost in minimization.

EXAMPLE. Let S be as shown in Fig. 3. If S is minimized, then S^M is formed, Fig. 4.

It is easily checked that S^M has no nontrivial right congruences and hence that S^M cannot be decomposed. On the other hand, S possesses a pair of permutable and complementary right congruences.

$$R_1 = \{[s_0, s_6], [s_1], [s_2], [s_3], [s_4], [s_5]\}$$
$$R_2 = \{[s_0][s_1, s_2, s_3, s_4, s_5, s_6]\}$$

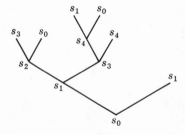

FIG. 4

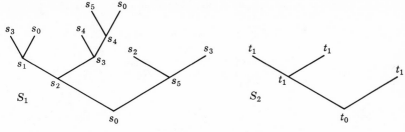

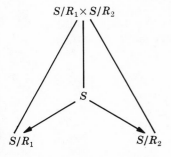

FIG. 5

S may be written as the direct product of S_1 and S_2, which are shown in Fig. 5 ($S_i = S/R_i$, $i = 1, 2$). For another example, see Hartmanis and Stearns.[4]

PROBLEMS

1. Show the converse of Theorem 2, that is, that if S is isomorphic to $S_1 \times S_2$, then there exists a pair of right-congruence relations on S which are permutable complements.

2. (Ádám, Fuchs, Szász) The following "theorem" is given by Birkhoff[1] (and applied by Hartmanis[1]) as a generalization of Theorem 2.
The representations of a sequential machine S as a direct product $S = S_1 \times \cdots \times S_r$ correspond one to one with sets of permutable right-congruence relations $R_1, \ldots, R_r$ on S satisfying

$$R_1 \cap \cdots \cap R_r = 0$$

and $\qquad (R_1 \cap \cdots \cap R_{i-1}) \cup R_i = 1 \qquad$ for $i = 2, \ldots, r$

Show that this "theorem" is false. Can you construct a counterexample. If not, consult the paper of Ádám.

3. Correctly generalize Theorem 2.

4. Show that there is a one-to-one *into* mapping from a sequential machine S into the direct product of two other machines iff there exist two nontrivial congruences R_1 and R_2 on S such that $R_1 \cap R_2 = 0$. (S is called the *subdirect product* of the two machines.)

5. The situation in Prob. 4 is shown in Fig. P5. That is, $S/R_1 \times S/R_2$ contains S as a submachine. It also contains $(S/R_1 \times S/R_2)^c$ as a submachine. Where

$S/R_1 \times S/R_2$

S

S/R_1 $\qquad$ S/R_2

FIG. P5

does $(S/R_1 \times S/R_2)^c$ go in the picture? That is, is $(S/R_1 \times S/R_2)^c$ smaller than S, isomorphic to S, etc.? Assume S is connected.

6. Realize the machine of Fig. P6 as a subdirect product. HINT:

$$R_1 = \{[s_0,s_1],[s_2,s_3], [s_4,s_5], [s_6,s_7]\}$$

and

$$R_2 = \{[s_0,s_4], [s_2,s_6],[s_1,s_5], [s_3,s_7]\}$$

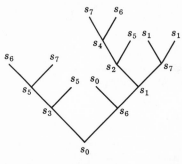

FIG. P6

7. Show the following converse of Theorem 5: If R_2 is a right congruence on S, then any right congruence R on S/R_2 uniquely determines a right congruence R_1 on S such that $R = R_1/R_2$.

8. Conclude that if S is a sequential machine and S/R is a quotient machine modulo a right-congruence relation R, then there is a one-to-one correspondence between the right-congruence relations on S/R and the right-congruence relations on S which include R.

9. Give rules for selecting the proper output sets for decomposed machines.

5 OTHER DECOMPOSITIONS AND GENERATION OF RIGHT - CONGRUENCE RELATIONS

The direct product decomposition is essentially one of connecting two machines in parallel as shown in Fig. 1. The next interesting decomposition is a *cascade* or *series connection* of two machines, which is sketched in Fig. 2.

The cascade decomposition depends on how the output function is defined on S_1. It is possible to give necessary and sufficient conditions

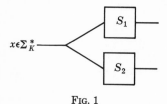

FIG. 1

FIG. 2

on a machine S for such a cascade decomposition. It should not be a surprise to learn that the condition, due to Yoeli[4], is that a certain type of right-congruence relation exists on S (Prob. 3). A less restricted definition is given by Hartmanis[2]; in that case, S is decomposable in a cascade connection iff there is a nontrivial right congruence on S. In the summary to this chapter a brief survey of decomposition theory for finite automata is given.

It has been seen that decompositions require a knowledge of the right-congruence relations on a machine. An algorithm is now presented for generating all the congruence relations on the states of a given machine. The method will require an algorithm for computing the least congruence relation which contains a given equivalence relation.

Algorithm 1. Let R be a given equivalence relation on a machine

$$S = \langle S, M, a \rangle$$

(1) Construct
$$E'_R = R \cup \{(u,v) | (\exists w_1, w_2)_S \quad w_1 R w_2 \wedge u = M(w_1, \sigma) \wedge v = M(w_2, \sigma)\}$$

(2) Construct $E_R = \widehat{E'_R}$, the transitive closure of E'_R.

Proposition 2. E_R is the least right-congruence relation containing R.

PROOF. E_R is reflexive and symmetric by construction. Step 2 guarantees that E_R is transitive, and the substitution property is satisfied in step 1. Suppose that Q is a right-congruence relation such that $R \subseteq Q$; then we shall show that $E_R \subseteq Q$.

Suppose $(u,v) \in E_R$. Since $E_R = \widehat{E'_R} = \bigcup_{i=1}^{\infty} (E'_R)^i$, $(u,v) \in (E'_R)^l$ that is $u E'_R z_1$, $z_1 E'_R z_2, \ldots, z_{l-1} E'_R v$. If we let $u = z_0$ and $v = z_l$, then the previous condition is

$$z_i E'_R z_{i+1} \quad \text{for } i = 0, \ldots, l-1$$

$$z_i E'_R z_{i+1} \Leftrightarrow z_i R z_{i+1} \vee (\exists w_i, w_{i+1})_S (\exists \sigma)_{\Sigma_k} \ [w_i R w_{i+1} \wedge M(w_i, \sigma) = z_i \wedge M(w_{i+1}, \sigma) = z_{i+1}]$$

If $z_i R z_{i+1}$, then, since $R \subseteq Q$, $z_i Q z_{i+1}$ and $u Q^l v$. Since Q is transitive, $Q^l \subseteq Q$ and $u Q v$. In the other case, $w_i R w_{i+1}$ implies $w_i Q w_{i+1}$. Since Q is a right congruence

$$M(w_i, \sigma) Q M(w_{i+1}, \sigma) \Leftrightarrow z_i Q z_{i+1}$$

and therefore $u Q^l v$, which implies $u Q v$. ∎

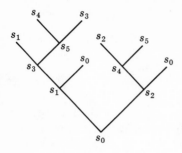

FIG. 3

EXAMPLE. Let S be the machine shown in Fig. 3 and let $R = \{[s_1,s_2], [s_0,s_3], [s_4], [s_5]\}$.

$$E'_R = R \cup \left\{\begin{matrix} (s_3,s_4) & (s_2,s_5) \\ (s_4,s_3) & (s_3,s_2) \end{matrix}\right\} = \left\{\begin{matrix} (s_1,s_2) & (s_3,s_0) & (s_2,s_5) \\ (s_2,s_1) & (s_3,s_4) & (s_5,s_2) \\ (s_0,s_3) & (s_4,s_3) \end{matrix}\right\}$$

$$E_R = \widehat{E'_R} = \{[s_1,s_2,s_5], [s_0,s_3,s_4]\}$$

Note that $S/\widehat{E'_R}$, shown in Fig. 4, is a clock.

Now a method for computing all the right congruences on the states of a sequential machine is given.

Algorithm 3. Let $S = \langle S,M,a \rangle$ be a sequential machine with n states.

(1) Define the $n(n-1)/2$ equivalence relations consisting of $n-2$ blocks of one element and one block of two elements.
(2) For each such relation R compute the least right congruence containing R by algorithm 1.
(3) Among the nontrivial right congruences generated, select a minimal set of congruences.
(4) Using the minimal congruences, construct all possible joins of the relations. Continue until the universal relation is reached.

While Algorithm 3 is exhaustive in nature, it actually is not too hard to compute.

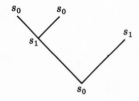

FIG. 4

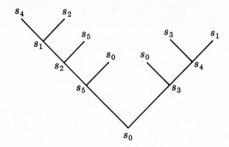

FIG. 5

EXAMPLE. Let S be as given in Fig. 5. The equivalence relations to be tested are

$$\{(s_0,s_1)\}$$
$$\{(s_1,s_2)\}$$
$$\{(s_0,s_2)\} \qquad \{(s_2,s_3)\}$$
$$\{(s_1,s_3)\} \qquad \{(s_3,s_4)\}$$
$$\{(s_0,s_3)\} \qquad \{(s_2,s_4)\} \qquad \{(s_4,s_5)\}$$
$$\{(s_1,s_4)\} \qquad \{(s_3,s_5)\}$$
$$\{(s_0,s_4)\} \qquad \{(s_2,s_5)\}$$
$$\{(s_1,s_5)\}$$
$$\{(s_0,s_5)\}$$

The least-congruence relations containing these relations are respectively

$$\{[s_0,s_1], [s_2,s_3], \qquad\qquad 1 \qquad \{[s_0,s_1], [s_2,s_3],$$
$$[s_4,s_5]\} \qquad\qquad\qquad\qquad\qquad [s_4,s_5]\}$$
$$1 \qquad\qquad 1$$
$$\{[s_1,s_3,s_5], \qquad\qquad\qquad\qquad\qquad \{[s_0,s_1], [s_2,s_3],$$
$$[s_0,s_2,s_4]\} \qquad\qquad\qquad\qquad\qquad [s_4,s_5]\}$$
$$1 \qquad\qquad 1$$
$$\{[s_0,s_2,s_4], \qquad \{[s_0,s_2,s_4],$$
$$[s_1,s_3,s_5]\} \qquad [s_1,s_3,s_5]\}$$
$$1 \qquad\qquad\qquad\qquad 1$$
$$\{[s_1,s_3,s_5],$$
$$[s_0,s_2,s_4]\}$$
$$1$$

The minimal nontrivial sets are

$$\{[s_0,s_1], [s_2,s_3], [s_4,s_5]\} \qquad \text{and} \qquad \{[s_0,s_2,s_4], [s_1,s_3,s_5]\}$$

The join of these relations is 1, so that the lattice of right-congruence relations is rather simple; cf. Fig. 6.

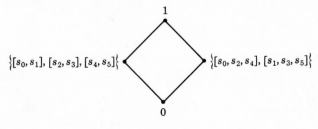

FIG. 6

PROBLEMS

1. Construct the lattice of right congruences for the machine shown in Fig. P1.

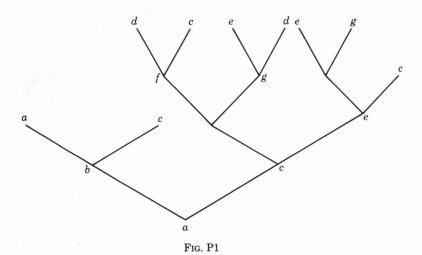

FIG. P1

2. The *cascade connection* of $S = \langle S,M,a,F \rangle$ over Σ_2 and $T = \langle T,N,b,G \rangle$ over $\{0,1\}$ is defined in the following way. First define $f: S \to \{0,1\}$ by

$$f(s) = \begin{cases} 1 & \text{if } s \in F \\ 0 & \text{otherwise} \end{cases}$$

then we define $S \circ T = \langle S \times T, P, (a,b), H \rangle$, where

$$P((s,t),\sigma) = (M(s,\sigma), N(t,f(M(s,\sigma))))$$

and $H = S \times G$. Construct $S \circ T$, where S and T are as given in Fig. P2.

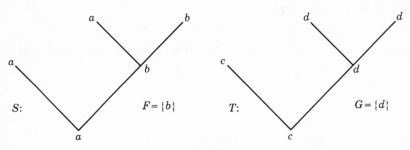

FIG. P2

3. (Yoeli[4]) Prove that a machine S can be decomposed as the cascade combination of two machines iff there exists a *uniform* right congruence on S, that is, a right congruence which has the same number of elements in each class.

6 SUMMARY

In this chapter the state-assignment problem has been mentioned and some results have been presented.   One approach, machine decomposition, has been briefly presented.

The decomposition of machines is an example of a problem which is important from both an engineering and a mathematical point of view. The original work on the decomposition of automata was a simple application by Hartmanis and Yoeli of the elementary decomposition theorems for abstract algebras. (Cf. the monograph by Jónsson and Tarski). Later, these results were extended by considering covers on the set of states rather than just right-congruence relations.   These extensions were due to Hartmanis, Hartmanis and Stearns, and Yoeli.

The first important and deep theorem on machine decomposition was obtained by Krohn and Rhodes who showed that every finite sequential machine has a cascade-parallel decomposition into prime machines and units, where the prime machines are those whose semigroup is a nontrivial finite simple group.   The set of units consists of four trivial machines. Because the proof of this theorem requires a knowledge of group and semigroup theory, it was omitted.   A number of the new concepts introduced in the proof have been included in the problems.   There are implications which arise from this theorem and lead to new decomposition theorems for continuous systems, a characterization of those sequential machines which can be built from counters, a theory of complexity for machines, semigroups, and context-free languages.

Maurer has studied the Krohn-Rhodes decomposition theorem for the case where the semigroup of the given machine is a group.   For this case, the decomposition is unique and formulas can be given which compute the connecting maps.   Recently, Zeiger has given a new proof of the Krohn-Rhodes theorem from the point of view of covers.   Zeiger's proof contains some new ideas and makes clearer the connection between the two different methods of decomposition; furthermore, the proof is more constructive.

The material in this chapter is taken mostly from the work of Hartmanis and Yoeli.

introduction to context-free languages

1 INTRODUCTION

Artificial languages are of interest to us for a number of reasons. The first consideration is that programming languages are artificial languages; perhaps a theory of artificial languages would yield some approach to the difficult problem of formulating a theory of programming. A more immediate reason is that artificial languages are generalizations of a language we have studied in some detail, the language of regular expressions.

The study of artificial languages was initiated by Chomsky, Bar-Hillel, and others as one method for studying natural languages. The basic problem in linguistics is the construction of a grammar for a given language.

2 THE INTUITIVE MODEL

So far, we have studied two kinds of devices: a recognition device, which examines an input string and ultimately gives a 1 output if the string is recognized; and a transformational device, e.g., a Mealy (Moore) machine, which maps one string onto another string of the same length. For the purposes of this chapter, we shall call a recognition device a *finite automaton* and we shall use the phrase *sequential machine* for a machine which transforms sequences into sequences. We are about to study a device of still a different type, called a *grammar*, which generates strings. Loosely speaking, a language L is just a set of strings from a finite set V which can be thought of as the vocabulary.

EXAMPLES. For work in languages, we think of V as a *vocabulary* and L as a set of *sentences*. An algebraist or automata theorist would think of V as an *alphabet* and L as a set of *words*. A programmer might think of V as an *instruction set* and L as *programs*.

Arbitrary sets of strings have no real interest to us unless there is a *grammar* or set of mechanical rules by which the strings can be generated. For linguists, a still stronger condition must be met. There should be a *structural description* of any string x which should tell how x was generated by the grammar in case $x \in L$. If $x \notin L$, a structural description might explain in what way x fails to be a member of L. For example, is the following sequence of words a grammatical English sentence: Peppermint hair plays swiftly?

Our interest will be rather narrow from the point of view of linguistics. We want to know only how a given sentence can be decomposed into phrases.

EXAMPLE. Consider the following sentence. "That stupid student gives me a pain." We list the parts of speech used in this sentence.

"That"	determiner	"me"	pronoun
"stupid"	adjective	"a"	article
"student"	noun	"pain"	noun
"gives"	verb		

The structure of the sentence is available from the parsing tree in which the sentence is decomposed in phrases as shown in Fig. 1. NP(VP) stands for noun (verb) phrase. Since it is known that trees are equivalent to bracketed strings (Prob. 7-2.5), the structural description can be given by

$$[\ \ [\ \ [\text{That}\ ]\ [\ \ [\text{stupid}\ ]\ \ [\text{student}]]]\ [\ [\text{gives}]\ \ [\ \ [\ \ \text{me}\ \ ]]\ \ [\ \ [a]\ [\text{pain}]]]]$$
$$\sigma\ \ \text{NP}\ \ \text{det}\ \ \ \ \text{NP}\ \text{adj}\ \ \ \ \ \ \text{N}\ \ \ \ \ \ \ \text{VP}\ \text{verb}\ \ \ \ \ \text{NP}\ \text{pronoun}\ \ \ \text{NP}\ \text{art}\ \ \text{N}$$

The grammar for generating such a sentence includes rewriting rules of the form

$$\sigma \rightarrow \text{NP VP}$$
$$\text{NP} \rightarrow \text{det NP}$$
$$\text{det} \rightarrow \text{That}$$
$$\text{NP} \rightarrow \text{adj N}$$
$$\text{adj} \rightarrow \text{stupid}$$
$$\text{N} \rightarrow \text{student}$$
$$\text{VP} \rightarrow \text{verb NP NP}$$
$$\text{verb} \rightarrow \text{gives}$$
$$\text{NP} \rightarrow \text{pronoun}$$
$$\text{pronoun} \rightarrow \text{me}$$
$$\text{NP} \rightarrow \text{art N}$$
$$\text{art} \rightarrow \text{a}$$
$$\text{N} \rightarrow \text{pain}$$

Two kinds of symbols are used in the decomposition. There are symbols of the generated sentence or *terminals*,† such as "that," there are *variables* or auxiliary

---

† A linguist would call the terminals *morphemes*.

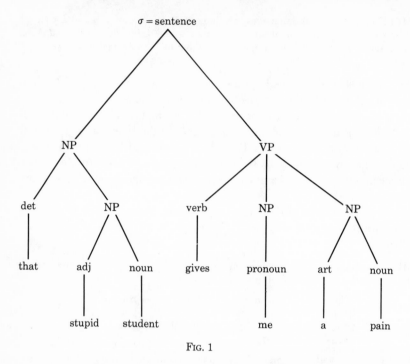

$\sigma = $ sentence

FIG. 1

symbols such as "det." Note that the rewriting rules involve only single variables on the left of the arrows.

The procedure that was followed in the example can be described by saying that we started with the original object, namely, the sentence σ itself. We then applied the rewriting rules and finally produced a string consisting of nothing but terminals. Such a string is called a *terminal string*. Grammars of this type are called *phrase-structure grammars*.

One of the problems concerning these generations is that a string may have several different structural descriptions; i.e., it may be ambiguous. Consider the following grammar which is of the *context-free type* since only nonterminals occur on the left-hand side of the rules.

$$\sigma \to NP\ VP$$
$$NP \to they$$
$$NP \to adj\ N$$
$$NP \to N$$
$$VP \to are\ NP$$
$$VP \to verb\ NP$$
$$verb \to are\ flying$$
$$adj \to flying$$
$$N \to planes$$

The sentence "They are flying planes," has the following two distinct structural descriptions:

$$[\quad [\text{They}] \quad [\quad [\text{are flying}] \quad [\quad [\text{planes}]]]]$$
$$\quad \sigma \quad \text{NP} \qquad \text{VP} \quad \text{verb} \qquad \text{NP} \quad \text{N}$$

$$[\quad [\text{They}] \quad [\text{are} \quad [\quad [\text{flying}] \quad [\text{planes}]]]]$$
$$\quad \sigma \quad \text{NP} \qquad \text{VP} \quad \text{NP} \quad \text{adj} \qquad \text{N}$$

These correspond to the distinct meanings of the sentence as illustrated below.

"My friends, who are pilots, are flying planes."

"Those spots in the sky are flying planes."

Thus, the context-free languages reflect the ambiguity of natural language. They are also very useful for the description of parts of artificial languages such as ALGOL.†

3 THE PRECISE FORMULATION

We now introduce context-free languages more precisely. The technique will be to generate the language from its grammar.

Definition 1. Let V be a finite nonvoid set called the *vocabulary*. V^* is the free monoid generated by V and includes the null word Λ.

Definition 2. Any subset of V^* is called a *language over* V.

Our interest will be in methods for generating the subsets and not in the subsets themselves. Generating systems for languages are called *grammars*.

Definition 3. A *context-free grammar* is defined as $G = \langle V, P, \sigma, T \rangle$, where V is a finite *vocabulary* and P is a set of *rewriting rules* or *productions*, i.e., P consists of a finite set of rules of the form

$$\nu \to x \qquad x \neq \nu \qquad \nu \,\epsilon\, V - T \qquad x \,\epsilon\, V^*$$

$T \subseteq V$ is called the *terminal vocabulary*; $\sigma \,\epsilon\, V - T$ is called the *initial symbol*. Sometimes $V - T$ is called the *auxiliary vocabulary*.

Note that the rewriting rules may contain productions of the form

$$\nu \to \Lambda \qquad \nu \,\epsilon\, V - T$$

The rules exclude productions of the form

$$\nu \to \nu$$

since such productions accomplish nothing.

---

† ALGOL is not a context-free language. Occasionally the phrase *ALGOL-like languages* is used as a synonym for context-free languages. This can lead to true sentences like "ALGOL is not an ALGOL-like language."

It should be noticed that phrase structure grammars are examples of the so-called semi-Thue systems discussed by Davis.

Definition 4. *y directly generates z* in G, symbolically $y \Rightarrow z$, iff there exist strings $u, v \in V^*$ such that $y = uvv$, $z = uxv$ and $(v \to x) \in P$.

Definition 5. *y generates z* in G, $(y \overset{*}{\Rightarrow} z)$, iff there exist strings $z_0, \ldots , z_r$ $(r \geq 0)$ such that $y = z_0, z_0 \Rightarrow z_1, \ldots , z_{r-1} \Rightarrow z_r$, and $z_r = z$.

EXAMPLE.   Let $V = \{\sigma, \alpha, \beta, 0, 1\}$, $T = \{0,1\}$; the rules are

$$\sigma \to \alpha\beta$$
$$\alpha \to 0$$
$$\beta \to 1$$

Consider $\sigma \overset{*}{\Rightarrow} 01$. We might have $\sigma \Rightarrow \alpha\beta \Rightarrow 0\beta \Rightarrow 01$ or $\sigma \Rightarrow \alpha\beta \Rightarrow \alpha1 \Rightarrow 01$. It is convenient to represent the derivation by a generation tree, Fig. 1. Such trees are read in lexicographic order. For example, in the tree shown in Fig. 2 the resulting generation is $\sigma \overset{*}{\Rightarrow} 0100$.

Proposition 6. $\overset{*}{\Rightarrow}$ is reflexive and transitive.

PROOF.   For any $y \in V^*$, choose $r = 0$, $z_0 = y = z_r$ so that $y \overset{*}{\Rightarrow} y$. Transitivity is clear. ▌

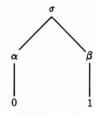

FIG. 1

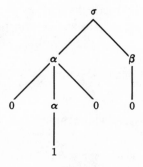

FIG. 2

Theorem 7. If $x_i \overset{*}{\Rightarrow} y_i$ $(i = 1, \ldots, n)$, then $x_1 \cdots x_n \overset{*}{\Rightarrow} y_1 \cdots y_n$.

PROOF.   It is sufficient to show the result for $n = 2$. Suppose $x_1 \overset{*}{\Rightarrow} y_1$; then there exist $z_0, \ldots, z_r$ such that $z_0 = x_1$, $z_r = y_1$, and $z_{i-1} \Rightarrow z_i$ for $i = 1, \ldots, r$. Similarly, there exist $w_0, \ldots, w_s$, where $w_0 = x_2$, $w_s = y_2$, and $w_{i-1} \Rightarrow w_i$ for $i = 1, \ldots, s$. Define $t_{2k} = z_k w_k$ and $t_{2k+1} = z_{k+1} w_k$ for $k = 0, \ldots, \min(r,s)$. For completeness, define $z_i = z_r$ for $i > r$ and $w_j = w_s$ for $j > s$. Clearly,

$$t_0 = z_0 w_0 = x_1 x_2 \quad \text{and} \quad t_{\max(r,s)} = z_r w_s = y_1 y_2$$

Note that $t_{i-1} \Rightarrow t_i$ for $i = 1, \ldots, \max(r,s)$. ∎

Theorem 8. If $x \overset{*}{\Rightarrow} y$ and $x = x_1 \cdots x_n$, then there exist words y_i $(i = 1, \ldots, n)$ such that $x_i \overset{*}{\Rightarrow} y_i$ and $y = y_1 \cdots y_n$.

PROOF.   The argument is an induction on the number of z's in the generation of y from x.

BASIS. $r = 0$; if $x = x_1 \cdots x_n$, then $y = x$ and $y_i = x_i$. $x_i \overset{*}{\Rightarrow} y_i$, since $y_i = x_i$. The result can also be quickly checked for $r = 1$.

INDUCTION STEP.   Assume the result true for all generation trees of length r. Consider a generation of length $r + 1$ from x to y. We have $z_0 = x$, $z_{r+1} = y$, and $z_i \Rightarrow z_{i+1}$ for $i = 0, \ldots, r$.

Note that $x \Rightarrow z_1$ and $z_1 \overset{*}{\Rightarrow} y$, where the length of the generation tree from z_1 to y is r. Since $x \Rightarrow z_1$, $x = u\nu v$ and $z_1 = uwv$, where $(\nu \to w) \epsilon P$. If $x = x_1 \cdots x_n$, let x_k be that string which contains ν. Define $t_i = x_i$ for $i = 1, \ldots, n$, but $i \neq k$ and $t_k = w$. Using $z_1 = t_1 \cdots t_n$, $z_1 \overset{*}{\Rightarrow} y$, and the induction hypothesis, there exist $y_1, \ldots, y_n$ such that $t_i \overset{*}{\Rightarrow} y_i$ and $y = y_1 \cdots y_n$. By transitivity, $x_i \overset{*}{\Rightarrow} y_i$ for $i = 1, \ldots, n$. ∎

Now we come to the sentences generated by these grammars. Intuitively, a sentence is a string produced from the initial symbol σ (standing for sentence) by repeated application of the rewriting rules. We also require that only terminals appear in the string. More carefully, we have the following definition.

Definition 9. x is a *sentence* of the grammar $G = \langle V, P, \sigma, T \rangle$ iff $\sigma \overset{*}{\Rightarrow} x$ and $x \epsilon T^*$. The *language generated by the grammar* G is denoted by

$$L(G) = \{x \mid x \epsilon T^* \wedge \sigma \overset{*}{\Rightarrow} x\}$$

A language L is said to be a *context-free language* iff there exists a context-free grammar G such that $L = L(G)$.

EXAMPLE.

$$G = \langle \{0,1,\sigma\}, P, \sigma, \{0,1\} \rangle \quad \text{where } P = \begin{Bmatrix} \sigma \to 0\sigma0 \\ \sigma \to 1 \end{Bmatrix}$$

A few generation trees for this language are shown in Fig. 3. Clearly, for our example, $L(G) = \{0^n 1 0^n \mid n \geq 0\}$. It should be noted that $L(G)$ is not regular. It will be shown shortly that every regular set is a context-free language. Thus the context-free languages are a generalization of the regular sets.

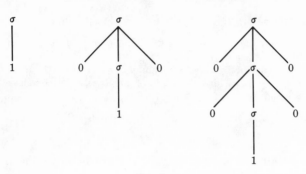

FIG. 3

EXAMPLE. $G = \langle \{0,1,\sigma\},P,\sigma,\{0,1\}\rangle$
where P contains

$$\sigma \to 0\sigma0$$
$$\sigma \to 1\sigma1$$
$$\sigma \to \Lambda$$

The language generated by G is given by

$$L(G) = \{xx^T | x \in T^*\}$$

PROBLEMS

1. If β is any infinite regular set contained in Σ^* show that $\{x\,\#\,x^T | x \in \beta, \; \# \notin \Sigma\}$ is not regular. This set is often called a *mirror language*. Is a similar result true without the center symbol $\#$?

2. Examine the examples of nonregular sets in Chap. 10. Give context-free grammars for as many of these sets as possible.

3. What is the language generated by the grammar shown below?

$$\sigma \to \sigma0$$
$$\sigma \to \alpha1$$
$$\alpha \to 0\alpha0$$
$$\alpha \to 1$$

4. Show that no infinite subset of the mirror language is regular. Cf. Prob. 1.

4   FINITE AUTOMATA AND LINEAR LANGUAGES

The first step in investigating the relations between machines and grammars is to show that every regular set is a language. This is easy.

Theorem 1. Given a finite automaton $S = \langle S,M,a,F\rangle$, there exists a context-free grammar G equivalent to S in the sense that $L(G) = \beta_S$. That is, every regular set is a context-free language.

PROOF. If S has input alphabet A, then choose $G = \langle V,P,a,A\rangle$, where $V = S \cup A$ (assuming $S \cap A = \emptyset$, which we may do with no loss of generality) and

$$P = \{s \to \alpha M(s,\alpha)|\alpha \in A, s \in S\} \cup \{s \to \Lambda|s \in F\}$$

$x \in L(G)$ iff $x \in A^*$ and $a \overset{*}{\Rightarrow} x$.   By the nature of the rules in P, $x \in A^*$, $a \overset{*}{\Rightarrow} x$ iff $x = ys$, where $y \in A^*$, $s = rp_S(y)$, and $s \to \Lambda$.   Thus $rp_S(x) = rp_S(y)$ and is in F.   We have shown $x \in L(G)$ iff $x \in \beta_S$. $\blacksquare$

The grammar constructed in the proof of Theorem 1 has a very special form.   The rules were of the form $\nu \to x\rho$ and $\mu \to y$.   Such a grammar is called a *right-linear grammar*.   It is convenient to define the various types of linear grammars at this time.

Definition 2.   A rule is called *right (left) linear* iff it is of the form $\nu \to x\rho$ ($\nu \to \rho x$) where $\nu, \rho \in V - T$, $x \in T^*$.   A rule is called *terminating* iff it is of the form $\nu \to x$ with $x \in T^*$.   A rule is called *linear* iff it is of the form $\nu \to x\rho y$ with $\nu, \rho \in V - T$; $x, y \in T^*$.   A grammar is called *right (left) linear* iff all of its rules are right (left) linear or terminating.   A grammar is *linear* iff all its rules are linear or terminating.   A grammar is *metalinear* iff each production is linear or of the form $\sigma \to x$ with $x \in V^*$ and there is no rule of the form $\nu \to x\sigma y$ where σ is the initial symbol, and $x, y, \in V^*$.

We have seen that every finite automaton gives rise to a right linear grammar.   The converse is also true (Prob. 1).

It is convenient to derive a substitution result of some generality.   First, a preliminary lemma is needed.

Lemma 3.   If $G = \langle V, P, \sigma, T \rangle$ is a context-free grammar and $\mu \in V - T$ is an auxiliary symbol, then let a new symbol $\rho \notin V$ be substituted for μ wherever it appears.   The modified grammar generates the same language as G.

PROOF.   The argument is an obvious induction on the length of the generation trees. $\blacksquare$

Theorem 4.   Let $M \subseteq U^*$ be a language and let φ map every $u \in U$ into a language $L_u \subseteq T_u^*$.   Let $L \subseteq (\bigcup_{u \in U} T_u)^*$ be constructed by substituting a string from L_u for each occurrence of u in a sentence of M, i.e.,

$$L = \{ y_{u_1} \cdots y_{u_k} | u_i \in U, y_{u_i} \in L_{u_i}, i = 1, \ldots, k, u_1 \cdots u_k \in M, k \geq 0 \}$$

L is a context-free language, and a grammar generating L can be constructed from the grammars which generate M and L_u with $u \in U$.

PROOF. M is generated by $G_M = \langle V_M, P_M, \sigma_M, U \rangle$.   For every $u \in U$, construct G_u which generates L_u where

$$G_u = \langle V_u, P_u, \sigma_u, T_u \rangle$$

Assume that all auxiliary vocabularies are disjoint.   If they are not disjoint, we use Lemma 3 to make them disjoint.   Define $G = \langle V, P, \sigma, T \rangle$, where

$$V = (V_M - U) \cup \bigcup_{u \in U} V_u \qquad T = \bigcup_{u \in U} T_u \qquad \text{and} \qquad P = P_M' \cup \bigcup_{u \in U} P_u$$

P_M' is obtained from P_M by substituting σ_u, the initial symbol of G_u, for all occurrences of $u \in U$ in every production.

$x \, \epsilon \, L$ implies x is generated by G, because σ first generates $\sigma_{u_1} \cdots \sigma_{u_k}$ from σ_M by applying P_M and y_{u_i} is obtained from σ_{u_i} by applying P_{u_i} for $i = 1, \ldots, k$.

Conversely, the argument is an induction on the length of the generation trees. $\blacksquare$

Corollary 5. If L is a language, $L \subseteq T^*$, and φ a homomorphism of T^* into U^*, then $\varphi(L)$ is a language.

We note that Theorem 4 and Corollary 5 also hold for regular sets.

PROBLEMS

1. Show that the languages generated by right-linear grammars are regular.

2. Show that all the left-linear languages are regular sets and conversely.

3. Show that there are linear languages which are not one-sided linear; i.e., one-sided means either left or right linear.

4. Show that there are metalinear languages which are not linear languages.

5 SOME USEFUL REDUCTIONS

It is important to be able to remove productions of the form $\nu \rightarrow \Lambda$ and $\nu \rightarrow \rho$, $\rho \, \epsilon \, V$. In other words, there are advantages to considering grammars with strictly length-increasing productions. We shall first work on eliminating rules of the form $\nu \rightarrow \Lambda$. It is useful to have an algorithm for deciding if $\Lambda \, \epsilon \, L(G)$.

Lemma 1. There is an algorithm for determining if $\Lambda \, \epsilon \, L(G)$.

PROOF. Define
$$V_1 = \{\nu | \nu \, \epsilon \, V - T \wedge (\nu \rightarrow \Lambda) \, \epsilon \, P\}$$
$$V_{k+1} = V_k \cup \{\nu | \nu \, \epsilon \, V - T \wedge (\exists x)_{V_k^*} \quad (\nu \rightarrow x) \, \epsilon \, P\} \qquad k = 1, \ldots$$

It is clear that all the V_k are finite and the construction is effective.

Note that $V_k \subseteq V_{k+1}$. V_{k+1} is the set of all letters which directly generate strings over V_k. Obviously, $V_k = V_{k+1}$ implies $V_k = V_l$ for every $l > k$. The chain must break off after $|V - T| = n$ steps. Let $V_n = \hat{V}$. It is clear that

$$\hat{V} = \{\nu | \nu \stackrel{*}{\Rightarrow} \Lambda\}$$

Thus $\Lambda \, \epsilon \, L(G)$ iff $\sigma \stackrel{*}{\Rightarrow} \Lambda$ iff $\sigma \, \epsilon \, \hat{V} = V_n$. Thus a constructive procedure has been given for deciding if $\Lambda \, \epsilon \, L(G)$. $\blacksquare$

EXAMPLE. Consider the grammar

$$\sigma \rightarrow \alpha\beta$$
$$\sigma \rightarrow 0$$
$$\alpha \rightarrow \Lambda$$
$$\beta \rightarrow \alpha\gamma$$
$$\gamma \rightarrow \Lambda$$

$$V_1 = \{\alpha, \gamma\}$$
$$V_2 = \{\alpha, \gamma\} \cup \{\beta\}$$
$$V_3 = \{\alpha, \beta, \gamma\} \cup \{\sigma\} = V_4 = \cdots$$

Thus all the nonterminals produce Λ and, in particular $\Lambda \, \epsilon \, L(G)$.

We can use the methods of Lemma 1 to reduce a grammar to a grammar without null rules.

Theorem 2. Given a grammar $G = \langle V,P,\sigma,T \rangle$, there exists a grammar $G' = \langle V,P',\sigma,T \rangle$ with no null rules such that

$$L(G') = \begin{cases} L(G) - \{\Lambda\} & \text{if } \Lambda \,\epsilon\, L(G) \\ L(G) & \text{otherwise} \end{cases}$$

PROOF. $P' = \{\nu \to x | x \neq \Lambda \wedge (\exists(\nu \to y))_P,$ x is obtained from y by omitting some (possibly no) elements of $V_n\}$. V_n is defined in the proof of Lemma 4. In other words, throw away the null rules and take the remaining rules and delete some of the auxiliaries which generate Λ. There is one special case; if $y \,\epsilon\, \hat{V}^*$ and $y \neq \Lambda$, then do not delete all the variables at once since that would produce $\nu \to \Lambda$.

Suppose that $\sigma \overset{*}{\Rightarrow} x$ in G' where $x \neq \Lambda$. There are strings $z_0, \ldots, z_r$ such that $\sigma = z_0$, $x = z_r$, and $z_i \Rightarrow z_{i+1}$ for $i = 1, \ldots, r - 1$. Each rule of P', say $\nu \to y$, has the property that there is a rule $(\nu \to y') \,\epsilon\, P$ where y' has y as a subsequence and furthermore the only symbols of y' which are not in y are variables of $\hat{V}$. Since the extra symbols in y' generate only Λ, it is clear that if $(\nu \to y) \,\epsilon\, P'$, then $\nu \to y' \overset{*}{\Rightarrow} y$ in G. Thus every string x in $L(G')$ is in $L(G)$.

Suppose that $\sigma \overset{*}{\Rightarrow} x$ in G where $x \neq \Lambda$. We sketch an induction on the length of the tree. Suppose $\sigma \Rightarrow v_1 \cdots v_k$ $x \overset{*}{\Rightarrow}$ where $v_i \,\epsilon\, V$. By Theorem 3-8, $x = b_1 \cdots b_k$, $b_i \,\epsilon\, T^*$ and $v_i \overset{*}{\Rightarrow} b_i$ for $i = 1, \ldots k$, furthermore $k > 0$ since $x \neq \Lambda$. The tree is shown in Fig. 1. Again because $x \neq \Lambda$, some of the b_i's are different from Λ. For any $b_j \neq \Lambda$, $v_j \overset{*}{\Rightarrow} b_j$ in G' by the induction hypothesis. For those v_{i_j} which generate Λ, $\sigma \Rightarrow v_1 \cdots v_k$ with v_{i_j} crossed out for all those v_{i_j} such that $v_{i_j} \overset{*}{\Rightarrow} \Lambda$ is a rule of P'; thus the whole generation is in P'. ∎

EXAMPLE.   Let the grammar G be given by

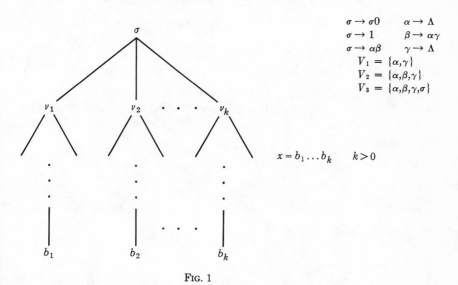

$$\begin{aligned} \sigma &\to \sigma 0 & \alpha &\to \Lambda \\ \sigma &\to 1 & \beta &\to \alpha\gamma \\ \sigma &\to \alpha\beta & \gamma &\to \Lambda \\ V_1 &= \{\alpha,\gamma\} \\ V_2 &= \{\alpha,\beta,\gamma\} \\ V_3 &= \{\alpha,\beta,\gamma,\sigma\} \end{aligned}$$

$x = b_1 \ldots b_k \qquad k > 0$

FIG. 1

The new set P' of rules are given

$$
\begin{array}{lll}
\sigma \to \sigma 0 & \sigma \to 0 & \sigma \to \alpha \\
\beta \to \alpha\gamma & \sigma \to 1 & \sigma \to \beta \\
\beta \to \alpha & \sigma \to \alpha\beta & \beta \to \gamma
\end{array}
$$

It is clear that $\sigma \to \alpha\beta$, $\sigma \to \alpha$, and $\sigma \to \beta$ can produce nothing. Note that if we allowed rules in which all elements of V_n were deleted, we would have deleted α and β from $\sigma \to \alpha\beta$ to produce $\sigma \to \Lambda$, and that would defeat our purpose.

Our next step is to show that it is possible to dispense with rules of the form

$$
\nu_i \to \nu_j \qquad \nu_i \,\epsilon\, V - T,\ \nu_j \,\epsilon\, V
$$

Theorem 3. If $G = \langle V,P,\sigma,T \rangle$ is a grammar with no null rules, one can effectively construct $G' = \langle V,P',\sigma,T \rangle$ such that

$$
(\forall x)_{T*} \quad \lg(x) \geq 2 \Rightarrow (x \,\epsilon\, L(G) \Leftrightarrow x \,\epsilon\, L(G'))
$$

where G' does not contain any rule of the form

$$
\nu_i \to \nu_j \qquad \text{with } \nu_i \epsilon\, V - T,\ \nu_j \,\epsilon\, V
$$

Furthermore, there is an algorithm for deciding if $t \,\epsilon\, L(G)$, where $t \,\epsilon\, T$.

PROOF.   Define for every $\nu \,\epsilon\, V$

$$
V_1(\nu) = \{\nu\}
$$
$$
V_{k+1}(\nu) = V_k(\nu) \,\cup\, \{\mu | \mu \,\epsilon\, V \,\wedge\, (\exists \lambda)_{V_k(\nu)} \quad (\lambda \to \mu) \,\epsilon\, P\}
$$

Clearly, $V_1(\nu) \subseteq \cdots \subseteq V_{n-1}(\nu) \subseteq V_n(\nu) = V_{n+1}(\nu) = \cdots$, where $n = |V|$. Clearly, $V_n(\nu) = \{\mu | \nu \overset{*}{\Rightarrow} \mu\}$, and the construction of $V_n(\nu)$ is effective. Note that $t \,\epsilon\, L(G)$ iff $\sigma \overset{*}{\Rightarrow} t \,\wedge\, t \,\epsilon\, T$, that is, $t \,\epsilon\, T \,\cap\, V_n(\sigma)$.

We construct P' by passing from P to $\hat{P}$ and then to P'. Define

$$
\hat{P} = \{\nu \to x | \lg(x) \geq 2 \,\wedge\, (\exists \mu)_{V_n(\nu)} \quad (\mu \to x) \,\epsilon\, P\}
$$

Define

$$
P' = \{\nu \to t_1 \cdots t_r | (\exists (\nu \to \rho_1 \cdots \rho_r))_{\hat{P}} \; t_j \,\epsilon\, V_n(\rho_j),\ 1 \leq j \leq r\}
$$

If $\sigma \overset{*}{\Rightarrow} x$ in G', then clearly $\sigma \overset{*}{\Rightarrow} x$ in G. The converse is easily proved by induction. ∎

These theorems enable us to determine if there are any words of length at most 1 in $L(G)$ and what they are. The grammar can then be effectively modified to a grammar with rules which are strictly length increasing.

EXAMPLE.   Consider the grammar

$$
\begin{array}{ll}
\sigma \to \alpha\beta & \alpha \to 0 \\
\alpha \to \sigma\alpha & \beta \to 1
\end{array}
$$

$$
V_5(\sigma) = \{\sigma\} \qquad V_5(\alpha) = \{\alpha,0\} \qquad V_5(\beta) = \{\beta,1\} \qquad V_5(0) = \{0\} \qquad V_5(1) = \{1\}
$$

Note that $0 \,\epsilon\, V_5(\alpha) \,\cap\, T$ and $1 \,\epsilon\, V_5(\beta) \,\cap\, T$.

$$
\hat{P} = \left\{ \begin{array}{l} \sigma \to \alpha\beta \\ \alpha \to \sigma\alpha \end{array} \right\}
$$
$$
P' = \{\sigma \to \alpha\beta,\ \sigma \to 0\beta,\ \sigma \to \alpha 1,\ \sigma \to 01,\ \alpha \to \sigma\alpha,\ \alpha \to \sigma 0\}
$$

It is easy to check that the language generated by P' is the same as the original language except for the strings of length 1.

We can now use a finiteness argument to give a very important necessary condition for a set to be a context-free language. We shall often use this theorem in proving that certain sets are not languages.

Theorem 4. Let $G = \langle V,P,\sigma,T \rangle$ be a grammar with strictly length-increasing rules. There exist natural numbers p and q such that if $z \,\epsilon\, L(G)$ and $\mathrm{lg}(z) > p$, then

$$z = xuwvy$$

where $u \neq \Lambda$ or $v \neq \Lambda$, $\mathrm{lg}(uwv) \leq q$, and all the strings z_k are in $L(G)$.

$$z_k = xu^k wv^k y \qquad \text{for } k = 1, 2, \ldots$$

PROOF. Let $n = |V|$. Consider all generation trees of G in which every path has length $\leq n$. The number of all such trees is finite. Let p be the maximal length of all terminal strings generated by these trees. Any string $z \,\epsilon\, L(G)$ such that $\mathrm{lg}(z) > p$ comes from a path whose length $> n$. Let $\nu_1 \cdots \nu_r (r > n)$ occur on a *longest* path in that tree. The sequence $\nu_{r-n}, \ldots, \nu_r$ [of length $r - (r - n) + 1 = n + 1$] must contain one symbol at least twice. Suppose $\nu_i = \nu_j = \nu$, $r - n \leq i < j \leq r$. Extract the subtree with root ν_i. In this tree $\nu_i \overset{*}{\Rightarrow} u'\nu_j v' = u'\nu_i v'$ and $\nu \overset{*}{\Rightarrow} u'vv'$ $\overset{*}{\Rightarrow} uwv$, where $u' \overset{*}{\Rightarrow} u$, $v' \overset{*}{\Rightarrow} v$, and $\nu \overset{*}{\Rightarrow} w$. Since G has only length-increasing rules, $u \neq \Lambda$ or $v \neq \Lambda$, where uwv is the string that ν finally generates; that is, it is a solid substring of z, namely, $z = xuwvy$.

The derivation $\nu \overset{*}{\Rightarrow} u'vv'$, $u' \overset{*}{\Rightarrow} u$, $v' \overset{*}{\Rightarrow} v$ can be repeated to yield $\nu \overset{*}{\Rightarrow} (u')^k \nu (v')^k \overset{*}{\Rightarrow}$ $u^k vv^k$. Finally, $\sigma \overset{*}{\Rightarrow} xu^k wv^k y$. Note that $\nu_{r-n} \cdots \nu_r$ is a longest path of the subtree. Thus the length of all subpaths in the subtree is bounded; thus $\mathrm{lg}(uwv) \leq q$. ∎

EXAMPLE. The proof of Theorem 4 may be illustrated by the following diagram of a typical subtree. The heavy line illustrates the maximal path under considera-

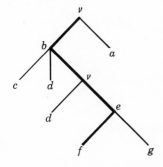

FIG. 2

tion. We have $\nu_i = \nu_j = \nu$. Clearly, $\nu \overset{*}{\Rightarrow} cd\nu a$; also $a \overset{*}{\Rightarrow} a$, $cd \overset{*}{\Rightarrow} cd$, and $\nu \overset{*}{\Rightarrow} dfg$. By repetition, $\nu \overset{*}{\Rightarrow} (cd)^k dfga^k$.

We shall now use this theorem to show that a particular set is not a language.

Theorem 5. $L = \{0^n1^n0^n | n \geq 1\}$ is not a context-free language.

PROOF.   Assume it is a language and represent it by a grammar G which has only length-increasing rules.   For every natural number n there is a production $\sigma \overset{*}{\Rightarrow} 0^n1^n0^n$. Let p be as in the proof of Theorem 4.   Then

$$0^p1^p0^p = xuwvy \qquad uv \neq \Lambda \qquad \text{and} \qquad xu^kwv^ky \in L$$

for $k = 1, 2, \ldots.$ The proof consists in showing that none of $x, u, w, v,$ or y can contain a 1.

CASE 1.   Suppose x contains a 1.   Then there exists $z \in \{0,1\}^*$ $x = 0^p1z$.   Let $t = xu^{2p}wv^{2p}y = 0^p1zu^{2p}wv^{2p}y \in L$.   Thus $t = 0^p1^p0^p$.   We   have $\lg(t) = 3p$ and $\lg(t) \geq 3p + 1$ which is a contradiction.   Symmetry disposes of the case where y contains a 1.

CASE 2.   Suppose $x \in 0^*$ and u contains a 1.
(a) Suppose there is a 0 in u.   Then $u = 0^i1z$ or $u = z10^i$ for some $i \geq 1$.   Then $xu^2wv^2y \in L$ and has a solid subtape $1z0^i1$ or 10^iz1 which contradicts that there is a 0 in u.
(b) Suppose $u = 1^j$ for $j \geq 1$.   Then $x = 0^p$.   Let $z = xu^{2p}wv^{2p}y = 0^p1^{2jp}wv^{2p}y \in L$, but $z = 0^p1^p0^p$ which is a contradiction.   The argument is similar if v contains a 1.

CASE 3.   Suppose there is a 1 in w and $xuvy \in 00^*$.   Let $r = \lg(w)$.   Then

$$xu^{2r}wv^{2r}y = 0^iw0^j \in L$$

which is a contradiction since $i > r$ or $j > r$. ∎

PROBLEMS

1.   Given the following grammar G, replace G by an equivalent grammar with length-increasing rules.   What is $L(G)$?

$$\begin{aligned} \sigma &\to \Lambda & \sigma &\to \alpha111\alpha \\ \sigma &\to 0\alpha & \sigma &\to \alpha000\alpha \\ \sigma &\to 11\alpha & \alpha &\to 0\alpha \\ \sigma &\to \alpha11 & \alpha &\to 1\alpha \\ \sigma &\to \alpha010\alpha & \alpha &\to \Lambda \end{aligned}$$

2.   Estimate p and q in Theorem 4.

3.   Show that $\{0^n10^n10^n | n \geq 0\}$ is not a language.

4.   Show that the set $\{a^nb^nc^n | n \geq 1\}$ is not a context-free language.

6   CLOSURE PROPERTIES OF LANGUAGES

We shall now check to see if languages are closed under some of the same operations as regular sets.

Theorem 1.   Every finite set is a context-free language.   If L is a context-free language, so is L^T.   If L is a context-free language, so is L^*.

PROOF.   If $L = \{x_1, \ldots, x_n\} \subseteq T^*$, choose $\sigma \notin T$ and define $G = \langle T \cup \{\sigma\}, P, \sigma, T \rangle$, where

$$P = \begin{Bmatrix} \sigma \to x_1 \\ \sigma \to x_2 \\ \cdot \cdot \cdot \cdot \\ \sigma \to x_n \end{Bmatrix}$$

$L(G) = L$.

Suppose that L is a language generated by $G = \langle V, P, \sigma, T \rangle$.   Then define $G^T = \langle V, P^T, \sigma, T \rangle$, where

$$P^T = \{\nu \to x^T | (\nu \to x) \in P\}$$

Clearly, $L(G^T) = L^T$.

Finally, suppose that L is a language generated by $G = \langle V, P, \sigma, P \rangle$ and ρ is a new symbol not in V.   Define $G^* = \langle V \cup \{\rho\}, P^*, \rho, T \rangle$, where

$$P^* = P \cup \{\rho \to \sigma\rho,\, \rho \to \Lambda\}$$

Clearly, $L(G^*) = L^*$. ▮

Theorem 2.   If L_1 and L_2 are context-free languages, then $L_1 \cup L_2$ and

$$L_1 L_2 = \{xy | x \in L_1 \wedge y \in L_2\}$$

are context-free languages.

PROOF.   Let L_i be generated by $G_i = \langle V_i, P_i, \sigma_i, T_i \rangle$ for $i = 1, 2$.   It is necessary to have a disjointness property of the vocabularies.   Assume $(V_1 - T_1) \cap V_2 = \emptyset$ and $(V_2 - T_2) \cap V_1 = \emptyset$.   This results in no loss of generality, since, by Lemma 4.3, such a substitution does not change the language generated by the grammar.

Let ρ be a new symbol not in V_1 or in V_2.   Define $G_1 \cup G_2 = \langle V_1 \cup V_2 \cup \{\rho\}$, $P', \rho, T_1 \cup T_2 \rangle$, where

$$P' = P_1 \cup P_2 \cup \{\rho \to \sigma_1,\, \rho \to \sigma_2\}$$

Clearly, $L(G_1 \cup G_2) = L(G_1) \cup L(G_2) = L_1 \cup L_2$.

Let ρ be a new symbol not in V_1 or in V_2.   Define

$$G_1 G_2 = \langle V_1 \cup V_2 \cup \{\rho\},\, P',\, \rho,\, T_1 \cup T_2 \rangle$$

where $P' = P \cup \{\rho \to \sigma_1 \sigma_2\}$.   Note that $L(G_1 G_2) = L(G_1)L(G_2) = L_1 L_2$. ▮

It will now be shown that context-free languages are not closed under complementation or intersection.

Let $G = \langle \{\sigma, \alpha, \beta, 0, 1\}, P, \sigma, \{0, 1\} \rangle$, where

$$\begin{array}{ll} \sigma \to \alpha\beta & \beta \to 0\beta \\ \alpha \to 0\alpha 1 & \beta \to 0 \\ \alpha \to 01 & \end{array}$$

Using the α rules n times will produce $\alpha \overset{*}{\Rightarrow} 0^n 1^n$, and using the β rule k times will produce 0^k.   Thus

$$L = \{0^n 1^n 0^k | n, k \geq 1\}$$

By Theorem 1, $L^T = \{0^p 1^q 0^q | p, q \geq 1\}$ is also a language.   Clearly, the intersection of L and L^T is

$$L \cap L^T = \{0^n 1^n 0^n | n \geq 1\}$$

and we have already seen that this set is not a language.

Theorem 3.   The context-free languages are not closed under intersection or complementation.

PROOF.   We have already seen that the context-free languages are not closed under intersection.   If they were closed under complementation, they would be closed under intersection because

$$L_1 \cap L_2 = (\overline{\overline{L_1} \cup \overline{L_2}}) \quad \blacksquare$$

Unlike the regular sets, the context-free languages do not form a boolean algebra.

PROBLEMS

1.   Show that the metalinear languages are the closure of the linear languages under finite concatenation and union.

2.   Show that even the linear languages with a single nonterminal symbol are not closed under either intersection or complementation.   (HINT: Choose $P_1 = \{\sigma \rightarrow 00\sigma 2, \sigma \rightarrow 1\sigma 2, \sigma \rightarrow 12\}$ and $P_2 = \{\sigma \rightarrow 0\sigma 22, \sigma \rightarrow 0\sigma 1, \sigma \rightarrow 01\}$.)

7   ALGORITHMS FOR DECIDABLE PROBLEMS

One of the pleasant features of our work with finite automata was that we were able to give algorithms for every interesting problem. For languages, the situation is more involved.   First we obtain some positive results.

Theorem 1.   There is a decision procedure for deciding if there exists $u, v \in V^*$ such that $v \overset{*}{\Rightarrow} uxv$, where $v \in V$, $x \in V^*$ under the assumption that G has no null rules.

PROOF.   We may assume that G has no rules of the form $v \rightarrow \Lambda$, where $v \in V - T$; we also assume $n = |V|$ and $\lg(x) = m$.   We define

$$R_1^m = \{y | \lg(y) \leq m \wedge (\exists u, v)_{V^*} \quad v \Rightarrow uyv\}$$
$$R_k^m = R_{k-1}^m \cup \{y | \lg(y) \leq m \wedge (\exists u, v, w) \quad w \in R_{k-1}^m \wedge w \Rightarrow uyv\}$$

Clearly, the R_k^m can be effectively constructed, since the definition involves $\Rightarrow$. $R_{k-1}^m \subseteq R_k^m$, $k = 2, \ldots$, and $R_{k-1}^m = R_k^m$ implies $R_{k-1}^m = R_{k+l}^m$ for all $l \geq 0$.   There exists an integer p such that $R_p^m = R_{p+1}^m$, and clearly

$$p \leq \frac{n^{m+1} - 1}{n - 1} - 1$$

Thus $x \in R_p^m$ iff $v \overset{*}{\Rightarrow} uxv$ for some $u, v \in V^*$.

$$[(\exists u, v)_{V^*} \quad v \overset{*}{\Rightarrow} uxv] \Leftrightarrow [(v = x) \vee (x = \Lambda) \vee (\exists k) \quad x \in R_k^m]$$
$$\Leftrightarrow [(v = x) \vee (x \in R_p^k)]$$

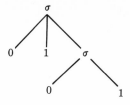

FIG. 1

Thus to decide if $\nu \overset{*}{\Rightarrow} uxv$, check to see if $\nu = x$. If it does not, construct R_p^m and see if $x \in R_p^m$. ▮

EXAMPLE. $\sigma \to 01\sigma$ Does $\sigma \overset{*}{\Rightarrow} u10v$ for some u, v?

       $\sigma \to 01$

Since $\sigma \neq x$, we start the construction

$$R_1^2 = \{\Lambda, 0, 1, 01, \sigma, 1\sigma\}$$
$$R_2^2 = R_1^2 \cup \{10\}$$
$$R_3^2 = R_2^2$$
$$10 \in R_2^2 \quad \text{so that } \sigma \overset{*}{\Rightarrow} u10v$$

In fact, a generation tree is given in Fig. 1.

Corollary 2. In a context-free grammar with no null rules, there is a decision procedure for deciding if $\nu \overset{*}{\Rightarrow} x$.

PROOF. Choose $u = v = \Lambda$ in the proof of Theorem 1. ▮

Corollary 3. In a context-free grammar with no null rules, there is an algorithm for determining if there exists $u \in V^*$ such that $\nu \overset{*}{\Rightarrow} ux$ and similarly if there exists $v \in V^*$ such that $\nu \overset{*}{\Rightarrow} xv$.

PROOF. $v = \Lambda$ and $u = \Lambda$, respectively. ▮

Corollary 4. In a context-free grammar with no null rules, there is an algorithm for deciding if there exist $u, v \in V^*$ such that $u \neq \Lambda$, $v \neq \Lambda$, $\nu \overset{*}{\Rightarrow} uxv$.

PROOF. The result holds iff

$$(\exists \rho_1, \rho_2)_V \; \nu \overset{*}{\Rightarrow} u\rho_1 x\rho_2 v \quad ▮$$

Corollary 5. In a context-free grammar with no null rules, there is a decision procedure for deciding if there is u, $u \neq \Lambda$ and $\nu \overset{*}{\Rightarrow} ux$, and similarly for deciding if $\exists v$, $v \neq \Lambda$ and $\nu \overset{*}{\Rightarrow} xv$.

As another corollary, we get an important result.

Corollary 6. There is an algorithm for deciding if $x \in L(G)$.

PROOF. If $x = \Lambda$, use Lemma 5.1. We effectively replace G by a grammar with no null rules which generates the same language except for the null string (Theorem 5.2). For $x \neq \Lambda$, we decide if $\sigma \overset{*}{\Rightarrow} x$ by Corollary 2. ▮

Now we turn to the problem of telling if a grammar generates a nonvoid word.

Theorem 7. Given a context-free grammar $G = \langle V,P,\sigma,T \rangle$, there is a decision procedure for deciding if $L(G) = \emptyset$.

PROOF. Let $T_0 = T$ and define

$$T_j = T_{j-1} \cup \{\nu | (\exists x) T^*_{j-1} \nu \Rightarrow x\}$$

$T_{j-1} \subseteq T_j$. $T_{j-1} = T_j$ implies $T_{j-1} = T_{j+l}$ for all $l > 0$. If $|V - T| = r$, then the chain breaks off in at most r steps and $T_r = \bigcup\limits_{j=0}^{\infty} T_j$. Clearly, T_r is the set of elements of V which generates strings over T. $(\exists x)\ x \epsilon L(G) \Leftrightarrow (\exists x)\ \sigma \xrightarrow{*} x \wedge x \epsilon T^* \Leftrightarrow [(\exists k)\ \sigma \epsilon T_k] \Leftrightarrow \sigma \epsilon T_r$. Thus $L(G) = \emptyset$ iff $\sigma \notin T_r$. ∎

EXAMPLE. Consider $G = \langle \{0,1,\sigma,\mu\},P,\sigma,\{0,1\} \rangle$, where P contains

$$\sigma \to 10\sigma 10$$
$$\sigma \to \sigma 0$$
$$\mu \to 0$$
$$T_0 = \{0,1\}$$
$$T_1 = T_0 \cup \{\mu\}$$
$$T_2 = T_1 = \{0,1,\mu\}$$

Since $\sigma \notin T_1$, $L(G) = \emptyset$.

PROBLEMS

1. It is convenient to have a *reduced form* for grammars. The idea is to eliminate all symbols in V which do not occur in some generation starting from σ and also eliminate those nonterminals which do not generate terminal strings. Prove that for any grammar G, there exists a reduced grammar G' such that $L(G) = L(G')$ and G' is in reduced form. Give an algorithm for constructing G'.

2. Let $G = \langle V,P,\sigma,T \rangle$ be a grammar. A symbol $\nu \epsilon V - T$ is called *an embedding symbol* iff there exist $u,\ v \epsilon V^*$ such that $u \neq \Lambda$ or $v \neq \Lambda$ and $\nu \xrightarrow{*} u\nu v$. Show that the language generated by a reduced grammar with length-increasing rules is infinite iff G has an embedding symbol.

3. Give an algorithm for determining if $L(G)$ is infinite.

4. In Prob. 2 is the condition "reduced grammar with length-increasing rules" necessary? Is the result true for just reduced grammars? Is the result true for just grammars with length-increasing rules?

5. A *context-sensitive* grammar is a system $G = \langle V,P,\sigma,T \rangle$ where V, σ, and T are as before. The rules P are of the form $x \to y$ where $x \epsilon V^*(V - T)V^*$, $y \epsilon V^*$, and $\lg(x) \leq \lg(y)$. Construct a context-sensitive grammar generating $\{0^n1^n0^n | n \geq 1\}$. Is there an algorithm for deciding if a given tape x is in $L(G)$ for a context-sensitive grammar G?

8 UNDECIDABLE PROBLEMS

One of the main differences between regular sets and languages is that there are many problems involving languages for which it is impossible to construct algorithms.

The usual method of establishing the unsolvability of a problem is to convert it to a problem which is known to be unsolvable. A very useful unsolvable problem is the *Post correspondence problem*, which can be stated as follows. Let $(a_1, \ldots ,a_n)$ and $(b_1, \ldots ,b_n)$ be two n-tuples of nonnull strings over some vocabulary V containing at least two symbols. Does there exist a sequence of indices $i_1, \ldots , i_k$ for $k \geq 1$ and $1 \leq i_j \leq n$ such that

$$a_{i_1} \cdots a_{i_k} = b_{i_1} \cdots b_{i_k} \tag{1}$$

Theorem 1. (Post[3]). The correspondence problem is recursively unsolvable when $|V| \geq 2$.

Notice that if there is one solution to the correspondence problem, then there are infinitely many solutions which are obtained by iteration of the one solution.

Summarizing, we get the following corollary.

Corollary 2. If $|V| \geq 2$ and if there is any solution to the correspondence problem, there are infinitely many solutions to the problem.

We now code the correspondence problem in a particular way.

Lemma 3. Given two lists of n symbols $\{a_i\}$ and $\{b_i\}$, the set

$$L = \{a_{i_1} \cdots a_{i_r}\#b_{i_r}{}^T \cdots b_{i_1}{}^T | r \geq 1\}$$

is a language.

PROOF. The reader can easily verify that the following grammar generates L.

$$\sigma \to a_i \sigma b_i{}^T \qquad i = 1, \ldots, n$$
$$\sigma \to a_i \# b_i{}^T \qquad i = 1, \ldots, n$$

where $G = \langle \{a_i, b_i, \sigma, \#\}, P, \sigma, \{a_i, b_i, \#\} \rangle$ ▮

Theorem 4. No algorithm exists for determining if the intersection of two context-free languages is empty, infinite, or regular when $|T| \geq 3$.

PROOF. Take L as in Lemma 3 and intersect it with the mirror language $L_M = \{x\#x^T | x \in T^*\}$. $x \in L \cap L_M$ iff there is a sequence of integers $i_1, \ldots , i_r$ such that $a_{i_1} \cdots a_{i_r} = b_{i_1} \cdots b_{i_r}$. How many elements are there in $L \cap L_m$? By Corollary 2, there are either none or infinitely many, but there is no algorithm for deciding which.

Since no infinite subset of L_m is regular (Prob. 3.5), $L \cap L_m$ is regular just in case it is finite, i.e., empty. ▮

By a more complex argument, Bar-Hillel, Perles, and Shamir have shown the following result.

Theorem 5. There is no algorithm for deciding if the complement of a context-free language is empty, finite, regular, or context-free.

Corollary 6. Given a grammar $G = \langle V, P, \sigma, T \rangle$, there is no algorithm for deciding if $L(G) = T^*$ or if $L(G)$ is regular.

Another problem of importance in automata theory is deciding if two automata have the same behavior.   By now, experience should suggest a pessimistic attitude toward the same problem for languages.

Theorem 7.   There is no algorithm for deciding if two context-free languages are equal or if one is contained in the other.

PROOF.   If one could decide if $L_1 \subseteq L_2$, one could decide equality.   If there were a decision procedure for equality, we could decide if $L = T^*$, which would contradict Corollary 6.   ∎

PROBLEMS

1.   Show that the complement of the mirror language $\{x \# x^T | x \in T^*\}$ is a language.

2.   Show that the complement of the double mirror language:

$$\{y \# x \# x^T \# y^T | x,y \in T^*\} = L_{m^2}$$

is a language.

3.   Show that the following set $L(a,b)$ is a language:

$$L(a,b) = \{\bar{\imath}_1 \cdots \bar{\imath}_k \# a_{i_k} \cdots a_{i_1} \# b_{j_1}{}^T \cdots b_{j_l}{}^T \# \bar{\jmath}_l{}^T \cdots \bar{\jmath}_1{}^T\}$$

where $\bar{\imath} = 10^i$; and similarly for $\bar{\jmath}$.

4.   Show that the complement of $L(a,b)$ is a language.

5.   Prove that there is no algorithm for deciding if the intersection of two languages is context-free.   [HINT: Consider $L(a,b) \cap L_{m^2}$.   Cf. Probs. 2 and 3.]

6.   Prove Theorem 5.

7.   Given a grammar $G = \langle V,P,\sigma,T \rangle$, a symbol ν is called *self-embedding* iff $(\exists u,v)\nu* \quad u \neq \Lambda,\ v \neq \Lambda,\ \nu \stackrel{*}{\Rightarrow} u\nu v$. G is called self-embedding iff G has a self-embedding symbol.   Show that this property is decidable.

8.   Prove that if G is not self-embedding, then $L(G)$ is regular.

9.   Problem 8 is an effective sufficient condition for a language to be regular. Prove that no effective necessary and sufficient condition can exist.

9   TWO FUNDAMENTAL THEOREMS

We shall now obtain some important theorems by a very useful and typical construction.   We shall prove that if a language is considered as a set of inputs to a sequential machine, then the set of outputs produced is again a language.   By a modification of the construction, it will be shown that the intersection of a language and a regular set is again a language.   This theorem is very useful, especially in proving that certain sets are not context-free languages.

Construction 1.   Given a sequential machine $S = \langle \Sigma,\Delta,S,f,s_0,g \rangle$ and a grammar $G = \langle V,P,\sigma,\Sigma \rangle$, we construct a grammar $G' = \langle V',P',\sigma',T' \rangle$, where

$$V' = (S \times V \times S) \cup \Delta \qquad \text{and} \qquad T' = \Delta$$

If $\nu \to \rho_1 \cdots \rho_k \epsilon P$, then P' contains

$$(s_i,\nu,s_j) \to (s_i,\rho_1,s_{i_1})(s_{i_1},\rho_2,s_{i_2})(s_{i_2},\rho_3,s_{i_3}) \cdots (s_{i_{k-1}},\rho_k,s_j)$$

for every possible sequence of states s_i, s_j, $s_{i_p} \epsilon S$. P' also contains $\sigma' \to (s_0,\sigma,s_i)$ for $i = 0, \ldots, n$, and $(s,\tau,s') \to \delta$ iff $f(s,\tau) = s'$ and $g(s,\tau) = \delta$ for $\tau \epsilon \Sigma$ and $\delta \epsilon \Delta$.

The following theorem is important and frequently used.

Theorem 2. Let $S = \langle \Sigma,\Delta,S,f,s_0,g \rangle$ be a sequential machine and let $G = \langle V,P,\sigma,\Delta \rangle$ be a context-free grammar which generates a language L. Then $g(L) = \{g(s_0,x)|x \epsilon L\}$ is a language.

PROOF. We shall show that G' has language $g(L)$. Suppose $x \epsilon L$, where $x = \rho_1 \cdots \rho_m$. There must exist a generation for x, say, $\sigma \Rightarrow z_1 \Rightarrow \cdots \Rightarrow z_{r-1} \Rightarrow z_r = x = \rho_1 \cdots \rho_m$. Every time a rule of P is used in the generation of x in G, use the corresponding rule of G'. If $P_1, \ldots, P_m$ are the rules used in G and $P'_1, \ldots, P'_m$ are the corresponding rules of G', then a derivation of x in G' goes as follows: Let

$$u_0 = s_0 \quad \text{and} \quad rp_S(\rho_1 \cdots \rho_l) = u_l \quad l = 1, \ldots, m$$

or equivalently $f(u_i,\rho_{i+1}) = u_{i+1}$.

The derivation is

$$\sigma' \to (s_0,\sigma,s_j) \overset{P_1'}{\Rightarrow} (\quad) \cdots (\quad) \overset{P_2'}{\Rightarrow} \cdots \overset{P_n'}{\Rightarrow} (s_0,\rho_1,s_{i_1}) \cdots (s_{i_{m-1}},\rho_m,s_j)$$

Finally, we get $(s_0,\rho_1,s_{i_1}) \cdots (s_{i_{m-1}},\rho_m,s_j)$. Since the s_{i_k} and s_j can be chosen arbitrarily select

$$s_j = rp_s(x) \quad \text{and} \quad s_{i_r} = u_r$$

Then the result of the G' derivation is

$$(u_0,\rho_1,u_1)(u_1,\rho_2,u_2) \cdots (u_{m-1},\rho_m,u_m)$$

where $\quad u_i = f(u_{i-1},\rho_i) \quad i = 1, \ldots, m$

and $\quad g(u_{i-1},\rho_i) = \delta_i \quad i = 1, \ldots, m$

Use the rules

$$(u_{i-1},\rho_i,u_i) \to \delta_i \quad i = 1, \ldots, m$$

and the derivation of $g(s_0,x)$ in G' is complete.

Conversely, assume $\delta_1 \cdots \delta_m \epsilon L(G')$. It is easy to reverse the argument and find $x = \rho_1 \cdots \rho_m$ in L such that $g(s_0,x) = \delta_1 \cdots \delta_m$. ▌

We now prove another important theorem which can be obtained by a modification of the previous argument.

Theorem 3. If L is a language and R is a regular set, then $L \cap R$ is a language.

PROOF. Let G generate L, where $G = \langle V,P,\sigma,T \rangle$ and R is recognized by $S = \langle S,M,s_0,F \rangle$ over alphabet T. Assume that G has no null rules. Define $G' = \langle V',P',\sigma',T \rangle$, where

$$V' = (S \times V \times S) \cup T$$

P' contains the same types of rules corresponding to $\nu \to \rho_1 \cdots \rho_m$ as in Construction 1. Only the terminal and the initial rules change.

$$\sigma' \to (s_0, \sigma, s_f) \qquad s_f \in F$$

If $\qquad (\forall \tau)_T \quad M(s, \tau) = t \quad$ then $\quad (s, \tau, t) \to \tau \in P'$

Suppose that $x \in L \cap R$, where $x = \rho_1 \cdots \rho_m$. Clearly, there is a sequence of states $s_0, \ldots, s_m$ such that

$$s_i = M(s_{i-1}, \rho_i) \qquad i = 1, \ldots, m$$

The following generation exists in G'.

$$\sigma' \to (s_0, \sigma, s_f) \qquad s_f \in F$$
$$\Downarrow *$$
$$(s_0, \rho_1, s_1)(s_1, \rho_2, s_2) \cdots (s_{m-1}, \rho_m, s_f) \, s_f \in F$$

Since $s_i = M(s_{i-1}, \rho_i)$, then $(s_{i-1}, \rho_i, s_i) \to \rho_i$

Thus $\qquad\qquad \sigma' \stackrel{*}{\Rightarrow} \rho_1 \cdots \rho_m$ and $x \in L(G')$

The argument is reversible. ▮

EXAMPLE. If $x \in T^*$, let $\#_a(x)$ denote the a's in the word x. Suppose $L_{abc} = \{x \mid \#_a(x) = \#_b(x) = \#_c(x)\}$ is a context-free language.

$$L_{abc} \cap a^* b^* c^* = \{a^n b^n c^n\}$$

which was proved to be a nonlanguage. Thus L_{abc} is not a context-free language.

The problem of ambiguity in languages is interesting and is related to a familiar problem in coding theory where codes with the unique decipherability property are important. Our discussion of this problem will be brief; it will be defined and proved to be unsolvable.

Definition 4. A grammar G is *ambiguous* if there is a string $x \in L(G)$ which has two different structural descriptions.

EXAMPLE. Consider the grammar

$$\sigma \to \sigma 1 \sigma \qquad \sigma \to 0$$

The string 01010 has two different generations shown in Fig. 1.

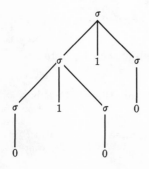 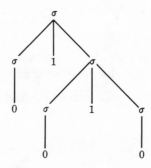

FIG. 1

The basic question about ambiguity is whether or not there is an algorithm to detect it.

Theorem 5. There is no algorithm for deciding if a context-free grammar is ambiguous.

PROOF. Suppose we have n elements a_i and n elements b_i in TT*. Pick n new symbols c_i and construct

$$G_1: \sigma_1 \rightarrow c_i \# a_i^T \qquad \sigma_1 \rightarrow c_i \sigma_1 a_i^T \qquad i = 1, \ldots, n$$
and
$$G_2: \sigma_2 \rightarrow c_i \# b_i^T \qquad \sigma_2 \rightarrow c_i \sigma_2 b_i^T \qquad i = 1, \ldots, n$$

It is easy to check that both G_1 and G_2 are unambiguous.

Consider the grammar $G_1 \cup G_2$, which consists of the rules for G_1, the rules for G_2, a new start symbol σ, and two additional rules $\sigma \rightarrow \sigma_1$, $\sigma \rightarrow \sigma_2$. A string can have two structural descriptions in $G_1 \cup G_2$ iff it has a generation in G_1 and a generation in G_2, that is,

$$c_{i_1} \cdots c_{i_r} \# a_{i_r}^T \cdots a_{i_1}^T = c_{i_1} \cdots c_{i_r} \# b_{i_r}^T \cdots b_{i_1}^T$$

The grammar is ambiguous iff there is an index sequence $i_1, \ldots, i_r$ such that $a_{i_1} \cdots a_{i_r} = b_{i_1} \cdots b_{i_r}$. The unsolvability of this problem follows from the Post correspondence theorem. █

A language may be ambiguous with respect to one grammar, but not ambiguous with respect to a second grammar.

Definition 6. A language L is *inherently ambiguous* iff every grammar for L is ambiguous.

It is not immediately clear that there are inherently ambiguous context-free languages.

Theorem 7. (Parikh) There exist inherently ambiguous languages.

PROOF. We shall give two examples that are inherently ambiguous, although we omit proofs.

$$\{x \mid x = 0^n 1^m 0^p 1^m \text{ or } 0^n 1^m 0^n 1^q, \, m,n,p,q \geq 1\}$$
$$\{0^n 1^m 2^p \mid n = m \text{ or } n = p\}$$

The following result is scarcely surprising.

Theorem 8. (Ginsburg-Ullian)   There is no algorithm for deciding if a context-free language is inherently ambiguous.

PROBLEMS

1. Given a context-free language L, prove that if a finite set is deleted from L, then the resulting set is also a language.

2. A *left transducer* or *generalized sequential machine* is defined as a system $S = \langle \Sigma, \Delta, S, f, a, g \rangle$, where $a \, \epsilon \, S$, and

$$f: S \times \Sigma \rightarrow S$$
$$g: S \times \Sigma \rightarrow \Delta^*$$

In other words, the response to a given input is a burst of output letters. A *right transducer* is defined in the analogous way except that the tape is read backwards. Show that right transducers and left transducers are not equivalent. (HINT: Consider the problem of designing a transducer which reproduces the input word if it ends in σ and prints Λ otherwise.)

3. A *transducer* is defined as $T = \langle \Sigma, \Delta, T, f_L, t_0, T', f_R, t_0', g \rangle$ where $\Sigma(\Delta)$ is the input alphabet, $T(T')$ are sets of states, t_0 and t_0' are the initial states, and f_L and f_R are the transition functions where f_L: $T \times \Sigma \to T$ and f_R: $T' \times \Sigma \to T'$. We write $t\sigma$ for $f_L(t,\sigma)$ and $\sigma t'$ for $f_R(t',\sigma)$. The output function g: $T \times \Sigma \times T' \to \Delta^*$ is intuitively the composition of a left and a right transducer. The rules for the extension of g are

$$g(t,\Lambda,t') = \Lambda$$
$$g(t,x\sigma,t') = g(t,x,\sigma t')g(tx,\sigma,t')$$

If β is regular and T is a transducer, show that $g(\beta) = \{g(t_0,x,t_0')\}|x \,\epsilon\, \beta\}$ is regular.

4. Show that β is regular iff there is a transduction g such that $g(\Sigma^*) = \beta$.

5. If L is a context-free language and g is a transduction, show that $g(L)$ is context-free.

6. Prove that, given two context-free languages L_1 and L_2 there is no algorithm for deciding if there exists a transduction g such that $g(L_1) = L_2$.

7. (Hodes) Show that the set of all well-formed formulas of the propositional (predicate) calculus is a context-free language. Show that the set of all theorems (closed formulas) of the propositional (predicate) calculus is not a context-free language.

8. Show that every regular set can be generated by an unambiguous context-free grammar.

10   SUMMARY AND HISTORY

In this chapter, we have studied the fundamentals of context-free languages. Our study of languages indicated the essential role which automata theory plays. In contrast to the regular sets, context-free

TABLE 1
Closure Properties of Regular Sets and Languages

Closed under	Regular sets	Context-free languages
Union	Yes	Yes
Intersection	Yes	No
Complementation	Yes	No
Transposition	Yes	Yes
Set product	Yes	Yes
*	Yes	Yes
Direct homomorphism	Yes	Yes
Inverse homomorphism	Yes	Yes
Sequential machine mapping	Yes	Yes
Transduction	Yes	Yes

TABLE 2
Decidability Questions for Regular Sets and Languages

Is there an algorithm for deciding if	α,β are regular	α,β are context-free languages
$x \in \alpha$	Yes	Yes
α is empty	Yes	Yes
α is finite	Yes	Yes
α is infinite	Yes	Yes
α is regular	Yes	No
$\alpha \subseteq \beta$	Yes	No
$\alpha = \beta$	Yes	No
$\alpha \cap \beta$ is empty	Yes	No
$\alpha \cap \beta$ is finite	Yes	No
$\alpha \cap \beta$ is regular	Yes	No
$\alpha \cap \beta$ is a context-free language	Yes	No
$\bar{\alpha}$ is empty	Yes	No
$\bar{\alpha}$ is finite	Yes	No
$\bar{\alpha}$ is regular	Yes	No
$\bar{\alpha}$ is a context-free language	Yes	No
α is inherently ambiguous	Yes	No
There exists a sequential machine mapping α into β	Yes	No
There exists a sequential machine mapping α onto β	Yes	No
There exists a left transducer mapping α into β such that the image of α is infinite when α is infinite	Yes	No
There exists a left transducer which maps α onto β	?	No

languages are very combinational and their theory is correspondingly more difficult. Many of the reasonable questions which arise do not have general solutions. In Table 1, the operations under which regular sets and languages are preserved are given. Table 2 summarizes the state-of-decision problems for regular sets and languages.

Artificial languages were introduced by Chomsky in order to study natural languages. The present chapter is based on papers by Chomsky,[4] Chomsky and Schützenberger, Ginsburg and Rose, and Parikh, but mostly the paper by Bar-Hillel, Perles, and Shamir.

APPENDIX 1 *cycle index polynomials for S_n*

n	Z_{S_n}
1	$f_1{}^2$
2	$\frac{1}{2}(f_1{}^4 + f_1{}^2 f_2)$
3	$\frac{1}{6}(f_1{}^8 + 3f_1{}^4 f_2{}^2 + 2f_1{}^2 f_3{}^2)$
4	$\frac{1}{24}(f_1{}^{16} + 6f_1{}^8 f_2{}^4 + 3f_1{}^4 f_2{}^6 + 8f_1{}^4 f_3{}^4 + 6f_1{}^2 f_2 f_4{}^3)$
5	$\frac{1}{120}(f_1{}^{32} + 10f_1{}^{16} f_2{}^8 + 15f_1{}^8 f_2{}^{12} + 20f_1{}^8 f_3{}^8 + 20f_1{}^4 f_2{}^2 f_3{}^4 f_6{}^2$ $+ 30f_1{}^4 f_2{}^2 f_4{}^6 + 24f_1{}^2 f_5{}^6)$
6	$\frac{1}{720}(f_1{}^{64} + 15f_1{}^{32} f_2{}^{16} + 45f_1{}^{16} f_2{}^{24} + 40f_1{}^{16} f_3{}^{16} + 15f_1{}^8 f_2{}^{28}$ $+ 120f_1{}^8 f_2{}^4 f_3{}^8 f_6{}^4 + 90f_1{}^8 f_2{}^4 f_4{}^{12} + 40f_1{}^4 f_3{}^{20} + 90f_1{}^4 f_2{}^6 f_4{}^{12}$ $+ 144f_1{}^4 f_5{}^{12} + 120f_1{}^2 f_2 f_3{}^2 f_6{}^9)$

APPENDIX 2 *cycle index polynomials for* G_n

n	Z_{G_n}
$n = 1$	$\frac{1}{2}(f_1{}^2 + f_2)$
$n = 2$	$\frac{1}{8}(f_1{}^4 + 3f_2{}^2 + 2f_1{}^2 f_2 + 2f_4)$
$n = 3$	$\frac{1}{48}(f_1{}^8 + 13f_2{}^4 + 8f_1{}^2 f_3{}^2 + 8f_2 f_6 + 6f_1{}^4 f_2{}^2 + 12f_4{}^2)$
$n = 4$	$\frac{1}{348}(f_1{}^{16} + 51f_2{}^8 + 48f_1{}^2 f_2 f_4{}^3 + 48f_8{}^2 + 12f_1{}^8 f_2{}^4 + 84f_4{}^4$ $+\ 12f_1{}^4 f_2{}^6 + 32f_1{}^4 f_3{}^4 + 96f_2{}^2 f_6{}^2)$
$n = 5$	$\frac{1}{3840}(f_1{}^{32} + 231f_2{}^{16} + 20f_1{}^{16}f_2{}^8 + 520f_4{}^8 + 80f_1{}^8 f_8{}^8 + 720f_2{}^4 f_6{}^4$ $+\ 160f_1{}^4 f_2{}^2 f_3 f_6{}^2 + 320f_4{}^2 f_{12}{}^2 + 240f_1{}^4 f_2{}^2 f_4{}^6 + 480f_8{}^4$ $+\ 240f_2{}^4 f_4{}^6 + 60f_1{}^8 f_2{}^{12} + 384f_1{}^2 f_5{}^6 + 384f_2 f_{10}{}^3)$
$n = 6$	$\frac{1}{46080}(f_1{}^{64} + 1{,}053f_2{}^{32} + 30f_1{}^{32}f_2{}^{16} + 4{,}920f_4{}^{16} + 180f_1{}^{16}f_2{}^{24}$ $+\ 160f_1{}^{16}f_3{}^{16} + 5{,}280f_2{}^8 f_6{}^8 + 120f_1{}^8 f_2{}^{28} + 960f_1{}^8 f_2{}^4 f_3{}^4 f_6{}^4$ $+\ 3{,}840f_4{}^4 f_{12}{}^4 + 720f_1{}^8 f_2{}^8 f_4{}^{12} + 5{,}760f_8{}^8 + 2{,}160f_2{}^8 f_4{}^{12}$ $+\ 640f_1{}^4 f_3{}^{20} + 1{,}920f_2{}^2 f_6{}^{10} + 1{,}440f_1{}^4 f_2{}^6 f_4{}^{12} + 2{,}304f_1{}^4 f_5{}^{12}$ $+\ 6{,}912f_2{}^2 f_{10}{}^6 + 3{,}840f_1{}^2 f_2 f_3{}^2 f_6{}^9 + 3{,}840f_4 f_{12}{}^5)$

APPENDIX 3 *table of representatives for F*₃

No.	Invariants	Standard sum	Group element
1	0;444;444;4	Null set	$(1,000,(1)(2)(3))$
2	1;333;555;3	7	$(1,000,(1)(2)(3))$
3	2;224;644;4	6,7	$(1,000,(1)(2)(3))$
4	2;244;442;6	4,7	$(1,001,(1)(2)(3))$
5	2;444;226;4	0,7	$(1,001,(1,3)(2))$
6	3;133;553;5	5,6,7	$(1,000,(1)(2)(3))$
7	3;333;337;3	1,6,7	$(1,000,(1,3)(2))$
8	3;333;333;7	3,5,6	$(1,000,(1)(2)(3))$
9	4;044;444;4	4,5,6,7	$(1,000,(1)(2)(3))$
10	4;444;044;4	2,3,4,5	$(1,000,(1)(2)(3))$
11	4;444;444;0	1,2,4,7	$(1,000,(1)(2)(3))$
12	4;222;444;6	3,5,6,7	$(1,000,(1)(2)(3))$
13	4;224;426;4	3,4,6,7	$(1,000,(1)(2)(3))$
14	4;244;224;6	0,5,6,7	$(1,011,(1)(2)(3))$

APPENDIX 4 *table of representatives for the functions of four variables*

This table consists of one representative for each of the 222 equivalence classes of functions of four variables under N^{G_4}. For the self-complementary classes, we list two representatives for convenience.

The representatives used are "good" representatives rather than the canonical forms. In general, picking the canonical form is not wise, since one may miss certain functions which possess useful structure. We have used the same functions as Ninomiya[3] and listed the invariants of the functions,† the standard sum, and the necessary group element for conversion.

The invariants were calculated by a computer program.

The group element listed in the table works as follows. The element is of the form

$$(k, i_1 \cdots i_n, \sigma)$$

where $\sigma \epsilon S_n$, $i_j \epsilon \{0,1\}$ for $j = 1, \ldots, n$, and $k \epsilon \{1, \eta\}$.

This element operates on boolean functions from the right, i.e.

$$(k, i_1 \cdots i_n, \sigma)f(x_1, \ldots, x_n) = f^k(x^{i_1}_{\sigma^{-1}(1)}, \ldots, x^{i_n}_{\sigma^{-1}(n)})$$

where
$$x_j^{i_j} = \begin{cases} \bar{x}_j & \text{if } i_j = 1 \\ x_j & \text{if } i_j = 0 \end{cases} \quad \text{for } j = 1, \ldots, n$$

and $f^1 = f$, while $f^\eta = \bar{f}$

† Ninomiya gives only the coordinates. We preferred to avoid minus signs, so we used invariants.

Thus, to find the transformation which takes a given function f into its representative, say, r, one finds the transformation which takes f into its canonical form.   This mapping α comes from the calculation of the invariants.   The transformation β which takes the canonical form into the representative r is listed under the column "group element." The entire transformation is then $\beta\alpha$.   (Remember the rule: This says do α first.)   The situation may be summarized by the following diagram:

$$f \xrightarrow{\alpha} \text{can. form } (f) \xrightarrow{\beta} r$$

An example of this calculation is given in Sec. 5-11.

Table — page 398

No.	Invariants	Standard sum	Group element
1	0 8 8 8 8 8 8 8 8 8 8 8 8 8 8	Null set	(1,0000,(1)(2)(3)(4)
2	1 8 7 7 9 9 9 9 9 9 9 9 7 7 9	15	(1,0000,(1)(2)(3)(4)
3	2 6 6 7 10 8 8 8 10 9 8 8 6 8 8	14 15	(1,0000,(1)(2)(3)(4)
4	2 6 6 8 8 8 10 8 7 9 10 10 8 8 6	12 15	(1,0001,(1)(2)(3)(4)
5	2 6 8 8 8 8 6 11 11 7 7 8 6 8 8	8 15	(1,0001,(2,4)(1)(3)
6	2 8 8 8 6 10 6 8 6 8 8 6 8 8 6	0 15	(1,0001,(1,4)(2)(3)
7	3 5 7 7 9 7 9 11 9 9 11 7 7 7 7	13 14 15	(1,0000,(1)(2)(3)(4)
8	3 5 7 7 11 7 9 9 9 9 9 5 7 8 7	9 14 15	(1,0000,(2,4)(1)(3)
9	3 5 7 9 7 9 9 7 9 9 9 5 9 11 .5	11 13 14	(1,0000,(1)(2)(3)(4)
10	3 7 7 11 7 11 7 7 7 7 7 7 9 11 7	1 14 15	(1,0000,(1,4)(2)(3)
11	3 7 7 7 11 7 7 11 7 7 11 7 7 7 11	3 12 15	(1,0000,(1,3)(2)(4)
12	3 7 7 7 7 11 11 7 7 7 7 7 7 7 7	3 13 14	(1,0000,(1,3)(2,4)
13	4 4 8 8 8 8 8 8 8 8 12 8 8 8 8	12 13 14 15	(1,0000,(1)(2)(3)(4)
14	4 4 8 8 4 12 8 8 8 8 8 8 8 8 8	8 9 14 15	(1,0010,(1)(2)(3)(4)
15	4 4 8 8 8 8 8 8 8 8 8 8 8 8 12	9 10 12 15	(1,0000,(1)(2)(3)(4)
16	4 8 8 8 8 12 8 8 4 4 8 8 8 8 8	0 1 14 15	(1,0010,(1,3)(2)(4)
17	4 8 8 8 8 8 4 8 4 4 8 8 8 12 8	0 3 12 15	(1,0101,(1)(2)(3)(4)
18	4 8 8 8 8 8 8 8 4 4 8 8 8 12 8	0 3 13 14	(1,0100,(1,2)(3)(4)
19	4 8 8 6 8 8 8 8 10 10 6 10 8 10 6	11 13 14 15	(1,0000,(1)(2)(3)(4)
20	4 8 6 8 10 8 6 8 10 10 8 8 8 8 8	10 13 14 15	(1,0000,(2,3)(1)(4)
21	4 6 8 8 8 6 8 10 8 10 8 10 8 8 6	8 13 14 15	(1,0011,(1)(2)(3)(4)
22	4 6 6 8 12 8 6 10 12 8 8 10 6 6 8	3 13 14 15	(1,0000,(1,3)(2,4)
23	4 6 6 8 8 8 8 12 8 8 6 10 6 6 8	7 11 13 14	(1,0000,(1)(2)(3)(4)
24	4 6 6 8 10 6 8 8 8 6 8 8 6 8 6	2 13 14 15	(1,0000,(1,3)(2)(4)
25	4 6 6 8 6 10 6 12 8 8 8 8 6 8 6	6 10 13 15	(1,0001,(1)(2)(3)(4)

398

n																					Notation
26		15	14	13	0	8	10	10	8	8	8	6	6	6	6	12	8	8	6	6	4	(1,0011,(1)(2)(3)(4))
27		15	12	11	4	8	6	6	8	8	12	10	10	6	6	8	8	8	6	3	5	(1,0000,(1,2)(3)(4))
28		15	14	9	4	8	6	10	8	12	8	10	6	6	6	8	8	8	6	3	5	(1,0010,(1,2)(3)(4))
29		14	13	8	7	4	10	10	8	8	8	10	10	6	6	8	8	8	6	3	5	(1,0000,(1)(2)(3)(4))
30		15	14	9	0	6	8	6	10	10	12	8	8	6	6	6	8	8	8	5	5	(1,0111,(2,4)(1)(3))
31		14	13	11	0	10	4	10	10	10	8	8	6	6	7	6	8	8	7	5	5	(1,0111,(1)(2)(3)(4))
32	15	14	13	12	11	7	9	7	9	9	7	7	9	9	7	11	7	7	7	5	5	(1,0000,(1)(2)(3)(4))
33	15	13	12	11	10	9	7	7	7	11	9	5	9	9	7	9	7	7	7	5	5	(1,0000,(1)(2)(3)(4))
34	15	14	13	11	8	5	11	7	7	7	9	9	9	9	7	9	7	7	7	5	5	(1,0000,(1)(2)(3)(4))
35	15	14	13	12	3	9	9	9	7	7	7	7	7	5	5	13	7	7	7	7	5	(1,0000,(1)(2)(3)(4))
36	15	14	9	8	7	7	7	5	9	9	13	9	9	7	9	5	7	7	7	7	5	(1,0000,(2,4)(1)(3))
37	13	12	11	10	7	7	7	9	9	13	9	5	9	7	9	9	7	7	7	7	5	(1,0000,(1)(2)(3)(4))
38	15	13	10	9	7	11	3	9	9	9	9	9	9	7	9	5	7	7	7	7	5	(1,0000,(1)(2)(3)(4))
39	14	13	11	8	7	3	11	9	9	9	9	9	9	7	9	5	7	7	7	7	5	(1,0000,(1)(2)(3)(4))
40	15	13	12	3	2	9	7	7	7	7	9	13	9	9	9	9	5	5	5	5	5	(1,0000,(1,3)(2)(4))
41	15	14	13	2	1	5	7	7	7	9	11	7	9	9	9	9	7	7	5	5	5	(1,0000,(1,3)(2,4))
42	15	14	13	3	0	9	7	7	11	7	5	7	11	11	7	9	7	7	5	5	5	(1,0000,(1,3)(2,4))
43	15	14	8	5	3	9	11	3	7	7	9	11	11	11	7	9	7	7	5	5	5	(1,0000,(2,4)(1)(3))
44	15	10	9	6	5	13	7	7	7	11	9	11	7	7	7	9	7	7	5	5	5	(1,0000,(1)(2)(3)(4))
45	15	14	13	11	7	5	9	9	11	11	9	7	7	7	7	9	5	5	5	5	5	(1,0000,(1)(2)(3)(4))
46	15	14	13	11	6	7	7	7	11	9	7	9	11	9	9	7	5	5	5	5	5	(1,0000,(1,3)(2)(4))
47	15	14	13	10	5	9	9	9	7	7	7	11	7	7	9	7	7	5	5	5	5	(1,0000,(1,2)(3)(4))
48	15	14	13	11	4	5	9	9	7	7	11	11	7	7	9	7	7	7	5	5	5	(1,0000,(1,2)(3)(4))
49	15	14	12	11	5	9	5	9	7	11	11	7	11	11	9	7	7	5	5	5	5	(1,0000,(1,2)(3,4))
50	14	13	12	11	7	5	9	9	11	11	7	7	11	11	9	7	7	7	5	5	5	(1,0000,(1)(2)(3)(4))

No.	Invariants															Standard sum					Group element
51	5	5	7	7	7	11	9	9	9	9	9	9	11	7	7	0	11	13	14	15	(1,0000,(1)(2)(3)(4))
52	5	5	7	7	7	11	9	9	5	9	9	5	7	11	7	1	11	12	14	15	(1,0000,(2,4,3)(1))
53	5	5	7	7	9	7	9	9	9	9	5	9	9	11	7	3	11	12	13	14	(1,0000,(2,4)(1)(3))
54	5	5	7	8	10	7	8	9	9	8	9	6	8	7	11	3	10	12	13	15	(1,0000,(2,3,4)(1))
55	5	5	7	8	10	7	8	9	9	8	9	6	8	11	7	3	8	13	14	15	(1,0000,(2,4)(1)(3))
56	5	5	7	7	5	9	11	9	5	9	7	7	7	7	9	6	7	9	11	12	(1,0000,(1)(2)(3)(4))
57	5	7	7	7	5	9	11	9	9	7	7	7	11	7	5	6	7	8	11	13	(1,0000,(1)(2)(3)(4))
58	5	7	7	9	9	9	11	9	9	11	7	7	11	11	5	0	7	11	13	14	(1,0000,(1)(2)(3)(4))
59	7	8	10	10	8	6	10	8	8	8	6	6	8	8	8	10	11	12	13	14	(1,0000,(1)(2)(3)(4))
60	6	8	10	8	8	8	8	6	8	8	6	6	6	10	10	8	11	12	13	14	(1,0001,(1)(2)(3)(4))
61	2	8	8	8	6	10	10	6	8	8	8	8	8	8	8	9	10	11	13	14	(1,0000,(1)(2)(3)(4))
62	6	6	8	8	8	8	6	8	8	6	8	8	8	8	8	2	3	12	14	15	(1,0000,(1,3)(2)(4))
63	6	6	8	8	2	14	8	8	8	8	8	8	8	8	8	6	7	10	12	13	(1,0000,(1)(2)(3)(4))
64	6	6	8	8	6	6	8	6	8	8	8	8	8	6	6	1	2	12	13	15	(1,0000,(1)(2)(3)(4))
65	6	8	8	2	10	10	8	2	8	6	8	6	6	10	10	4	7	8	11	15	(1,0001,(1)(2)(3)(4))
66	6	6	8	6	6	6	8	6	8	8	8	8	8	6	6	4	7	9	13	14	(1,0000,(1,2)(3)(4))
67	6	6	8	6	8	8	8	8	8	8	8	6	8	6	14	5	6	9	12	15	(1,0000,(1)(2)(3)(4))
68	6	8	8	10	2	10	6	10	6	2	8	8	6	10	8	1	6	8	14	15	(1,0010,(1)(2)(3)(4))
69	6	8	8	10	6	6	6	6	6	6	8	8	6	14	8	1	6	10	11	13	(1,0000,(2,4)(1)(3))
70	8	2	6	8	10	10	6	6	8	6	6	8	10	8	10	1	2	3	12	14	(1,0100,(1)(2)(3)(4))
71	6	8	8	6	6	6	6	6	8	8	8	8	8	8	8	3	5	6	9	12	(1,0000,(1)(2)(3)(4))
72	6	4	6	8	8	8	10	8	6	4	6	8	8	8	6	7	11	12	13	15	(1,0000,(1)(2)(3)(4))
73	6	4	8	6	6	10	8	10	8	4	8	6	8	6	8	6	11	12	13	15	(1,0000,(1,2)(3)(4))
74	6	4	8	6	10	10	8	10	8	4	8	8	8	8	6	4	11	12	13	15	(1,0000,(1,2)(3)(4))
75	6	4	6	12	8	6	8	10	8	6	6	8	10	8	8	3	11	12	13	14	(1,0000,(2,4)(1)(3))

No.																				Expression
76	6	4	6	6	8	8	8	6	10	10	8	8	6	8	7	10	11	12	13	15	$(1,0000,(1)(2)(3)(4))$
77	6	4	6	6	8	8	8	10	10	10	8	8	6	4	7	8	11	13	14	15	$(1,0000,(1)(2)(3)(4))$
78	6	4	6	8	12	8	6	6	8	8	10	12	8	10	2	11	12	13	14	15	$(1,0001,(2,3)(1)(4))$
79	6	4	6	8	8	8	6	10	8	12	10	8	8	6	7	8	10	13	14	15	$(1,0000,(2,3)(1)(4))$
80	6	4	6	8	8	8	6	6	8	8	10	12	8	6	6	10	11	12	13	15	$(1,0001,(1)(2)(3)(4))$
81	6	4	6	8	6	8	6	8	8	8	8	10	10	10	6	8	13	14	15	15	$(1,0001,(1)(2)(3)(4))$
82	6	4	6	8	8	12	6	10	10	8	8	6	8	8	0	11	13	14	15	15	$(1,0011,(1)(2)(3)(4))$
83	6	4	4	8	8	8	10	8	8	12	6	6	8	8	4	10	12	13	15	15	$(1,0011,(3,4)(1)(2))$
84	6	4	6	8	6	8	6	10	6	8	10	10	8	8	4	9	10	13	14	15	$(1,0011,(1)(2)(3)(4))$
85	6	4	6	8	10	8	10	10	10	10	8	8	4	4	4	8	11	13	14	15	$(1,0011,(1)(2)(3)(4))$
86	8	4	8	6	10	6	10	6	10	8	8	12	6	6	0	8	11	12	13	15	$(1,0111,(1)(2)(3)(4))$
87	8	4	8	6	10	6	10	10	10	8	8	8	10	8	0	11	13	14	15	$(1,0111,(1)(2)(3)(4))$
88	8	6	6	6	6	10	8	12	8	6	12	8	8	8	5	8	10	13	14	15	$(1,0000,(1)(2)(3)(4))$
89	8	6	6	10	6	6	8	4	10	10	8	8	8	8	5	7	10	12	14	14	$(1,0000,(1,2)(3)(4))$
90	8	6	6	10	10	6	8	8	10	10	8	8	4	8	0	6	11	13	14	15	$(1,0001,(1)(2)(3)(4))$
91	6	8	8	6	4	10	8	6	4	8	8	8	12	12	2	4	11	13	14	15	$(1,0001,(1,3)(2)(4))$
92	6	8	6	6	8	10	8	8	8	4	8	12	8	8	3	4	10	13	14	15	$(1,0000,(1,2,3)(4))$
93	6	8	6	6	10	10	8	8	8	8	8	4	12	12	2	7	11	12	13	14	$(1,0001,(1,3)(2)(4))$
94	6	6	10	6	10	8	10	4	10	8	4	10	10	6	0	4	11	13	14	15	$(1,0011,(1)(2)(3)(4))$
95	6	6	6	10	6	12	10	8	8	8	8	10	10	6	6	7	8	9	12	15	$(1,0001,(1)(2)(3)(4))$
96	6	6	8	10	10	6	8	8	6	8	4	8	10	10	0	5	10	13	14	15	$(1,0011,(1)(2)(3)(4))$
97	6	6	6	6	4	8	12	12	8	10	8	8	6	10	6	7	8	11	12	13	$(1,0001,(1)(2)(3)(4))$
98	6	6	6	10	4	8	8	8	12	10	6	10	6	6	1	4	10	13	14	15	$(1,0011,(1)(2)(3)(4))$
99	8	6	8	10	8	8	4	12	10	6	6	6	6	10	3	4	13	13	14	15	$(1,0001,(1)(2)(3)(4))$
100	6	6	8	4	4	8	10	10	6	10	8	8	8	8	0	1	10	13	14	15	$(1,0110,(1)(2)(3)(4))$

No.	Invariants	Standard sum	Group element
101	6 6 8 8 4 8 8 6 10 10 10 10 4 8	0 3 8 13 14 15	(1,0100,(1)(2)(3)(4))
102	6 6 8 8 4 8 8 6 6 10 10 6 8 12	1 2 8 13 14 15	(1,0100,(1)(2)(3)(4))
103	6 6 8 8 8 8 8 6 10 6 8 10 4 12	0 7 9 10 12 15	(1,0011,(1)(2)(3)(4))
104	6 8 8 8 6 8 6 6 10 8 8 4 12 10	2 3 4 8 13 15	(1,0001,(1,3)(2,4))
105	6 6 6 6 10 6 10 10 10 10 10 10 10 6	0 7 11 13 14 15	(1,0000,(1)(2)(3)(4))
106	6 6 6 6 6 6 10 10 10 6 6 6 10 6	1 6 11 13 14 15	(1,0000,(1,4)(2)(3))
107	6 6 6 6 6 6 10 10 6 10 10 6 6 10	3 5 10 13 14 15	(1,0000,(1,3,2,4))
108	6 6 6 6 6 6 10 6 10 10 10 10 10 6	3 7 11 12 13 14	(1,0000,(13)(2)(4))
109	7 1 7 7 9 7 9 7 7 9 9 9 7 9	9 10 11 12 13 14	(1,0000,(1)(2)(3)(4))
110	7 7 7 7 7 7 7 15 7 7 7 7 7 7	1 2 3 12 13 14	(1,0000,(1,3)(2,4))
111	7 3 7 7 7 7 7 7 7 7 7 7 15 7	1 6 7 11 12 13	(1,0000,(1,4)(2)(3))
112	7 3 7 7 11 7 7 7 7 7 7 7 7 15	3 5 6 10 12 15	(1,0000,(1)(2)(3)(4))
113	7 3 5 9 5 11 11 7 9 11 9 9 7 7	7 10 11 13 14 15	(1,0000,(1)(2)(3)(4))
114	7 3 7 9 7 7 9 7 9 9 7 9 9 9	5 10 11 13 14 15	(1,0000,(3,4)(1)(2))
115	7 3 5 7 7 7 9 7 11 7 9 9 9 5	7 8 11 13 14 15	(1,0000,(1)(2)(3)(4))
116	7 7 7 7 9 9 7 9 11 9 9 11 5 9	7 9 10 12 13 14 15	(1,0000,(1)(2)(3)(4))
117	7 7 5 7 7 7 9 7 7 13 7 11 7 7	1 10 11 12 13 14 15	(1,0000,(2,4)(1)(3))
118	7 7 9 9 5 11 11 7 9 7 7 7 7 7	3 8 11 11 12 14 15	(1,0000,(2,4)(1)(3))
119	7 3 7 7 9 9 7 11 9 7 7 7 9 7	7 8 9 10 13 14 15	(1,0000,(2,4)(1)(3))
120	7 3 7 7 9 9 7 7 7 7 9 7 9 11	3 9 10 12 13 14 15	(1,0000,(2,4)(1)(3))
121	7 3 7 7 7 7 9 7 7 11 11 11 7 7	7 9 10 11 12 13 14	(1,0000,(1)(2)(3)(4))
122	7 5 5 5 7 9 7 7 9 7 13 7 7 9	6 7 10 11 12 13 15	(1,0000,(1)(2)(3)(4))
123	7 5 7 7 5 9 9 13 7 9 7 9 9 7	4 5 10 11 13 14 15	(1,0000,(1,2)(3)(4))
124	7 5 7 7 9 9 9 7 9 9 7 9 9 11	5 6 9 10 13 14 15	(1,0000,(1)(2)(3)(4))
125	7 5 5 7 9 9 9 7 9 7 7 5 13 7	4 7 9 10 13 14 15	(1,0000,(1,2)(3)(4))

n																								code
126	15	14	13	11	8	7	4	3	9	9	7	7	11	9	9	9	9	7	7	7	5	5	7	(1,0000,(1)(2)(3)(4))
127	15	14	13	12	9	3	2	9	7	9	5	9	7	7	7	13	9	5	7	7	7	5	7	(1,0000,(2,3,4)(1))
128	15	14	13	12	11	3	0	9	11	9	9	9	7	7	11	13	9	9	7	7	7	5	7	(1,0000,(2,4)(1)(3))
129	14	13	12	11	10	5	3	9	11	9	9	9	3	7	7	9	9	5	7	7	7	5	7	(1,0000,(2,4)(1)(3))
130	15	13	12	11	10	5	2	9	7	9	5	9	11	7	3	9	9	9	7	7	7	5	7	(1,0000,(2,3)(1)(4))
131	15	14	13	12	11	2	1	5	7	9	9	5	7	7	7	13	9	9	7	7	7	5	7	(1,0000,(2,4)(1)(3))
132	13	12	11	10	9	7	6	9	7	9	9	13	7	7	7	9	5	5	7	7	7	5	7	(1,0000,(1)(2)(3)(4))
133	15	12	11	10	9	7	4	9	3	9	9	9	11	7	7	9	9	5	7	7	7	5	7	(1,0000,(1)(2)(3)(4))
134	15	13	12	11	10	7	0	9	7	9	9	13	11	11	7	9	9	9	7	7	7	5	7	(1,0000,(1)(2)(3)(4))
135	14	13	12	11	10	7	1	5	7	13	9	9	7	7	7	9	9	5	7	7	7	5	7	(1,0000,(2,4)(1)(3))
136	15	13	12	11	10	6	1	9	7	13	5	5	7	7	7	9	9	9	7	7	7	5	7	(1,0000,(2,4)(1)(3))
137	15	12	11	10	9	6	5	13	7	5	9	9	7	7	7	9	9	5	7	7	7	5	7	(1,0000,(1)(2)(3)(4))
138	15	11	10	8	7	5	4	7	7	7	7	7	11	11	11	11	7	3	7	7	7	7	7	(1,0000,(1,2)(3)(4))
139	15	11	10	9	6	5	4	11	7	7	7	7	7	11	11	7	7	3	7	7	7	7	7	(1,0000,(1,2)(3)(4))
140	14	11	10	9	7	5	4	7	11	7	7	11	7	7	7	7	7	3	7	7	7	7	7	(1,0000,(1,2)(3,4))
141	12	11	10	9	7	6	5	11	7	7	11	11	7	7	7	7	7	3	5	7	7	7	7	(1,0000,(1)(2)(3)(4))
142	15	14	13	9	4	3	2	7	7	11	11	7	7	11	7	7	7	7	5	7	7	7	7	(1,0000,(1,3,4)(2))
143	15	14	12	9	5	3	2	11	11	3	3	7	11	7	7	7	7	7	7	7	7	7	7	(1,0000,(1,3)(2,4))
144	15	14	13	11	4	2	1	3	7	7	7	7	11	11	7	11	7	7	7	7	7	7	7	(1,0000,(1,4)(2)(3))
145	14	13	12	11	7	2	1	3	11	11	7	7	11	7	7	7	7	7	7	7	7	7	7	(1,0000,(1,3)(2,4))
146	15	14	13	12	11	7	3	7	9	9	9	9	7	7	11	11	7	7	5	5	5	5	7	(1,0000,(1,3)(2)(4))
147	15	14	13	12	10	7	3	9	7	7	11	9	9	5	11	9	7	7	5	5	5	5	7	(1,0000,(1,3,2)(4))
148	15	14	13	12	11	7	2	5	11	7	7	9	9	9	11	9	7	7	5	5	5	5	7	(1,0000,(1,3)(2)(4))
149	15	14	13	12	8	7	3	7	9	9	7	7	11	9	9	5	5	11	7	5	5	5	7	(1,0000,(1)(2)(3)(4))
150	15	14	13	12	9	6	3	11	9	9	7	7	11	5	9	9	5	11	7	5	5	5	7	(1,0000,(1)(2)(3)(4))

No.	Invariants														Standard sum								Group element
151	7	5	5	7	7	5	9	9	9	11	7	11	9	7		2	7	9	12	13	14	15	(1,0000,(1)(2)(3)(4))
152	7	5	5	7	7	9	9	11	11	11	11	9	5	7		0	7	11	12	13	14	15	(1,0000,(1)(2)(3)(4))
153	7	5	5	7	7	5	9	9	11	7	11	7	9	7		6	7	9	11	12	13	14	(1,0000,(1)(2)(3)(4))
154	7	5	5	7	7	5	9	9	11	11	5	11	9	7		6	7	8	11	12	13	15	(1,0000,(1)(2)(3)(4))
155	7	5	5	7	7	5	9	9	7	11	7	7	5	11		6	7	9	10	12	13	15	(1,0000,(1)(2)(3)(4))
156	7	7	5	7	7	7	9	11	5	9	5	7	9	9		6	7	8	9	11	12	15	(1,0000,(1)(2)(3)(4))
157	7	5	5	7	7	7	11	11	9	9	5	7	7	5		6	7	8	9	11	13	14	(1,0000,(1)(2)(3)(4))
158	7	5	5	7	7	11	9	9	5	9	9	11	5	5		4	7	8	10	11	13	15	(1,0000,(1)(2)(3)(4))
159	7	5	9	7	7	11	11	9	9	5	9	11	5	5		0	7	8	11	13	14	15	(1,0000,(1)(2)(3)(4))
160	7	5	5	7	7	7	7	9	5	5	5	9	5	9		5	6	8	9	11	14	15	(1,0000,(3,4)(1)(2))
161	7	5	9	7	7	9	9	7	11	5	9	11	5	5		1	6	8	11	13	14	15	(1,0000,(2,4)(1)(3))
162	7	7	7	7	7	11	11	11	11	7	7	11	11	7		0	1	6	11	13	14	15	(1,0000,(1,4)(2)(3))
163	7	7	7	7	7	11	11	11	7	7	7	11	5	5		0	3	5	10	13	14	15	(1,0000,(1,3,2,4))
164	7	7	7	7	7	11	11	11	11	11	11	11	11	7		0	3	7	11	12	13	14	(1,0000,(1,3)(2)(4))
165	8	0	8	8	8	8	8	8	8	8	8	8	8	8	8	9	10	11	12	13	14	15	(1,0000,(1)(2)(3)(4))
166	8	0	8	8	8	8	8	8	8	8	8	8	8	8	4	5	6	7	8	9	10	11	(1,0000,(1)(2)(3)(4))
167	8	8	8	8	8	8	8	8	0	8	8	8	8	8	2	3	4	5	8	9	14	15	(1,0000,(1)(2)(3)(4))
168	8	8	8	8	8	8	8	8	8	8	8	8	0	8	1	2	4	7	8	11	13	14	(1,0000,(1)(2)(3)(4))
169	8	2	6	6	8	8	10	10	10	10	10	6	8	8	7	9	10	11	12	13	14	15	(1,0000,(1)(2)(3)(4))
170	8	2	8	8	6	8	10	8	8	8	8	8	6	8	6	9	10	11	12	13	14	15	(1,0001,(1)(2)(3)(4))
171	8	2	6	8	6	10	8	8	8	8	8	6	8	8	4	9	10	11	12	13	14	15	(1,0011,(1)(2)(3)(4))
172	8	2	6	8	6	8	8	10	10	8	8	8	8	6	0	9	10	11	12	13	14	15	(1,0111,(1)(2)(3)(4))
173	8	6	8	6	8	8	8	6	6	6	8	6	14	8	1	6	7	10	11	12	13	15	(1,0000,(1,4)(2)(3))
174	8	6	8	6	8	2	8	10	10	6	6	8	8	10	2	4	6	9	11	13	14	15	(1,0001,(1)(2)(3)(4))
175	8	6	8	6	8	6	6	8	8	6	14	8	8	6	1	6	7	10	11	12	13	14	(1,0000,(1)(2)(3)(4))

No.	Values	Expression
176	15 14 12 10 9 6 5 3	14 8 8 8 6 6 6 8 6 8 8 8 6 6 8	(1,0000,(1)(2)(3)(4))
177	15 14 12 11 10 5 4 1	8 10 10 8 8 8 6 10 6 2 8 8 8 6 8	(1,0010,(1)(2)(3)(4))
178	14 13 12 10 9 7 4 3	8 14 6 8 8 8 6 6 6 6 8 8 8 6 8	(1,0000,(1,2)(3)(4))
179	15 14 13 12 8 3 2 1	10 8 6 10 10 8 8 8 6 6 2 8 8 8 8	(1,0100,(1)(2)(3)(4))
180	13 12 11 10 8 7 6 1	6 8 14 6 6 8 8 8 6 6 6 8 8 8 8	(1,0000,(2,4)(1)(3))
181	15 12 10 9 8 6 5 3	14 8 6 6 6 8 8 8 6 6 6 8 8 8 8	(1,0000,(1)(2)(3)(4))
182	15 14 13 12 11 10 7 6	8 8 8 8 12 8 8 6 8 8 8 4 8 4 8	(1,0000,(1)(2)(3)(4))
183	15 14 13 12 9 8 7 6	8 8 8 8 8 8 8 12 4 8 8 8 8 4 8	(1,0000,(1)(2)(3)(4))
184	15 14 13 12 10 9 6 5	12 8 6 10 8 8 8 8 8 8 8 8 8 4 8	(1,0000,(1)(2)(3)(4))
185	15 14 13 12 11 8 6 5	8 12 14 6 8 8 8 6 8 6 8 8 8 4 8	(1,0000,(1)(2)(3)(4))
186	15 15 13 12 11 10 1 0	8 8 8 8 12 8 8 4 8 8 8 8 8 8 8	(1,0110,(1)(2)(3)(4))
187	15 14 13 12 11 8 3 0	8 12 8 8 8 4 8 8 4 8 8 8 8 8 8	(1,0101,(1)(2)(3)(4))
188	15 14 13 10 9 8 7 0	8 8 12 8 8 8 4 8 4 4 8 8 8 8 8	(1,0011,(1)(2)(3)(4))
189	15 14 13 12 10 9 3 0	12 8 4 8 8 8 8 4 8 8 8 8 8 8 8	(1,0101,(1)(2)(3)(4))
190	14 13 12 11 10 9 7 0	8 12 12 4 4 8 8 8 10 8 6 8 8 4 8	(1,0001,(2,4)(1)(3))
191	15 14 13 10 5 2 1 0	8 8 8 8 12 4 8 8 8 4 8 8 8 8 8	(1,0011,(1,3)(2,4))
192	15 14 13 11 4 2 1 0	12 8 8 8 8 8 8 8 4 4 8 8 8 8 8	(1,0111,(1)(2)(3)(4))
193	15 14 12 11 5 2 1 0	8 8 12 8 8 8 8 8 4 4 8 8 8 8 8	(1,0110,(1)(2)(3)(4))
194	14 13 12 11 7 2 1 0	12 8 8 8 8 8 8 8 8 4 8 8 8 8 8	(1,0100,(1)(2)(3)(4))
195	15 14 13 12 11 10 7 5	8 8 8 10 10 8 6 10 10 8 6 6 4 4 8	(1,0000,(1,2)(3)(4))
196	15 14 13 12 11 10 7 4	10 6 10 8 10 6 8 10 8 6 8 6 6 4 8	(1,0001,(1,2)(3)(4))
197A	15 14 13 12 11 10 5 3	6 10 8 8 8 6 8 12 10 6 6 6 6 4 8	(v,1111,(1)(2)(3)(4))
197B	15 14 13 11 9 8 7 6	6 10 8 8 8 8 8 12 10 6 6 6 6 4 8	(1,0000,(1)(2)(3)(4))
198A	15 14 13 12 11 10 7 1	10 6 8 8 12 8 8 8 10 6 6 6 6 4 8	(v,1111,(1)(2)(3)(4))
198B	15 15 12 11 10 9 7 6	10 6 8 8 12 8 8 8 10 6 6 6 6 4 8	(1,0000,(1)(2)(3)(4))

No.	Invariants	Standard sum	Group element
199	8 4 6 6 8 6 10 4 8 10 8 6 10 8 8	2 6 9 11 12 13 14 15	$(1,0001,(2,3)(1)(4))$
200A	8 4 6 6 8 6 6 8 12 6 8 6 10 8 8	2 5 10 11 12 13 14 15	$(\eta,1110,(2,3)(1)(4))$
200B	8 4 6 6 8 6 6 8 12 6 8 6 10 8 8	6 7 8 9 11 12 14 15	$(1,0000,(1)(2)(3)(4))$
201A	8 4 6 6 8 8 6 8 8 6 12 6 10 8 8	0 7 10 11 12 13 13 15	$(\eta,1111,(1)(2)(3)(4))$
201B	8 4 6 6 8 8 6 8 8 4 12 6 10 8 8	6 7 9 10 11 12 13 14	$(1,0000,(1)(2)(3)(4))$
202	8 4 6 6 8 6 8 8 8 10 8 6 10 4 8	3 6 8 11 12 13 14 15	$(1,0001,(2,3)(1)(4))$
203	8 4 6 6 8 6 8 8 8 6 8 6 10 8 12	2 7 8 11 12 13 14 15	$(1,0001,(2,3)(1)(4))$
204A	8 4 8 8 8 6 8 8 8 8 10 10 10 10 6	0 5 10 11 13 13 14 15	$(\eta,1111,(1)(2)(3)(4))$
204B	8 4 8 8 8 6 6 8 8 8 10 10 10 10 6	6 7 8 9 11 12 13 14	$(1,0000,(1)(2)(3)(4))$
205A	8 4 8 8 8 6 6 8 8 4 10 10 10 10 10	0 7 8 11 12 13 14 15	$(\eta,1111,(1)(2)(3)(4))$
205B	8 4 6 6 8 6 6 8 10 4 10 10 10 10 10	5 6 9 10 11 12 13 14	$(1,0000,(1)(2)(3)(4))$
206A	8 4 6 6 8 6 6 8 6 8 10 6 10 6 6	3 4 9 10 12 13 14 15	$(\eta,1100,(1)(2)(3)(4))$
206B	8 4 6 6 8 6 6 8 6 8 10 6 10 6 6	4 7 8 9 10 13 14 15	$(1,0011,(1)(2)(3)(4))$
207	8 6 6 4 6 12 10 8 12 8 6 10 6 10 8	2 3 7 9 12 13 14 15	$(1,0000,(1,3,4,2))$
208A	8 6 6 4 6 8 8 8 8 4 10 10 10 10 8	0 3 7 11 12 13 14 15	$(\eta,1111,(1)(2)(3)(4))$
208B	8 6 6 4 6 8 8 8 8 4 10 10 10 10 8	5 6 7 9 10 11 13 14	$(1,0000,(1)(2)(3)(4))$
209A	8 6 6 4 6 8 8 8 8 8 10 6 10 6 12	1 2 7 11 12 13 14 15	$(\eta,1111,(1)(2)(3)(4))$
209B	8 6 6 4 6 8 8 8 8 8 10 6 10 6 12	5 6 7 9 10 11 12 15	$(1,0000,(1)(2)(3)(4))$
210	8 6 6 6 8 12 10 8 12 6 8 6 6 10 10	2 3 7 8 12 13 14 15	$(1,0001,(1,3,2)(4))$
211A	8 6 6 4 6 8 8 6 8 6 12 10 10 8 8	0 2 7 11 12 13 14 15	$(\eta,1111,(1)(2)(3)(4))$
211B	8 6 6 4 6 8 8 6 8 6 12 10 10 8 8	5 6 7 9 10 11 12 14	$(1,0000,(1)(2)(3)(4))$
212A	8 6 6 4 6 8 8 8 8 10 8 10 8 12 8	0 3 7 10 12 13 14 15	$(\eta,1111,(1,2)(3)(4))$
212B	8 6 6 4 6 8 8 8 8 10 8 10 8 12 8	4 6 7 9 10 11 13 14	$(1,0000,(1,2)(3)(4))$
213	8 6 6 6 8 10 8 6 8 8 8 4 8 6 8	2 5 7 8 11 12 14 15	$(1,0001,(1,2,3)(4))$
214A	8 6 6 4 6 8 8 8 8 10 10 10 8 10 8	0 3 4 11 12 13 14 15	$(\eta,1100,(1,2)(3)(4))$

214B	8	6	8	4	6	10	6	8	10	10	8	5	6	7	8	9	10	13	14	(1,0000,(1)(2)(3)(4))
215A	8	6	8	4	6	6	6	8	12	6	8	0	1	6	11	12	13	14	15	(η,1110,(1,2)(3)(4))
215B	8	6	8	4	6	6	6	8	12	6	8	5	6	7	8	10	11	12	13	(1,0000,(1)(2)(3)(4))
216	8	6	8	8	6	6	6	8	8	10	8	0	6	7	8	11	12	13	15	(1,0001,(3,4)(1)(2))
217A	8	6	8	4	6	10	6	12	8	6	12	1	2	4	11	12	13	14	15	(η,1100,(1,2)(3)(4))
217B	8	6	8	4	6	10	6	8	8	6	12	5	6	7	8	9	10	12	15	(1,0000,(1)(2)(3)(4))
218A	8	6	8	8	6	6	6	8	4	10	12	0	4	7	8	11	13	14	15	(η,1111,(1)(2)(3)(4))
218B	8	6	8	8	6	6	6	8	4	10	12	3	5	6	9	10	12	13	14	(1,0000,(1)(2)(3)(4))
219	8	6	8	8	6	10	6	8	8	6	8	0	6	7	9	11	12	13	14	(1,0001,(3,4)(1)(2))
220	8	6	8	8	6	6	6	8	8	10	12	2	4	5	8	11	13	14	15	(1,0001,(1,2)(3,4))
221	8	6	8	6	6	4	8	10	12	8	6	0	6	7	8	9	10	13	15	(1,0001,(2,4,3)(1))
222A	8	6	8	6	6	4	8	10	10	12	10	0	1	6	8	11	13	14	15	(η,1111,(1)(2)(3)(4))
222B	8	6	8	6	6	4	8	10	10	12	10	3	5	6	8	10	11	12	13	(1,0000,(1)(2)(3)(4))

APPENDIX 5 *table of minimal switching circuits for functions of four variables*

1 INTRODUCTION

A table which contains minimal networks for each equivalence class of functions is presented. Minimal relay networks (in the sense of both the number of contacts and the number of springs), along with minimal diode, vacuum-tube, and transistor circuits, are given.

This table has been worked out by Prof. I. Ninomiya, who has very kindly consented to its reproduction here.

2 MINIMAL RELAY NETWORKS

For each equivalence class, a network which is minimal in contacts and in springs is given. Except for five classes, the networks given are minimal with respect to both criteria. Whenever possible, Ninomiya chose series-parallel networks. The series-parallel networks are not drawn but are denoted by the appropriate boolean forms. The number of contacts required is listed in column C, and S denotes the number of springs. It is also apparent from the table that $\lambda(4) = 13$ and only two classes (112 and 112') require 13 contacts.

3   MINIMAL DIODE CIRCUITS

The top line in each block gives the form corresponding to the minimal two-level diode circuit.† The number of diodes is given in the column under R. Ninomiya observed that no more than 40 diodes are ever needed.

If an asterisk appears, then the minimal product form must be used to synthesize the circuit. In this case, see the minimal sum representation for the complementary class.

4   MINIMAL VACUUM - TUBE CIRCUITS

In order to specify the minimal vacuum-tube circuits, it is convenient to introduce a symbolic representation.

Definition 1.   Let $P_n(e_1, \ldots ,e_n) = \bar{e}_1 \cdots \bar{e}_n$
$$S_n(e_1, \ldots ,e_n) = \bar{e}_1 + \cdots + \bar{e}_n$$
$$F_n(e_1, \ldots ,e_n) = e_1 + \cdots + e_n$$
$$B_n(e_1, \ldots ,e_n) = e_1 \cdots e_n$$

Thus $P_1(e)$ denotes a simple triode inverter. $P_n(e_1, \ldots ,e_n)$ specifies a triode gate with inputs $e_1, \ldots , e_n$. $S_2(e_1,e_2)$ denotes a pentode gate with inputs e_1 and e_2. $F_n(e_1, \ldots ,e_n)$ symbolizes a cathode follower with inputs $e_1, \ldots , e_n$. No vacuum-tube circuit represents S_n, $n > 2$ and B_n.

Using these symbols, it is easy to characterize any vacuum-tube circuit with the convention that connecting together two plate resistors corresponds to the product of the symbols.

EXAMPLE.   Refer to Fig. 1. $S_2(x,p)S_2[\bar{x},P_1(p)]$, where $p = P_2(y,z)$.

A measure of the cost of synthesis in this technology is the number of control grids used. This is given in column G. Ninomiya constructed

† Under the assumption that both variables and their complements are available.

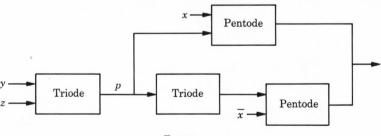

FIG. 1

better networks than the Harvard table† in 151 cases; these are marked by an asterisk. The serial number of the Harvard class is listed in column H. The maximum number of grids required is 16, not 20 as was listed in the Harvard table.

5   MINIMAL TRANSISTOR CIRCUITS

Again we suppose that variables and their complements are available as inputs. The same symbolic notation is used as with vacuum tubes. The interpretation is shown in the accompanying table. By convention,

Symbol	Action	pnp gate	npn gate
$P_1(e)$	$\bar{e}$	. . . .	Complement gate
$S_1(e)$	$\bar{e}$	Complement gate	
$P_n(e_1, \ldots ,e_n)$	$\bar{e}_1 \cdots \bar{e}_n$	Series gate	Parallel gate
$S_n(e_1, \ldots ,e_n)$	$\bar{e}_1 + \cdots + \bar{e}_n$	Parallel gate	Series gate
$F_n(e_1, \ldots ,e_n)$	$e_1 + \cdots + e_n$	. . . .	Emitter follower gate
$B_n(e_1, \ldots ,e_n)$	$e_1 \cdots e_n$	Emitter follower gate	

let $+$ ($\cdot$) denote the common resistor connection of pnp (npn) gates. Note that S_n, $n > 2$ is now possible (cf. Chap. 3), whereas symbols such as $P_2(e_1,e_2) + B_2(e_1,e_2)$ are meaningless.

The number of transistors required is shown in the column headed T. Only npn circuits are given, but the corresponding pnp circuit can be obtained from the npn circuit of the complementary type by interchanging P and S symbols, F and B symbols, and $+$ and $\cdot$ symbols and complementing every literal.

For the classes of weight 8, both circuits are given. The blocks with only one expression have the property that the one expression denotes both the vacuum-tube and transistor circuits. The least upper bound of the number of transistors is 16.

† An improved version of the Harvard table is reprinted in Higonnet and Grea.

Table of Minimal Switching Circuits for
Boolean Functions for Four Variables

Table of symbols for vacuum tube and transistor switching circuits

Symbol	Switching action	Vacuum tube gate	npn transistor gate	pnp transistor gate
$P_1(e)$	e'	Complement gate	Complement gate	
$P_n(e_1, \ldots ,e_n)$	$e_1' \cdots e_n'$	Triode gate	Series gate	Parallel gate
$S_1(e)$	e'			Complement gate
$S_n(e_1, \ldots ,e_n)$	$e_1' + \cdots + e_n'$	Pentode gate $(n = 2)$	Series gate	Parallel gate
$F_n(e_1, \ldots ,e_n)$	$e_1 + \cdots + e_n$	Cathode follower gate	Emitter follower gate	
$B_n(e_1, \ldots ,e_n)$	$e_1 \cdots e_n$			Emitter follower gate
	Multiplication	Common plate resistor connection	Common collector resistor connection	
$+$	Addition			Common collector resistor connection

N	H	Switching Circuit	R	C	S	G
1	0	0	0	0	0	0
2	1	$wxyz$	4	4	8	
		$P_4(w', x', y', z')$				4
3	2	wxy	3	3	6	
		$P_3(w', x', y')$				3
4	3	$wxyz+wxy'z'$	10*			
		$wx(yz+y'z')$		6	10	
		$P_2(w', x')S_2(y, z')S_2(y', z)$				6
5	4	$wxyz+wx'y'z'$	10			
		$w(xy+x'z')(y'+z)$		7	11	
		$P_1(w') S_2(x, y') S_2(x', z) S_2(y, z')$				7
6	5	$wxyz+w'x'y'z'$	10			
		$(wx+w'y')(yz+x'z')$		8	12	
		$S_2(w, x') S_2(w', z) S_2(x, y') S_2(y, z')$				8
7	6	$wxy+wxz$	8*			
		$wx(y+z)$		4	8	
		$P_2(w', x') S_2(y', z')$				4

N	H	Switching Circuit	R	C	S	G	T
8	7	$wxy+wx'y'z$	9				
		$w(xy+x'zy')$		6	10		
		$P_1(w')S_2(x,y')S_2(x',y)S_2(x',z')$				7	7
9	9	$wxyz'+wxy'z+wx'yz$	15*				
				8	13		
		$P_1(w')S_2(x,p)S_2[x',P_1(p)]S_2(y',z'),\ p=P_2(y',z')$				10	10
10	8	$wxy+w'x'y'z$	9				
		$(wx+w'zy')(x'+y)$		7	11		
		$S_2(w',x)S_2(w,y')S_2(w',z')S_2(x',y)$				8	8
11	10	$wxyz+wxy'z'+w'x'yz$	15				
				9	14		
		$S_2(w,x')S_2(w',x)S_2(w',y')S_2(y,z')S_2(y',z)$				10	10
12	11	$wxyz'+wxy'z+w'x'yz$	15				
				9	14		
		$S_2(w,x')S_2(y',z')S_2(w',p)S_2[x,P_1(p)],\ p=S_2(y,z)$				11*	11
13	12	wx	2	2	4		
		$P_2(w',x')$				2	2
14	19	$wxy+wx'y'$	8*				
		$w(xy+x'y')$		5	8		
		$P_1(w')S_2(x,y')S_2(x',y)$				5	5
15	25	$wxyz+wxy'z'+wx'yz'+wx'y'z$	20*				
				9	14		
		$P_1(w')S_2(x,p)S_2[x',P_1(p)],\ p=S_2(y,z)S_2(y',z')$				10	10
16	24	$wxy+w'x'y'$	8				
		$(wx+w'y')(x'+y)$		6	9		
		$S_2(w,x')S_2(w',y)S_2(x,y')$				6	6
17	29	$wxyz+wxy'z'+w'x'yz+w'x'y'z'$	20*				
		$(wx+w'x')(yz+y'z')$		8	12		
		$S_2(w,x')S_2(w',x)S_2(y,z')S_2(y',z)$				8	8

N	H	Switching Circuit	R	C	S	G	T
18	30	$wxyz'+wxy'z+w'x'yz+w'x'y'z'$	20*				
		(diagram)		8	16		
		(diagram)		10	15		
		$S_2(w,\ x')\,S_2(w',\ p)\,S_2[x,\ P_1(p)],\ p=S_2(y,\ z)\,S_2(y',\ z')$				11	11
19	13	$wxy+wxz+wyz$	12*				
		(diagram)		6	11		
		$P_1(w')\,S_2(x',\ y')\,S_2(x',\ z')\,S_2(y',\ z')$				7	7
20	14	$wxz+wyz'$	8*				
		$w(xz+yz')$		5	9		
		$P_1(w')\,S_2(x',\ z)\,S_2(y',\ z')$				5	5
21	15	$wxy+wxz+wx'y'z'$	13*				
		(diagram)		7	11		
		$P_1(w')\,S_2(x,\ p)\,S_2[x',\ P_1(p)],\ p=P_2(y,\ z)$				8	8
22	16	$wxy+wxz+w'x'yz$	13				
		(diagram)		7	12		
		$S_2(w,\ x')\,S_2(y',\ z')\,S_2[w',F_3(x,\ y',\ z')]$				9	9
23	26	$wxyz'+wxy'z+wx'yz+w'xyz$	20				
		(diagram)		10	16		
		$S_2(p,\ q)\,P_1[P_2(p,\ q)],$ $p=P_2(w',\ x')\,S_2(y',\ z'),\ q=P_2(y',\ z')\,S_2(w',\ x')$				13*	13
24	17	$wxy+wxz+w'x'yz'$	13*				
		$(w'+x)(w+x'z')(y+z)$		7	11		
		$S_2(w,\ x')\,S_2(w',\ x)\,S_2(w',\ z)\,S_2(y',\ z')$				8	8

N	H	Switching Circuit	R	C	S	G	T
25	20	$wxz+wx'yz'+w'xyz'$	14				

| | | $S_2(w',\ x')\ S_2(z,\ p)\ S_2[z',\ S_2(y,\ p)],\ p=S_2(w,\ x)$ | | | | 10* | 10 |

| | | | | 8 | 13 | | |

N	H	Switching Circuit	R	C	S	G	T
26	18	$wxy+wxz+w'x'y'z'$	13				

| | | | | 8 | 12 | | |
| | | $S_2(w',\ x)\ S_2(w,\ p)\ S_2[x',\ P_1(p)],\ p=P_2(y,\ z)$ | | | | 9 | 9 |

N	H	Switching Circuit	R	C	S	G	T
27	22	$wyz+xy'z'$	8				
		$ywz+y'xz'$		6	10		
		$F_2[P_3(w',\ y',\ z'),\ P_3(x',\ y,\ z)]$				8	
		$P_1[S_3(w,\ y,\ z)\ S_3(x,\ y',\ z')]$					7

N	H	Switching Circuit	R	C	S	G	T
28	21	$wxy+wx'y'z+w'xy'z'$	14				

| | | | | 8 | 12 | | |
| | | $S_2(w',\ z)\ S_2(x',\ z')\ S_2(y,\ p)\ S_2[y',\ P_1(p)],\ p=S_2(w,\ x)$ | | | | 11 | 11 |

N	H	Switching Circuit	R	C	S	G	T
29	27	$wxyz'+wxy'z+wx'y'z'+w'xyz$	20				

| | | | | 10 | 16 | | |
| | | $S_2(w',\ z')\ S_2(x',\ z)\ S_2(y',\ p)\ S_2[y,\ P_1(p)],\ p=P_1(x')\ S_2(w,\ z)$ | | | | 12* | 12 |

N	H	Switching Circuit	R	C	S	G	T
30	23	$wxy+wx'y'z+w'x'y'z'$	14				

| | | | | 8 | 12 | | |
| | | $F_2[P_3(w',\ x',\ y'),\ P_2(x,\ y)\ S_2(w,\ z')\ S_2(w',\ z)]$ | | | | 11 | 11 |

N	H	Switching Circuit	R	C	S	G	T
31	28	$wxyz'+wxy'z+wx'yz+w'x'y'z'$	20				

| | | | | 10 | 15 | | |

$S_2(w',\ p)\ S_2[P_2(w',\ x),\ q]\ P_1[P_1(x')\ S_2(p,\ q)],$ 14*

$S_2(w',\ p)\ S_3(w,\ x',\ q)\ P_1[P_1(x')\ S_2(p,\ q)],$ 13

$p=S_2(\underline{y',\ z'}),\ q=S_2(y,\ z)$

N	H	Switching Circuit	R	C	S	G	T
32	31	$wx+wyz$	7				
		$w(x+yz)$		4	8		
		$P_1(w')\,S_2(x',\,y')\,S_2(x',\,z')$				5	5
33	38	$wxy'+wx'y+wxz$	12*				
		$w(x+y)(x'+y'+z)$		6	10		
		$P_1(w')\,S_2(x',\,y')\,S_2[x,\,P_2(y',\,z)]$				7	
		$P_1(w')\,S_2(x',\,y')\,S_3(x,\,y,\,z')$					6
34	33	$wxy+wxz+wyz+wx'y'z'$	17*				
				8	13		
		$S_2(x,\,p)\,P_2[w',\,P_2(x,\,p)\,S_2(y,\,z)],\ p=P_2(y,\,z)$				10	10
35	32	$wx+w'x'yz$	8				
		$wx+w'yzx'$		6	10		
		$S_2(w,\,x')\,S_2[w',\,F_3(x,\,y',\,z')]$				7	7
36	46	$wxy+wx'y'+xyz$	12				
				7	11		
		$S_2(w',\,x')\,S_2(w',\,z')\,S_2(x,\,y')\,S_2(x',\,y)$				8	8
37	50	$wxy'+wx'y+w'xyz$	13				
				8	13		
		$S_2(x',\,y')\,S_2(w,\,p)\,S_2[w',\,S_2(z,\,p)],\ p=P_2(x',\,y')$				10	10
38	51	$xyz+wxy'z'+wx'yz'+wx'y'z$	19				
				9	14		
		$S_2(w',\,x')\,S_2(z,\,p)\,S_2[z',\,S_2(w,\,p)],\ p=S_2(x,\,y)\,S_2(x',\,y')$				12	
		$S_2(y,\,q)\,P_1[P_1(y)\,S_2(w,\,q)],\ q=S_2(x,\,z)\,S_3(w,\,x',\,z')$					11
39	55	$wxyz'+wxy'z+wx'yz+wx'y'z'+w'xyz$	25				
				11	17		
		$S_2(w',\,y')\,S_2(w',\,z')\,S_2(x,\,p)\,S_2[x',\,P_1(p)],$ $p=P_1(w')\,S_2(y,\,z')\,S_2(y',\,z)$				14*	14

N	H	Switching Circuit	R	C	S	G	T
40	49	$wxy'+wxz+w'x'y$	12				
		$(w+x')[w'y+x(y'+z)]$		7	11		
		$F_2[P_2(w',\ x')\,S_2(y,\ z'),\ P_3(w,\ x,\ y')]$				9	9
41	48	$wxy+wxz+w'x'yz'+w'x'y'z$	18*				
		$(w'+x)[w+x'(y'+z')](y+z)$		8	12		
		$S_2(w,\ x')\,S_2(w',\ x)\,S_2(y',\ z')\,P_1[P_3(w,\ y',\ z')]$				10	
		$S_2(w,\ x')\,S_2(w',\ x)\,S_2(y',\ z')\,S_3(w',\ y,\ z)$					9
42	47	$wxy+wxz+w'x'yz+w'x'y'z'$	18				

				9	14		
		$F_2[P_2(w',\ x')\,S_2(y',\ z'),\ P_2(w,\ x)\,S_2(y,\ z')\,S_2(y',\ z)]$				12	12

| 43 | 52 | $wxy+wx'y'z'+w'xy'z+w'x'yz$ | 19 | | | | |

				9	17		

				10	15*		
		$S_2(w,\ p)\,P_1[S_2(w,y)\,S_2(w,\ z')\,S_2(z,\ p)],\ p=S_2(x,y)\,S_2(x',\ y')$				13*	13

| 44 | 57 | $wxyz+wx'yz'+wx'y'z+w'xyz'+w'xy'z$ | 25* | | | | |

				10	16		
		$S_2(w',\ x')\,S_2(y',\ z')\,S_2(p,\ q)\,P_1[P_2(p,\ q)],$				13*	13
		$p=S_2(w,\ x),\ q=P_2(y',\ z')$					

| 45 | 34 | $wxy+wxz+wyz+xyz$ | 16 | | | | |

				8	14		
		$S_2(w',\ x')\,S_2(y',\ z')\,P_1[S_2(w,\ x)\,S_2(y,\ z)]$				9	9

| 46 | 35 | $wxz+wyz+xyz'$ | 12 | | | | |

				6	11		
		$S_2(w',\ z)\,S_2(x',\ y')\,S_2(x',\ z')\,S_2(y',\ z')$				8	8

N	H	Switching Circuit	R	C	S	G	T
47	39	$wxy+wyz'+xy'z$	12*				
		$(w+y')(y+z)(x+z')$		6	10		
		$S_2(w', y) S_2(x', z) S_2(y', z')$				6	6
48	36	$wxy+wxz+wyz+w'xy'z'$	17*				
				9	14		
		$S_2(x', y') S_2(x', z') S_2(w, p) S_2[w', P_1(p)],\ p=P_2(y, z)$				11	11
49	40	$wxz'+wyz+w'xy'z$	13				
				7	11		
		$S_2(w', p) P_1[P_1(p) S_2(w', x)],\ p=S_2(y', z) S_2(x', z')$				10*	10
50	42	$wxy'+wxz'+wx'yz+w'xyz$	18				
				9	14		
		$S_2(p, q) P_1[P_2(p, q)],\ p=P_2(w', x'),\ q=S_2(w', x') P_2(y', z')$				11	11
51	37	$wxy+wxz+wyz+w'x'y'z'$	17				
				9	15		
		$S_2(x, p) P_2[P_2(w, p), P_2(w', x) S_2(y, z)],\ p=P_2(y, z)$				12*	12
52	41	$wxz'+wyz+w'x'y'z$	13				
				8	12*		
		$S_2(w', x) S_2(w', y) S_2(x', z') P_1[P_3(w', y, z')]$				10	
		$S_2(w', x) S_2(w', y) S_2(x', z') S_3(w, y', z)$					9
53	45	$wxy'+wxz'+x'yz$	12				
				7	11		
		$S_2(x', p) S_2[x, S_2(w, p)],\ p=S_2(y, z)$				8*	8

N	H	Switching Circuit	R	C	S	G	T
54	44	$wxy'+wxz+wx'yz+w'x'yz$	18*				

					9	14	
		$S_2(x,\ p)\ P_1[P_1(p)\ S_2(w,\ x)],\ p=P_1(y')\ S_2(w,\ z)\ S_2(w',\ z')$				11*	11
55	43	$wxy+wxz+wx'y'z'+w'x'yz$	18				

					9	14	
		$S_2(x,\ p)\ P_1[P_1(p)\ S_2(w,\ x)],\ p=S_2(w',\ y')\ S_2(w,\ z)\ S_2(y,\ z')$				12*	12
56	54	$w'xy+wx'z+wxy'z'$	13				

					8	12	
		$S_2(w',\ x')\ S_2(w',\ y')\ S_2(x',\ z')\ P_1[P_2(w',\ x')\ S_2(y',\ z')]$				11	11
57	53	$w'xy+wxy'z+wx'yz+wx'y'z'$	19				

					10	15	
		$S_2(w',\ p)\ S_2(z,\ q)\ P_1[P_1(w')\ S_2[p,\ F_2(z,\ q)]],$ $p=S_2(x,\ y),\ q=P_2(x,\ y)$				14*	14
58	56	$wxyz'+wxy'z+wx'yz+w'xyz+w'x'y'z'$	25				

					12	18	
		$S_2[p,\ P_1(q)]S_2[q,\ P_1(p)],$ $p=S_2(w',\ x')\ S_2(y,\ z),\ q=S_2(w,\ x')\ S_2(w',\ x)\ S_2(y',\ z')$				16*	16
59	58	$wx+wy$	6*				
		$w(x+y)$		3	6		
		$P_1(w')\ S_2(x',\ y')$				3	3
60	59	$wx+wyz+wy'z'$	11*				
		$w(x+yz+y'z')$		6	10		
		$P_1(w')\ S_2[x',\ S_2(y,\ z)\ S_2(y',\ z')]$				7	7
61	79	$wxy'+wx'z+wyz'$	12*				
		$w(x+y+z)(x'+y'+z')$		7	11		
		$P_2[w',\ S_2(x,\ y')\ S_2(x',\ z)\ S_2(y,\ z')]$				8	
		$P_1(w')\ S_3(x,\ y,\ z)\ S_3(x',\ y',\ z')$					7

N	H	Switching Circuit	R	C	S	G	T
62	66	$wx+w'x'y$	7				
		$wx+w'yx'$		5	8		
		$S_2(w,\ x')\,S_2(w',\ x)\,S_2(w',\ y')$				6	6
63	101	$wxy'+wx'y+w'xy$	12				

				7	11		
		$S_2(w',\ x')\,S_2(y',\ p)\,S_2[y,\ P_1(p)],\ p=S_2(w,\ x)$				9	9
64	67	$wx+w'x'yz'+w'x'y'z$	13				
		$(w'+x)[w+x'(y+z)(y'+z')]$		8	12		
		$F_2[P_2(w',\ x'),\ P_2(w,\ x)\,S_2(y,\ z)\,S_2(y',\ z')]$				10	10
65	98	$wyz+wy'z'+xyz+xy'z'$	16*				
		$(w+x)(yz+y'z')$		6	10		
		$S_2(w',\ x')\,S_2(y,\ z')\,S_2(y',\ z)$				6	6
66	102	$wyz'+wy'z+w'xyz+w'xy'z'$	18				

				9	14		
		$S_2(w,\ p)\,S_2[w',\ S_2(x,\ p)],\ p=S_2(y,\ z')\,S_2(y',\ z)$				10	10
67	106	$wxyz+wxy'z'+wx'yz'+wx'y'z+w'xyz'+w'xy'z$	30*				

				11	17		
		$S_2(p,\ q)\,P_1[P_2(p,\ q)],$ $p=P_2(w',\ x'),\ q=S_2(w',\ x')\,S_2(y,\ z)\,S_2(y',\ z')$				13	13
68	99	$wxy+wx'y'+xyz'+x'y'z$	16*				

				7	11		
		$F_2[P_2(x',\ y')\,S_2(w,\ z),\ P_2(x,\ y)\,S_2(w',\ z')]$				10	10
69	103	$wxy'+wx'y+w'xyz'+w'x'y'z$	18				

| | | | | 10 | 14 | | |
| | | $F_2[P_1(w')\,S_2(x,y)\,S_2(x',\ y'),\ P_1(w)\,S_2(x',\ y)\,S_2(x,\ z)\,S_2(y',\ z')]$ | | | | 14 | 14 |

N	H	Switching Circuit	R	C	S	G	T
70	100	$wxy'+w'x'y+wxz'+w'x'z$	16*				
		$(w+x')[w'(y+z)+x(y'+z')]$		8	12		
		$F_2[P_2(w, x) S_2(y', z'), P_2(w', x') S_2(y, z)]$				10	10
71	107	$wxy'z'+wx'yz'+wx'y'z+w'xyz'+w'xy'z+w'x'yz$	30				
				12	18		
		$S_2[p, P_1(q)] S_2[q, P_1(p)],$				14*	14
		$p=S_2(w, x) S_2(y, z), q=S_2(w', x') S_2(y', z')$					
72	60	$wx+wyz+xyz$	11				
				6	11		
		$S_2(w', x') P_1[S_2(w, x) S_2(y, y)]$				7*	7
73	61	$wx+wyz+xyz'$	11				
				5	9		
		$P_2[P_1(w) S_2(y, z'), P_1(x) S_2(y, z)]$				8	8
74	62	$wx+wyz+xy'z'$	11				
		$(w+y'z')(x+zy)$		6	11		
		$P_2[P_1(w) S_2(y', z'), P_1(x) S_2(y, z)]$				8	8
75	63	$wx+x'yz$	7				
		$wx+yzx'$		5	9		
		$S_2(w', x) S_2(x', y') S_2(x', z')$				6	6
76	73	$wxy'+wx'y+xyz$	12				
				7	12		
		$S_2(x', y') S_2(w', p) S_2[z', P_1(p)], p=S_2(x, y)$				9*	9
77	68	$wxy+wxz+wyz+xyz+wx'y'z'$	21				
				9	15		
		$S_2(w', x') S_2(x, p) P_1[P_1(p) S_2(w, x) S_2(y, z)], p=P_2(y, z)$				12*	12

N	H	Switching Circuit	R	C	S	G	T
78	64	$wx+wyz+w'x'yz'$	12				

		$S_2(x', y') S_2(w, p) S_2[w', P_1(p)], \ p=P_2(x, z)$				9	9

(row spanning: 7 11 under C S for N78)

N	H	Switching Circuit	R	C	S	G	T
79	74	$wxz+wx'z'+wyz'+xyz$	16*				

| | | $F_2[P_2(w', z) S_2(x, y'), \ P_2(x', z') S_2((w', y')]$ | | | | 10 | |
| | | $S_2(w', y') S_2(w', z') S_2(x', z) S_3(x, y', z')$ | | | | | 9 |

(7 12 under C S for N79)

| 80 | 81 | $wxy'+wx'y+wxz+w'xyz'$ | 17 | | | | |

| | | $S_2(w, p) S_2[w', P_1(p)] S_2(x', y'), \ p=P_3(x', y'z)$ | | | | 10 | 10 |

(9 14 under C S for N80)

| 81 | 69 | $wxz+wyz+xyz'+wx'y'z'$ | 17 | | | | |

| | | $P_2[S_2(w, y') S_2(w, z) S_2(x, z'), \ P_1(y) S_2(x, z) S_2(x', z')]$ | | | | 13 | 13 |

(9 15 under C S for N81)

| 82 | 65 | $wx+wyz+w'x'y'z'$ | 12 | | | | |

| | | $P_2[P_1(w) S_2(x', z'), \ P_1(x) S_2(w', y') S_2(y, z)]$ | | | | 10* | 10 |

(8 12 under C S for N82)

83	82	$wx'y+wxz+xy'z'$	12				
		$(x+y)[w(x'+z)+y'z']$		7	12		
		$S_2(x', y') S_2(w', p) S_2[y, P_1(p)], \ p=S_2(x, z')$				9	9

| 84 | 80 | $wxy+wyz'+wy'z+w'xy'z'$ | 17 | | | | |

| | | $S_2(w', p) P_1[P_1(p) S_2(w', x)], \ p=S_2(y', z') P_1[P_3(x, y', z')]$ | | | | 12* | |
| | | $S_2(w, q) S_2[w', S_2(x, q)] S_3(x', y, z), \ q=P_2(y, z)$ | | | | | 11 |

(8 13 under C S for N84)

N	H	Switching Circuit	R	C	S	G	T

85 70 $wxy+wxz+wyz+wx'y'z'+w'xy'z'$ R = 22

C = 10 S = 16

$S_2(p,\ q)\,P_1[P_2(p,\ q)]$,   G = 13* T = 13
$p=P_1(w')\,S_2(x',\ z'),\ q=P_1(y)\,S_2(w',\ x')\,S_2(x,\ z)$

---

86 83 $wxy'+wx'y+wxz+w'x'y'z'$ R = 17

C = 9 S = 14

$S_2(w,\ p)\,S_2[w',\ S_2(z',\ p)]P_1[P_3(x',\ y',\ z)]$,   G = 12
$S_2(w,\ p)\,S_2[w',\ S_2(z',\ p)]\,S_3(x,\ y,\ z')$,   T = 11
$p=P_2(x,\ y)$

---

87 71 $wxy+wxz+wyz+x'y'z'$ R = 16

C = 8 S = 14

$S_2(z,\ p)\,P_1[P_2[p,\ P_3(w',\ x',\ y')]\,S_2(w,\ z)]$,   G = 12
$S_2(z,\ p)\,P_1[P_1(p)\,S_2(w,\ z)\,S_3(w,\ x,\ y)]$,   T = 11
$p=P_2(x,\ y)$

---

88 85 $wxy+wx'z'+w'xz$ R = 12*
   $(w'+x'+y)(wz'+xz)$ C = 7 S = 11*
   $S_2(w',\ z')\,S_2(x',\ z)\,P_1[P_3(w',\ x',\ y)]$ G = 8
   $S_2(w',\ z')\,S_2(x',\ z)\,S_3(w,\ x,\ y')$ T = 7

---

89 89 $wx'y+wxz'+w'xz$ R = 12

C = 7 S = 11

$S_2(w',\ p)\,S_2[w,\ P_1(p)]\,S_2(x',\ y'),\ p=S_2(x,\ z)$ G = 9 T = 9

---

90 76 $wxz+wyz+xyz'+w'x'y'z'$ R = 17*

C = 9 S = 14

$S_2(w',\ z)\,S_2(w,\ p)\,P_1[P_2(z,\ p)\,S_2(x,\ y)],\ p=P_2(x,\ y)$ G = 11 T = 11

N	H	Switching Circuit	R	C	S	G	T
91	77	$wxy+wxz+wyz+w'xy'z'+w'x'yz'$	22*				

$S_2(x', y') S_2(w, p) S_2[w', P_1(p)], \ p=P_1(z) S_2(x, y)$

						10*	1(
					9	14	

N	H	Switching Circuit	R	C	S	G	T
92	87	$wxz+wyz'+w'xy'z'+w'x'yz$	18				

$S_2(x', y') S_2(w, p) S_2[w', P_1(p)], \ p=S_2(x, z) S_2(y, z')$

| | | | | | 9 | 14 | |
| | | | | | | 11 | 11 |

N	H	Switching Circuit	R	C	S	G	T
93	92	$wxy'+wxz'+wx'yz+w'xyz+w'x'yz'$	23				

$S_2(x', y') S_2(w, p) S_2[w', P_1(p)], \ p=P_1(y') S_2(x, z') S_2(x',z)$

| | | | | | 10 | 15 | |
| | | | | | | 12* | 12 |

N	H	Switching Circuit	R	C	S	G	T
94	78	$wxy+wxz+wyz+w'y'z'$	16				

$S_2(w', p) S_2[w, S_2(x, p) S_2(y, z)], \ p=S_2(y', z')$

| | | | | | 9 | 14* | |
| | | | | | | 10 | 10 |

N	H	Switching Circuit	R	C	S	G	T
95	97	$wx'y'+w'xy+wy'z'+xyz$	16*				

$S_2(y', p) P_1[P_1(p) S_2(w, y')], \ p=P_1(x) S_2(w, z')$

| | | | | | 8 | 12 | |
| | | | | | | 9* | 9 |

N	H	Switching Circuit	R	C	S	G	T
96	86	$wxy+wyz'+xy'z+w'x'y'z'$	17*				
		$(w+y')(w'x'+y+z)(x+z')$			8	12	
		$S_2(w, y) S_2(x', z) P_1[S_2(w', x') P_2(y, z)]$				9	9

N	H	Switching Circuit	R	C	S	G	T
97	94	$wxy'+w'xy+wy'z'+wx'yz$	17				

$S_2(w', x') S_2(y, p) S_2[y', P_1(p)], \ p=P_1(w') S_2(x', z)$

| | | | | | 9 | 14 | |
| | | | | | | 10* | 10 |

N	H	Switching Circuit	R	C	S	G	T
98	88	$wxz+wyz'+w'xy'z'+w'x'y'z$	18				
					9	15	
		$F_2[P_1(w')\,S_2(x',z)\,S_2(y',z'),\,P_2(w,y)\,S_2(x,z)\,S_2(x',z')]$				13	13
99	91	$wxy+wxz+wx'y'z'+w'xy'z'+w'x'yz$	23				
					11	17	
		$S_2(w,p)\,S_2[w',P_1(p)],$				15*	15
		$p=S_2(x,q)\,S_2[x',S_2(w,q)\,S_2(y,z)],\ q=S_2(y',z')$					
100	90	$w'x'y'+wxz+wyz'$	12				
		$w(zx+z'y)+w'x'y'$		8		13	
		$F_2[P_1(w')\,S_2(x',z)\,S_2(y',z'),\,P_3(w,x,y)]$				10	10
101	95	$wxy+wxz+x'y'z'+w'x'yz$	17				
					9	14	
		$S_2(x,p)\,P_1[P_1(p)\,S_2(w,x)],\ p=S_2(w,y)\,S_2(y,z')\,S_2(y',z)$				12*	
		$S_2(x',q)\,P_1[P_1(x')\,S_2(w,q)],\ q=S_2(y',z')\,S_3(w',y,z)$					11
102	96	$wxy+wxz+wx'y'z'+w'x'yz'+w'x'y'z$	23				
					10	17	
		$S_2[w',S_2(y,z')\,S_2(y',z)]\,S_2(x',p)\,S_2[x,P_1(p)],$				14	14
		$p=P_1(w')\,S_2(y',z')$					
103	104	$xyz+wxy'z'+wx'yz'+wx'y'z+w'x'y'z'$	24				
					11	17	
		$S_2(x',p)\,S_2[x,P_1(p)],$				15*	15
		$p=S_2(w',q)\,P_1[P_1(q)\,S_2(w',x')\,S_2(y,z)],\ q=P_2(y,z)$					

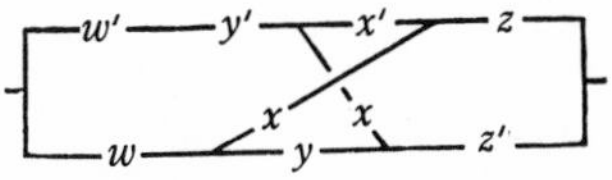

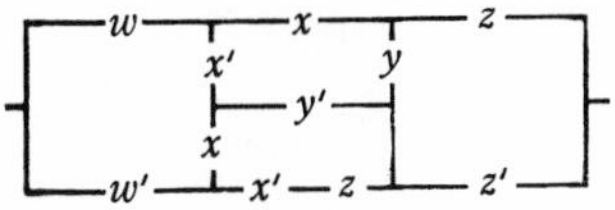

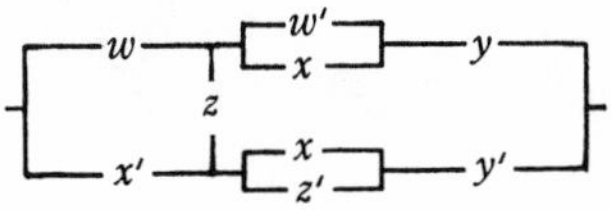

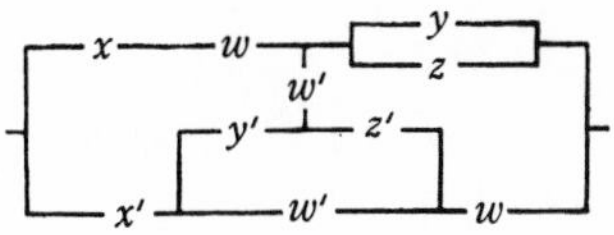

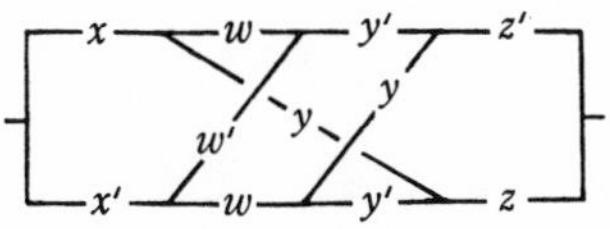

N	H	Switching Circuit	R	C	S	G	T
104	105	$w'x'y+wxz+wx'y'z'+w'xy'z'$	18				
				10	15		
		$S_2(y', p)S_2(z', q)P_1[P_2(p, q)S_2(y', z')]$, $p=P_2(w, x)$, $q=P_2(w', x')$				13*	13
105	72	$wxy+wxz+wyz+xyz+w'x'y'z'$	21				
				11	17		
		$P_2[S_2(w, y)S_2(x, y)S_2(y', z'), S_2(w', x')S_2(w, z)S_2(x, y)]$				14*	14
106	75	$wxz+wyz'+xy'z+w'x'yz$	17				
				9	14		
		$S_2(x', z')S_2(y', z')S_2(w, p)P_1[P_3(w, z', p)], p=P_2(x, y)$				12	12
107	84	$wxy+wyz'+xy'z+w'x'yz$	17				
				8	12		
		$S_2(p, q)P_1[P_2(p, q)], p=P_2(w, y'), q=S_2(x', z)S_2(y', z')$				11*	11
108	93	$wxy'+wxz'+w'yz+x'yz$	16				
				8	12		
		$S_2(p, q)P_1[P_2(p, q)], p=S_2(w, x), q=S_2(y, z)$				9	9
109	108	$wx+wy+wz$	9*				
		$w(x+y+z)$		4	8		
		$P_2[w', P_3(x, y, z)]$				5	
		$P_1(w')S_3(x', y', z')$					4
110	127	$wx+w'x'y+w'x'z$	11*				
		$wx+w'(y+z)x'$		8	10		
		$S_2(w, x')S_2(w', x)P_1[P_3(w, y, z)]$				8	
		$S_2(w, x')S_2(w', x)S_3(w', y', z')$					7

N	H	Switching Circuit	R	C	S	G	T
111	162	$wxy' + wx'y + w'xy + w'x'y'z$	17				

| | | | | | 9 | 14 | |

$S_2(w', p) P_1[P_2(w) S_2(y', z'), p]]$,
$p = S_2(x, y) S_2(x', y')$

| | | | | | | 12 | 12 |

N	H	Switching Circuit	R	C	S	G	T
112	163	$wxyz + wxy'z' + wx'yz + wx'y'z + w'xyz' + w'xy'z + w'x'yz$	35				

| | | | | | 13 | 20 | |

$S_2(p, q) P_1[P_1(p) S_2[q, S_2(w', y')]]]$,
$p = S_2(w, x) S_2(w', x')$, $q = S_2(y, z_2) S_2(y', z)$

| | | | | | | 16 | 16 |

N	H	Switching Circuit	R	C	S	G	T
113	109	$wx + wy + xyz$	10				

| | | | | | 6 | 11 | |

$S_2(x', y') S_2[w', F_3(x', y', z')]$

| | | | | | | 7 | 7 |

N	H	Switching Circuit	R	C	S	G	T
114	110	$wx + wy + xy'z$	10*				
		$(w + zy')(x + y)$			5	9	
		$S_2(w', y) S_2(w', z') S_2(x', y')$				6	6

N	H	Switching Circuit	R	C	S	G	T
115	112	$wx + wyz + wy'z' + xyz$	15				

| | | | | | 8 | 14 | |

$F_2[P_1(w') S_2(x', y) S_2(x', z), S_2(w', x') P_2(y', z')]$

| | | | | | | 11 | 11 |

N	H	Switching Circuit	R	C	S	G	T
116	113	$wx + wyz' + wy'z + xyz$	15*				

| | | | | | 7 | 12 | |

$P_2[P_1(w) S_2(y, z), P_1(x) S_2(y, z') S_2(y', z)]$

| | | | | | | 10* | 10 |

N	H	Switching Circuit	R	C	S	G	T
117	111	$wx + wy + w'x'y'z$	11				

| | | | | | 7 | 11 | |

$S_2(w, p) S_2[w', S_2(z, p)]$, $p = P_2(x, y)$

| | | | | | | 8 | 8 |

N	H	Switching Circuit	R	C	S	G	T
118	114	$wx+wy'z'+x'yz$	11				
		(contact network)			7	12	
		$S_2(w', x) S_2(w', y') S_2[x', S_2(y, z) S_2(y', z')]$				10	
		$P_1[S_2(w, x) S_3(w, y', z') S_3(x', y, z)]$					9
119	136	$wx'y'+wyz'+wy'z+xyz$	16*				
		(contact network)			8	13*	
		$F_2[P_2(w', y) S_2(x, z'), P_1(y') S_2(w', z') S_2(x', z)]$				11	
		$S_2(w', p) S_2[x', P_1(p)] S_3(x, y', z'), p=S_2(y, z)$					10
120	115	$wx+wyz'+wy'z+w'x'yz$	16				
		(contact network)			9	14	
		$S_2(w, p) P_1[P_1(w) S_2(y, p)], p=P_1(x) S_2(y, z') S_2(y', z)$				11*	11
121	146	$wxy'+wx'z+wyz'+w'xyz$	17				
		(contact network)			9	14	
		$S_2(w, p) S_2[w', P_1(p)] P_1[P_3(x, y, z)],$				12	
		$S_2(w, p) S_2[w', P_1(p)] S_3(x', y', z'),$					11
		$p=P_3(x', y', z')$					
122	137	$wxy'+wx'y+w'xy+wxz$	16*				
		(contact network)			8	13	
		$S_2(w', p) P_1[P_3(w', z, p)] S_2(x', y'), p=S_2(x, y)$				10*	10
123	123	$wy+w'xy'+xy'z$	11*				
		$wy+(w'+z)xy'$			6	10	
		$S_2(w', y) S_2(x', y') P_1[P_3(w', y, z)]$				8	
		$S_2(w', y) S_2(x', y') S_3(w, y', z')$					7
124	140	$wxy+wyz'+wy'z+xyz'+xy'z$	20*				
		(contact network)			8	13	
		$S_2(w', x') S_2(y', z') P_1[S_2(w, x) P_2(y', z')]$				9	9

N	H	Switching Circuit	R	C	S	G	T
125	130	$wyz' + wy'z + xyz + w'xy'z'$	17				
				8	15		
		$S_2(w', p) P_1[P_2[P_1(x') S_2(w, y'), p]],$ $p = S_2(y, z) S_2(y', z')$				12*	12
126	128	$wxy + wxz + wyz + xyz + wx'y'z' + w'xy'z'$	26*				
				10	16		
		$S_2(w', x') S_2(p, q) P_1[P_2(p, q) S_2(y, z)],$ $p = P_2(w', x'), q = P_2(y, z)$				13*	13
127	126	$wx + w'x'y + wy'z$	11				
				7	11		
		$S_2(w', x) S_2(w', y') P_1[P_2(w', x) S_2(y', z)]$				9	9
128	124	$wx + x'yz + w'x'y'z'$ $xw + x'(y'+z)(y+z'w')$ $S_2(w', x) S_2[x', S_2(y, z) P_1[P_3(w, y, z)]]$ $S_2(w', x) S_2[x', S_2(y, z) S_3(w', y', z')$	12	8	12	10	9
129	152	$wxz' + wyz' + xy'z + x'yz$ $(w+z)(x'+y'+z')(x+y)$ $S_2(w', z') S_2(x', y') P_1[P_3(x', y', z')]$ $S_2(w', z') S_2(x', y') S_3(x, y, z)$	16*	7	11	8	7
130	142	$wxy' + wyz + xy'z + x'yz'$	16*				
				8	13		
		$S_2(x', y') P_2[P_2(x', z) S_2(w, y'), P_3(w, y', z')]$ $S_2(x', y') P_1[P_2(x', z) S_2(w, y')] S_3(w', y, z)$				11	10
131	125	$wx + wyz + w'x'yz' + w'x'y'z$	17				
				9	14		
		$S_2(w, p) S_2[w', S_2[p, S_2(y', z')]], p = P_1(x) S_2(y, z)$				11*	11

N	H	Switching Circuit	R	C	S	G	T
132	149	$wxy' + wx'y + w'xy + wx'z$	16*				

| | | | | 8 | 13 | | |

$$S_2(w', p)\, S_2[w,\, P_1(p)]\, P_1[P_3(x,\, y,\, z)],\ p = S_2(x,\, y)$$

| | | | | | | 11 | |

$$S_2(w', p)\, S_2[w,\, P_1(p)]\, S_3(x',\, y',\, z'),\ p = S_2(x,\, y)$$

| | | | | | | | 10 |

| 133 | 133 | $wx'y + wx'z + xyz + xy'z'$ | 16* | | | | |

| | | | | 8 | 13 | | |

$$F_2[P_1(x')\, S_2(y,\, z')\, S_2(y',\, z),\ P_2(w',\, x)\, S_2(y',\, z')]$$

| | | | | | | 11 | 11 |

| 134 | 139 | $wxy' + wx'y + xyz + w'x'y'z'$ | 17 | | | | |

| | | | | 10 | 15* | | |

$$P_2[S_2(w,\, x')\, S_2(x,\, z)\, S_2(y',\, z'),\ P_1(y)\, S_2(w,\, x)\, S_2(w',\, x')]$$

| | | | | | | 13* | 13 |

| 135 | 151 | $wxy' + wx'y + wxz' + w'xyz + w'x'y'z$ | 22* | | | | |

| | | | | 10 | 15 | | |

$$S_2(w', p)\, P_1[P_1(p)\, S_2(w',\, z)],\ p = S_2(x',\, y')\, P_1[P_3(x',\, y',\, z')]$$

| | | | | | | 12 | |

$$S_2(w', q)\, P_1[P_1(q)\, S_2(w',\, z)],\ q = S_2(x',\, y')\, S_3(x,\, y,\, z)$$

| | | | | | | | 11 |

| 136 | 147 | $wxy' + wx'y + wxz + w'xyz' + w'x'y'z$ | 22* | | | | |

| | | | | 10 | 15 | | |

$$S_2(w, p)\, S_2[w',\, S_2[p,\, S_2(y',\, z')]],$$
$$p = S_2(x,\, y')\, S_2(x',\, y)\, S_2(x,\, z)$$

| | | | | | | 14* | |

$$S_2(w', q)\, P_1[P_2[P_1(w)\, S_2(y',\, z'),\ q]],$$
$$q = S_2(x',\, y')\, S_3(x,\, y,\, z)$$

| | | | | | | | 13 |

| 137 | 134 | $wx'y + wx'z + wyz + wxy'z' + w'xyz' + w'xy'z$ | 27* | | | | |

| | | | | 11 | 17 | | |

$$S_2(w, p)\, P_1[P_2[P_1(w')\, S_2(x',\, q),\ p]],$$
$$p = P_2(x',\, q)\, S_2(y,\, z),\ q = P_2(y,\, z)$$

| | | | | | | 14* | 14 |

N	H	Switching Circuit	R	C	S	G	T
138	155	$wx'y+w'xy'+wx'z'+xyz$	16*				
		$(w+x)[(w'+y)(y'+z)+x'z']$		8	12		
		$S_2(w', x') P_1[S_2(w', y') S_2(x', z') S_2(y, z)]$				9*	9
139	145	$wx'y+w'xy'+wx'z+w'xz'+wyz$	20*				

N	H	Switching Circuit	R	C	S	G	T
				10	15*		
		$S_2(w, p) P_1[P_2[P_1(w') S_2(y', z'), p]], \; p = P_1(x') S_2(y, z)$					11* 11
140	157	$w'xy'+wx'z+w'xz+wyz'$	16*				

N	H	Switching Circuit	R	C	S	G	T
				8	13		
		$S_2(w, p) S_2[w', S_2(x, p)], \; p = S_2(x', z) S_2(y, z')$					10 10
141	161	$wx'y+w'xy+wx'z+w'xz+wxy'z'$	21*				

N	H	Switching Circuit	R	C	S	G	T
				9	14		
		$S_2(p, q) P_1[P_2(p, q)],$					11* 11
		$p = S_2(w', x') S_2(y', z'), \; q = P_2(w', x')$					
142	156	$wxy+w'x'y+wy'z+w'xy'z'$	17				

N	H	Switching Circuit	R	C	S	G	T
				9	14		
		$S_2(w, p) S_2[w', S_2[p, S_2(x', y')]], \; p = S_2(x, y) S_2(y', z)$					12 12
143	158	$wxy+w'x'y+wxz'+wx'y'z+w'xy'z$	22				

N	H	Switching Circuit	R	C	S	G	T
				10	18		

N	H	Switching Circuit	R	C	S	G	T
				11	17		
		$S_2(w, p) P_1[P_2[p, P_1(w') S_2(x', z')]],$				14	
		$p = S_2(x, y) S_2(x', y')S_2(x, z')$					
		$S_2(w', q) S_2[w, S_2[q, S_2(x', z')]], \; q = S_2(x', y) S_3(x, y', z)$					13

N	H	Switching Circuit	R	C	S	G	T
144	144	$wxy+wxz+wyz+w'xy'z'+w'x'yz'+w'x'y'z$	27				
				11	17		
		$S_2(w',\,p)\,S_2[w,\,P_1(p)\,S_2(x',\,q),$ $p=S_2(x',\,y')\,S_2(x',\,z')\,P_1(q),\ q=P_2(y,\,z)$				14	14
145	160	$wxy'+wxz'+wx'yz+w'xyz+w'x'yz'+w'x'y'z$	28				
				12	18		
		$S_2(p,\,q)\,P_1[P_2(p,\,q)],$ $p=S_2(y,\,z),\ q=S_2(w,\,x)\,P_1[P_2(w,\,x)\,S_2(y',\,z')]$				14*	14
146	116	$wx+yz$ $P_1[S_2(w,\,x)\,S_2(y,\,z)]$	6	4	8	5	5
147	119	$wx+wyz'+w'yz$	11				
				6	10		
		$F_2[P_2(w',\,x'),\,P_1(y')\,S_2(w,\,z)\,S_2(w',\,z')]$				9	9
148	117	$wx+wyz+xyz+w'x'yz'$	16				
				8	13		
		$S_2(z,\,p)\,P_1[S_2(w,\,x)\,S_2[y,\,F_2(z,\,p)]],\ p=P_2(w,\,x)$				11*	11
149	121	$wx+wy'z'+w'yz$ $w(x+y'z')+w'yz$ $P_2[P_1(w)\,S_2(y,\,z),\,P_2(w',\,x)\,S_2(y',\,z')]$	11	7	12	9	9
150	122	$wx+wy'z+xyz'+w'x'yz$	16*				
				8	12*		
		$S_2(w',\,y')\,S_2(x',\,z')\,P_1[P_2(y',\,z')\,S_2(w,\,x)\,S_2(w',\,x')]$				11*	11
151	120	$wx+wy'z+xyz+w'x'yz'$	16*				
				8	12		
		$P_2[P_1(w)\,S_2(x',\,y)\,S_2(y,\,z),\,P_1(x)\,S_2(w',\,z')\,S_2(y',\,z)]$				12	
		$S_2(w',\,y')\,S_3(w,\,x',\,z')\,S_3(w',\,x,\,z')\,S_3(x',\,y,\,z)$					11

N	H	Switching Circuit	R	C	S	G	T
152	118	$wx+wyz+xyz+w'x'y'z'$	16				

| | | | | 9 | 14 | | |

$P_2[S_2(w, x) S_2(w', x') S_2(y, z), P_2(w, x), S_2(y', z')]$ 12* 12

| 153 | 150 | $wxy'+w'xy+wxz'+wx'z$ | 16* | | | | |

| | | | | 8 | 12 | | |

$S_2(x', z') S_2(w', p) P_1[P_3(w', z', p)],\ p=S_2(x, y)$ 10 10

| 154 | 138 | $wxy'+w'xy+wyz+wy'z'$ | 16* | | | | |

| | | | | 8 | 13 | | |

$F_2[P_1(y') S_2(w', x') S_2(w, z'), P_2(w', y) S_2(x', z)]$ 11*
$S_2(w', x') S_2(w', y') S_3(w, y, z') S_3(x', y', z)$ 10

| 155 | 131 | $wxy'+w'xy+wy'z+xyz+wx'yz'$ | 21* | | | | |

| | | | | 10 | 15 | | |

$S_2(p, q) P_1[P_2(p, q)],$ 13* 13
$p=S_2(w', y') S_2(x', y), q=P_2(w', z) S_2(x, y')$

| 156 | 153 | $wx'y'+w'xy+wyz+wy'z'$ | 16* | | | | |

| | | | | 8 | 12* | | |

$S_2(w', x') S_2(y, p) P_1[P_3(x', y, p)],\ p=P_2(w', z)$ 10* 10

| 157 | 135 | $wx'y'+w'xy+wx'z+wy'z+xyz'$ | 20* | | | | |

| | | | | 9 | 15* | | |

$S_2(p, q) P_1[P_2(p, q)],$ 12* 12
$p=P_2(x', y'), q=P_1(w') S_2(x, z') S_2(y, z')$

N	H	Switching Circuit	R	C	S	G	T
158	141	$wxz+wx'z'+wyz+xyz+w'xy'z'$	21*				

$$S_2(w', x') S_2(z, p) P_1[P_3(x',z, p)], \ p=P_1(y) S_2(w, x)$$

					9	15	
						11*	11
159	129	$wxy+wxz+wyz+xyz+x'y'z'$	20				

$$F_3[P_2(w', x') S_2(y', z'), S_2(w', x') P_2(y', z'), P_3(x, y, z)]$$
$$S_3(x, y', z') P_1[S_2(w, x) S_2(y', z') P_1[S_2(w', x') P_2(y', z')]]]$$

					10	16	
						14	
							13
160	148	$wx'y'+wyz+xyz'+w'xy'z$	17				

$$S_2(w', x')S_2(y', z') P_1[P_2(y', p)S_2(w', z)], \ p=P_1(x)S_2(w', z)$$

					9	14*	
						12*	12
161	132	$wxz+wyz+xyz'+wx'y'z'+w'x'y'z$	22				

$$S_2(p, q) P_1[P_2(p, q)],$$
$$p=P_2(x, y) S_2(w', z'), \ q=S_2(w', z) S_2(x', z') S_2(y', z')$$

					10	16	
						15*	15
162	143	$w'x'y'+wxz+wyz+xyz'$	16				

$$S_2(w, p) P_1[S_2(w, z) P_2[p, P_3(x', y', z)]], \ p=P_2(x, y)$$
$$S_2(w, p) P_1[P_1(p) S_2(w, z) S_3(x, y, z')], \ p=P_2(x, y)$$

					9	14	
						12*	
							11
163	154	$wxy+wyz'+xy'z+w'x'yz+w'x'y'z'$	22				

$$S_2(p, q) P_1[P_2(p, q)],$$
$$p=P_1(w) S_2(x, y') S_2(y', z'), \ q=S_2(x', z) S_2(y', z')$$

					10	16*	
						14*	14

N	H	Switching Circuit	R	C	S	G	T
164	159	$wxy'+wxz'+w'yz+x'yz+w'x'y'z'$	21				

| | | | | 10 | 16 | | |

$S_2(p, q) P_1[P_2(p, q) P_1[P_4(w, x, y, z)]]$,
$S_2(p, q) P_1[P_2(p, q) S_4(w', x', y', z')]$,
$p=P_2(w', x')$, $q=P_2(y', z')$

| | | | | | | 14* | |
| | | | | | | | 13 |

N	H	Switching Circuit	R	C	S	G	T
165	164	w	0	1	2	0	0
166	204	$wx'+w'x$	6	4	6		
		$S_2(w, x) S_2(w', x')$				4	4
		$P_2(w, x')+P_2(w', x)$					4
167	236	$wxy+wx'y'+w'xy'+w'x'y$	16				

| | | | | 8 | 12 | | |

$S_2(w, p) S_2[w', P_1(p)]$, $p=S_2(x, y) S_2(x', y')$
$P_2(w, q)+P_2(w', S_1(q)]$, $q=P_2(x, y)+P_2(x', y')$

| | | | | | | 9 | 9 |
| | | | | | | | 9 |

N	H	Switching Circuit	R	C	S	G	T
168	237	$wxyz'+wxy'z+wx'yz+wx'y'z'+w'xyz+w'xy'z'+w'x'yz'$ $+w'x'y'z$	40				

| | | | | 12 | 18 | | |

$S_2(p, q) P_1[P_2(p, q)]$,
$p=S_2(w, x) S_2(w', x')$, $q=S_2(y, z) S_2(y', z')$
$P_2(r, s)+S_1[S_2(r, s)]$,
$r=P_2(w, x')+P_2(w', x)$, $s=P_2(y, z)+P_2(y', z')$

| | | | | | | 13* | 13 |
| | | | | | | | 13 |

N	H	Switching Circuit	R	C	S	G	T
169	165	$wx+wy+wz+xyz$	13				

| | | | | 5 | 10 | | |

$S_2[w', F_3(x', y', z')] P_1[P_3(x, y, z)]$
$S_2[w', S_3(x, y, z)] S_3(x', y', z')$
$P_2[w', P_3(x, y, z)]+P_3(x', y', z')$

						9	
							8
							8

N	H	Switching Circuit	R	C	S	G	T
170	166	$wx+wy+wz+xyz'$	13				

| | | | | 7 | 12 | | |

$S_2[w', F_3(x', y', z)] P_1[P_3(x, y, z)]$
$S_2[w', S_3(x, y, z')] S_3(x', y', z')$
$P_2[w', P_3(x, y, z)]+P_3(x', y', z)$

						9	
							8
							8

N	H	Switching Circuit	R	C	S	G	T
171	167	$wy+wz+xy'z'$	10				

$$S_2(w', p) S_2[x', P_1(p)], \ p=S_2(y', z')$$
$$P_2(w', q)+P_2[x', S_1(q)], \ q=P_2(y, z)$$

				6	10		
						7*	7
							7

| 172 | 168 | $wx+wy+wz+w'x'y'z'$ | 14 | | | | |

$$S_2(w, p) S_2[w', P_1(p)], \ p=P_3(x, y, z)$$
$$P_2(w, q)+P_2[w', S_1(q)], \ q=S_3(x', y', z')$$

				8	12		
						8	8
							8

| 173 | 208 | $wxy'+wx'y+w'xy+wxz+w'x'y'z$ | 21 | | | | |

$$S_2(w', p) S_2(z', q) P_1[P_2(w', p) S_2(y, z)],$$
$$p=P_1(q) S_2(x, y), \ q=P_2(x, y)$$
$$P_2(w', r)+P_2(z', s)+S_1[S_2(w', r)+P_2(y, z)],$$
$$r=S_1(s)+P_2(x, y), \ s=S_2(x, y)$$

				10	16		
						14*	14
							14

| 174 | 201 | $wz+w'xz'+w'yz'+xyz'$ | 15 | | | | |

$$S_2(w', z) P_1[P_1(z) S_2(w', x) S_2(w', y)S_2(x, y)]$$
$$P_2(w', z')+S_1[S_1(z')+P_2(w', x)+P_2(w', y)+P_2(x, y)]$$

				7	13		
						10*	10
							10

| 175 | 220 | $wx\dot{y}'+wx'y+w'xy+wxz'+w'x'y'z$ | 21 | | | | |

$$S_2(w', p) S_2(z', q) P_1[P_2(w', p) S_2(x, z')],$$
$$p=P_1(q) S_2(x, y), \ q=P_2(x, y)$$
$$P_2(w', r)+P_2(z, s)+S_1[S_2(w', r)+P_2(x, z)],$$
$$r=S_1(s)+P_2(x, y), \ s=S_2(x, y)$$

				10	15		
						14*	14
							14

N	H	Switching Circuit	R	C	S	G	T

176 205 | $wxy+wxz'+wyz'+xyz'+wx'y'z+w'xy'z+w'x'yz$ | 31

                                                          12   18*

$S_2(p, q) P_1[P_2(p, q)], \; p=P_1(r) S_2(y', z)$ 16* 16
$q=S_2(w, x) S_2(y, z') S_2(y', r), \; r=P_2(w, x)$
$P_2(s, t)+S_1[S_2(s, t)], \; s=S_1(u)+P_2(y', z')$ 16
$t=P_2(w, x)+P_2(y, z)+P_2(y', u), \; u=S_2(w, x)$

---

177 202 | $wy+w'y'z+xy'z'$ | 11
$yw+y'(zw'+z'x)$ 7   11
$S_2(w', y) P_1[P_1(y) S_2(w', z) S_2(x, z')]$ 8* 8
$P_2(w', y')+S_1[S_1(y')+P_2(w', z')+P_2(x, z)]$ 8

---

178 210 | $wyz'+wy'z+w'yz+xy'z'$ | 16

                                                           9   14

$S_2(w, p) S_2(x', q) P_1[P_3(w, p, q)],$ 12   12
$p=P_2(y', z'), \; q=P_2(y, z)$
$P_2(w, r)+P_2(x', s)+S_1[S_3(w, r, s)],$ 12
$r=S_2(y, z), \; s=S_2(y', z')$

---

179 203 | $wx+w'x'y+w'x'z+wy'z'$ | 15

                                                           8   12

$S_2(w', p) S_2(w, P_1(p)], \; p=P_1(x) S_2(y', z')$ 8   8
$P_2(w', q)+P_2[w, S_1(q)], \; q=S_1(x')+P_2(y, z)$ 8

---

180 228 | $wxy'+wx'y+w'xy+wx'z'+w'x'y'z$ | 21

                                                            10   15

$S_2(w, p) S_2[w', P_1(p)], \; p=S_2(x, y') S_2(x', y) S_2(y', z')$ 11
$S_2(w', q) S_2[w, P_1(q)], \; q=S_2(x, y) S_3(x', y', z)$ 10
$P_2(w', r)+P_2[w, S_1(r)], \; r=P_2(x', y')+P_3(x, y, z')$ 10

N	H	Switching Circuit	R	C	S	G	T
181	215	$wx'y'+wx'z'+wy'z'+wxyz+w'xyz'+w'xy'z+w'x'yz$	32				

| | | | | 12 | 18 | | |

$S_2(w,\,p)\,S_2[w',\,P_1(p)],$
$p=S_2(x,\,q)\,S_2[x',\,P_1(q)]\,S_2(y',\,z'),\ q=P_2(y',\,z')$
$P_2(w,\,r)+P_2[w',\,S_1(r)],$
$r=P_2(x',\,s)+P_2[x,\,S_1(s)]+P_2(y,\,z),\ s=S_2(y,\,z)$

| | | | | | | 14 | 14 |
| | | | | | | | 14 |

| 182 | 169 | $wx+wy+xy$ | 9 | | | | |

| | | | | 5 | 9 | | |

$S_2(w',\,x')\,S_2(w',\,y')\,S_2(x',\,y')$
$P_2(P_2(w',\,x')+P_2(w',\,y')+P_2(x',\,y'))$

| | | | | | | 6 | 6 |
| | | | | | | | 6 |

183	174	$wy'+xy$	6	4	7		
		$S_2(w',\,y')\,S_2(x',\,y)$				4	4
		$(w',\,y)+P_2(x',\,y')$					4

| 184 | 180 | $wx+wyz'+wy'z+xyz'+xy'z$ | 19 | | | | |

| | | | | 8 | 13 | | |

$S_2(w',\,x')\,P_1[S_2(w,\,x)\,S_2(y,\,z')\,S_2(y',\,z)]$
$P_2(w',\,x')+S_1[P_2(w,\,x)+P_2(y,\,z)+P_2(y',\,z')]$

| | | | | | | 9* | 9 |
| | | | | | | | 9 |

| 185 | 184 | $wyz+wy'z'+xyz'+xy'z$ | 16 | | | | |

| | | | | 8 | 13 | | |

$S_2(w',\,p)\,S_2[x',\,P_1(p)],\ p=S_2(y,\,z')\,S_2(y',\,z)$
$P_2(w',\,q)\,P_2[x',\,S_1(q)],\ q=P_2(y,\,z')+P_2(y',\,z)$

| | | | | | | 9 | 9 |
| | | | | | | | 9 |

| 186 | 179 | $wx+wy+w'x'y'$ | 10 | | | | |

| | | | | 6 | 9 | | |

$S_2(w,\,p)\,S_2[w',\,P_1(p)],\ p=P_2(x,\,y)$
$P_2(w,\,q)+P_2[w',\,S_1(q)],\ q=S_2(x',\,y')$

| | | | | | | 7 | 7 |
| | | | | | | | 7 |

N	H	Switching Circuit	R	C	S	G	T
187	189	$wx+x'yz+x'y'z'$	11				
		$xw+x'(yz+y'z')$		7	11		
		$S_2(w', x) S_2[x', S_2(y, z) S_2(y', z')]$				8	8
		$P_2(w', x')+P_2[x, P_2(y, z')+P_2(y', z)]$					8

| 188 | 219 | $wyz'+wy'z+xyz+x'y'z'$ | 16 | | | | |

				9	14		
		$S_2(x, p) S_2(x', q) P_1[P_3(w, p, q)]$,				12	12
		$p=P_2(y, z),\ q=P_2(y', z')$					
		$P_2(x, r)+P_2(x', s)+S_1[S_3(w, r, s)]$,					12
		$r=S_2(y', z'),\ s=S_2(y, z)$					

| 189 | 190 | $wx+wyz'+wy'z+w'x'yz+w'x'y'z'$ | 21 | | | | |

				10	15		
		$S_2(w, p) S_2[w', P_1(p)]$, $p=P_1(x) S_2(y, z') S_2(y', z)$				10	10
		$P_2(w, q)+P_2[w', S_1(q)]$, $q=S_1(x')+P_2(y, z')+P_2(y', z)$					10

| 190 | 226 | $wxy'+wx'z+wyz'+w'xyz+w'x'y'z'$ | 22 | | | | |

				11	17		
		$S_2(w, p) S_2[w', P_1(p)]$, $p=S_2(x, y') S_2(x', z) S_2(y, z')$				11	11
		$P_2(w, q)+P_2[w', S_1(q)]$, $q=P_2(x', y)+P_2(x, z')+P_2(y', z)$					11

| 191 | 233 | $wxz+w'x'z'+wyz'+w'y'z$ | 16 | | | | |

				8	14		
		$F_2[S_2(w, x') S_2(w', y) S_2(y', z'),\ P_2(x, z) S_2(w, y')]$				12	12
		$B_2[P_2(w, x)+P_2(w', y')+P_2(y, z'),\ S_2(x', z)+P_2(w, y)]$					12

| 192 | 225 | $wxy+w'x'y'+wxz+w'x'z'+wyz+w'y'z'$ | 24 | | | | |

				10	15		
		$S_2(w, p) S_2[w', P_1(p)]$, $p=S_2(x, y) S_2(x, z) S_2(y, z)$				11	11
		$P_2(w, q)+P_2[w', S_1(q)]$, $q=P_2(x', y')+P_2(x', z')+P_2(y', z')$					11

N	H	Switching Circuit	R	C	S	G	T
193	234	$wxz'+w'x'z'+wyz+w'y'z$	16				

N	H	Switching Circuit	R	C	S	G	T
				8	12		
		$S_2(w,\ p)\,S_2[w',\ P_1(p)],\ p=S_2(x,\ z')\,S_2(y,\ z)$				9	9
		$P_2(w,\ q)+P_2[w',\ S_1(q)],\ q=P_2(x',\ z)+P_2(y',\ z')$					9
194	235	$wxy'+w'x'y'+wxz'+w'x'z'+wx'yz+w'xyz$	26				

N	H	Switching Circuit	R	C	S	G	T
				10	15		
		$S_2(p,\ q)\,P_1[P_2(p,\ q)],$				11*	11
		$p=S_2(w,\ x)\,S_2(w',\ x'),\ q=S_2(y,\ z)$					
		$P_2(r,\ s)+S_1[S_2(r,\ s)],$					11
		$r=P_2(w,\ x')+P_2(w',\ x),\ s=P_2(y',\ z')$					
195	170	$wx+wy+xz$	9				

N	H	Switching Circuit	R	C	S	G	T
				5	9		
		$S_2(w',\ x')\,S_2(w',\ z')\,S_2(x',\ y')$				6	6
		$P_2(w',\ x')+P_2(w',\ y')+P_2(x',\ z')$					6
196	171	$wx+wy+xyz+xy'z'$	14				

N	H	Switching Circuit	R	C	S	G	T
				7	12		
		$F_2[P_1(w')\,S_2(x',\ y'),\ P_1(x')\,S_2(y,\ z')\,S_2(y',\ z)]$				10	10
		$B_2[S_1(x')+P_2(w',\ y'),\ S_1(w')+P_2(y,\ z)+P_2(y',\ z')]$					10
197 a	175	$wx+wy+xy'z+x'yz$	14*				
		$[w+z(x'+y')](x+y)$		6	10		
		$S_2(w',\ z')\,S_2(x',\ y')\,P_1[P_3(w,\ x',\ y')]$				8	
		$S_2(w',\ z')\,S_2(x',\ y')\,S_3(w',\ x,\ y)$					7
		$S_1[P_2(w,\ z)+P_2(x,\ y)+P_3(w,\ x',\ y')]$					8
197 b	181	$wz+xy+wx'y'$	10				
		$w(z+x'y')+xy$		6	10		
		$P_1[S_2(w,\ z)\,S_2(x,\ y)\,P_1[P_3(w',\ x,\ y)]]$				9	
		$P_1[S_2(w,\ z)\,S_2(x,\ y)\,S_3(w,\ x',\ y')]$					8
		$P_2(w',\ z')+P_2(x',\ y')+P_3(w',\ x,\ y)$					7

N	H	Switching Circuit	R	C	S	G	T
198 a	172	$wx+wy+xyz+w'x'y'z$	15				

N	H	Switching Circuit	R	C	S	G	T
				8	13		
		$S_2(w,\ p)\,S_2(w',\ z')\,P_1[P_2(w,\ p)\,S_2(x,\ y)],\ p=P_2(x,\ y)$				11	11
		$P_2(w',\ q)+S_1[S_2(w',\ z)+P_2[q,\ P_2(x',\ y')]],\ q=P_2(x,y)$					11
198 b	186	$wz+wxy'+wx'y+w'xy$	15				

N	H	Switching Circuit	R	C	S	G	T
				8	13		
		$S_2(w',\ p)P_1[P_2(w',\ z)S_2[p,\ S_2(x',\ y')]],\ p=S_2(x,\ y)$				11*	11
		$P_2(w,\ q)+P_2(w',\ z')+S_1[S_2(w,\ q)+P_2(x,\ y)],\ q=S_2(x,\ y)$					11
199	177	$wx+wz+w'yz'$	10				
		$w(x+z)+w'yz'$		6	10		
		$S_2(w',\ y')\,S_2(w',\ z)\,P_1[P_3(w',\ x,\ z)]$				8	
		$S_2((w',\ y')\,S_2(w',\ z)\,S_3(w,\ x',\ z')$					7
		$P_2(w',\ x')+P_2(w',\ z')+P_3(w,\ y',\ z)$					7
200 a	176	$wx+wy+xy'z+x'yz'$	14*				
		$(x+y)(w+x'z'+y'z)$		7	11		
		$S_2(x',\ y')\,P_1[P_1(w)\,S_2(x',\ z')\,S_2(y',\ z)]$				8	8
		$B_2[S_2(x',\ y'),\ S_1(w')+P_2(x,\ z)+P_2(y,\ z')]$					9
200 b	194	$xy+wx'z+wy'z'$	11				

N	H	Switching Circuit	R	C	S	G	T
				7	11*		
		$F_2[P_2(x',\ y'),\ P_1(w')\,S_2(x,\ z)\,S_2(y,\ z')]$				9*	9
		$P_2(x',\ y')\,S_1[S_1(w)+P_2(x',\ z')+P_2(y',\ z)]$					8
201 a	173	$wx+wy+xyz+w'x'y'z'$	15				

N	H	Switching Circuit	R	C	S	G	T
				9	14		
		$P_2[P_1(w)\,S_2(x,\ z)\,S_2(y',\ z'),\ P_1(y)\,S_2(w,\ x)\,S_2(w',\ x')]$				12	
		$S_2[w',\ S_3(x,\ y,\ z)\,S_3(x',\ y',\ z)]\,S_3(w,\ x',\ y')$					11
		$P_2(w',\ p)+S_1[S_3(w',\ z',\ p)]+P_3(x',\ y',\ z'),\ p=P_2(x,\ y)$					11

N	H	Switching Circuit	R	C	S	G	T
201 b	217	$wx'y+w'xy+wxz'+wy'z$	16*				

| | | | | 9 | 14 | | |

$F_2[P_1(w')\,S_2(x',\,z')\,S_2(y,\,z),\,P_1(y')\,S_2(w,\,x)\,S_2(w',\,x')]$ — 12

$S_2(w',\,p)\,P_1[P_3(w',\,z',\,p)]\,S_3(x',\,y',\,z'),\ p=S_2(x,\,y)$ — 11

$P_2[w',\,P_3(x,\,y,\,z)+P_3(x',\,y',\,z')+P_3(w,\,x',\,y')$ — 11

| 202 | 185 | $wx+wy'z+xyz'+x'yz$ | 15 | | | | |

| | | | | 7 | 11 | | |

$S_2(w',\,y')\,S_2(z',\,p)\,P_1[P_2(z',\,p)\,S_2(w,\,x)],\ p=P_2(x,\,y')$ — 11* 11

$P_2(w',\,x')+P_2(z',\,q)+S_1[S_2(z',\,q)+P_2(w,y)],\ q=S_2(x',\,y)$ — 11

| 203 | 182 | $wx+wyz+wy'z'+xyz+w'x'yz'$ | 20 | | | | |

| | | | | 9 | 14 | | |

$S_2(w',\,y')\,S_2(w,\,p)\,P_1[P_2(w,\,p)\,S_2(x,\,z)],$ — 14* 14

$p=P_1(x)\,S_2(y,\,z)\,S_2(y',\,z')$

$P_2(w',\,x')+P_2(w,\,q)+S_1[S_2(w,\,q)+P_2(y,\,z')],$ — 14

$q=S_1(y)+P_2(x,\,z')+P_2(x',\,z)$

| 204 a | 178 | $wx+wy+xy'z+w'x'y'z'$ | 15 | | | | |

| | | | | 8 | 12 | | |

$S_2(p,\,q)\,P_1[P_2(p,\,q)],\ p=S_2(x',\,y'),\ q=P_1(w)\,S_2(y',\,z)$ — 10* 10

$P_2(r,\,s)+S_1[S_2(r,\,s)],\ r=S_2(x',\,y'),\ s=S_1(w')+P_2(y,\,z')$ — 10

| 204 b | 188 | $wy'+w'xy+wx'z+xyz'$ | 15 | | | | |

| | | | | 8 | 12 | | |

$S_2(p,\,q)\,P_1(P_2(p,\,q)],\ p=P_2(x',\,y'),\ q=P_1(w')\,S_2(y,\,z')$ — 10* 10

$P_2(r,\,s)+S_1[S_2(r,\,s)],\ r=P_2(x',\,y'),\ s=S_1(w)+P_2(y',\,z)$ — 10

N	H	Switching Circuit	R	C	S	G	T
205 a	183	$wx+wyz+xyz+x'y'z'$	15				
		(circuit diagram)		8	14		
		$F_3[P_2(w',\ x'),\ S_2(w',\ x')P_2(y',\ z'),\ P_3(x,\ y,\ z)]$				12	
		$P_1[S_2(w,\ x)P_1[S_2(w',\ x')P_2(y',\ z')]S_3(x',\ y',\ z')]$					11
		$P_2(w',\ x')+S_1[P_2(w,\ x)+S_2(y,\ z)]+P_3(x,\ y,\ z)$					10
205 b	218	$wx'y+wxz'+wy'z+xyz'+xy'z$	20*				
		(circuit diagram)		8	13		
		$S_2(w',\ x')P_2[S_2(w,\ x)P_2(y,\ z),\ P_3(x',\ y',\ z')]$					11
		$S_2(w',\ x')P_1[S_2(w,\ x)P_2(y,\ z)]S_3(x,\ y,\ z)$					10
		$S_1[P_2(w,\ x)+S_1[P_2(w',\ x')+S_2(y',\ z')]+P_3(x',\ y',\ z')]$					11
206 a	187	$wx+wyz'+wy'z+xy'z'+w'x'yz$	20				
		(circuit diagram)		9	14		
		$S_2(w,\ p)\,S_2(x',\ q)\,P_1[P_3(w,\ p,\ q)],$				13*	13
		$p=P_3(x,\ y',\ z'),\ q=P_2(y,\ z)$					
		$P_2(w,\ r)+P_2(x',\ s)+S_1[S_3(w,\ r,\ s)],$					13
		$r=S_3(x',\ y,\ z),\ s=S_2(y',\ z')$					
206 b	207	$wx'y'+wxz+wyz'+xyz+w'xy'z'$	21*				
		(circuit diagram)		9	16		
		$S_2(w,\ p)\,S_2(x',\ q)\,P_1[P_3(w,\ p,\ q)],$				13*	13
		$p=P_3(x',\ y,\ z),\ q=P_2(y',\ z')$					
		$P_2(w,\ r)+P_2(x',\ q)+S_1[S_3(w,\ r,\ s)],$					13
		$r=S_3(x,\ y',\ z'),\ s=S_2(y,\ z)$					
207	195	$wx+w'x'y+wy'z+w'yz$	15				
		(circuit diagram)		7	12		
		$F_2[P_2(w,\ y')S_2(x,\ z'),\ P_1(w')S_2(x',\ y)S_2(x',\ z')]$				11*	
		$S_2(w',\ y')P_1[P_2(w',\ x)S_2(y',\ z)]S_3(w',\ x,\ z')$					10
		$P_2(w',\ x')+S_1[S_2(w',\ y)+P_2(x',\ z)]+P_3(w',\ y,\ z')$					10

N	H	Switching Circuit	R	C	S	G	T
208 a	191	$wx+yz+w'x'y'z$	11				
		$wx+(y+w'z')(z+y'x')$		8	12		
		$P_1[S_2(w,\ x)\,S_2(y,\ z)\,P_1[P_4(w,\ x,\ y,\ z)]]$				10	
		$P_1[S_2(w,\ x)\,S_2(y,\ z)\,S_4(w',\ x',\ y',\ z')]$					9
		$P_2(w',\ x')+P_2(y',\ z')+P_4(w,\ x,\ y,\ z)$					8
208 b	231	$w'xy+wx'z+wyz'+xy'z$	16*				
		$(w+x)(w'+x'+y'+z')(y+z)$		8	12		
		$S_2(w',\ x')\,S_2(y',\ z')\,P_1[P_4(w',\ x',\ y',\ z')]$				9	
		$S_2(w',\ x')\,S_2(y',\ z')\,S_4(w,\ x,\ y,\ z)$					8
		$S_1[P_2(w,\ x)+P_2(y,\ z)+P_4(w',\ x',\ y',\ z')]$					9
209 a	192	$wx+wyz+xyz+w'x'yz'+w'x'y'z$	21				
		[circuit diagram]		10	16		
		$S_2[p,\ P_1(q)]\,S_2[q,\ P_1(p)],$				14*	14
		$p=S_2(w,\ x)\,S_2(y,\ z),\ q=P_2(w,\ x)\,S_2(y',\ z')$					
		$P_2(r,\ s)+S_1[S_2(r,\ s)],$					13
		$r=P_2(w',\ x')+P_2(y',\ z'),\ s=S_2(w',\ x')+P_2(y,\ z)$					
209 b	211	$wx'y+w'xy+wx'z+w'xz+wyz+wxy'z'$	25*				
		[circuit diagram]		10	16		
		$S_2(p,\ q)\,P_1[P_2(p,\ q)],$				13	13
		$p=S_2(w',\ x')\,S_2(y',\ z'),\ q=P_2(w',\ x')\,S_2(y,\ z)$					
		$P_2[r,\ S_1(s)]+P_2[s,\ S_1(r)],$					14
		$r=P_2(w,\ x)+P_2(y,\ z),\ s=S_2(w,\ x)+P_2(y',\ z')$					
210	198	$wx+w'x'y+wy'z'+w'yz$	15				
		$[w+y(x'+z)](w'+x+z'y')$		8	13*		
		$F_2[P_2(w,\ y')\,S_2(x,\ z'),\ P_1(w')\,S_2(x',\ y)\,S_2(x',\ z)]$				11	
		$S_2(w',\ y')\,P_1[P_2(w',\ x)\,S_2(y',\ z')]\,S_3(w',\ x,\ z')$					10
		$P_2(w',\ x')+S_1[S_2(w',\ y)+P_2(x',\ z)]+P_3(w',\ y,\ z)$					10
211 a	193	$wx+wyz+xyz+w'x'z'$	15				
		[circuit diagram]		8	13		
		$S_2(z,\ p)\,P_1[P_1(p)\,S_2(w,\ x)\,S_2(y,\ z)],\ p=P_2(w,\ x)$				10*	10
		$P_2(w',\ x')+P_2(z,\ q)+S_1[S_3(y,\ z,\ q)],\ q=S_2(w',\ x')$					10

N	H	Switching Circuit	R	C	S	G	T
211 b	221	$wx'y+w'xy+wxz'+wx'z+w'xz$	20*				
		(circuit diagram)		8	13		
		$S_2(w', x')S_2(z, p)P_1[P_3(y, z, p)], \; p=P_2(w', x')$				10	10
		$P_2(z, q)+S_1[S_1(q)+P_2(w, x)+P_2(y, z)], \; q=S_2(w, x)$					10
212 a	196	$wx+wyz'+w'yz+w'x'y'z'$	16				
		(circuit diagram)		9	14		
		$P_2[p_2(w', x)S_2(y, z'), \; P_2[w, P_3(x, y, z)]S_2(y, z)]$				13*	
		$P_2[P_2(w', x)S_2(y, z'), \; P_1(w)S_2(y, z)S_3(x', y', z')]$					12
		$B_2[S_2(w, x')+P_2(y', z), \; S_1(w')+P_2(y', z')+P_3(x, y, z)]$					12
212 b	213	$wx'y+w'xy+w'xz'+wyz'+wy'z$	20*				
		(circuit diagram)		9	14		
		$F_2[P_2(w, x')S_2(y', z), \; P_2[w', P_3(x', y', z')]S_2(y', z')]$				13	
		$F_2[P_2(w, x')S_2(y', z), \; P_1(w')S_2(y', z')S_3(x, y, z')]$					12
		$S_2[S_2(w', x)+P_2(y, z'), \; S_1(w)+P_2(y, z)+P_3(x', y', z')]$					12
213	209	$wxz'+w'xz+wyz+wy'z'+w'x'yz'$	21				
		(circuit diagram)		10	16		
		$S_2(w, p)P_1[P_1(w)S_2(y, p)S_2(x, z)],$ $p=S_2(x, y)S_2(y, z)S_2(y', z')$				14*	14
		$P_2(w, q)+S_1[S_1(w)+P_2(x, q)+P_2(y, z')],$ $q=P_2(x, y)+P_2(x, z')+P_2(x', z)$					14
214 a	199	$wx+w'y'z'+x'yz$	11				
		$wx+(z+w'y')(z'+yz')$		8	12		
		$F_3[P_2(w', x'), \; P_3(w, y, z), \; P_3(x, y', z')]$				11	
		$P_1[S_2(w, x)S_3(w', y', z')S_3(x', y, z)]$					9
		$P_2(w', x')+P_3(w, y, z)+P_3(x, y', z')$					8
214 b	232	$wx'y'+w'xy+wyz'+xy'z$	16*				
		$[z(w'+y)+z'(x'+y')](w+x)$		8	12		
		$S_2(w', x')P_2[P_3(w', y', z'), \; P_3(x', y, z)]$				10	
		$S_2(w', x')S_3(w, y, z)S_3(x, y', z')$					8
		$S_1[P_2(w, x)+P_3(w', y', z')+P_3(x', y, z)]$					9

N	H	Switching Circuit	R	C	S	G	T
215 a	197	$wx+w'x'y'+wyz+xyz'$	15				

		$S_2[p,\ P_1(q)]\,S_2[q,\ P_1(p)],$				12	12
		$p=P_1(w)\,S_2(y,\ z'),\ q=P_1(x)\,S_2(y,\ z)$					
		$P_2(r,\ s)+S_1[S_2(r,\ s)],$					11
		$r=S_1(w')+P_2(y',\ z),\ s=S_1(x')+P_2(y',\ z')$					

| 215 b | 230 | $wx'y+w'xy+wy'z'+xy'z$ | 16* | | | | |

		$S_2(p,\ q)\,P_1[P_2(p,\ q)],$				11*	11
		$p=P_1(w')\,S_2(y',\ z),\ q=P_1(x')\,S_2(y',\ z')$					
		$P_2[r,\ S_1(s)]+P_2[s,\ S_1(r)],$					12
		$r=S_1(w)+P_2(y,\ z'),\ s=S_1(x)+P_2(y,\ z)$					

| 216 | 222 | $wxy'+w'xy+wyz+x'y'z'$ | 16 | | | | |

		$F_2[P_1(y')\,S_2(w',\ x')\,S_2(w,\ z'),\ P_1(y)\,S_2(w',\ x)\,S_2(x',\ z)]$				12*	12
		$B_2[S_1(y')+P_2(w',\ x')+S_2(x,\ z),\ S_1(y)+P_2(w,\ x')$					12
		$+P_2(w',\ z')]$					

| 217 a | 200 | $wx+wyz+xy'z'+w'x'yz'+w'x'y'z$ | 21 | | | | |

		$S_2[p,\ P_1(q)]\,S_2[q,\ P_1(p)],$				12*	12
		$p=P_1(w)\,S_2(y',\ z'),\ q=P_1(x)\,S_2(y,\ z)$					
		$P_2(r,\ s)+S_1[S_2(r,\ s)],$					11
		$r=S_1(w')+P_2(y,\ z),\ s=S_1(x')+P_2(y',\ z')$					

| 217 b | 216 | $wx'y'+w'xy+wx'z'+w'xz+wy'z'+xyz$ | 24* | | | | |

		$S_2(p,\ q)\,P_1[P_2(p,\ q)],$				11*	11
		$p=P_1(w')\,S_2(y,\ z),\ q=P_1(x')\,S_2(y',\ z')$					
		$P_2[r,\ S_1(s)]+P_2[s,\ S_1(r)],$					12
		$r=S_1(w)+P_2(y',\ z'),\ s=S_1(x)+P_2(y,\ z)$					

N	H	Switching Circuit	R	C	S	G	T

218 a   206 $wxy+wxz+wyz+w'y'z'+xyz+x'y'z'$ 24

11 17

$S_2(p,\ q)\,P_1[P_2(p,\ q)]$,   14* 14
$p=S_2(w,\ x)\,P_1[P_2(y',\ z')\,S_2(w',\ x')]$, $q=S_2(y',\ z')$
$P_2(r,\ s)+S_1[S_2(r,\ s)]$,   14
$r=P_2(w',\ x')+S_1[S_2(y,\ z)+P_2(w,\ x)]$, $s=S_2(y',\ z')$

---

218 b   223 $wxy'+wyz'+wy'z+xyz'+xy'z+w'x'yz$ 25*

11 17*

$S_2(p,\ q)\,P_1[P_2(p,\ q)]$,   14* 14
$p=S_2(w',\ x')\,P_1[P_2(y,\ z)\,S_2(w,\ x)]$, $q=P_2(y',\ z')$
$P_2(r,\ s)+S_1[S_2(r,\ s)]$,   14
$r=P_2(w,\ x)+S_1[S_2(y',\ z')+P_2(w',\ x')]$. $s=P_2(y',\ z')$

---

219   227 $wxy'+w'xy+wx'z+xyz'+w'x'y'z'$ 21

10 16

$S_2(p,\ q)\,P_1[P_2(p,\ q)]$,   14*
$p=P_1(w')\,S_2(y,\ z')$, $q=S_2(x,\ y')\,S_2(x',\ y)\,S_2(x',\ z)$
$S_2(r,\ s)\,P_1[P_2(r,\ s)]$,   13
$r=P_1(w)\,S_2(y,\ z')$, $s=S_2(x',\ z')\,S_3(x,\ y,\ z)$
$P_2(t,\ u)+S_1[S_2(t,\ u)]$,   13
$t=S_1(w)+P_2(y',\ z)$, $u=P_2(x',\ y')+P_3(x,\ y,\ z)$

---

220   212 $wxy+w'xy'+wxz+wyz+wx'y'z'+w'x'yz'$ 26

11 17*

$S_2(p,\ q)\,P_1[P_2(p,\ q)]$,   14*
$p=P_1(w')\,S_2(y',\ z)$, $q=S_2(x,\ y)\,S_2(x',\ y')\,S_2(y,\ z)$
$S_2(r,\ s)\,P_1[P_2(r,\ s)]$,   13
$r=P_1(x)\,S_2(y,\ z)$, $s=S_2(w',\ y)\,S_3(w,\ y',\ z')$
$P_2(t,\ u)+S_1[S_2(t,\ u)]$,   13
$t=S_1(w)+P_2(y,\ z')$, $u=P_2(x',\ y)+P_3(x,\ y',\ z)$

N	H	Switching Circuit	R	C	S	G	T
221	224	$wx'y'+w'xy+wxz+wx'z'+x'y'z'$	20				

$$S_2(p,\ q)\,P_1[P_2(p,\ q),$$
$$p=P_1(x)\,S(y',\ z),\ q=S_2(w',\ y')\,S_2(w,\ z')$$
$$P_2(r,\ s)+S_1[S_2(r,\ s)],$$
$$r=S_1(x')+P_2(y,\ z),\ s=P_2(w,\ y')+P_2(w',\ z')$$

(C = 9, S = 15, G = 12*, T = 12, T = 12)

N	H	Switching Circuit	R	C	S	G	T
222 a	214	$w'x'y'+wxz+wyz+xyz'+x'y'z'$	20				

$$S_2(p,\ q)\,P_1[P_2(p,\ q)],$$
$$p=P_1(x)\,S_2(y,\ z),\ q=S_2(w',\ z)\,S_2(y',\ z')$$
$$P_2(r,\ s)+S_1[S_2(r,\ s)],$$
$$r=S_1(x')+P_2(y',\ z'),\ s=P_2(w',\ z')+P_2(y',\ z)$$

(C = 10, S = 15, G = 12*, T = 12, T = 12)

N	H	Switching Circuit	R	C	S	G	T
222 b	229	$wx'z'+wy'z'+xy'z+x'yz+w'xyz'$	21*				

$$S_2(p,\ q)\,P_1[P_2(p,\ q)],$$
$$p=P_1(x')\,S_2(y',\ z'),\ q=S_2(w',\ z')\,S_2(y',\ z)$$
$$P_2(r,\ s)+S_1[S_2(r,\ s)],$$
$$r=S_1(x)+P_2(y,\ z),\ s=P_2(w',\ z)+P_2(y',\ z')$$

(C = 10, S = 15, G = 12*, T = 12, T = 12)

N	H	Switching Circuit	R	C	S	G	T
1'	401	1	0	0	0	0	0
2'	400	$w'+x'+y'+z'$	4	4	8		
		$F_4(w',\ x',\ y',\ z')$				4	4
3'	396	$w'+x'+y'$	3	3	6		
		$F_3(w',\ x',\ y')$				3	3
4'	397	$w'+x'+yz'+y'z$	8	6	10		
		$F_3[w',\ x',\ S_2(y,\ z)\,S_2(y',\ z')]$				7	7
5'	398	$w'+xy'+x'z+yz'$	12				
		$w'+(x+y+z)(x'+y'+z')$		7	11		
		$P_1[P_1(w')\,S_2(x,\ y')\,S_2(x',\ z)\,S_2(y,\ z')]$				8	8
6'	399	$wx'+w'z+xy'+yz'$	12*				
		$(w+x+y+z)(w'+x'+y'+z')$		8	12		
		$P_1[S_2(w,\ x')\,S_2(w',\ z)\,S_2(x,\ y')\,S_2(y,\ z')]$				9	
		$S_4(w,\ x,\ y,\ z)\,S_4(w',\ x',\ y',\ z')$					8
7'	390	$w'+x'+y'z'$	5	4	8		
		$F_3[w',\ x',\ P_2(y,\ z)]$				5	5
8'	391	$w'+xy'+x'y+x'z'$	10*				
		$w'+(x'+y')(x+y+z')$		6	10		
		$F_2[w',\ S_2(x,\ y)\,P_1[P_3(x,\ y,\ z')]]$				8	
		$S_3(w,\ x,\ y)\,S_4(w,\ x',\ y',\ z)$					7
9'	393	$w'+x'y'+x'z'+y'z'+xyz$	14				

N	H	Switching Circuit	R	C	S	G	T
				8	13		
		$F_2[w',\ S_2(x',\ p)P_1[P_2(x',\ p)\,S_2(y',\ z')]]],\ p=P_2(y',\ z')$				11	11
10'	392	$w'x+wy'+w'z'+x'z$	12*				
		$(w'+x'+y')(w+x+y+z')$		7	11		
		$P_2[P_3(w',\ x',\ y'),\ P_4(w,\ x,\ y,\ z')]$				9	
		$S_3(w,\ x,\ y)\,S_4(w',\ x',\ y',\ z)$					7
11'	394	$wx'+w'x+w'y'+yz'+y'z$	15				

N	H	Switching Circuit	R	C	S	G	T
				9	14		
		$P_1[S_2(w,\ x')\,S_2(w',\ x)\,S_2(w',\ y')\,S_2(y,\ z')\,S_2(y',\ z)]$				11	11

N	H	Switching Circuit	R	C	S	G	T
12'	395	$wx'+w'y'+w'z'+y'z+xyz$	16*				
		(circuit diagram: w — x', y' — w' z — y, z', w' — x)		9	14		
		$P_2[P_2(w',\,x')\,S_2(y,\,z)\,S_2(y',\,z'),\,P_4(w,\,x,\,y',\,z')]$				12	
		$P_1[P_2(w',\,x')\,S_2(y,\,z)\,S_2(y',\,z')]S_4(w',\,x',\,y,\,z)$					11
13'	371	$w'+x'$	2	2	4		
		$S_2(w,\,x)$				2	2
14'	378	$w'+xy'+x'y$	7	5	8		
		· $F_2[w',\,S_2(x,\,y)\,S_2(x',\,y')]$				6	6
15'	384	$w'+xyz'+xy'z+x'yz+x'y'z'$	17				
		(circuit diagram: w'; z — y — z', x — x', z' — z)		9	14		
		$F_2[w',\,S_2(x,\,p)S_2[x',\,P_1(p)]],\ p=S_2(y,\,z')\,S_2(y',\,z)$				11	11
16'	383	$wx'+w'y+xy'$	9				
		$(w+x+y)(w'+x'+y')$		6	9		
		$P_1[S_2(w,\,x')\,S_2(w',\,y)\,S_2(x,\,y')]$				7	
		$S_3(w,\,x,\,y)\,S_3(w',\,x',\,y')$					6
17'	388	$wx'+w'x+yz'+y'z$	12	8	12		
		$P_1[S_2(w,\,x')\,S_2(w',\,x)\,S_2(y,\,z')\,S_2(y',\,z)]$				9	9
18'	389	$wx'+w'yz'+w'y'z+xyz+xy'z'$	19				
		(circuit diagram: w' — x, y; z — z', y'; w — x')				8	12
		$S_2[P_2(w',\,x'),\,p]P_1[P_3(w,\,x,\,p)],$				12	
		$S_3(w,\,x,\,p)\,P_1[P_3(w,\,x,\,p)],$					11
		$p=S_2(y,\,z)\,S_2(y',\,z')$					
19'	372	$w'+x'y'+x'z'+y'z'$	10				
		(circuit diagram: w'; x' — y'; y'' — z', y)		6	11		
		$F_3[w',\,P_2(y,\,z),\,P_1(x)S_2(y,\,z)]$				8	8
20'	373	$w'+x'z+y'z'$	7	5	9		
		$F_2[w',\,S_2(x,\,z)\,S_2(y,\,z')]$				6	6

N	H	Switching Circuit	R	C	S	G	T
21'	374	$w'+x'y+x'z+xy'z'$	11				

				7	11		
		$F_2[w',\ S_2(x',\ p)\ S_2[x,\ P_1(p)]],\ p=P_2(y,\ z)$				9	9

N	H	Switching Circuit	R	C	S	G	T
22'	375	$wx'+w'x+w'y'+w'z'+y'z$	15*				

				7	12		
		$P_2[P_2(w',\ x')\ S_2(y',\ z'),\ P_4(w,\ x,\ y',\ z')]$				10	
		$P_1[P_2(w',\ x')\ S_2(y',\ z')]\ S_4(w',\ x',\ y,\ z)$					9

N	H	Switching Circuit	R	C	S	G	T
23'	385	$w'x'+w'y'+w'z'+x'y'+x'z'+y'z'+wxyz$	23*				

				10	16		
		$S_2(w',\ p)\ P_1[P_2(w',\ p)\ S_2(y',\ z')\ S_2(x',\ q)],$				13*	13
		$p=P_2(x',\ q),\ q=S_2(y,\ z)$					

N	H	Switching Circuit	R	C	S	G	T
24'	376	$wx'+w'x+w'z+y'z'$	12				
		$wx'+w'(x+z)+y'z'$		7	11		
		$P_1[S_2(w,\ x')\ S_2(w',\ x)\ S_2(w',\ z)\ S_2(y',\ z')]$				9	9

N	H	Switching Circuit	R	C	S	G	T
25'	379	$w'x'+w'z+x'z+y'z'+wxz'$	16*				

				8	13		
		$S_2(z,\ p)\ P_1[S_2(w',\ x')\ P_3(y,\ z,\ p)],\ p=P_2(w',\ x')$				10	10

N	H	Switching Circuit	R	C	S	G	T
26'	377	$w'x+x'y+x'z+wy'z'$	13				

				8	12		
		$P_2[P_2(w',\ x')\ S_2(y',\ z'),\ P_4(w,\ x,\ y,\ z)]$				10	
		$S_3(w,\ x,\ p)\ P_1[P_3(w,\ x,\ p)],\ p=S_2(y',\ z')$					9

N	H	Switching Circuit	R	C	S	G	T
27'	381	$w'y+x'y'+yz'+y'z$	12*				
		$(w'+y'+z')(x'+y+z)$		6	10		
		$P_2[P_3(w',\ y',\ z'),\ P_3(x',\ y,\ z)]$				8	
		$S_3(w,\ y,\ z)\ S_3(x,\ y',\ z')$					6

N	H	Switching Circuit	R	C	S	G	T
28'	380	$w'y+w'z+x'y+x'z'+wxy'$	16*				

N	H	Switching Circuit	R	C	S	G	T
				8	12		
		$S_2(y, p)P_1[P_2(y, p) S_2(w, z) S_2(x, z')]$, $p=P_2(w', x')$				11*	11
29'	386	$w'y'+w'z'+x'y+x'z+wyz+xy'z'$	20				

N	H	Switching Circuit	R	C	S	G	T
				10	15		
		$S_2(y, p) P_1[P_3(w', y, p) S_2(x', z)]$, $p=P_1(x')S_2(w, z)S_2(w', z')$				13*	13
30'	382	$w'y+w'z+xy'+x'y+wy'z'$	16*				

N	H	Switching Circuit	R	C	S	G	T
				8	12		
		$P_2[P_3(w', x', y'), P_2(x, y) S_2(w, z') S_2(w', z)]$				11	
		$S_3(w, x, y) S_3[x', y', S_2(w, z') S_2(w', z)]$					10
31'	387	$w'y+w'z+wx'y'+wx'z'+xyz+xy'z'$	22*				

N	H	Switching Circuit	R	C	S	G	T
				10	16*		
		$S_2(x', p) P_1[P_3(w', x', p) S_2(y', z')]$,				14	14
		$p=S_2(w, y') S_2(w', z) S_2(y, z')$					
32'	344	$w'+x'y'+x'z'$	7				
		$w'+x'(y'+z')$		4	8		
		$F_2[w', P_1(x) S_2(y, z)]$				5	5
33'	351	$w'+x'y'+xyz'$	8				
		$w'+x'y'+xz'y$		6	10		
		$F_3[w', P_2(x, y), P_3(x', y', z)]$				8	
		$P_1[P_1(w') S_2(x', y') S_3(x, y, z')]$					7
34'	346	$w'+xy'z'+x'yz'+x'y'z$	13				

N	H	Switching Circuit	R	C	S	G	T
				8	13		
		$F_2[w', S_2(y, z) S_2(x', p)S_2(x, P_1(p))]$, $p=P_2(y, z)$				11	11

N	H	Switching Circuit	R	C	S	G	T
35′	345	$wx'+w'x+w'y'+w'z'$	12*				
		$(w'+x')(w+x+y'+z')$		6	10		
		$S_2(w,\ x)P_1(P_4(w,\ x,\ y',\ z'))]$				7	
		$S_2(w,\ x)S_4(w',\ x',\ y,\ z)$					6
36′	359	$w'x'+xy'+x'y+w'z'$	12				
		(circuit diagram)		7	11		
		$P_2[S_2(w',\ z')P_2(x',\ y'),\ P_3(w',\ x,\ y)]$				9	
		$P_1[S_2(w',\ z')P_2(x',\ y')]S_3(w,\ x',\ y')$					8
37′	363	$w'x'+w'y'+w'z'+x'y'+wxy$	16*				
		(circuit diagram)		8	13		
		$S_2(w,\ p)P_1[P_4(w,\ x',\ z',\ p)],\ p=S_2(x,\ y)S_2(x',\ y')$				11	
		$S_3(w,\ x,\ y')S_3(w.\ x',\ y)S_4(w',\ x,\ y,\ z)$					10
38′	364	$w'y'+w'z'+xyz'+xy'z+x'yz+x'y'z'$	22*				
		(circuit diagram)		9	16		
		$S_2(z,\ p)P_1[P_3(w',\ z,\ p)],\ p=S_2(w',\ x')S_2(x,\ y')S_2(x',\ y)$				12*	
		$S_3(w,\ z',\ q)P_1[P_2(z',\ q)],\ q=S_2(x,\ y)S_3(w,\ x',y')$					11
39′	368	$w'x'+w'y'+w'z'+xy'z'+x'yz'+x'y'z+wxyz$	26*				
		(circuit diagram)		11	17		
		$S_2(y',\ p)P_1[P_2(y',\ p)S_2(w',\ x')S_2(w',\ z')],$				14*	14
		$p=P_1(w')S_2(x,\ z')S_2(x',\ z)$					
40′	362	$wx'+w'x+w'y'+wyz'$	13*				
		$(w+x+y')(w'+x'+yz')$		7	11		
		$P_2[P_2(w',\ x')S_2(y,\ z'),\ P_3(w,\ x,\ y')]$				9	
		$P_1[P_2(w',\ x')S_2(y,\ z')]S_3(w',\ x',\ y)$					8
41′	361	$wx'+w'x+y'z'+w'yz$	13				
		$wx'+w'(x+yz)+y'z'$		8	13		
		$F_2[P_2(y,\ z),\ S_2(w,\ x)P_1[P_2(w,\ x)S_2(y,\ z)]]$				11	
		$P_1[S_2(w,\ x')S_2(w',\ x)S_2(y',\ z')S_3(w',\ y,\ z)]$					10

N	H	Switching Circuit	R	C	S	G	T
42′	360	$wx'+w'x+wy'z'+w'yz'+w'y'z$	18				

				9	14		
		$P_2[P_2(w', x') S_2(y', z'), P_2(w, x) S_2(y, z') S_2(y', z)]$				12	12
43′	365	$w'z'+wxy'+wx'y+w'xy+x'y'z$	19				

				9	14*		
		$S_2[P_2(w, z'), p] P_1[P_2(w', p) S_2(y', z)],$				13*	
		$S_3(w', z, p) P_1[P_2(w', p) S_2(y', z)],$					12
		$p=S_2(x, y) S_2(x', y')$					
44′	370	$w'x'+y'z'+wxy'+wxz'+w'yz+x'yz$	22				

				10	16		
		$S_2(p, q) P_1[P_2(p, q) S_2(w', x') S_2(y', z')],$				13*	13
		$p=P_2(w', x'), q=P_2(y', z')$					
45′	347	$w'x'+w'y'+w'z'+x'y'+x'z'+y'z'$	18*				

				8	14		
		$P_2[P_2(w', x') S_2(y', z'), S_2(w', x') P_2(y', z')]$				10	10
46′	348	$w'z+x'y'+x'z'+y'z'$	12				

				6	11		
		$P_2[P_2(w', z') S_2(x', y'), P_3(x', y', z)]$				9	
		$P_1[P_2(w', z') S_2(x', y')] S_3(x, y, z')$					8
47′	352	$w'y+x'z+y'z'$	9				
		$w'y+zx'+z'y'$		6	10		
		$P_1[S_2(w', y) S_2(x', z) S_2(y', z')]$				7	7

N	H	Switching Circuit	R	C	S	G	T
48'	349	$w'y+w'z+x'y'+x'z'+wy'z'$	16				

		$P_2[P_2(w', y') S_2(x', z'), P_2(x', y) S_2(w, z') S_2(w', z)]$		9	14	12	12

N	H	Switching Circuit	R	C	S	G	T
49'	353	$w'x'+w'y+w'z'+x'z'+wy'z$	16*				

		$S_2(w, p) P_1[P_3(w, x', p)],\ p=S_2(x', z') S_2(y', z)$		7	11	10*	10

N	H	Switching Circuit	R	C	S	G	T
50'	355	$w'x'+w'y'+w'z'+x'y'+x'z'+wxyz$	20*				

		$S_2(p, q) P_1[P_2(p, q)],$ $p=S_2(w, x),\ q=S_2(w', x') P_2(y', z')$		9	14	11	11

N	H	Switching Circuit	R	C	S	G	T
51'	350	$w'y+w'z+wx'y'+wx'z'+xy'z'$	18*				

| | | $P_2[P_1(w') S_2(x', y') S_2(x', z') S_2(y', z'), P_4(w, x, y, z)]$ | | 9 | 15 | 13 | |
| | | $P_1[P_1(w') S_2(x', y') S_2(x', z') S_2(y', z')] S_4(w', x', y', z')$ | | | | | 12 |

N	H	Switching Circuit	R	C	S	G	T
52'	354	$w'x+w'y+x'z'+wy'z$	13				
		$x'z'+(w+x+y)(w'+y'z)$		8	12		
		$P_2[P_1(w') S_2(x', z') S_2(y', z), P_4(w, x, y, z')]$				11	
		$S_3(w, x, z') S_3(w, y, z) S_4(w', x', y', z)$					10

N	H	Switching Circuit	R	C	S	G	T
53'	358	$w'x+x'y'+x'z'+xyz$	13*				

		$S_2(x', p) P_1[P_3(w', x', p)],\ p=P_2(y', z')$		7	11	8*	8

N	H	Switching Circuit	R	C	S	G	T
54'	357	$w'x+w'z'+x'y'+wx'z+xyz'$	17				

		$S_2(x', p) P_1[P_3(w', x', p)],\ p=P_1(y') S_2(w, z) S_2(w', z')$		9	14	11*	11

N	H	Switching Circuit	R	C	S	G	T
55'	356	$w'x+w'y'+wx'z+xy'z'+x'yz'$	18				
				9	14		
		$S_2(x', p) P_1[P_3(w', x', p)]$, $p=S_2(w', y') S_2(w, z) S_2(y, z')$				12*	12
56'	367	$w'x'+w'y'+x'z'+wxy+wxz$	17*				
				8	12		
		$S_2(w', p) P_1[P_2(w', p) S_2(x, z) S_2(x', z')]$, $p=P_2(x', y')$				11*	11
57'	366	$w'x'+w'y'+wxy+wxz'+wyz'+x'y'z$	22*				
				10	15		
		$S_2(x, p) P_1[P_3(w', x, p) S_2(y, z')]$, $p=S_2(w, y) S_2(w', y') S_2(y', z')$				14*	14
59'	369	$wx'y'+w'xy'+wx'z'+w'x'z+wy'z'+w'yz'+wxyz$	29*				
				12	19		
		$S_2(p, q) P_1[P_2(p, q)]$, $p=S_2(w', x') S_2(y, z)$, $q=S_2(w, x') S_2(w', x) S_2(y', z')$				15*	15
59'	294	$w'+x'y'$ $S_2(w, x) S_2(w, y)$	4	3	6	4	4
60'	295	$w'+x'yz'+x'y'z$ $w'+x'(yz'+y'z)$ $F_2[w', P_1(x) S_2(y, z) S_2(y', z')]$	9	6	10	7	7
61'	315	$w'+xyz+x'y'z'$ $w'+(xy+x'z')(y'+z')$ $F_2[w', S_2(x, y') S_2(x', z) S_2(y, z')]$	9	7	11	8	8
62'	302	$wx'+w'x+w'y'$ $(w'+x')(w+x+y')$ $S_2(w, x) P_1[P_3(w, x, y')]$ $S_2(w, x) S_3(w', x', y)$	9*	5	8	6	5

N	H	Switching Circuit	R	C	S	G	T

63′ 337 $w'x'+w'y'+x'y'+wxy$ — R = 13*

C = 7, S = 11

$S_2[y,\ S_2(w',\ x')P_1(p)]\,S_2(y',\ p),\ p=P_2(w',\ x')$ — G = 9, T = 9

64′ 303 $wx'+w'x+w'yz+w'y'z'$ — R = 14*

$(w'+x')(w+x+yz+y'z')$ — C = 8, S = 12

$S_2(w,\ x)P_1[P_2(w,\ x)S_2(y,\ z)S_2(y',\ z')]$ — G = 9*, T = 9

65′ 334 $w'x'+yz'+y'z$ — R = 9, C = 6, S = 10

$P_1[S_2(w',\ x')S_2(y,\ z')S_2(y',\ z)]$ — G = 7, T = 7

66′ 338 $w'x'+wyz+wy'z'+w'yz'+w'y'z$ — R = 19*

C = 9, S = 14

$S_2(w,\ p)P_1[P_3(w,\ x',\ p)],\ p=S_2(y,\ z)S_2(y',\ z')$ — G = 10, T = 10

67′ 342 $w'x'+w'yz+w'y'z'+x'yz+x'y'z'+wxyz'+wxy'z$ — R = 29

C = 11, S = 17

$S_2(p,\ q)P_1[P_2(p,\ q)],$ — G = 13, T = 13
$p=S_2(w,\ x),\ q=S_2(w',\ x')S_2(y,\ z)S_2(x',\ z')$

68′ 335 $xy'+x'y+w'yz+w'y'z'$ — R = 14

C = 7, S = 11

$P_2[P_2(x',\ y')S_2(w',\ z),\ P_2(x,\ y)S_2(w',\ z')]$ — G = 10, T = 10

69′ 339 $wxy+wx'y'+w'x'y+w'xz+w'y'z'$ — R = 20*

C = 9, S = 14*

$S_2(w,p)P_1[P_2(w,p)S_2(x,\ z)S_2(y',\ z')],p=S_2(x,y)S_2(x',y')$ — G = 13*, T = 13

70′ 336 $wx'+w'x+wyz+w'y'z'$ — R = 14

$(w+x+y'z')(w'+x'+zy)$ — C = 8, S = 13

$P_2[P_2(w,\ x)S_2(y',\ z'),\ P_2(w',\ x')S_2(y,\ z)]$ — G = 10, T = 10

N	H	Switching Circuit	R	C	S	G	T
71'	343	$wxy+w'x'y'+wxz+w'x'z'+wyz+w'y'z'+xyz+x'y'z'$	32*				

| | | $S_2(p, q) P_1[P_2(p, q)],$ | | 12 | 18 | | |
| | | $p=S_2(w, x) S_2(y, z),\ q=S_2(w', x') S_2(y', z')$ | | | | 13* | 13 |

| 72' | 296 | $w'x'+w'y'+w'z'+x'y'+x'z'$ | 15* | | | | |

| | | $S_2(w, x) P_1[S_2(w', x') P_2(y', z')]$ | | 6 | 11 | | |
| | | | | | | 7 | 7 |

| 73' | 297 | $w'y'+w'z+x'y'+x'z'$ | 12* | | | | |

| | | $S_2(w, x) P_1[P_1(y') S_2(w', z) S_2(x', z')]$ | | 5 | 9 | | |
| | | | | | | 8 | 8 |

74'	298	$w'y+w'z+x'y'+x'z'$	12*				
		$w'(y+z)+x'(y'+z')$		6	10		
		$F_2[P_1(w) S_2(y', z'),\ P_1(x) S_2(y, z)]$				8	8

75'	299	$w'x+x'y'+x'z'$	9*				
		$(w'+x')(x+y'+z')$		5	9		
		$S_2(w, x) P_1[P_3(x, y', z')]$				6	
		$S_2(w, x) S_3(x', y, z)$					5

| 76' | 309 | $w'x'+w'y'+x'y'+xyz'$ | 13* | | | | |

| | | $S_2(z, p) P_1[P_2(w', p) S_2(x', y')],\ p=P_2(x', y')$ | | 7 | 12 | | |
| | | | | | | 9* | 9 |

| 77' | 304 | $w'x'+w'y'+w'z'+xy'z'+x'yz'+x'y'z$ | 21 | | | | |

| | | $P_1[S_2(w', x')S_2(x, p) P_1[P_1(p) S_2(w, x) S_2(y, z)]], p=P_2(y, z)$ | | 9 | 15 | | |
| | | | | | | 13* | 13 |

N	H	Switching Circuit	R	C	S	G	T
78'	300	$w'x+w'z+x'y'+wx'z'$	13*				
		(circuit diagram)		7	11		
		$S_2(w, x) P_1[P_2(x, y') S_2(w, z') S_2(w', z)]$				9*	9
79'	310	$w'y'+w'z'+x'z+xy'z'$	13				
		(circuit diagram)		7	12		
		$P_2[P_2(w', z) S_1(x, y'), P_2(x', z') S_2(w', y')]$				10	10
80'	317	$w'x'+w'y'+w'z+x'y'+wxyz'$	17				
		(circuit diagram)		9	14		
		$S_2(w', p) P_1[P_2(w', p) S_2(x', y')], \; p=P_3(x', y', z)$				10*	10
81'	305	$w'x'+w'z+xy'z'+x'yz'+x'y'z$	18*				
		(circuit diagram)		9	15		
		$F_2[S_2(w, y') S_2(w, z) S_2(x, z'), P_1(y) S_2(x, z) S_2(x', z')]$				13	
		$S_3(x, y, z') S_2[w, S_2(z', p) S_2[z, P_1(p)]], \; p=S_2(x', y')$					12
82'	301	$w'x+w'z+wx'y'+x'yz'$	14*				
		(circuit diagram)		8	12		
		$F_2[P_1(w) S_2(x', z'), P_1(x) S_2(w', y') S_2(y, z)]$				10*	
		$S_2(w, x) S_3(w, y, z) S_4(w', x', y', z')$					9
83'	318	$w'x'+w'z+x'y'+xyz'$	13*				
		$x'y'+(w'+xz')(y+z)$		7	11		
		$S_2(y', p) P_1[P_2(w', p) S_2(x', y')], \; p=P_2(x', z)$				9	9
84'	316	$w'x'+w'y+w'z+wy'z'+x'yz$	17				
		(circuit diagram)		8	13		
		$S_2(w, p) P_1[P_3(w, x', p)], \; p=S_2(y', z') P_1[P_3(x, y', z')]$				12*	
		$S_2(w, q) P_1[P_3(w, x', q)], \; q=S_2(y', z') S_3(x', y, z)$					11

N	H	Switching Circuit	R	C	S	G	T
85′	306	$w'x'+w'y+w'z+x'yz'+x'y'z+wxy'z'$	22				
				10	16*		
		$S_2(p,\ q)\,P_1[P_2(p,\ q)],$ $p=S_2(w',\ x')\,P_2(y,\ z),\ q=F_2[w',\ P_1(x)\,S_2(y,\ z)]$				14*	14
86′	319	$w'x+w'y+w'z+wx'y'+xyz'$	17				
				9	14		
		$S_2[P_2(w,\ z),\ p]\,P_1[P_1[P_3[w',\ p,\ P_3(x',\ y',\ z)]]],$			13		
		$S_3(w',\ z',\ p)\,P_1[P_2(w',\ p)\,S_3(x,\ y,\ z')],$					11
		$p=P_2(x,\ y)$					
87′	307	$w'x+w'y+xyz'+x'yz'+x'y'z$	18*				
				8	15		
				9	14*		
		$S_2(x',\ p)\,P_1[P_2(w',\ p)\,S_2(x',\ y')\,S_2(x',\ z')],\ p=P_2(y,\ z)$				11*	11
88′	321	$w'z'+x'z+wxy'$	10				
		$wy'x+(w'+z)(x'+z')$		7	11*		
		$F_2[S_2(w,\ z')\,S_2(x,\ z),\ P_3(w',\ x',\ y)]$				9	
		$P_1[S_2(w',\ z')\,S_2(x',\ z)\,S_3(w,\ x,\ y')]$					8
89′	325	$w'x'+w'z'+x'y'+wxz$	13*				
				7	11		
		$S_2(w',\ p)\,P_1[P_2(w',\ p)\,S_2(x',\ y')],\ p=P_2(x',\ z')$				9*	9
90′	312	$w'z+wx'y'+xy'z'+x'yz'$	15				
				9	14*		
		$P_1[S_2(w',\ z)\,S_2(w,\ p)\,P_1[P_2(z,\ p)\,S_2(x,\ y)]],\ p=P_2(x,\ y)$				12	12

N	H	Switching Circuit	R	C	S	G	T
91'	313	$w'z+x'y'+w'xy+wx'z'+wy'z'$	18				

$$P_1[S_2(x', y')\, S_2(w, p)\, S_2[w', P_1(p)]], \quad p=P_1(z)\, S_2(x, y)$$

N	H	Switching Circuit	R	C	S	G	T
				9	14		
						11*	11
92'	323	$x'y'+wx'z+w'xz+wy'z'+w'yz$	19*				

$$S_2(w, p)\, P_1[P_2(w, p)\, S_2(x', y')], \quad p=S_2(x', z)\, S_2(y', z')$$

N	H	Switching Circuit	R	C	S	G	T
				9	14		
						11*	11
93'	328	$w'y'+x'y'+wx'z'+w'xz'+w'x'z+wxyz$	23				

$$S_2(w', p)\, P_1[P_2(w', p)\, S_2(x', y')], \quad p=P_1(y')\, S_2(x, z')\, S_2(x', z)$$

N	H	Switching Circuit	R	C	S	G	T
				10	15		
						12*	12
94'	314	$w'y+w'z+wx'y'+wx'z'+wy'z'$	18*				

$$S_2(w', p)\, P_1[P_2(w', p)\, S_2(x', y')\, S_2(x', z')], \quad p=P_2(y, z)$$

N	H	Switching Circuit	R	C	S	G	T
				9	14		
						11	11
95'	333	$w'y'+x'y+wyz'+xy'z$	14				
		$(w'+y+zx)(x'+y'+wz')$		8	13		
		$S_2(y, p)\, P_1[P_3(w', y, p)], \quad p=P_1(x')\, S_2(w, z')$				9*	9
96'	322	$w'y+x'z+wy'z'+xy'z'$	14				
		$yw'+zx'+y'z'(w+x)$		8	13		
		$P_1[S_2(w', y)\, S_2(x', z)\, P_1[S_2(w', x')\, P_2(y, z)]]$				10	10
97'	330	$w'x'+w'y'+wxy+wyz'+x'y'z$	18*				

$$S_2(y', p)\, P_1[P_2(y', p)\, S_2(w', x')], \quad p=P_1(w')\, S_2(x', z)$$

N	H	Switching Circuit	R	C	S	G	T
				9	14		
						10*	10
98'	324	$w'y+wx'z+w'xz+w'x'z'+wy'z'$	19*				

$$S_2(w, p)\, P_1[P_3(w, y, p)\, S_2(x', z')], \quad p=S_2(x', z)\, S_2(y', z')$$

N	H	Switching Circuit	R	C	S	G	T
				9	14		
						12*	12

N	H	Switching Circuit	R	C	S	G	T
99'	327	$wx'y+w'x'y'+wx'z+w'xz+w'yz'+wxy'z'$	25*				

N	H	Switching Circuit	R	C	S	G	T
				11	17		
		$S_2(w',\ p)\,P_1[P_2(w',\ p)\,S_2(x',\ y)\,S_2(x',\ z)]$, $p=S_2(x,\ y)\,S_2(x',\ z')\,S_2(y',\ z)$				15*	15
100'	326	$w'x+w'y+wx'z+wy'z'$	14*				
		$(w+x+y)\,(w'+x'z+y'z')$		8	12		
		$P_2[P_1(w')\,S_2(x',\ z)\,S_2(y',\ z'),\ P_3(w,\ x,\ y)]$				10	
		$S_3(w',\ x',\ y')\,S_3(w,\ x,\ z)\,S_3(w,\ y,\ z')$					9
101'	331	$w'x+wx'y+xy'z'+x'yz'+x'y'z$	19*				

N	H	Switching Circuit	R	C	S	G	T
				9	14		
		$S_2(x',\ p)\,P_1[P_3(w',\ x',\ p)]$, $p=S_2(w,\ y)\,S_2(y,\ z')\,S_2(y',\ z)$				12*	
		$S_3(w,\ x,\ q)\,P_1[P_2(x,\ q)]$, $q=S_2(y',\ z')\,S_3(w',\ y,\ z)$					11
102'	332	$w'x+wx'y+wx'z+w'yz+w'y'z'+xy'z'$	23				

N	H	Switching Circuit	R	C	S	G	T
				10	16		
		$S_2(x,\ p)\,P_1[P_2(x,\ p)\,S_2(y,\ z)\,S_2(w',\ q)]$, $p=P_2(w',\ q)$, $q=P_2(y,\ z)$				13*	13
103'	340	$w'xy'+w'x'z+w'yz'+xyz'+xy'z+x'yz+wx'y'z'$	29*				

N	H	Switching Circuit	R	C	S	G	T
				11	17		
		$S_2(y,\ p)\,P_1[P_2(y,\ p)\,S_2(w',\ x)\,S_2(w',\ z)]$, $p=S_2(w',\ x')\,S_2(x,\ z')\,S_2(x',\ z)$				15*	15
104'	341	$wx'y+w'xy+w'x'y'+wxz'+wx'z+w'xz$	24*				

N	H	Switching Circuit	R	C	S	G	T
				10	15		
		$S_2(y,\ p)\,S_2(z,\ q)\,P_1[P_4(y,\ z,\ p,\ q)]$, $p=P_2(w,\ x)$, $q=P_2(w',\ x')$				13*	13

N	H	Switching Circuit	R	C	S	G	T
105'	308	$wx'y'+w'xy'+wx'z'+w'x'z+wy'z'+w'yz'$	24*				

$F_2[S_2(w, y) S_2(x, z) S_2(y', z'), S_2(w', x')S_2(x, y) S_2(w, z)]$

$S_3(w, x, p) S_3(y, z, q) P_1[P_2(p, q)], p = F_2(y, z), q = F_2(w, x)$

				11	17*		
						14	
							13

N	H	Switching Circuit	R	C	S	G	T
106'	311	$x'z'+y'z'+wx'y'+w'xz+w'yz$	18*				

$S_2(p, q) P_1[P_2(p, q)],$

$p = S_2(w, z), q = S_2(x', y) S_2(x, z) S_2(y', z')$

$S_3(x, y, z') P_1[P_1(z') S_2(w, r) S_2(w', P_1(r)]], r = P_2(x, y)$

				9	14		
						13	
							12

N	H	Switching Circuit	R	C	S	G	T
107'	320	$w'z'+x'y'+y'z'+w'xy+wx'z$	17				

$S_2(p, q) P_1[P_2(p, q)], p = S_2(w', y), q = S_2(x', z) S_2(y', z')$

| | | | | 8 | 12 | | |
| | | | | | | 11* | 11 |

N	H	Switching Circuit	R	C	S	G	T
108'	329	$w'y'+w'z'+x'y'+x'z'+wxyz$	17*				

$S_2(p, q) P_1[P_2(p, q)], p = S_2(w, x), q = P_2(y', z')$

| | | | | 8 | 12 | | |
| | | | | | | 9 | 9 |

N	H	Switching Circuit	R	C	S	G	T
109'	238	$w'+x'y'z'$	5	4	8		
		$F_2[w', P_3(x, y, z)]$				5	5

N	H	Switching Circuit	R	C	S	G	T
110'	257	$wx'+w'x+w'y'z'$	10				
		$(w'+x')(w+x+y'z')$		6	10		
		$S_2(w, x) P_1[P_2(w, x) S_2(y', z')]$				7	7

N	H	Switching Circuit	R	C	S	G	T
111'	292	$wxy+wx'y'+w'xy'+w'x'y+w'x'z'$	20*				

$S_2(w, p) P_1[P_2(w, p) S_2(y', z')], p = S_2(x, y) S_2(x', y')$

| | | | | 9 | 16 | | |
| | | | | | | 11 | 11 |

N	H	Switching Circuit	R	C	S	G	T
112'	293	$w'x'y'+w'x'z'+w'y'z'+x'y'z'+wxyz'+wxy'z$ $+wx'yz+w'xyz$	36*				

| | | $S_2(p,\ q)\,P_1[P_2(p,\ q)\,S_2(w',\ y')]$, $p=S_2(w,\ x)\,S_2(w',\ x'),\ q=S_2(y,\ z)\,S_2(y',\ z')$ | | 13 | 20 | 15 | 15 |

| 113' | 239 | $w'x'+w'y'+w'z'+x'y'$ | 12* | | | | |

| | | $S_2(w,\ x)\,S_2(w,\ y)\,P_1[P_3(x',\ y',\ z')]$ $S_2(w,\ x)\,S_2(w.\ y)\,S_3(x,\ y,\ z)$ | | 6 | 11 | 8 | 7 |

| 114' | 240 | $w'y+w'z'+x'y'$ $w'(y+z')+x'y'$ $F_2[P_2(x,\ y),\ P_1(w)\,S_2(y',\ z)]$ | 9 | 5 | 9 | 7 | 7 |

| 115' | 242 | $w'x'+w'y'+w'z'+x'yz'+x'y'z$ | 17* | | | | |

| | | $P_2[P_1(w')\,S_2(x',\ y)\,S_2(x',\ z),\ S_2(w',\ x')\,P_2(y',\ z')]$ $S_2(w,\ x)\,P_1[S_2(w',\ x')\,P_2(y',\ z')]\,S_3(w,\ y',\ z')$ | | 8 | 13 | 11 | 10 |

| 116' | 243 | $w'y'+w'z'+x'yz+x'y'z'$ | 14 | | | | |

| | | $F_2[P_1(w)\,S_2(y,\ z),\ P_1(x)\,S_2(y,\ z')\,S_2(y',\ z)]$ | | 7 | 12 | 10* | 10 |

| 117' | 241 | $w'x+w'y+w'z'+w'z'+wx'y'$ | 13* | | | | |

| | | $S_2(w,\ p)\,P_1[P_3(w,\ z',\ p)],\ p=S_2(x',\ y')$ | | 7 | 11 | 8 | 8 |

| 118' | 244 | $w'x+w'y'+x'yz'+x'y'z'$ | 14* | | | | |

| | | $S_2(z,\ p)\,P_1[P_2(w',\ p)\,S_2(x',\ z)],\ p=P_2(x,\ y')$ $S_2(w,\ x)\,S_3(w,\ y',\ z')\,S_3(x',\ y,\ z)$ | | 7 | 11 | 9* | 8 |

N	H	Switching Circuit	R	C	S	G	T

$119'$ 266 $w'y'+w'z'+xy'z'+x'yz$ 14

            8 $13*$

$P_2[P_3(w', y', z), S_2(w', y')S_2(x', y)S_2(x, z')]$ 11

$S_2(w, y, z')P_1[S_2(w', y')S_2(x', y)S_2(x, z')]$ 10

$120'$ 245 $w'x+w'y'+w'z'+x'y'z'+wx'yz$ $18*$

            9 14

$S_2[P_2(w, y'), p]P_1[P_2(w', p)], p=P_1(x)S_2(y, z')S_2(y', z)$ 12

$S_3(w', y, p)P_1[P_2(w', p)], p=P_1(x)S_2(y, z')S_2(y', z)$ 11

$121'$ 276 $w'x'+w'y'+w'z'+x'y'z'+wxyz$ $18*$

            9 14

$S_2(w', p)P_1[P_3[w', p, P_3(x, y, z)]], p=P_3(x', y', z')$ $12*$

$S_2(w', p)P_1[P_2(w', p)S_3(x', y', z')], p=P_3(x', y', z')$ 11

$122'$ 267 $w'x'+w'y'+x'y'+wxyz'$ 14

            8 13

$S_2(w', p)S_2[w, S_2(x', y')S_2(z', p)], p=P_2(x', y')$ 10 10

$123'$ 253 $w'y+x'y'+wy'z'$ 10

            $(w'+y')(x'+y+wz')$ 6 10

            $S_2(w, y)P_1[P_2(x', y)S_2(w, z')]$ 7 7

$124'$ 270 $w'x'+y'z'+w'yz+x'yz$ 14

            8 13

$P_1[S_2(w', x')S_2(y', z')P_1[S_2(w, x)P_2(y', z')]]]$ 10 10

$125'$ 260 $w'x'+wy'z'+w'yz'+w'y'z+x'yz$ $19*$

            8 13

$S_2(w, p)P_1[P_2(x', p)S_2(w, y')], p=S_2(y, z)S_2(y', z')$ $11*$ 11

N	H	Switching Circuit	R	C	S	G	T
126′	258	$w'x'+w'yz'+w'y'z+x'yz'+x'y'z+wxy'z'$	24				

$S_2(p,\ q)\,P_1[P_1(p)\,S_2(w',\ x')\,S_2[q,\ S_2(y,\ z)]],$
$p=P_2(w',\ x'),\ q=S_2(y',\ z')$

N	H	Switching Circuit	R	C	S	G	T
				10	16		
						14*	14
127′	256	$w'x+w'y'+wx'y+wx'z'$	14*				

$S_2(w',\ p)\,P_1[P_2(w',\ p)\,S_2(x',\ z')],\ p=P_2(x',\ y')$
$S_2(w,\ x)\,S_3(w',\ x',\ y)\,S_3(w,\ y',\ z)$

N	H	Switching Circuit	R	C	S	G	T
				7	11		
						9	
							8
128′	254	$w'x+wx'y'+x'yz'+x'y'z$	15*				
		$(w'+x')[x+(w+y+z)(y'+z')]$		8	12		
		$S_2(w,\ x)\,S_2[x',\ S_2(w,\ y')\,S_2(y,\ z')\,S_2(y',\ z)]$				10	
		$S_2(w,\ x)\,S_3(x',\ y,\ z)\,S_4(w',\ x',\ y',\ z')$					9
129′	282	$w'z'+x'y'+xyz$	10				
		$w'z'+(x+y')(x'+yz)$		7	11		
		$P_1[S_2(w',\ z')\,S_2(x',\ y')\,P_1[P_3(x',\ y',\ z')]]$				9	
		$P_1[S_2(w',\ z')\,S_2(x',\ y')\,S_3(x,\ y,\ z)]$					8
130′	272	$x'y'+w'xz'+w'yz+xyz'$	15				

$P_2[P_2(x',\ y)\,S_2(w',\ z'),\ P_1(y')\,S_2(w',\ z)\,S_2(x,\ z')]$

N	H	Switching Circuit	R	C	S	G	T
				8	13		
						11	11
131′	279	$w'x+wx'y'+wx'z'+w'yz+w'y'z'$	19*				

$S_2(w,\ p)\,P_1[P_2(w,\ p)\,S_2(y',\ z')],\ p=S_2(x',\ y')\,S_2(x',\ z')$

N	H	Switching Circuit	R	C	S	G	T
				9	14		
						11*	11
132′	279	$w'x'+w'y'+wxy+x'y'z'$	14				

$S_2(w',\ p)\,S_2[w,\ P_2[p,\ P_3(x,\ y,\ z)]],\ p=P_2(x',\ y')$
$S_2(w',\ p)\,P_1[P_2(w',\ p)\,S_3(x',\ y',\ z')],\ p=P_2(x',\ y')$

N	H	Switching Circuit	R	C	S	G	T
				8	13		
						11	
							10

N	H	Switching Circuit	R	C	S	G	T

133' 263 $w'x'+xyz'+xy'z+xy'z+x'y'z'$ 15

    8   13

$P_2[P_1(x')S_2(y, z')S_2(y', z), P_2(w', x)S_2(y', z')]$ 11   11

134' 269 $wx'y'+w'xy'+w'x'z+w'yz'+xyz'$ 20* ~

    10   15

$F_2[S_2(w, x')S_2(x, z)S_2(y', z'),P_1(y)S_2(w, x)S_2(w', x')]$ 13* 13

135' 281 $w'z'+wx'y'+w'xy'+w'x'y+wxyz$ 20

    10   15*

$S_2(w, p)P_1[P_3(w, z', p)], p=S_2(x', y')P_1[P_3(x', y', z')]$ 12
$S_2(w, q)P_1[P_3(w, z', q)], q=S_2(x', y')S_3(x, y, z)$ 11

136' 277 $wx'y'+w'xy'+w'x'z'+w'yz+wxyz'$ 21

    10   16

$S_2(w, p)P_1[P_2(w, p)S_2(y', z')],$ 13*
$p=S_2(x', y')P_1[P_3(x', y', z')]$
$S_2(w, q)P_1[P_2(w, q)S_2(y', z')],$ 12
$q=S_2(x', y')S_3(x, y, z)$

137' 264 $w'x'+w'yz+w'y'z'+x'y'z'+wxyz'+wxy'z$ 25

    11   17*

$S_2(w', p)P_1[P_2(w', p)S_2(x', q)],$ 13* 13
$p=P_2(x', q)S_2(y, z), q=P_2(y, z)$

138' 285 $w'x'+wxy'+wy'z+xyz'$ 15
           $w'x'+(w+y)(y'+z')(x+z)$ 8   12
           $P_1[S_2(w', x')P_1[S_2(w', y')S_2(x', z')S_2(y, z)]]$ 10*   10

N	H	Switching Circuit	R	C	S	G	T
139'	275	$w'x'+wxy'+wxz'+wy'z'+w'yz$	19				
		(circuit: w — z' — x; y', z; y; w' — x' — x'; z')		10	16		
		$S_2(w',\ p)\,P_1[P_2(w',\ p)\,S_2(y',\ z')],\ p=P_1(x')\,S_2(y,\ z)$				10*	10
140'	287	$w'x'+wxz+wy'z'+w'yz'$	15				
		(circuit: w' — x'; y; z'; y'; w — x — z)		8	13		
		$S_2(w,\ p)\,P_1[P_3(w,\ x',\ p)],\ p=S_2(x,\ z)\,S_2(y',\ z')$				10	10
141'	291	$w'x'+wxy+wxz+w'y'z'+x'y'z'$	19				
		(circuit: w' — y' — z'; x', y; w — w'/x — z)		9	14		
		$S_2(p,\ q)\,P_1[P_2(p,\ q)],\ p=S_2(w',\ x')\,S_2(y',\ z'),\ q=S_2(w,\ x)$				11	11
142'	286	$wx'y+w'xy+w'x'y'+w'xz+wy'z'$	20*				
		(circuit: x' — y' — z'; w, x', y; x — w' — z)		9	14*		
		$S_2(w,\ p)\,P_1[P_2(w,\ p)\,S_2(x',\ y')],\ p=S_2(x',\ y)\,S_2(y',\ z')$				11	11
143'	288	$wx'y+w'xy+w'x'y'+wx'z'+w'xz'+wxy'z$	25*				
		(circuit: x — x'; y, z'; w — w'; y'; x' — x — z)		10	16		
		$S_2(w',\ p)\,P_1(P_2(w',\ p)\,S_2(x',\ z')],$ $p=S_2(x,\ y)\,S_2(x',\ y')\,S_2(x,\ z')$				13	13
144'	274	$wx'y'+w'xy+wx'z'+w'xz+wy'z'+w'yz+x'y'z'$	28*				
		(circuit: w — w'; x', x, x'; y, y', y — y'; z — z')		11	17		
		$S_2(w,\ p)\,P_1[P_2(w,\ p)\,S_2(x',\ q)],$ $p=P_1(q)\,S_2(x',\ y')\,S_2(x',\ z'),\ q=P_2(y,\ z)$				14*	14

N	H	Switching Circuit	R	C	S	G	T

145′ 290 $wx'y'+w'xy+wx'z'+w'xz'+w'y'z'+wxyz+w'x'yz$ R = 30*

C = 12 S = 18*

$S_2(p, q) P_1[P_2(p, q)],$
$p=P_2(y', z'),\ q=S_2(w, x) P_1[P_2(w, x) S_2(y', z')]$ G = 14 T = 14

146′ 246 $w'y'+w'z'+x'y'+x'z'$ R = 12*
$(w'+x')(y'+z')$ C = 4 S = 8
$S_2(w, x) S_2(y, z)$ G = 4 T = 4

147′ 249 $w'y'+w'z'+x'y'+wx'z$ R = 13*

C = 6 S = 10

$S_2(w, x) S_2[y, S_2(w, z) S_2(w', z')]$ G = 8 T = 8

148′ 247 $w'y'+x'y'+wx'z'+w'xz'+w'x'z$ R = 18*

C = 8 S = 13

$S_2(w, x) P_1[P_1(y') S_2(z, p) S_2[z', P_1(p)]],\ p=P_2(w, x)$ G = 11* T = 11

149′ 251 $w'y'+w'z'+wx'y+wx'z$ R = 14*
$wx'(y+z)+w'(y'+z')$ C = 7 S = 11
$F_2[P_1(w) S_2(y, z),\ P_2(w', x) S_2(y', z')]$ G = 9
$S_2(w, x) S_3(w, y', z') S_3(w', y, z)$ T = 8

150′ 252 $w'y'+x'z'+wx'y+w'xz$ R = 14

C = 8 S = 12*

$S_2(w, x) P_1[S_2(w, y) S_2(w', y') S_2(x, z) S_2(x', z')]$ G = 11* T = 11

151′ 250 $w'y'+wx'z'+w'xz'+x'yz$ R = 15

C = 8 S = 12

$F_2[P_1(w) S_2(x', y) S_2(y, z),\ P_1(x) S_2(w', z') S_2(y', z)]$ G = 12 T = 12

N	H	Switching Circuit	R	C	S	G	T
152'	248	$wx'y'+w'xy'+wx'z'+w'x'z+w'yz'$	20*				
		(circuit diagram)		9	14		
		$F_2[S_2(w,\ x)\ S_2(w',\ x')\ S_2(y,\ z),\ P_2(w,\ x)\ S_2(y',\ z')]$				12	
		$S_2(w,\ x)\ P_1[S_2(w',\ x')\ P_2(y',\ z')]\ S_4(w',\ x',\ y',\ z')$					11
153'	280	$w'x'+w'y'+x'z'+wxyz$	14				
		(circuit diagram)		8	12		
		$S_2[S_2(w,\ z),\ p]\ P_1[P_2(w',\ p)\ S_2(x',\ z')],\ p=P_2(x',\ y')$				11	11
154'	268	$w'x'+w'y'+wyz'+x'y'z$	14				
		(circuit diagram)		8			
		$P_2[P_1(y')\ S_2(w',\ x')\ S_2(w,\ z'),\ P_2(w',\ y)\ S_2(x',\ z)]$				11*	11
155'	261	$w'x'+w'y'+x'yz+x'y'z'+wxyz'$	19				
		(circuit diagram)		10	15		
		$S_2(p,\ q)\ P_1[P_2(p,\ q)]$,				13*	13
		$p=S_2(w,\ y')\ S_2(x,\ y),\ q=P_2(w',\ z)\ S_2(x,\ y')$					
156'	283	$w'x'+w'y'+wyz'+xy'z$	14				
		(circuit diagram)		8	12		
		$P_2[P_3(w',\ y,\ z),\ S_2(w',\ x')\ S_2(w,\ z')\ S_2(x,\ y')]$				11	
		$S_3(w,\ y',\ z')\ P_1[S_2(w',\ x')\ S_2(w,\ z')\ S_2(x,\ y')]$					10

N	H	Switching Circuit	R	C	S	G	T

| 157′ | 265 | $w'x'+w'y'+xy'z'+x'yz'+wxyz$ | 19 | | | | |

| | | | | 9 | 16* | | |

| | | | | 10 | 15* | | |

$S_2(p, q) P_1[P_2(p, q)]$,
$p = S_2(x, y), \quad q = P_1(w') S_2(x, z') S_2(y, z')$

| | | | | | | 12* | 12 |

| 158′ | 271 | $w'x'+wxz'+w'yz'+w'y'z+x'y'z$ | 19 | | | | |

| | | | | 9 | 15 | | |

$P_1[S_2(w', x') S_2(z, p) P_1[P_3(x', z, p)]]$, $p = P_1(y) S_2(w, x)$

| | | | | | | 12* | 12 |

| 159′ | 259 | $w'xy'+w'x'z+w'yz'+xy'z'+x'yz'+x'y'z$ | 24* | | | | |

| | | | | 10 | 16 | | |

$S_2(x', p) P_2[P_3(w', x', p)], \quad S_2(w', x') P_2(y', z')]$, $p = P_2(y, z)$

| | | | | | | 13 | 13 |

| 160′ | 278 | $w'x'+wxy'+w'yz+xy'z'+x'yz'$ | 19* | | | | |

| | | | | 9 | 14* | | |

$S_2(p, q) P_1[P_2(p, q)]$,
$p = P_2(x', y'), \quad q = S_2(w, y') S_2(w, z) S_2(x, z')$

| | | | | | | 13* | 13 |

| 161′ | 262 | $w'xz+w'yz+w'y'z'+xy'z'+x'yz'+wx'y'z$ | 25* | | | | |

| | | | | 10 | 16 | | |

$S_2(p, q) P_1[P_2(p, q)]$,
$p = P_2(x, y) S_2(w', z'), \quad q = S_2(w, z) P_1[P_3(x', y', z)]$
$S_2(r, s) P_1[P_2(r, s)]$,
$r = P_2(x, y) S_2(w', z'), \quad s = S_2(w, z) S_3(x, y, z')$

| | | | | | | 15* | |
| | | | | | | | 14 |

N	H	Switching Circuit	R	C	S	G	T
162'	273	$wx'y'+w'x'y+w'xz+xy'z'+x'yz'$	20*				

		$S_2(w',\ p)\,P_2[P_3(w',\ z',\ p),\ P_3(x',\ y',\ z)]$,		9	14		
		$S_2(w',\ p)\,P_1[P_3(w',\ z',\ p)]\,S_3(x,\ y,\ z')$,				12	
		$p=P_2(x,\ y)$					11

N	H	Switching Circuit	R	C	S	G	T
163'	284	$w'xy+wx'z+wy'z'+w'yz'+xy'z'+x'y'z$	24*				

| | | $S_2(p,\ q)\,P_1[P_2(p,\ q)]$, | | 10 | 16 | | |
| | | $p=P_1(w)\,S_2(x,\ y')\,S_2(y',\ z')$, $q=S_2(x,\ z)\,S_2(y,\ z')$ | | | | 14* | 14 |

N	H	Switching Circuit	R	C	S	G	T
164'	289	$wx'y'+w'xy+w'yz'+w'y'z+x'yz'+x'y'z+wxyz$	29*				

		$S_2(p,\ q)\,P_2[P_2(p,\ q),\ P_4(w,\ x,\ y,\ z)]$,		10	16		
		$S_2(p,\ q)\,P_1[P_2(p,\ q)]\,S_4(w',\ x',\ y',\ z')$,				14*	
		$p=P_2(w',\ x')$, $q=S_2(y,\ z)$					13

APPENDIX 6 *a guide to the literature*

The literature of switching and automata theory is widely scattered and in many languages. Perhaps even more unfortunate is that the level of the literature (even within a given journal) is often uneven— sometimes sophisticated and sometimes simple. This means that it is difficult to give a general guide to obtaining information from the literature.

The following books and journals are very important and contain a number of basic papers.

1. *Automata Studies*, Annals of Mathematics Study, 34, Princeton University Press, Princeton, N.J., 1956.

2. *Cornell Summer Institute on Symbolic Logic (notes)*, Cornell University, Ithaca, N.Y., 1959.

3. *Proceedings of an International Symposium on the Theory of Switching*, The Annals of the Computation Laboratory of Harvard University, vols. XXIX and XXX, 1959.

4. *Proceedings of a Symposium on the Mathematical Theory of Automata*, Polytechnic Institute of Brooklyn, 1962.

5. *Automation Express*

6. *Bell System Technical Journal*

7. *Bulletin of the Research Council of Israel*

8. *Doklady Akademii Nauk SSSR*

9. *IBM Journal of Research and Development*

10. *Information and Control*

11. *IRE (IEEE)*† *Transactions on Circuit Theory*
12. *IRE (IEEE)*† *Transactions on Electronic Computers*
13. *IRE (IEEE)*† *Transactions on Information Theory*
14. *Journal of the Association for Computing Machinery*
15. *Journal of the Franklin Institute*
16. *Journal of the Society for Industrial and Applied Mathematics*
17. *Proceedings of the AIEE Symposium on Switching Circuit Theory and Logical Design*, annually since 1962.

It is very fortunate that there are journals which review most of the papers in the field.   The following list of journals which review papers includes comments on the relative merits of the journals.

1. *Mathematical Reviews.*   The reviews are good, and papers from all over the world are reviewed.   The reader must search under several different headings for relevant papers.   Naturally, only papers of mathematical interest are reviewed.

2. *IEEE Professional Group on Electronic Computers.*   The reviews are good; but with few exceptions, only papers which appear in English-language journals are reviewed.

3. *Journal of Symbolic Logic.*   Many excellent and detailed reviews appear in this journal.   The papers are chosen from all over the world. This journal is particularly important to the theoretician who does not read Russian or Roumanian.

4. *Computing Reviews.*   An enormous area is covered by this journal. It is useful, mainly, as a source for finding out what has been published.

5. *Referativnyy Zhurnal-Mathematika* (Russian).   This journal provides wide coverage of pertinent papers in all languages.   The reviews are thorough, and new papers are reviewed very rapidly.   Starting in 1964, an English translation of the theoretical cybernetics section of the journal has been published as *Theoretical Cybernetics Abstracts.*

BIBLIOGRAPHY

Ádám, A.: On the Definitions of Direct Product in Universal Algebra, *Publ. Math.*, tomus 6, fasc. 1–2, pp. 303–310, 1959.

Aizermann, M. A., L. A. Gusev, L. I. Rozonoer, I. M. Smirnov, and A. A. Tal': *Logic, Automata, and Algorithms*, Gas. Insdat., Fiz.-Mat. Lit., Moscow, 1963.

Aranovich, B. I.: Ispol' zovanie matrichnykh metodov v vôprosakh strukturnogo analiza relejno-kontaktnykh skhem, *Automatika i Telemekhanika*, vol. 10, no. 6, pp. 437–451, 1949.

† The Institute of Radio Engineers has changed its name to the Institute of Electrical and Electronics Engineers.   Both names refer to the same journal in the references.

Arbib, M.: (1) Turing Machines, Finite Automata and Neural Nets, *J. Assoc. Computing Machinery*, vol. 8, pp. 467–475, 1961.
(2) *Brains, Machines, and Mathematics*, McGraw-Hill Book Company, New York, 1964.

Arnold, R. F., and M. A. Harrison: Algebraic Properties of Symmetric and Partially Symmetric Boolean Functions, *IEEE Trans. Electron. Computers*, vol. EC-12, no. 3, pp. 244–251, 1963.

Ashenhurst, R. L.: (1) The Application of Counting Techniques, *Proc. Assoc. Computing Machinery*, Pittsburgh, Pa., Meeting, pp. 293–305, May, 1952.
(2) A Method of Determining Functional Invariance, *Harvard Computation Lab.*, BL-2, sec. II, pp. 1–12, 1953.
(3) The Theory of Abstract Two-terminal Switching Networks, *Harvard Computation Lab. BL-5*, sec. VII, pp. 1–15, 1954.
(4) A Uniqueness Theorem for Abstract Two-terminal Switching Networks, *Harvard Computation Lab. BL-10*, sec. VI, pp. 1–8, 1955.
(5) The Decomposition of Switching Functions, in *Proc. Intern. Symp. Theory of Switching*, Harvard University, pp. 74–116, 1957.

Asser, G.: Turing-Maschinen und Markowsche Algorithmen," *Z. Math. Logik Grundlagen Math.*, vol. 5, pp. 346–365, 1959.

Aufenkamp, D. D.: Analysis of Sequential Machines II, *IRE Trans. Electron. Computers*, vol. EC-7, pp. 299–306, December, 1958.

Aufenkamp, D. D., and F. E. Hohn: Analysis of Sequential Machines, *IRE Trans. Electron. Computers*, vol. EC-6, pp. 276–285, December, 1957.

Bach, E.: *An Introduction to Transformational Grammars*, Holt, Rinehart and Winston, Inc., New York, 1964.

Bacon, G. C.: The Decomposition of Stochastic Automata, *Inform. Control*, vol. 7, no. 3, pp. 320–339, 1964.

Bar-Hillel, Y.: *Language and Information*, John Wiley & Sons, Inc., New York, 1964.

Bar-Hillel, Y., and E. Shamir: Finite State Languages, *Bull. Res. Council Israel*, vol. 8F, pp. 155–166, 1960.

Bar-Hillel, Y., M. Perles, and E. Shamir: On Formal Properties of Simple Phrase Structure Grammars, *Z. Phonetik Sprachwiss. Kommunikationsforsch.*, vol. 14, pp. 143–172, 1961.

Bartee, T. C.: Computer Design of Multiple Output Logical Networks, *IRE Trans. Electron. Computers*, vol. EC-10, no. 1, pp. 21–30, 1961.

Bartee, T. C., I. L. Lebow, and I. S. Reed: *Theory and Design of Digital Machines*, McGraw-Hill Book Company, New York, 1962.

Bazilevskii, Yu, Ya: *The Theory of Mathematical Machines*, Pergamon Press, New York, 1963.

Berge, C.: *The Theory of Graphs*, John Wiley & Sons, Inc., New York, 1962.

Birkhoff, G.: (1) *Lattice Theory*, American Mathematical Society Colloquium Publications, Providence, R.I., vol. XXV, 1948.
(2) On the Structure of Abstract Algebras, *Proc. Cambridge Phil. Soc.*, vol. 31, pp. 433–454, 1933.
(3) Subdirect Unions in Universal Algebra, *Bull. Am. Math. Soc.*, vol. 50, pp. 764–768, 1944.
(4) Universal Algebra, *Proc. Can. Math. Congr.*, pp. 310–326, 1945.

Birkhoff, G., and S. MacLane: *A Survey of Modern Algebra*, The Macmillan Company, New York, 1954.

Blokh, A., Sh.: On Soluble Problems in Sequential Machines, *Probl. Kibernetki*, vol. 3, pp. 81–88, 1960.

Bodnarchuk, V. G.: (1) Systems of Equations in the Algebra of Events, *Zh. Vych. Mat. i Mat. Fiz.*, vol. 3, no. 6, pp. 1077–1088, 1963. Also see, *Automation Express*, vol. 6, no. 9, pp. 5–10, 1964.
(2) Automata and Events, *Ukr. Mat. Zh.*, vol. 14, no. 4, pp. 351–361, 1962.

Bourbaki, N.: *Éléments de Mathématique: I, Les Structures Fondamentales de l' Analyse; Libre II, Algebre*, Hermann & Cie, Paris, 1959.

Braffort, P., and D. Hirschberg (eds.): *Computer Programming and Formal Systems*, North Holland Publishing Company, Amsterdam, 1963.

Braun, E. L.: *Digital Computer Design, Logic, Circuitry, and Synthesis*, Academic Press Inc., New York, 1963.

Brzozowski, J. A.: (1) Canonical Regular Expressions and Minimal State Graphs for Definite Events, *Proc. Symp. Math. Theory Automata*, Polytechnic Institute of Brooklyn, pp. 529–561, April, 1962.
(2) A Survey of Regular Expressions and Their Applications, *IRE Trans. Electron. Computers*, vol. EC-11, pp. 324–335, June, 1962.
(3) Derivatives of Regular Expressions, *J. Assoc. Computing Machinery*, vol. 11, no. 4, pp. 481–494, 1964.

Bruck, R. H.: *A Survey of Binary Systems*, Ergebnisse, Neue Folge, Heft 20, Springer-Verlag OHG, Berlin, 1958.

Büchi, J. R.: (1) Regular Canonical Systems and Finite Automata, *Univ. Mich. Res. Inst. Tech. Rept.* 03105, 2794-7-T, 1959.
(2) Weak Second Order Arithmetic and Finite Automata, *Z. Math. Logik Grunklagen Math.*, vol. 6, pp. 66-92, 1960.
(3) On a Decision Method in Restricted Second Order Arithmetic, in *Logic, Methodology, and Philosophy of Science; Proceedings of the 1960 International Congress*, Stanford University Press, Stanford, Calif., 1962.
(4) Mathematische Theorie des Verhaltens Endlicher Automaten, *Z. Angew. Math. Mech.*, band 42, pp. 9–16, 1962.
(5) Turing-machines and the Entscheidungs Problem, *Math. Ann.*, vol. 148, pp. 201–213, 1962.

Büchi, J. R., and J. B. Wright: *Class Notes on a Mathematical Theory of Automata*, 1960.

Burks, A. W., and H. Wang: The Logic of Automata, *J. Assoc. Computing Machinery*, vol. 4, no. 2, pp. 193–218, and no. 3, pp. 279–297, 1957.

Burks, A. W., and J. B. Wright: (1) Theory of Logical Nets, *Proc. IRE*, vol. 41, no. 10, pp. 1357–1365, 1953.
(2) Sequence Generators and Digital Computers, *Recursive Function Theory, Proc. Symp. Pure Math.*, vol. 5, American Mathematical Society, 1963.
(3) Sequence Generators, Graphs and Formal Languages, *Inform. Control*, vol. 5, no. 3, pp. 204–212, 1963.

Burks, A. W., R. McNaughton, C. H. Pollmar, D. W. Warren, and J. B. Wright: (1) Complete Decoding Nets: General Theory and Minimality, *J. Soc. Indus. Appl. Math.*, vol. 2, no. 4, pp. 201–243, 1954.
(2) The Folded Tree, *J. Franklin Inst.*, vol. 260, no. 1, pp. 9–24; no. 2, pp. 115–126, 1955.

Burnside, W.: *Theory of Groups of Finite Order*, 2d ed., Cambridge University Press, London, 1911.

Calabi, L.: (1) A Solution of the Minimization Problem for Boolean Formulas, *Parke Math. Lab. Rept.* 7-3471, December, 1960.
(2) Relations between Switching Networks and Boolean Formulas, *Parke Math. Lab. Rept.* 8-3471, March, 1961.

Calabi, L., and J. A. Riley: (1) Inessentiality in Minimal Networks and Formulas, *IRE Trans. Electron. Computers*, vol. EC-11, no. 5, pp. 711–713, 1962.
(2) The Algebra of Boolean Formulas: Some Criteria for Minimality, *Proc. Third Ann. Symp. Switching Circuit Theory Logical Design*, S-141, pp. 33–47, September, 1962.

Calabi, L., and E. W. Samson: (1) On the Theory of Boolean Formulas: Minimal Including Sums, I, *J. Soc. Indus. Appl. Math.*, vol. 11, no. 2, pp. 212–234, 1963.

Caldwell, S. H.: (1) *Switching Circuits and Logical Design*, John Wiley & Sons, Inc., New York, 1958.
(2) The Recognition and Identification of Symmetric Switching Functions, *Trans. AIEE, Part II*, vol. 73, no. 12, pp. 142–146, 1954.

Cardot, C.: Quelques résultats sur l'application de l'algèbre de Boole à synthèse des circuits à relais, *Ann. Télé Communications*, vol. 7, no. 2, pp. 75–84, 1952.

Carlyle, J. W.: Reduced Forms for Stochastic Sequential Machines, *J. Math. Analysis Appl.*, vol. 7, no. 2, pp. 167–175, 1963.

Cherniavskii, V. C., and V. A. Kosmidiadi: On the Ordering of the Set of Automata, *Vopr. Teorii Math. Mashin.*, no. 2, pp. 34–51, 1962.

Chevalley, C.: (1) *Fundamental Concepts of Algebra*, Academic Press Inc., New York, 1956.
(2) *The Construction and Study of Certain Important Algebras*, The Mathematical Society of Japan, 1955.

Chomsky, N.: (1) Three Models for the Description of Language, *IRE Trans. Inform. Theory*, vol. 2, pp. 113–124, 1956.
(2) On Certain Formal Properties of Grammars, *Inform. Control*, vol. 2, pp. 137–167, 1959.
(3) A Note on Phrase Structure Grammars, *Inform. Control*, vol. 2, pp. 393–395, 1959.
(4) Formal Properties of Grammars, *Handbook of Mathematical Psychology*, vol. II, John Wiley & Sons, Inc., New York, 1963.
(5) On the Notion "Rule of Grammar," *Structure of Language and Its Mathematical Aspects, Proc. Symp. Appl. Math.*, vol. 12, pp. 6–24, 1961.

Chomsky, N., and G. A. Miller: (1) Finite State Languages, *Inform. Control*, vol. 1, pp. 91–112, 1958.
(2) Introduction to the Formal Analysis of Natural Languages, *Handbook of Mathematical Psychology*, vol. II, John Wiley & Sons, Inc., New York, 1963.

Chomsky, N., and M. P. Schützenberger: The Algebraic Theory of Context-free Languages, in P. Braffort and D. Hirschberg (eds.), *Computer Programming and Formal Systems*, Studies in Logic Series, North Holland Publishing Company, Amsterdam, 1962.

Church, A.: (1) *Introduction to Mathematical Logic*, vol. I, Princeton University Press, Princeton, N.J., 1956.
(2) Application of Recursive Arithmetic to the Problem of Circuit Synthesis, in *Notes from the Summer Institute of Symbolic Logic*, Cornell University, pp. 3–50, 1957.
(3) Application of Recursive Arithmetic in the Theory of Computing and

Automata, in *Notes in Advanced Theory of the Logical Design of Digital Computers,* University of Michigan Summer Session, 1959.

Clifford, A. H., and G. B. Preston: *The Algebraic Theory of Semigroups,* American Mathematical Society, Providence, R.I., 1961.

Copi, I., C. Elgot, and J. Wright: Realization of Events by Logical Nets, *J. Assoc. Computing Machinery,* vol. 5, no. 2, pp. 181–196, 1958.

Copilowish, I. M.: Matrix Development of the Calculus of Relations, *J. Symbolic Logic,* vol. 13, pp. 193–203, 1948.

Coxeter, H. S. M.: *Regular Polytopes,* Methuen & Co., Ltd., London, 1948.

Coxeter, H. S. M., and W. O. J. Moser: *Generators and Relations for Discrete Groups,* Springer-Verlag OHG, Berlin, 1957.

Curtis, H. A.: *A New Approach to the Design of Switching Circuits,* D. Van Nostrand Company, Inc., Princeton, N.J., 1962.

Davis, M.: *Computability and Unsolvability,* McGraw-Hill Book Company, New York, 1958.

Davis, R. L.: The Number of Structures of Finite Relations, *Proc. Am. Math. Soc.,* vol. 4, pp. 486–495, June, 1953.

De Bruijn, N. G.: Generalization of Pólya's Fundamental Theorem in Enumerative Combinatorial Analysis, *Koninkl. Ned. Akad. Wetenschap.,* Ser. A, vol. 62, no. 2, pp. 56–59, 1959.

Dickson, L. E.: *Linear Groups with an Exposition of the Galois Field Theory,* Dover Publications, Inc., New York, 1958.

Durst, L. K.: On Certain Subsets of Finite Boolean Algebras, *Proc. Am. Math. Soc.,* vol. 6, pp. 695–697, 1955.

Eggan, L. C.: Transition Graphs and the Star Height of Regular Events, *Mich. Math. J.,* vol. 10, pp. 385–397, 1963.

Elgot, C. C.: (1) The Non-existence of Certain Finite Automata Design Algorithms, in *Advanced Theory of Logical Design of Digital Computers,* The University of Michigan Press, Ann Arbor, Mich., 1958.
(2) Lectures on Switching and Automata Theory, *Univ. Mich. Res. Inst. Tech. Rept.* 2755-3-T, 1959.
(3) Decision Problems of Finite Automata Design and Related Arithmetics, *Trans. Am. Math. Soc.,* vol. 98, no. 1, pp. 21–51, 1961.

Elgot, C. C., and J. Mezei: (1) Two-sided Finite-state Transductions, *Proc. AIEE Symp. Switching Theory and Logical Design,* S-143, 1963. Also, IBM Research Report RC1017.
(2) On Relations Defined by Generalized Finite Automata, *IBM J. Res. Develop.,* vol. 9, no. 1, pp. 47–68, 1965.

Elgot, C. C., and A. Robinson: Random-access Stored-program Machines: An Approach to Programming Languages, *J. Assoc. Computing Machinery,* vol. 11, no. 4, pp. 365–399, 1964.

Elgot, C. C., and J. D. Rutledge: (1) Operations on Finite Automata, Extended Summary, *Proc. AIEE Second Ann. Symp. Switching Circuit Theory and Logical Design,* S-134, September, 1961.
(2) Machine Properties Preserved under State Minimization, *Proc. AIEE Third Ann. Symp. Switching Circuit Theory and Logical Design,* S-141, pp. 62–70, September, 1962.

(3) RS Machines with Almost Blank Tape, *J. Assoc. Computing Machinery*, vol. 11, no. 3, pp. 313–337, 1964.

Elgot, C. C., and J. B. Wright: Series Parallel Graphs and Lattices, *Duke Math. J.*, vol. 26, no. 2, pp. 325–338, 1959.

Elspas, B.: (1) Autonomous Linear Sequential Networks, *IRE Trans. Circuit Theory*, CT-6, pp. 45–60, March, 1959.
(2) Self-complementary Symmetry Types of Boolean Functions, *IRE Trans. Electron. Computers*, vol. EC-9, No. 2, pp. 264–266, 1960.

Esary, J. D., and F. Proschan: (1) The Reliability of Coherent Systems, in *Redundancy Techniques for Computing Systems*, Spartan Books, Washington, D.C., 1962.
(2) Coherent Structures of Non-identical Components, *Technometrics*, vol. 5, no. 2, pp. 191–209, 1963.

Fabian, V.: Structural Unambiguity of Formal Languages, *Czech. Math. J.*, vol. 14, no. 3, pp. 394–430, 1964.

Feller, W.: *An Introduction to Probability Theory and Its Applications*, John Wiley & Sons, Inc., New York, 1950.

Fischer, P. C.: On Computability by Certain Classes of Restricted Turing Machines, *Proc. Fourth Ann. Symp. Switching Circuit Theory and Logical Design*, S-156, pp. 23–32, September, 1963.

Fielder, D. C.: On Shannon's Almost Uniform Distribution, *IEEE Trans. Electron. Computers*, vol. EC-13, no. 1, pp. 53–54, 1964.

Fleck, A.: Isomorphism Groups of Automata, *J. Assoc. Computing Machinery*, vol. 9, no. 4, pp. 469–476, 1962.

Friedman, Joyce: (1) Some Results in Church's Restricted Recursive Arithmetic, *J. Symbolic Logic*, vol. 22, pp. 337–342, 1957.
(2) A Decision Procedure for Computations of Finite Automata, *J. Assoc. Computing Machinery*, vol. 9, no. 3, pp. 315–323, 1962.

Gilbert, E. N.: (1) Lattice Theoretic Properties of Frontal Switching Functions, *J. Math. Phys.*, vol. 33, no. 1, pp. 57–67, 1954.
(2) Gray Codes and Paths on the *n*-cube, *Bell System Tech. J.*, vol. 37, no. 3, pp. 815–826, 1958.
(3) The Number of Internal State Assignments for a Sequential Machine, *Internal Tech. Mem.* MM-59-121-4, *Bell Telephone Lab.*, 1959.

Gill, A.: *Introduction to the Theory of Finite-state Machines*, McGraw-Hill Book Company, New York, 1962.

Ginsburg, S.: (1) *An Introduction to Mathematical Machine Theory*, Addison-Wesley Publishing Company, Inc., Reading, Mass., 1962.
(2) On the Length of the Smallest Uniform Experiment Which Distinguishes the Terminal States of a Machine, *J. Assoc. Computing Machinery*, vol. 5, pp. 266–280, 1958.
(3) Some Remarks on Abstract Machines, *Trans. Am. Math. Soc.*, vol. 96, pp. 400–444, 1960.
(4) Sets of Tapes Accepted by Different Types of Automata, *J. Assoc. Computing Machinery*, vol. 8, no. 1, pp. 81–86, 1961.

Ginsburg, S., and T. N. Hibbard: (1) Solvability of Machine Mappings of Regular Sets to Regular Sets, *J. Assoc. Computing Machinery*, vol. 11, no. 3, pp. 302–312, July, 1964.
(2) Two Theorems about Regular Bases of Sets of Words, *SDC Tech. Memo. TM-738/004/00*.

Ginsburg, S., T. N. Hibbard, and J. S. Ullian: Sequences in Context-free Languages, *SDC Tech. Memo. TM-738/001/01.*

Ginsburg, S., and H. G. Rice: Two Families of Languages Related to ALGOL, *J. Assoc. Computing Machinery,* vol. 9, no. 3, pp. 350–371, July, 1962.

Ginsburg, S., and G. F. Rose: (1) Operations Which Preserve Definability in Language, *J. Assoc. Computing Machinery,* vol. 10, no. 2, pp. 175–195, 1963.
(2) Some Recursively Unsolvable Problems in ALGOL-like Languages, *J. Assoc. Computing Machinery,* vol. 10, no. 1, pp. 29–47, 1963.
(3) A Comparison of the Work Done by Generalized Sequential Machines and Turing Machines, *Trans. Am. Math. Soc.,* vol. 103, no. 3, pp. 394–402, 1962.
(4) A Characterization of Machine Mappings, *SDC Tech. Memo. TM-738/009/00,* August, 1964.

Ginsburg, S., and E. H. Spanier: (1) Quotients of Context-free Languages, *J. Assoc. Computing Machinery,* vol. 10, no. 4, pp. 487–492, 1963.
(2) Distinguishability of a Semi-group by a Machine, *Proc. Am. Math. Soc.,* vol. 12, no. 4, pp. 661–668, 1961.
(3) Bounded ALGOL-like Languages, *Trans. Am. Math. Soc.,* vol. 113, no. 2, pp. 333–368, 1964.
(4) Mappings of Languages by Two Tape Devices, *Proc. Fifth Ann. Symp. Switching Circuit Theory and Logical Design,* S-164, pp. 57–67, 1964.
(5) Semi-groups, Presberger Formulas and Languages, *SDC Tech. Memo. TM-738/008/00.*

Ginsburg, S., and J. Ullian: (1) Ambiguity in Context-free Languages, *SDC Tech. Memo. TM-738/005/00,* January, 1964.
(2) Some Remarks about Sequences in Context-free Languages, *SDC Tech. Memo. TM-738/001/00,* January, 1963.

Give'on, Y.: Lattice Matrices, *Inform. Control,* vol. 7, no. 4, pp. 477–484, 1964.

Glushkov, V. M.: (1) On a Synthesis Algorithm for Abstract Automata, *Ukr. Mat. J.,* vol. 12, no. 2, pp. 147–156, 1960.
(2) The Abstract Theory of Automata, *Russian Math. Surveys,* vol. 16, no. 5, pp. 1–53, 1961.
(3) Abstract Automata and Partitions of Free Semigroups, *Dokl. Akad. Nauk SSSR,* 1961.
(4) *Synthesis of Digital Automata,* Fizmatgiz, Moscow, 1962.

Golomb, S.: (1) On the Classification of Boolean Functions, *IRE Trans. Inform. Theory,* vol. IT-5, pp. 176–186, 1959.
(2) A Mathematical Theory of Discrete Classification, *Proc. Fourth London Symp. Inform. Theory,* pp. 404–425, 1961.

Gould, R.: (1) Graphs and Vector Spaces, *J. Math. Phys.,* vol. 37, pp. 193–214, 1958.
(2) Application of Graph Theory to the Synthesis of Contact Networks, in *Proceedings of an International Symposium on the Theory of Switching,* pp. 244–292, Harvard University Press, Cambridge, Mass., 1959.

Gross, M.: Inherent Ambiguity of Minimal Linear Grammars, *Inform. Control,* vol. 7, no. 3, pp. 366–368, 1964.

Haines, L. H.: Note on the Complement of a (Minimal) Linear Language, *Inform. Control,* vol. 7, no. 3, pp. 307–314, 1964.

Hall, M.: *Theory of Groups,* The Macmillan Company, New York, 1959.

Harary, F.: The Exponentation of Permutation Groups, *Am. Math. Monthly,* vol. 66, pp. 572–575, 1959.

Haring, D. R. : Some Aspects of the State Assignment Problem for Sequential Circuits, *MIT Electron. System Lab. Rept. ESL-R*-147, September, 1962.

Harrison, M. A.: (1) The Number of Classes of Invertible Boolean Functions, *J. Assoc. Computing Machinery*, vol. 10, no. 1, pp. 25–28, 1963.
(2) Combinatorial Problems in Boolean Algebras and Applications to the Theory of Switching, doctoral thesis, University of Michigan, 1963.
(3) On the Number of Classes of (n,k) Switching Networks, *J. Franklin Inst.*, vol. 276, no. 4, pp. 313–327, 1963.
(4) The Number of Transitivity Sets of Boolean Functions, *J. Soc. Indus. Appl. Math.*, vol. 11, no. 3, pp. 808–828, 1963.
(5) The Number of Equivalence Classes of Boolean Functions under Groups Containing Negation, *IEEE Trans. Electron. Computers*, vol. EC-12, no. 5, pp. 559–561, 1963.
(6) On the Classification of Boolean Functions by the General Linear and Affine Groups, *J. Soc. Appl. Ind. Math.*, vol. 12, no. 2, pp. 285–299, 1964.
(7) A Remark on Uniform Distribution, *IEEE Trans. Electron. Computers*, vol. EC-13, no. 5, pp. 630–631, 1964.
(8) A Census of Finite Automata, *Can. J. Math.*, vol. 17, pp. 100–113, 1965.

Hartmanis, J.: (1) Symbolic Analysis of a Decomposition of Information Processing Machines, *Inform. Control*, vol. 3, no. 2, pp. 151–178, June, 1960.
(2) On the State Assignment Problem for Sequential Machines I, *IRE Trans. Electron. Computers*, vol. EC-10, no. 2, pp. 157–165, June, 1961.
(3) Maximal Autonomous Clocks of Sequential Machines, *IRE Trans. Electron. Computers*, vol. EC-11, no. 1, pp. 83–86, 1962.
(4) Loop-free Structure of Sequential Machines, *Inform. Control*, vol. 5, no. 1, pp. 25–43, 1962.
(5) Further Results on the Structure of Sequential Machines, *J. Assoc. Computing Machinery*, vol. 10, no. 1, pp. 78–88, 1963.

Hartmanis, J., and R. E. Stearns: (1) On the State Assignment Problem for Sequential Machines II, *IRE Trans. Electron. Computers*, vol. EC-10, no. 4, pp. 593–603, December, 1961.
(2) Regularity Preserving Modifications of Regular Expressions, *Inform. Control*, vol. 6, no. 1, pp. 55–69, 1963.
(3) A Study of Feedback and Errors in Sequential Machines, *IEEE Trans. Electron. Computers*, vol. EC-12, no. 3, pp. 223–232, 1963.
(4) Some Dangers in State Reduction of Sequential Machines, *Inform. Control*, vol. 5, no. 3, pp. 252–260, 1962.
(5) On Computational Complexity of Algorithms, *Trans. Am. Math. Soc.* To appear in 1965.
(6) Pair Algebra and Its Application to Automata Theory, *Inform. Control*, vol. 7, no. 4, pp. 485–507, 1964.

Hellerman, L. : Equivalence Classes of Logical Functions, *IBM Tech. Publ. TR* 00.819, November, 1961.

Hennie, F. C.: *Iterative Arrays of Logical Circuits*, The M.I.T. Press, Cambridge, Mass., 1961.

Hermes, H.: *Einführung in die Verbandstheorie*, Springer-Verlag OHG, Berlin, 1955.

Higonnet, R., and R. Grea: *Logical Design of Electrical Circuits*, McGraw-Hill Book Company, New York, 1958.

Hohn, F. E., and L. R. Schissler: Boolean Matrices and the Design of Combinational Relay Switching Circuits, *Bell System Tech. J.*, vol. 34, no. 1, pp. 177–202, 1955.

Hu, S. T.: On the Decomposition of Switching Functions, *ASTIA Tech. Rept.* *AD*265 563, June, 1961.

Huffman, D. A.: (1) The Synthesis of Sequential Switching Circuits, *J. Franklin Inst.*, vol. 257, no. 3, pp. 161–190, 1954; no. 4, pp. 275–303, 1954.
(2) Canonical Forms for Information-lossless Finite-state Logical Machines, *IRE Trans. Inform. Theory*, vol. IT-5, pp. 41–59, May, 1959.

Huzino, S.: Theory of Finite Automata, *Mem. Fac. Sci., Kyushu Univ. Ser. A*, vol. 15, no. 2, pp. 97–159, 1962.

Ibuki, K., K. Naemura, and A. Nozaki: The General Theory of Complete Sets of Logical Functions, *J. Inst. Elec. Comm. Engrs. of Japan*, vol. 46, no. 7, pp. 934–1490, 1963.

Iverson, K. E.: *A Programming Language*, John Wiley & Sons, Inc., New York, 1962.

Janov, Ju. I.: Identical Transformations of Regular Expressions, *Dokl. Akad. Nauk*, pp. 327–330, 1962. See *Soviet Math.*, vol. 3, no. 6, pp. 1630–1634.

Jeffrey, R. C.: (1) Some Recent Simplifications of the Theory of Finite Automata, *MIT Res. Lab. Electron. Tech. Rept.* 219, May, 1959.
(2) Finite State Transformations, *Inform. Control*, vol. 7, no. 1, pp. 45–54, 1964.

Jónsson, B., and A. Tarski: *Direct Decompositions of Finite Algebraic Systems*, Notre Dame Math. Lectures, no. 5, South Bend, Ind., 1947.

Karatsuba, A. A.: On the Solution of a Problem in the Theory of Finite Automata, *Usp. Mat. Nauk*, vol 15, no. 3, pp. 157–159, 1960.

Karnaugh, M.: The Map Method for Synthesis of Combinational Logic Circuits, *Trans. AIEE*, Part I, vol. 72, no. 9, pp. 593–599, 1953.

Karp, R. M.: Functional Decomposition and Switching Circuit Design, *J. Soc. Indus. Appl. Math.*, pp. 291–335, June, 1963.

Kautz, W. H.: State-logic Relations in Autonomous Sequential Networks, *Proc. Eastern Joint Computer, Conf.*, 1958.

Kemeny, J. G., and J. L. Snell: *Finite Markov Chains*, D. Van Nostrand Company, Inc., Princeton, N.J., 1960.

Kleene, S. C.: (1) *Introduction to Metamathematics*, D. Van Nostrand Company, Inc., Princeton, N.J., 1952.
(2) Representation of Events in Nerve Nets and Finite Automata, in *Automata Studies*, Princeton University Press, Princeton, N.J., 1956.

Kobrinskii, N. E., and B. A. Traktenbrot: *Introduction to the Theory of Finite Automata*, Gosudarstv, Izdat. Fiz.-Mat. Lit., Moscow, 1962.

Kochen, M.: Extension of Moore-Shannon Model for Relay Circuits, *IBM J. Res. Develop.*, vol. 3, no. 2, pp. 169–186, 1959.

König, D.: *Theorie der Endlichen und Unendlichen Graphen*, Akademische Verlagsgesellschaft M.B.H., Leipzig, 1936.

Korpelevich, G. M.: The Relationship between the Concepts of Solvability and Enumerability for Finite Automata, *Dokl. Akad. Nauk SSSR*, vol. 149, no. 5, pp. 1023–1025, 1964. See *Automation Express*, vol. 6, no. 3, pp. 35–37, 1963.

Krohn, K. B., and J. L. Rhodes: (1) *Algebraic Theory of Machines: I, The Main Decomposition Theorem, Prime Decomposition Theorem for Finite Semigroups*, Seminar Notes, University of California, Berkeley, 1963.
(2) Results on Finite Semigroups Derived from the Algebraic Theory of Machines, *Proc. Natl. Acad. Sci. U.S.A.*, vol. 53, no. 3, pp. 499–501, 1965.

Kuroda, S. Y.: Classes of Languages and Linear-bounded Automata, *Inform. Control*, vol. 7, no. 2, pp. 207–223, 1964.

Lechner, R.: Affine Equivalence of Switching Functions, doctoral thesis, Harvard University, 1963.

Lee, C. Y.: (1) Switching Functions on an n-dimensional Cube, *Trans. AIEE, Part I*, vol. 73, no. 14, pp. 289–291, 1954.
(2) Automata and Finite Automata, *Bell System Tech. J.*, vol. 39, no. 5, pp. 1267–1295, 1960.

Letičevskiĭ, A. A.: Automaton Decomposition of Mappings of Free Semi-groups, *Z. Vycisl. Mat. i Mat. Fiz.*, vol. 2, pp. 467–474, 1962.

Le Veque, W. G.: *Topics in Number Theory*, vols. I and II, Addison-Wesley Publishing Company, Inc., Reading, Mass., 1956.

Löfgren, L.: (1) Automata of High Complexity and Methods of Increasing Their Reliability by Redundancy, *Inform. Control*, vol. 1, pp. 127–147, May, 1958.
(2) On the Realizability Problem for Irredundant Boolean Networks, *Nuovo Cimento*, 1959.
(3) Irredundant and Redundant Boolean Branch Networks, *IRE Trans. Inform. Theory*, vol. IT-5, pp. 158–175, May, 1959.
(4) A Theory of Uniform Switching Nets, *Res. Inst. of Natl. Defense Rept.* A510, Sweden, 1962.

Lorens, C. S.: Invertible Boolean Functions, *IEEE Trans. Electron. Computers*, vol. EC-13, no. 5, pp. 529–541, 1964.

Luce, R. D.: A Note on Boolean Matrix Theory, *Proc. Am. Math. Soc.*, vol. 3, pp. 382–388, 1952.

Lunts, A. G.: (1) The Application of Boolean Matrix Algebra to the Analysis and Synthesis of Relay Contact Networks, *Dokl. Akad. Nauk SSSR*, vol. 70, no. 3, pp. 421–423, 1950.
(2) The Synthesis and Analysis of Relay Contact Networks with the Aid of Characteristic Functions, *Dokl. Akad. Nauk SSSR*, vol. 75, no. 2, pp. 201–204, 1950.
(3) A Method of Analyzing Finite Automata, *Dokl. Akad. Nauk SSSR*, vol. 160, no. 4, pp. 778–780, 1965.

Lupanov, O. B.: (1) On the Synthesis of Contact Networks, *Dokl. Akad. Nauk SSSR*, vol. 119, no. 1, pp. 23–26, 1958.
(2) On the Asymptotic Estimates of the Complexities of Formulas Which Realize Logic Algebra Functions, *Dokl. Akad. Nauk SSSR*, vol. 128, no. 3, pp. 464–467, 1959.
(3) On the Realization of Logic Algebra Functions Using Formulas of Limited Depth in the Basis &, V and ¯, *Dokl. Akad. Nauk SSSR*, vol. 136, no. 5, pp. 1041–1042, 1961.

Lyubick, Y. I.: On the Properties of the Periodicity of Events Represented in Finite Automata, *Ukr. Mat. Zh.*, vol. 16, no. 3, pp. 396–401, 1964.

Marcus, M. P.: (1) *Switching Circuits for Engineers*, Prentice-Hall Inc., Englewood Cliffs, N.J., 1962.
(2) Minimization of the Partially Developed Transfer Tree, *IRE Trans. Electron. Computers*, vol. EC-6, no. 2, pp. 92–95, 1957.

Marimont, R. B.: A New Method of Checking the Consistency of Precedence Matrices, *J. Assoc. Computing Machinery*, vol. 6, no. 2, pp. 164–171, 1959.

Markov. A. A.: *Theory of Algorithms*, Moscow, 1954.   English translation available from U. S. Dept. of Commerce.

Maurer, W. D.: Ph.D. Thesis, Univ. of California, Berkeley, Calif., 1965.

Mautner, F. I.: An Extension of Klein's Erlanger Program; Logic as Invariant Theory, *Am. J. Math.*, vol. 68, pp. 345–384, 1946.

McCarthy, J., and C. E. Shannon (eds.): *Automata Studies*, Princeton University Press, Princeton, N.J., 1956.

McCluskey, E. J., Jr.: (1) Detection of Group Invariance or Total Symmetry of a Boolean Function, *Bell System Tech. J.*, vol. 35, no. 6, pp. 1445–1466, 1956.
(2) Reduction of Feedback Loops in Sequential Circuits and Carry Leads in Iterative Networks, *Inform. Control*, vol. 6, no. 2, pp. 99–118, 1963.

McCluskey, E. J., Jr., and S. Unger: A Note on the Number of Internal Variable Assignments for Sequential Switching Circuits, *IRE Trans. Electron. Computers*, vol. EC-8, no. 4, pp. 439–440, 1959.

McCulloch, W.: Stable Reliable and Flexible Nets of Unreliable Formal Neurons, *MIT Res. Lab. Electron. Progr. Rept.* 49, April, 1958.

McCulloch, W., and W. Pitts: Logical Calculus of the Ideas Immanent in Nervous Activity, *Bull. Math. Biophys.*, vol. 5, pp. 115–133, 1943.

McKinsey, J. C. C.: On Boolean Functions of Many Variables, *Trans. Am. Math. Soc.*, vol. 40, pp. 343–362, 1936.

McKnight, J. D.: (1) Fine Quotients of Semigroups, *G.E. Computer Lab. Rept.* 63-*CDL*-8, 1963.
(2) Generalized Kleene Quotient Theorems, *G.E. Computer Lab. Rept.* 63-*CDL*-10, 1963.

McNaughton, R.: (1) The Theory of Automata: A Survey, *Advan. Computers*, vol. 2, 1961.
(2) On Nets Made Up of Badly Timed Elements, *Notes from Moore School of Electrical Engineering*, University of Pennsylvania, 1961.
(3) Unate Truth Functions, *IRE Trans. Electron. Computers*, vol. EC-10, no. 1, pp. 1–6, 1961.

McNaughton, R., and H. Yamada: Regular Expressions and State Graphs for Automata, *IRE Trans. Electron. Computers*, vol. EC-9, pp. 39–47, March, 1960.

Mealy, G. H.: A Method for Synthesizing Sequential Circuits, *Bell System, Tech. J.*, vol. 34, no. 5, pp. 1045–1079, 1955.

Medvedev, I. T.: On a Class of Events Representable in a Finite Automation, *Automaty*, Moscow.   Also *Lincoln Lab. Group Rept.* 34-73, June, 1958.   (Translated by J. J. Schonn-Kor.)

Minsky, M. L.: Recursive Unsolvability of Post's Problem of "Tag" and Other Topics in the Theory of Turing Machines, *Ann. Math.*, vol. 74, pp. 437–454, 1961.

Moisil, G. C.: (1) *Teoria Algebrica a Mecanismelor Automate* (*Algebraic Theory of Automatic Machines*) Editura Tehnica, Bucharest, 1959.
(2) *Functionarea in Mai Multi Timpi a Schemelor cu Relee Ideale* (*Time Sequential Operation of Circuits with Ideal Relays*), Editura Academiei Republicii Popolare Romine, Bucharest, 1960.

Moore, E. F.: (1) Gedanken Experiments on Sequential Machines, in *Automata Studies*, Princeton University Press, Princeton, N.J., 1956.
(2) Minimal Complete Relay Decoding Networks, *IBM J. Res. Dev.*, vol. 4, no. 5, pp. 525–531, 1960.

(3) Machine Models of Self-reproduction, *Math. Prob. Biol. Sci., Proc. Symp. Appl. Math.*, vol. 14, pp. 17–33, 1962.
(4) *Sequential Machines, Selected Papers*, Addison-Wesley Publishing Company, Inc., Reading, Mass., 1964.

Moore, E. F., and C. Shannon: Reliable Circuits Using Less Reliable Relays I–II, *J. Franklin Inst.*, vol. 262, no. 3, pp. 191–208, no. 4, pp. 281–297, 1956.

Mostow, G. D., J. H. Sampson, and J. Meyer: *Fundamental Structures of Algebra*, McGraw-Hill Book Company, New York, 1963.

Muller, D. E.: (1) Application of Boolean Algebra to Switching Circuit Design and to Error Detection, *IRE Trans. Electron. Computers*, vol. EC-3, no. 3, pp. 6–12, 1954.
(2) Complexity in Electronic Switching Circuits, *IRE Trans. Electron. Computers*, vol. EC-5, no. 1, pp. 15–19, 1956.
(3) Infinite Sequences and Finite Machines, *Proc. IEEE Symp. on Switching Circuit Theory and Logical Design*, S-156, pp. 3–16, September, 1963.

Mullin, A.: Reliable Stochastic Sequential Switching Circuits, *Trans. AIEE*, Part II, vol. 77, pp. 606–611, 1958.

Myhill, J.: (1) Finite Automata and the Representation of Events, *WADC Tech. Rept.* 57-624, November, 1957.
(2) Linear Bounded Automata, *WADD Tech. Note* 60-165, Wright-Patterson Air Force Base, Ohio, 1960.

Nechiporuk, E. I.: On the Synthesis of Networks Using Linear Transformations of the Variables, *Dokl. Akad. Nauk SSSR*, vol. 123, no. 4, pp. 610–612, 1958. (Available in English in *Automation Express*, pp. 12–13, April, 1959.)

Nerode, A.: Linear Automation Transformations, *Proc. Am. Math. Soc.*, vol. 9, pp. 541–544, 1958.

Netherwood, D. B.: Minimal Sequential Machines, *IRE Trans. Electron. Computers*, vol. EC-8, no. 3, pp. 339–345, 1959.

Neumann, P. G.: (1) A Note on Cyclic Permutation Error-correcting Codes, *Inform. Control*, vol. 5, pp. 72–86, March, 1962.
(2) Efficient Error-limiting Variable-length Codes, *IRE Trans. Inform. Theory*, vol. IT-8, pp. 292–304, July, 1962.
(3) Encoding and Decoding for Cyclic Permutation Codes, *IRE Trans. Electron. Computers*, vol. EC-11, pp. 507–511, August, 1962.
(4) On a Class of Efficient Error-limiting Variable-length Codes, *IRE Trans. Information Theory*, vol. IT-8, pp. 260–266, September, 1962.
(5) Error-limiting Coding Using Information-lossless Sequential Machines, *IEEE Trans. Inform. Theory*, vol. IT-9, pp. 108–115, April, 1964.

Ninomiya, I.: (1) On the Number of Types of Symmetric Boolean Output Matrices, *Mem. Fac. Eng. Nagoya Univ.*, vol. 7, no. 2, pp. 115–124, 1955.
(2) On the Number of Genera of Boolean Functions of *n* Variables, *Mem. Fac. Eng. Nagoya Univ.*, vol. 11, no. 1, pp. 54–58, 1959.
(3) A Study of the Structures of Boolean Functions and Its Applications to the Synthesis of Switching Circuits, *Mem. Faculty Eng. Nagoya Univ.*, vol. 13, no. 2, 149–363, 1961.

Norman, R. Z., and M. O. Rabin: An Algorithm for a Minimum Cover of a Graph, *Proc. Am. Math. Soc.*, vol. 10, no. 1, pp. 315–319, 1959.

Okada, S.: Topology Applied to Switching Circuits, *Proc. Symp. Inform. Networks*, Polytechnic Institute of Brooklyn, vol. 3, pp. 267–290, April, 1954.

Ore, O.: (1) *Theory of Graphs,* American Mathematical Society Colloquium Publications, vol. XXXVIII, Providence, R.I., 1962.
(2) On the Foundations of Abstract Algebra, I, *Ann. Math.,* vol. 36, no. 2, pp. 406–437, 1935.
(3) On the Foundations of Abstract Algebra, II, *Ann. Math.,* vol. 37, no. 2, pp. 265–292, 1936.
(4) Theory of Monomial Groups, *Trans. Am. Math. Soc.,* vol. 516, no. 1, pp. 15–64, 1942.
(5) Theory of Equivalence Relations, *Duke Math. J.,* vol. 9, pp. 573–627, 1942.

Ott, G., and N. Feinstein: Design of Sequential Machines from Their Regular Expressions, *J. Assoc. Computing Machinery,* vol. 8, no. 4, pp. 585–600, 1961.

Parikh, R. J.: Language Generating Devices, *MIT Res. Lab. Electron. Quart. Progr. Rept.* 60, pp. 199–212, January, 1961.

Paull, M., and S. Unger: Minimizing the Number of States in Incompletely Specified Sequential Switching Functions, *IRE Trans. Electron. Computers,* vol. EC-8, no. 3, pp. 356–367, 1959.

Pawlak, Z.: Decoding Nets and the Theory of Graphs, *J. Soc. Indus. Appl. Math.,* vol. 7, no. 1, pp. 1–5, 1959.

Paz, A.: (1) Homomorphisms between Finite Automata, *Bull. Res. Council Israel,* vol. 10F, no. 3, 93–100, 1962.
(2) Some Aspects of Probabilistic Automata, *Information Control.* To appear in 1965.

Perles, M., M. O. Rabin, and E. Shamir: The Theory of Definite Automata, *IEEE Trans. Electron. Computers,* vol. EC-12, no. 3, pp. 233–243, 1963.

Peterson, W. W.: *Error Correcting Codes,* John Wiley & Sons, Inc., New York, 1961.

Phister, M.: *Logical Design of Digital Computers,* John Wiley & Sons, Inc., New York, 1956.

Piatowski, T. F.: *n*-head Finite State Machines, doctoral thesis, University of Michigan, 1963.

Pólya, G.: (1) Kombinatorische Anzahlbestimmungen für Gruppen, Graphen, und chemische Verbindungen, *Acta Math.,* vol. 68, pp. 145–253, 1937.
(2) Sur les types des propositions composées, *J. Symbolic Logic,* vol. 5, no 3, pp. 98–103, 1940.

Post, E. L.: (1) A General Theory of Elementary Propositions, *Am. J. Math.,* vol. 43, pp. 163–185, 1921.
(2) Finite Combinatory Processes—Formulation I, *J. Symbolic Logic,* vol. 1, pp. 103–105, 1936.
(3) A Variant of a Recursively Unsolvable Problem, *Bull. Am. Math. Soc.,* vol. 52, pp. 264–268, 1946.

Povarov, G. N.: (1) Functional Separability of Boolean Functions, *Dokl. Akad. Nauk SSSR,* vol. 94, no. 5, pp. 801–803, 1954.
(2) On the Study of Symmetric Boolean Functions from the Relay Circuit Theory Viewpoint, *Dokl. Akad. Nauk SSSR,* vol. 104, no. 2, pp. 183–185, 1955.
(3) On a Method of Analysing Symmetric Switching Circuits, *Automatika i Telemekhanika,* vol. 16, no. 4, pp. 364–366, 1955.
(4) A Mathematical Theory for the Synthesis of Contact Networks with One Input and *k* Outputs, in *Proceedings of an International Symposium on the Theory of Switching,* Part II, pp. 74–94, Harvard University Press, Cambridge, Mass., 1959.

Presburger, M.: Über die Vollständigkeit eines gewissen Systems der Arithmetik ganzer Zahler in welchen die Addition als einzige Operation hervortritt, *Sprawozdanie z I Kongresu Matematykow Krajow Slowianskich,* Warsaw, pp. 92–101, 1930.

Quine, W. V.: (1) The Problem of Simplifying Truth Functions, *Am. Math. Monthly,* vol. 59, pp. 521–531, 1952.
(2) Two Theorems about Truth Functions, *Bol. Soc. Math. Mexicana,* vol. 10, pp. 64–70, 1953.
(3) A Way to Simplify Truth Functions, *Am. Math. Monthly,* vol. 62, pp. 627–631, 1955.

Rabin, M. O.: (1) Probabilistic Automata, *Inform. Control,* vol. 6, no. 3, pp. 230–245, 1963.
(2) Real-time Computation, *Israel J. Math.,* vol. 1, no. 4, pp. 203–211, 1963.

Rabin, M. O., and D. Scott: Finite Automata and Their Decision Problems, *IBM J. Res. Dev.,* vol. 3, no. 2, pp. 114–125, 1959.

Rabin, M. O., and H. Wang: Words in the History of a Turing Machine with a Fixed Input, *J. Assoc. Computing Machinery,* vol. 10, no. 4, pp. 526–527, 1963.

Rado, T.: On Non-computable Functions, *Bell System Tech. J.,* vol. 41, pp. 877–884, 1962.

Raney, G.: Sequential Functions, *J. Assoc. Computing Machinery,* vol. 5, pp. 177–180, April, 1958.

Red'ko, V. N.: (1) On the Determining Set of Relations in the Algebra of Regular Events, *Ukr. Mat. Z.,* vol. 16, no. 1, pp. 120-126, 1964.
(2) On the Algebra of Commutative Events, *Ukr. Mat. Zh.,* vol. 16, no. 2, pp. 185–195, 1964.
(3) On Commutative Closures of Events, *Dopovidi Akad. Nauk Ukr. RSR,* vol.9, pp. 1156–1159, 1963.

Riley, J. A.: Foundations for a General Theory of Boolean Formulas, *Parke Math. Lab. Repts.* 3–3471 and 9–3471, July, 1960, and March, 1961. (Two reports.)

Riordan, J.: *An Introduction to Combinatorial Analysis,* John Wiley & Sons, Inc., New York, 1958.

Riordan, J., and C. Shannon: The Number of Two-terminal Series-Parallel Networks, *J. Math. Phys.,* vol. 21, no. 2, pp. 83–93, 1942.

Ritchie, R. W.: (1) Classes of Predictably Computable Functions, *Trans. Am. Math. Soc.,* vol. 106, no. 1, pp. 139–173, 1963.
(2) Finite Automata and the Set of Squares, *J. Assoc. Computing Machinery,* vol. 10, no. 4, pp. 528–531, 1963.

Rosenbloom, P. C.: *The Elements of Mathematical Logic,* Dover Publications, Inc. New York, 1950.

Roth, J. P.: (1) Algebraic Topological Methods in Synthesis, in *Proceedings of an International Symposium on the Theory of Switching,* Harvard University Press, Cambridge, Mass., 1959.
(2) Minimization over Boolean Trees, *IBM J. Res. Dev.,* vol. 4, no. 5, pp. 543–558, 1960.

Roth, J. P., and R. M. Karp: Minimization over Boolean Graphs, *IBM J. Res. Dev.,* vol. 6, no. 2, pp. 227–238, 1962.

Rutledge, J. D.: On Ianov's Program Schemata, *J. Assoc. Computing Machinery,* vol. 11, no. 1, pp. 1–9, 1964.

Salomaa, A.: (1) Theorems on the Representation of Events in Moore-Automata, *Ann. Univ. Turku., Ser. AI*, vol. 69, 1964.

(2) Axiom Systems for Regular Expressions of Finite Automata, *Ann. Univ. Turku., Ser. AI*, vol. 75, pp. 4–29, 1964.

Scheinberg, S.: Note on the Boolean Properties of Context Free Languages, *Inform. Control*, vol. 3, pp. 372–375, 1960.

Schützenberger, M. P.: (1) On the Definition of a Family of Automata, *Inform. Control*, vol. 4, pp. 245–270, September, 1961.

(2) A Remark on Finite Transducers, *Inform. Control*, vol. 4, pp. 185–196, September, 1961.

(3) Finite Counting Automata, *Inform. Control*, vol. 5, pp. 91–107, 1962.

(4) On Context-free Languages and Push-down Automata, *Inform Control*, vol. 6, pp. 246–264, September, 1963.

(5) Certain Families of Elementary Automata, *Proc. Symp. Math. Theory Automata*, vol. XII, MRI Symposia Series, pp. 139–153, 1962.

(6) On a Theorem of R. Jungen, *Proc. Am. Math. Soc.*, vol. 13, pp. 885–890, December, 1962.

Semon, W.: (1) Synthesis of Series-parallel Network Switching Functions, *Bell System Tech. J.*, vol. 37, no. 4, pp. 877–898, 1958.

(2) Matrix Methods in the Theory of Switching, in *Proceedings of an International Symposium on the Theory of Switching*, pp. 13–50, Harvard University Press, Cambridge, Mass., 1959.

(3) E-algebras in Switching Theory, *Trans. AIEE*, Part I, vol. 80, pp. 265–269, July, 1961.

(4) General E-algebras, in *Switching Theory in Space Technology*, pp. 174–184, Stanford University Press, Stanford, Calif., 1963.

Seshu, S., and M. Reed: *Graph Theory and Electrical Networks*, Addison-Wesley Publishing Company, Inc., Reading, Mass., 1961.

Shamir, E.: (1) A Remark on Discovery Algorithms for Grammars, *Inform. Control*, vol. 5, pp. 246–251, 1962.

(2) On Sequential Languages, *Appl. Logic Branch Hebrew Univ. Tech. Rept. 7*, Jerusalem, 1961.

Shannon, C. E.: (1) A Symbolic Analysis of Relay and Switching Circuits, *Trans. AIEE*, vol. 57, pp. 713–723, 1938.

(2) The Synthesis of Two-terminal Switching Circuits, *Bell System Tech. J.*, vol. 28, pp. 59–98, January, 1949.

Shannon, C. E., and W. Weaver: *The Mathematical Theory of Communication*, The University of Illinois Press, Urbana, Ill., 1949.

Shepherdson, J. C.: The Reduction of Two-way Automata to One-way Automata, *IBM J. Res. Dev.*, vol. 3, no. 2, pp. 198–200, 1959.

Shepherdson, J. C., and H. E. Sturgis: Computability of Recursive Functions, *J. Assoc. Computing Machinery*, vol. 10, no. 2, pp. 217–255, 1963.

Shestakoff, V. I.: Algébra dvuhpolúsnyh shém, postroénnyh iskúčitel' no iz dvuhpolúsnikov (Algébra Ashém), *Automatika i Telemekhanika*, no. 2, pp. 15–24, 1941.

Sikorski, R.: *Boolean Algebras*, Springer-Verlag OHG, Berlin, 1960.

Simon, J.: A Note on Memory Aspects of Sequence Transducers, *IRE Trans. Circuit Theory*, vol. CT-6, p. 26–29, 1959.

Slepian, D.: (1) On the Number of Symmetry Types of Boolean Functions of n Variables, *Can. J. Math.*, vol. 5, no. 2, pp. 185–193, 1953.

(2) Some Further Theory of Group Codes, *Bell System Tech. J.*, vol. 39, no. 5, pp. 1219–1252, 1960.

Sorkin, Y. I.: The Algebra of Automata, *Probl. Kibernetiki*, 1961.

Staff of the Computation Laboratory: *Synthesis of Electronic and Control Circuits*, Annals of the Computation Laboratory of Harvard University, vol. 27, Harvard University Press, Cambridge, Mass., 1951.

Stoll, R. R.: *Sets, Logic, and Axiomatic Theories*, W. H. Freeman and Company, San Francisco, 1961.

Stone, M. H.: (1) Subsumption of Boolean Algebras under the Theory of Rings, *Proc. Natl. Acad. Sci.*, vol. 21, pp. 103–105, 1935.
(2) The Theory of Representations for Boolean Algebras, *Trans. Am. Math. Soc.*, vol. 40, pp. 37–111, July, 1936.

Traktenbrot, B. A.: (1) Sintéz logičéskih sétéj, opératory kotoryh opisany srédstvami isčisléniá odnoméstnyh prédikatov, *Dokl. Akad. Nauk SSSR*, vol. 118, no. 4, pp. 646–648, 1958.
(2) Nékotorýe postroéniá v logiké odnomestynh prédikatov, *Dokl. Akad. Nauk SSSR*, vol. 138, no. 2, pp. 320–321, 1961.

Tsetlin, M. L.: The Application of Matrix Calculus to the Synthesis of Relay Contact Networks, *Dokl. Akad. Nauk SSSR*, vol. 86, no. 3, pp. 525–528, 1952.

Turing, A.: On Computable Numbers with Applications to the Entscheidungsproblem, *Proc. London Math. Soc.*, Ser. 2, vol. 42, pp. 230–265, 1936.

Van der Waerden, B. L.: *Modern Algebra*, vols. I and II, Frederick Ungar Publishing Co., New York, 1949, 1950.

Von Neuman, J.: (1) The General and Logical Theory of Automata, in *Cerebral Mechanisms in Behavior: The Hixon Symposium*, John Wiley & Sons, Inc., New York, 1951.
(2) The Theory of Automata, Construction, Reproduction, and Homogeneity, unpublished manuscript.
(3) Probabilistic Logics and the Synthesis of Reliable Organisms from Unreliable Components, *Automata Studies*, pp. 43–98, Princeton University Press, Princeton, N.J., 1956.

Vučkocíc, V.: On a Class of Regular Sets, *Notre Dame J. of Formal Logic*, vol. 5, no. 2, pp. 113–124, 1964.

Wagner, E. G.: An Approach to Modular Computers, I: Spider Automata and Embedded Automata, *IBM Res. Rept. RC* 1107, 1964.

Wang, H.: (1) Circuit Synthesis by Solving Sequential Boolean Equations, *Z. Math. Logik Grundlagen Math.*, vol. 5, no. 3, pp 291–322, 1959.
(2) A Variant to Turing's Theory of Computability, *J. Assoc. Computing Machinery*, vol. 4, pp. 63–92, 1957.

Wedderburn, J. H. M.: Boolean Linear Associative Algebras, *Ann. Math.*, vol. 35, pp. 185–194, 1934.

Weeg, G.: The Structure of an Automaton and Its Operation Preserving Transformation Group, *J. Assoc. Computing Machinery*, vol. 9, no. 3, pp. 345–349, 1962.

Weyl, H.: *Classical Groups*, Princeton University Press, Princeton, N.J., 1946.

Whitney, H.: (1) Nonseparable and Planar Graphs, *Trans. Am. Math. Soc.*, vol. 34, pp. 339–362, 1932.
(2) On the Classification of Graphs, *Am. J. Math.*, vol. 55, pp. 236–244, 1933.
(3) Planar Graphs, *Fundamentica Math.*, vol. 21, pp. 73–84, 1933.

(4) 2-isomorphic Graphs, *Am. J. Math.*, vol. 55, pp. 245–254, 1933.

(5) On the Abstract Properties of Linear Dependence, *Am. J. Math.*, vol. 57, pp. 509–533, 1935.

Wilcox, R. H., and W. C. Mann (eds.): *Redundancy Techniques for Computing Systems*, Spartan Books, Washington, D. C., 1962.

Winograd, S.: (1) Bounded Transient Automata, *Proc. Third. Annual AIEE Symp. Switching Circuit Theory and Logical Design*, S-141, pp. 138–141, September, 1962.

(2) Coding for Logical Operations, *IBM J. Res. Dev.*, vol. 6, pp. 430–436, October, 1962.

(3) Redundancy and Complexity of Logical Elements, *Inform. Control*, vol. 6, no. 3, pp. 177–194, 1963.

(4) Input Error Limiting Automata, *J. Assoc. Computing Machinery*, vol. 11, no. 3, pp. 338–351, 1964.

Winograd, S., and J. D. Cowan: *Reliable Computation in the Presence of Noise*, The M.I.T. Press, Cambridge, Mass., 1963.

Yoeli, M.: (1) The Theory of Switching Nets, *IRE Trans. Inform. Theory*, vol. IT-5, pp. 152–157, May, 1959.

(2) Counting with Nonlinear Binary Feedback Shift Registers, *IEEE Trans. Electron. Computers*, vol. EC-21, no. 4, pp. 357–361, 1963.

(3) A Note on a Generalization of Boolean Matrix Theory, *Am. Math. Monthly*, vol. 68, no. 6, pp. 552–557, 1961.

(4) The Cascade Decomposition of Sequential Machines, *IRE Trans. Electron. Computers*, vol. EC-10, no. 4, pp. 587–592, 1961.

(5) Binary Ring Sequences, *Am. Math. Monthly*, vol. 69, no. 9, pp. 852–855, 1962.

(6) Decompositions of Finite Automata, *Technion, Israel Inst. Technology, Tech. Rept.* 10, March, 1963.

(7) Cascade-parallel Decompositions of Sequential Machines, *IEEE Trans. Electron. Computers*, vol. EC-12, no. 3, pp. 322–324, 1963.

(8) Cascaded Counters with Feedbacks, *MRC Tech. Rept. No. 467*, March, 1964.

(9) Lattice Ordered Semi-groups, Graphs, and Automata, *MRC Tech. Rept. No. 451*, January, 1964.

(10) Canonical Representations of Chain Events, *MRC Tech. Rept. No. 462*, March, 1964.

(11) Multi-valued Homomorphic Mappings and Subdirect Covers of Partial Algebras, *MRC Tech. Rept. No. 493*, July, 1964.

(12) Generalized Cascade Decompositions of Automata, *SRI Tech. Rept. No. 64-1*, October, 1964.

Yoeli, M., and A. Ginzburg: On Homomorphic Images of Transition Graphs, *J. Franklin Inst.*, vol. 278, no. 5, pp. 291–296, 1964.

Yoeli, M., and S. Rinon: Application of Ternary Algebra to the Study of Static Hazards, *J. Assoc. Computing Machinery*, vol. 11, no. 1, pp. 84–97, 1964.

Zadeh L. A., and C. A. Desoer: *Linear System Theory*, McGraw-Hill Book Company, New York, 1963.

Zeiger, H. P.: Loop-free Synthesis of Finite State Machines, Ph.D. Thesis, MIT, Cambridge, Mass., 1964.

INDEX